THE
BRITISH CATALOGUE
OF MUSIC

1973

A record of music and books about music recently published in Great Britain, based upon the material deposited at the Copyright Receipt Office of the British Library, arranged according to a system of classification with a Composer and Title Index, a Subject Index, and a list of music publishers

Managing Editor: A. J. WELLS, O.B.E., F.L.A.

THE COUNCIL OF THE BRITISH NATIONAL BIBLIOGRAPHY, LTD.

7 RATHBONE STREET, LONDON, W1P 2AL

in association with The Music Department of the British Library, The U.K. Branch of the International Association of Music Libraries, The Music Publishers Association and The Central Music Library

ISBN 0 900220 45 7

CONTENTS

1974

Printed in Great Britain by William Clowes & Sons, Limited, London, Beccles and Colchester
and published by the Council of the British National Bibliography, Ltd., 7 Rathbone Street, London, W1P 2AL
(Registered Office: British Museum, London, W.C.1)

The Council of the British National Bibliography, Ltd., by whom this work is published, is a non-profit making organisation set up at the wish of those bodies whose representatives form the Council for the purpose of "compiling, editing and publishing in appropriate bibliographical form lists of books, pamphlets and other recorded material of whatever nature published in Great Britain, the Dominions and Colonies and/or foreign countries, together with such annotations or further information as may be desirable for the use of librarians, bibliographers and others."

During 1973 the Council consisted of the following representatives:

Miss M. F. Webb, B.SC., A.L.A. and
R. J. Fulford, M.A.
  representing The British Museum.

T. E. Callander, F.L.A. (*Chairman of the Council*), and
Miss J. M. Plaister, B.SC. (ECON.), F.L.A.
  representing The Library Association.

Haddon Whitaker, O.B.E., M.A. (*Vice-Chairman of the Council*) and
M. Turner
  representing The Publishers Association.

P. A. Stockham, B.A. and
R. G. Heffer
  representing The Booksellers Association of Great Britain and Ireland.

Clifford Simmons and
Miss R. Myers, M.A.
  representing The National Book League.

R. A. Flood, M.B.E., F.L.A.
  representing The British Council.

Professor O. V. S. Heath, F.R.S.
  representing The Royal Society.

L. W. Wilson, M.A.
  representing ASLIB.

M. B. Line, M.A., F.L.A.
  representing The National Central Library.

E. B. Ceadel, M.A.
  representing The Joint Committee of the Four Copyright Libraries.

THE
BRITISH CATALOGUE
OF MUSIC
1973

PREFACE

The British Catalogue of Music is a record of new music —with the exception of certain types of popular music— published in Great Britain. In addition, it records foreign music available in this country through a sole agent and books about music. It is based on the works deposited at the British Museum where copies of all new publications must be sent by law and is the most complete list of current British music available.

Hints for tracing information

The Catalogue is presented in three sections:
Classified Section
Composer and Title Index
Subject Index

The purpose of the Classified Section is to arrange works according to the various voices, instruments, and combinations for which they are written. It is not essential to understand the system of classification. To find information, first consult the Composer and Title Index, which makes it possible to find details of which the composer, title, arranger, or any similar fact, is known. The Subject Index provides an alphabetical index of instruments, musical forms, etc., appearing in the Classified Section.

Composer

When the composer or author of a work is known, look under his name in the Composer and Title Index. The information given here, including the publisher and price, will be adequate for most purposes. If, on the other hand, the fullest information about a work is required, turn to the entry in the Classified Section. This may be found by means of the class symbol (group of letters) at the end of the composer or author entry. In tracing class symbols which include ( ) "brackets" or / "stroke", it should be borne in mind that these signs precede letters in the arrangement.

Thus:

	A
is followed by	A(. . . .)
which is followed by	A/ . . . .
which is followed by	AA
which is followed by	AB
which is followed by	B, etc.

Titles, series, editors and arrangers

Entries are made in the Composer and Title Index under the titles of all works, so that, if you do not know the composer or author, a work can be found by looking up its title in the Composer and Title Index.

If you do not know either the composer or the title, it may still be possible to trace the work if the name of the editor or arranger is known and, in the case of vocal works, the author of the words.

Instrument, musical form and character

While the Classified Section displays the works systematically according to the instrument or combination for which a work is written, the Subject Index lists the principal musical forms and musical character and it shows by means of the class symbol where works having such forms or musical character are to be found in the Classified Section. For example, in the Subject Index under the word Sonatas the following entries may be found:

Sonatas: Arrangements for 2 pianos	QNUK/AE
Sonatas: Organ	RE
Sonatas: Piano duets, 4 hands	QNVE
Sonatas: Piano solos	QPE
Sonatas: Violin solos, Unaccompanied	SPME

It will be seen that this group of entries enables you to assemble all the works in sonata form no matter for what instrument the music is, or was originally, written.

Under the word Violin the following may be found:

Violin	S
Violin: Accompanying female voices: Choral works	FE/S
Violin: Books	AS
Violin & orchestra	MPS
Violin & string orchestra	RXMPS

This group directs you first to the place S in the Classified Section, where music for the violin is found, including works composed originally for other instruments and arranged for violin. It also directs you to works in which the violin figures in combination with other instruments.

It thus provides at one and the same time the link between an instrument and its place in the Classified Section and an exhaustive guide to all the works in which that particular instrument figures.

Musical literature

Books about music which normally appear in the *British National Bibliography* are also included in this catalogue. They occur in the sequences lettered A and B. They are indexed in exactly the same way as musical works in the Composer and Title Index and are designated by the qualification "Books" in the Subject Index. Thus, in the second group above, the entry Violin: Books, directing you to AS, indicates that books about the violin will be found at that place.

Prices

Prices given are those current at the time of the first recording of an entry in this catalogue. In a few cases prices of parts are not given but can be obtained on application to the publisher.

Abbreviations

Most of the abbreviations used in describing musical works are self-explanatory. The size of a musical work is indicated by one of the following conventional symbols: *8vo* for works up to 10½ in. in height, *4to* for works between 10½ and 12 in. in height, and *fol.* for works over 12 in. in height. The abbreviation *obl.* (oblong) is added to show when a work is of unusual proportions, and a single sheet is designated by the abbreviations *s.sh.* The abbreviations used for the description of books in the sections A and B are those in use in the *British National Bibliography*.

OUTLINE OF THE CLASSIFICATION

The following outline is given for general information only. Users are advised to consult the Subject Index to discover the exact location of required material in the Classified Section.

MUSICAL LITERATURE

A	General works
	Common sub-divisions
A(B)	Periodicals
A(C)	Encyclopaedias
A(D)	Composite works, symposia, essays by several writers
A(E)	Anecdotes, personal reminiscences
A(K)	Economics
A(M)	Persons in music
A(MM)	Musical profession
A(MN)	Music as a career
A(P)	Individuals
A(Q)	Organisations
A(QT)	Terminology
A(QU)	Notation
A(R)	Printing
A(S)	Publishing
A(T)	Bibliographies
A(U)	Libraries
A(V)	Musical education
A(X)	History of music
A(Y)	Music of particular localities
A/AM	Theory of music
A/CC	Aesthetics
A/CY	Technique of music
A/D	Composition
A/E	Performance
A/F	Recording
A/FY	Musical character
A/G	Folk music
A/GM	Music associated with particular occupations
A/H	Dance music
A/HM	Ballet music
A/J	Music accompanying drama
A/JR	Film music
A/KD	Music to accompany social customs
A/L	Religious music
A/LZ	Elements of music
A/R	Harmony
A/S	Forms of music
A/Y	Fugue
AB	Works on vocal music
AC	Works on opera
ACM	Works on musical plays
AD-AX	Works on music for particular vocal or instrumental performers, enumerated like D–X below
B	Works on individual composers (including libretti and other verbal texts of particular musical works)
BZ	Works on non-European music

MUSIC (SCORES AND PARTS)

C/AY	Collections not limited to work of particular composer, executant, form or character
C/AZ	Collections of a particular composer not otherwise limited
C/G-C/Y	Collections illustrating music of particular form, character, etc., enumerated like A/G-A/Y above
CB	Vocal music
CC	Opera. Vocal scores with keyboard
CM	Musical plays. Vocal scores with keyboard
D	Choral music
DC	Religious choral music
DF	Liturgical music
DH	Motets, Anthems, Hymns
DTZ	Secular choral music
DX	Cantatas
DW	Songs, etc.
E	Choral music with instruments other than keyboard
EZ	Choral music unaccompanied
F	Choral music. Female voices
G	Choral music. Male voices
J	Unison vocal works
K	Vocal solos
L	Instrumental music
M	Orchestral music
N	Chamber music
PVV	Music for individual instruments and instrumental groups
PW	Keyboard instruments
Q	Piano
R	Organ
RW	String instruments
S	Violin
SQ	Viola
SR	Cello
SS	Double bass
TQ	Harp
TS	Guitar
U	Wind instruments
V	Woodwind
VR	Flute
VS	Recorder
VT	Oboe
VU	Saxophone
VV	Clarinet
VW	Bassoon
W	Brass
WS	Trumpet
WT	Horn
WU	Trombone
WX	Bass tuba
X	Percussion instruments
Z	Non-European music

CLASSIFIED SECTION

This section contains entries under subjects, executants and instruments according to a system of classification, a synopsis of which appears in the preliminary pages. The key to the classification and to this section is found in the Subject Index at the end of this volume, which is followed by a list of music publishers and their addresses.

The following are used in giving the sizes of musical works:—

8vo for works up to 10½″ in height.
4to for works between 10½″ and 12″ in height.
fol. for works over 12″ in height.
obl. indicates a work of unusual proportions.
s.sh. means a single sheet.

A — MUSICAL LITERATURE
Doe, Paul Maurice
The craft of music: an inaugural lecture delivered in the University of Exeter on 2 November 1972/ [by] P.M. Doe. — Exeter: University of Exeter, 1973. — 19p; 22cm. — (University of Exeter. Inaugural lectures)
ISBN 0 900771 69 0 Sd: £0.30

(B73-06588)

Glennon, James
Understanding music/ [by] James Glennon. — London: Hale, 1973. — [10],342,[14]p: ill(some col), music, ports; 26cm.
Index.
ISBN 0 7091 3539 4 : £6.00

(B73-04214)

A(C) — Encyclopaedias
Jacobs, Arthur
A new dictionary of music/ [by] Arthur Jacobs. — 3rd ed. — Harmondsworth: Penguin, 1973. — 425p: music; 18cm. — (A Penguin reference book)
Previous ed.: 1967.
ISBN 0 14 051012 5 Pbk: £0.50

(B73-31504)

Scholes, Percy Alfred
The concise Oxford dictionary of music/ by Percy A. Scholes. — 2nd ed. [reprinted with corrections]/ edited by John Owen Ward. — London: Oxford University Press, 1973. — xxx,636p: ill, music; 20cm.
Second ed. originally published 1964. — Also available in a boxed set with 'The concise Oxford dictionary of opera'.
ISBN 0 19 311302 3 Pbk: £1.50
ISBN 0 19 311307 4 Pbk: £0.75

(B73-30855)

A(D) — Essays
Blythe, Ronald
Aldeburgh anthology/ edited by Ronald Blythe. — Aldeburgh: Snape Maltings Foundation Ltd; London (38 Russell Sq., W.C.1): [Distributed by] Faber Music Ltd, 1972. — xiii,437,[83]p: ill, facsims, map, music, ports; 26cm.
Ill. on lining papers.
ISBN 0 571 10003 1 : £6.00

(B73-04215)

Cairns, David, *b.1926*
Responses: musical essays and reviews/ [by] David Cairns. — London: Secker and Warburg, 1973. — xiv,266p: music; 23cm.
ISBN 0 436 08090 7 : £3.75

(B73-13013)

Wagner, Richard
Wagner writes from Paris: stories, essays and articles by the young composer/ edited and translated [from the German] by Robert L. Jacobs and Geoffrey Skelton. — London: Allen and Unwin, 1973. — 197p: port; 23cm.
Index.
ISBN 0 04 780022 4 : £3.85

(B73-19496)

A(KK/P) — Mayer, Sir Robert. Biographies
Mayer, *Sir* **Robert**
My first hundred years: the revised version of an informal address given at the British Institute of Recorded Sound, on Friday 3rd December 1971/ by Sir Robert Mayer. — Gerrards Cross: Smythe, 1972. — 23p,2 leaves: port; 22cm.
Limited ed. of 600 copies.
ISBN 0 900675 77 2 Sd: £0.85(non-net)

(B73-29206)

A(QU/XN53) — Notation. History, 1920-1972
Karkoschka, Erhard
Notation in new music: a critical guide to interpretation and realisation/ [by] Erhard Karkoschka; translated from the German by Ruth Koenig. — [Tonbridge] (c/o A. Kalmus, 38 Eldon Way, Paddock Wood, Tonbridge, Kent): Universal Edition, 1972. — xiii,183p(16fold): ill, facsims, music; 31cm.
Translation of 'Das Schriftbild der neuen Musik'. Altencelle: Moeck Verlag, 1966. — Bibl.p.179-183.
ISBN 0 900938 28 5 : £8.00

(B73-06589)

A(RC/XLK36) — Printing. Music covers, 1890-1925
Wilk, Max
Memory lane, 1890 to 1925: ragtime, jazz, foxtrot and other popular music and music covers/ selected by Max Wilk. — London (14 West Central St., WC1A 1JH): Studioart, 1973. — 88,[36]p: chiefly ill(chiefly col), music; 30cm.
ISBN 0 902063 14 6 : £6.75
ISBN 0 902063 13 8 Pbk: £3.75

(B73-30839)

A(V) — Education
Markel, Roberta
Parents' and teachers' guide to music education/ [by] Roberta Markel. — New York: Macmillan; London: Collier-Macmillan, 1972. — xi,209p: ill; 22cm.
Index.
ISBN 0 02 579750 6 : £2.65

(B73-05833)

A(VC) — Teaching
Cambridge Ward Method Centre
The Ward method of teaching music/ [Cambridge Ward Method Centre]. — Cambridge (12 Grange Rd, Cambridge CB3 9DX): Cambridge Ward Method Centre, [1973]. — [18]p: chiefly ill, music; 24cm.
ISBN 0 9502782 0 3 Sd: Unpriced

(B73-08419)

A(VF) — Schools
Schools Council. *Music Committee*
Music and integrated studies in the secondary school: a bulletin/ prepared by a working party of the Schools Council Music Committee. — London (160 Great Portland St., W.1): Schools Council, [1972]. — [1],34p; 30cm.
ISBN 0 901681 28 8 Sd: Free

(B73-11781)

A(VF/GR) — Education. Schools. Activities
Buzzing, Pauline
Let's sing and make music: ideas and advice for those who are engaged in Christian education with children and young people/ [by] Pauline Buzzing. — Redhill: Denholm House Press, 1972. — 112p: music; 20cm.
ISBN 0 85213 062 7 Pbk: £1.20

(B73-04906)

A(VG) — Primary schools
Nye, Robert Evans
Music in the elementary school/ [by] Robert Evans Nye, Vernice Trousdale Nye. — 3rd ed. — Englewood Cliffs; [Hemel Hempstead]: Prentice-Hall, 1970. — xii,660p: ill, music; 24cm.
Fold sheet ('A scope and sequence chart of conceptual learnings related to the elements of music') in pocket. — Previous ed. 1964. — Bibl. — Index.
ISBN 0 13 608141 x : £4.75

(B73-03023)

A(VMX) — Handicapped children
Bailey, Philip
They can make music/ [by] Philip Bailey; with a preface by Lady Hamilton. — London: Oxford University Press, 1973. — xii,143, [4]p,leaf: ill, music; 20cm.
Bibl.p.137-141.
ISBN 0 19 311913 7 : £1.75

(B73-16551)

A(W/Q/P) — Concerts. British Broadcasting Corporation
Curran, Charles John
Music and the BBC/ [by] Charles Curran. — London: British Broadcasting Corporation, [1970]. — 12p; 22cm.
'The original article was published in "The Listener" 11 June 1970'.
ISBN 0 563 10209 8 Sd: Free

(B73-07798)

A(W/Q/P) — Sir Robert Mayer Concerts
Reid, Charles, *b.1900*
 Fifty years of Robert Mayer concerts, 1923-1972/ [by] Charles
 Reid. — Gerrards Cross: Smythe, 1972. — 31,[13]p: ill, ports;
 22cm.
 ISBN 0 900675 78 0 Sd: £0.55(non-net)

(B73-28190)

A(W/Q/YDN/XA1972) — Concerts. Dublin. Ceol Chumann na nOg
Ceol Chumann na nOg
 The story of Ceol Chumann na nOg/ [by] James Blanc. —
 Gerrards Cross: Smythe, 1972. — 17p; 22cm.
 ISBN 0 900675 80 2 Sd: £0.50(non-net)

(B73-28189)

A(W/YD/XLQ76) — Concerts. England. History, 1895-1970
Mayer, *Sir* Robert
 The anatomy of a miracle: Campbell-Orde memorial lecture 1972/
 [by] Sir Robert Mayer. — Gerrards Cross: Smythe, 1972. — 21p;
 21cm. — (Campbell-Orde memorial lectures; 1972)
 ISBN 0 900675 87 x Sd: £0.45(non-net)

(B73-28188)

A(X) — History
Ingman, Nicholas
 The story of music/ text by Nicholas Ingman; illustrations by
 Bernard Brett. — London: Ward Lock, 1972. — 128p: ill(chiefly
 col), facsims, music, ports(some col); 29cm.
 Index.
 ISBN 0 7063 1306 2 : £2.00

(B73-00877)

The **new** Oxford history of music. — London: Oxford University
 Press.
 Vol.7: The Age of Enlightenment, 1745-1790/ edited by Egon Wellesz and
 Frederick Sternfeld. — 1973. — xx,724p,[9] leaves: ill, music; 26cm.
 Bibl.p.637-691. — Index.
 ISBN 0 19 316307 1 : £8.00

(B73-31506)

Rosen, Charles
 The classical style: Haydn, Mozart, Beethoven/ [by] Charles
 Rosen. — London: Faber, 1972. — 3-467p: music; 22cm.
 Originally published 1971. — Bibl.p.13. — Index.
 ISBN 0 571 10234 4 Pbk: £2.00

(B73-04668)

Sternfeld, Frederick William
 A history of Western music/ general editor F.W. Sternfeld. —
 London: Weidenfeld and Nicolson.
 1: Music from the Middle Ages to the Renaissance/ edited by F.W.
 Sternfeld. — 1973. — 524p: music; 25cm.
 Bibl.p.439-486. — List of gramophone records p.431-437. — Index.
 ISBN 0 297 99594 4 : £7.00

(B73-32161)

 5: Music in the modern age/ edited by F.W. Sternfeld. — 1973. — 515p:
 music; 25cm.
 List of records p.443-461. — Bibl.p.463-490. — Index.
 ISBN 0 297 99561 8 : £6.50

(B73-18797)

A(XHK111) — History, 1830-1940
Palmer, Christopher
 Impressionism in music/ [by] Christopher Palmer. — London:
 Hutchinson, 1973. — 248p: music; 23cm.
 Bibl.p.241-243. — Index.
 ISBN 0 09 115140 6 : £3.00
 ISBN 0 09 115141 4 Pbk: £1.75

(B73-20236)

A(Y) — MUSIC OF PARTICULAR LOCALITIES
A(YB/X) — Europe. History
Grout, Donald Jay
 A history of western music/ by Donald Jay Grout. — Revised ed.
 — London: Dent, 1973. — xiv,818p: ill, facsims, music, ports;
 25cm.
 Revised ed. also published, New York: Norton, 1973. — Previous ed., New
 York: Norton, 1960; London: Dent, 1962. — Bibl.p.738-775. — Index.
 ISBN 0 460 03517 7 : £5.95

(B73-18798)

A(YC/BC) — Great Britain. Directories
Music trade directory. — Tunbridge Wells (10a High St., Tunbridge
 Wells, Kent): Music Industry Publications.
 1972-73: [5th ed.]. — [1972]. — 148p: ill; 30cm.
 ISBN 0 903224 00 3 Pbk: £1.80

(B73-05003)

Music trades international year book. — Watford (157 Hagden La.,
 Watford, Herts. WD1 8LW): Trade Papers (London) Ltd.
 1973/ editor R.E.B. Hickman. — 1973. — 206p: ill; 24cm.
 Previous issues published as ' "Piano World and Music Trades Review" year
 book'.
 ISBN 0 903462 01 x Sp: £1.55

(B73-14513)

A(YC/Q/MM) — Great Britain. Incorporated Society of Musicians
Incorporated Society of Musicians
 Handbook and register of members/ Incorporated Society of
 Musicians. — London (48 Gloucester Place, W1H 3HJ):
 Incorporated Society of Musicians.
 1972-73. — 1973. — 319p: ill; 23cm.
 Index.
 ISBN 0 902900 04 8 Pbk: £2.50
 ISBN 0 902900 05 6 Pbk: £2.00

(B73-04667)

A(YC/WE/Q) — England. Festivals. Organisations
British Federation of Music Festivals
 Year book/ British Federation of Music Festivals. — London (106
 Gloucester Place, W1H 3DB): British Federation of Music
 Festivals.
 1973. — 1973. — [2],82p; 24cm.
 ISBN 0 901532 04 5 Sd: £0.60

(B73-12433)

A(YD/XDY81/ZB) — English music, 1560-1640 - compared with
 English poetry, 1558-1625
Johnson, Paula
 Form and transformation in music and poetry of the English
 Renaissance/ by Paula Johnson. — New Haven; London: Yale
 University Press, 1972. — ix,170p: music; 23cm. — (Yale studies
 in English; 179)
 Bibl.p.155-162. — List of records p.163-165. — Index.
 ISBN 0 300 01544 5 : £3.50
 Also classified at 821'.3'09

(B73-03716)

A(YDL/X) — History. Scotland
Elliott, Kenneth
 A history of Scottish music/ [by] Kenneth Elliott and Frederick
 Rimmer. — London: British Broadcasting Corporation, 1973. —
 84p: music; 20cm.
 Bibl.p.6.
 ISBN 0 563 12192 0 Pbk: £0.90

(B73-25526)

A(YDLH) — Edinburgh
Music in Edinburgh: consumers' guide to places of music. —
 Edinburgh (19 Coates Cres., Edinburgh EH3 7AF): Ramsay Head
 Press, 1972. — 23p: ill, ports; 30cm. — (The Edinburgh scene; 3)
 ISBN 0 902859 10 2 Sd: £0.25

(B73-08420)

A(YE/XCS79) — Germany, 1440-1518
Cuyler, Louise
 The Emperor Maximilian I and music/ [by] Louise Cuyler. —
 London: Oxford University Press, 1973. — xii,257,[5]p: ill(incl 1
 col), 2maps, music; 23cm.
 Gramophone record (2s., 7in., 33-1/3rpm) in pocket. — Bibl.p.250-253. —
 Index.
 ISBN 0 19 315223 1 : £10.75
 Also classified at 781.7'43

(B73-24453)

A(YH/XCQ316) — France. History, 1400-1715
Isherwood, Robert M
 Music in the service of the king: France in the seventeenth
 century/ [by] Robert M. Isherwood. — Ithaca; London: Cornell
 University Press, 1973. — xv,422p: ill, music; 24cm.
 Bibl.p.397-414. — Index.
 ISBN 0 8014 0734 6 : £7.90

(B73-17451)

A(YH/XDZA153) — France, 1581-1733
Anthony, James R
 French baroque music: from Beaujoyeulx to Rameau/ [by] James
 R. Anthony. — London: Batsford, 1973. — xi,429,[8]p: ill, music,
 port; 23cm.
 Bibl.p.379-391. — Index.
 ISBN 0 7134 0755 7 : £6.00

(B73-32162)

A(YJ/XCL91/T) — Italy, 1320-1410. Bibliographies
Hagopian, Viola L
 Italian Ars Nova music: a bibliographic guide to modern editions
 and related literature/ [by] Viola L. Hagopian. — 2nd ed., revised
 and expanded. — Berkeley; London: University of California
 Press, 1973. — xv,175p,leaf: 1 ill; 24cm.
 Previous ed. 1964. — Index.
 ISBN 0 520 02223 8 : £4.50

(B73-20592)

A(YM/XA1950) — Russia. History, to 1950
Swan, Alfred Julius
Russian music and its sources in chant and folk-song/ [by] Alfred
J. Swan. — London: J. Baker, 1973. — 234,[17]p: ill, facsim,
music, ports; 23cm.
Bibl.p.217-219. — Index.
ISBN 0 212 98421 7 : £4.50
(B73-22799)

A(YT/T) — United States. Bibliographies
University of Exeter. *Library*
The literature of American music: a fully annotated catalogue of
the books and song collections in Exeter University Library/
compiled by David Horn. — Exeter (Northcote House, The
Queen's Drive, Exeter, Devon): University of Exeter (American
Arts Documentation Centre): University of Exeter Library, 1972.
— [2],170p; 22cm.
Index.
ISBN 0 902746 02 2 Sp: £1.00
(B73-13195)

A(Z) — MUSIC IN RELATION TO OTHER SUBJECTS
A(ZD/B) — Music-influencing postage stamps. Periodicals
The **Baton**: official journal of the Philatelic Music Circle. — Kenton
(c/o Hon. Editor, Irene Lawford, 22 Bouverie Gardens, Kenton,
Middx HA3 0RG): Philatelic Music Circle.
Vol.1, no.1- ; [1969-]. — 1969-. — ill, music; 21cm.
Quarterly. — 28p. in vol. 3, no.4.
Sd: Unpriced
(B73-18101)

A(ZF) — Music-influenced by painting
Lockspeiser, Edward
Music and painting: a study in comparative ideas from Turner to
Schoenberg/ [by] Edward Lockspeiser. — London: Cassell, 1973.
— [9],197,[12]p: ill; 23cm.
Index.
ISBN 0 304 29149 8 : £4.25
Also classified at 759.05
(B73-14124)

A/CC — AESTHETICS
Coker, Wilson
Music & meaning: a theoretical introduction to musical aesthetics/
by Wilson Coker. — New York: Free Press; London:
Collier-Macmillan, 1972. — xv,256p: music; 24cm.
Bibl.p.234-249. — Index.
ISBN 0 02 906350 7 : £4.50
(B73-05832)

A/D — COMPOSITION
Palmer, King
Compose music/ [by] King Palmer. — 2nd ed. — London: Teach
Yourself Books, 1972. — viii,276p: music; 18cm. — (Teach
yourself books)
Previous ed., London: Hodder and Stoughton for the English Universities
Press, 1947. — Bibl.p.270. — Index.
ISBN 0 340 05552 9 : £0.65
(B73-07097)

A/D(M/XML61/C) — Composers, 1911-1971. Encyclopaedias
Thompson, Kenneth
A dictionary of twentieth-century composers, 1911-1971/ [by]
Kenneth Thompson. — London: Faber, 1973. — 666p; 25cm.
ISBN 0 571 09002 8 : £12.00
(B73-09574)

A/D(VG) — Primary schools
Hope-Brown, Margaret
Music with everything/ [by] Margaret Hope-Brown. — London:
F. Warne, 1973. — xii,67,[8]p: ill(some col), music; 26cm.
Bibl.p.65-66.
ISBN 0 7232 1722 x : £3.00
(B73-30643)

A/D(YB/M) — Composers. Europe
Hughes, Gervase
Fifty famous composers/ [by] Gervase Hughes. — Revised and
enlarged ed. — London: Pan Books, 1972. — vii,293p; 18cm.
Previous ed. published as 'The Pan book of great composers'. 1964. —
Index.
ISBN 0 330 13064 1 Pbk: £0.60
(B73-00359)

A/DZ(VF) — Improvisation. Schools
Dankworth, Avril
Voices and instruments/ [by] Avril Dankworth; illustrations by
Leslie Priestley. — St Albans: Hart-Davis, 1973. — 119p: ill,
music; 24cm.
ISBN 0 247 12513 x Pbk: £1.50
(B73-27555)

A/E — PERFORMANCE
A/E(M/EM) — Performances. Illustrations
Auerbach, Erich
An eye for music/ [by] Erich Auerbach; introduction by Lord
Goodman. — London: Hart-Davis, 1971. — 248p: of ill, facsim,
ports; 31cm.
Limited ed. of 1000 signed and numbered copies.
ISBN 0 246 98552 6 : £15.75
(B73-09575)

A/E(XDYQ176) — History, 1575-1750
Donington, Robert
A performer's guide to Baroque music/ [by] Robert Donington. —
London: Faber, 1973. — 320p: music; 26cm.
Bibl.p.301-306. — Index.
ISBN 0 571 09797 9 : £7.00
(B73-27556)

A/EC(P) — Boult, Sir Adrian. Biographies
Boult, *Sir* Adrian
My own trumpet/ [by] Adrian Cedric Boult. — London:
Hamilton, 1973. — x,213,[12]p: ill, ports; 24cm.
Index.
ISBN 0 241 02445 5 : £3.25
(B73-26819)

A/EC(P) — Klemperer, Otto
Heyworth, Peter
Conversations with Klemperer/ compiled and edited by Peter
Heyworth. — London: Gollancz, 1973. — 128,[12]p: ill, ports;
27cm.
List of gramophone records p.105-122. — Index.
ISBN 0 575 01652 3 : £3.00
(B73-16148)

A/EC(P) — Previn, André. Biographies
Greenfield, Edward
André Previn/ [by] Edward Greenfield; with a foreword by
Edward Heath. — [Shepperton]: Allan, 1973. — 96p: ill, ports;
25cm. — [Recordmasters; 4]
Title page imprint: London. — List of records p.93-96.
ISBN 0 7110 0370 x : £2.25
(B73-21633)

A/EC(P) — Sargent, Sir Malcolm. Biographies
Reid, Charles, *b.1900*
Malcolm Sargent: a biography/ by Charles Reid. — London:
Hodder and Stoughton, 1973. — xviii,491,[8]p: ill, ports; 18cm.
Originally published, London: Hamilton, 1968. — Index.
ISBN 0 340 17662 8 Pbk: £0.60
(B73-25531)

A/EC(P/D) — Stokowski, Leopold. Essays
Johnson, Edward
Stokowski: essays in analysis of his art/ edited by Edward
Johnson. — London: Triad Press, 1973. — 116p: ill, music, ports;
30cm.
Limited ed. of 400 copies. — List of films p.83-84. — List of records
p.87-106. — Index.
ISBN 0 902070 06 1 Pbk: £1.95
(B73-14763)

**A/EC(P/XA1923) — Beecham, Sir Thomas, bart. Biographies, to
1923**
Beecham, *Sir* Thomas, *bart*
A mingled chime: leaves from an autobiography/ [by] Sir Thomas
Beecham, bart. — London: White Lion Publishers, 1973. — 198p;
23cm.
Originally published, London: Hutchinson, 1944.
ISBN 0 85617 163 8 : £2.25
(B73-20240)

A/FD — RECORDED MUSIC
A/FD(WM) — Trade lists. Decca
Decca Group records, musicassettes and stereo 8 cartridges, main
catalogue. — London: Decca Record Co.
1973: up to and including September 1972. — 1973. — 742p in various
pagings; 26cm.
ISBN 0 901364 04 5 : £5.00
(B73-07316)

A/FD(WT) — Lists
The **art** of record buying: a list of recommended microgroove
recordings. — London: E.M.G.
1973. — [1973]. — [2],304p: map; 23cm.
ISBN 0 900982 04 7 : £2.15
(B73-15041)

A/FD(XNC51/D) — History, 1923-1973. Essays
Wimbush, Roger
'The Gramophone' jubilee book/ [compiled by Roger Wimbush].
— Harrow (177 Kenton Rd, Harrow, Middx): General
Gramophone Publications Ltd, 1973. — x,310,[17]p: ill, facsims,
ports; 22cm.
ISBN 0 902470 04 3 : £2.50
(B73-13020)

A/FF(WT) — Stereophonic records. Lists
The **stereo** record guide. — [Blackpool] (Squires Gate, Station
Approach, Blackpool, Lancs. FY82 SP): Long Playing Record
Library Ltd.
Vol.8: Composer index Me-Z/ by Edward Greenfield, Robert Layton, Ivan
March; edited by Ivan March. — 1972. — vi p,p1331-1611; 23cm.
ISBN 0 901143 06 5 : £1.95

(B73-08019)

A/FH — MECHANICAL MUSIC
A/FH/B — Mechanical music. Automata
Ord-Hume, Arthur Wolfgang Julius Gerald
Clockwork music: an illustrated history of mechanical musical
instruments from the musical box to the pianola, from automaton
lady virginal players to orchestrion/ [by] Arthur W.J.G.
Ord-Hume; illustrated with contemporary material. — London:
Allen and Unwin, 1973. — 3-334p: ill, facsims; 26cm.
Index.
ISBN 0 04 789004 5 : £5.95

(B73-14765)

A/FM — Fair organs
Fair Organ Preservation Society
Organs, rides and engines on parade/ Fair Organ Preservation
Society. — [Manchester] (3 Bentley Rd, Denton, Manchester M34
AH2): F.O.P.S.
Vol.2. — [1972]. — [1],40p: of ill; 25cm.
ISBN 0 9502701 0 5 Sd: £0.50

(B73-04221)

A/FY — MUSICAL CHARACTER
A/G(BC) — Folk music. Directories
Folk directory. — London: English Folk Dance and Song Society.
1973/ edited by Tony Wales. — 1973. — 184p: ill, ports; 23cm.
ISBN 0 85418 087 7 : £1.25 (£0.75 to members of the English Folk Dance
and Song Society)
ISBN 0 85418 086 9 Pbk: £0.60 (£0.30 to members of the English Folk
Dance and Song Society)

(B73-07790)

A/G/E(YDL/Q) — Folk music. Performance. Scotland. Organisations
Scottish folk directory. — [Perth] (12 Mansfield Rd, Scone, Perth):
[Sheila Douglas].
1973. — [1973]. — [19]p; 22cm.
ISBN 0 903919 00 1 Sd: £0.20

(B73-14762)

A/GB — Popular music
Taylor, Derek
As time goes by/ [by] Derek Taylor. — London: Davis-Poynter,
1973. — 159p; 23cm.
Index.
ISBN 0 7067 0027 9 : £2.00

(B73-21631)

A/GB(B) — Popular music. Periodicals
Listen Easy. — Hitchin (43 Queen St., Hitchin, Herts.): B.C.
Enterprises.
No.1- ; Oct. 1972-. — 1972-. — ill, ports(some col); 28cm.
Monthly. — 40p. in 1st issue.
Sd: £0.20

(B73-08998)

A/GB(XHS65) — Popular music. History, 1837-1901
Pearsall, Ronald
Victorian popular music/ [by] Ronald Pearsall. — Newton Abbot:
David and Charles, 1973. — 240p: facsims, table, music, ports;
23cm.
Bibl.p.233-236. — Index.
ISBN 0 7153 5689 5 : £3.50

(B73-03713)

A/H/G/(YD) — Folk dances. England
Kidson, Frank
English folk-song and dance/ by Frank Kidson and Mary Neal.
— Wakefield: E.P. Publishing, 1972. — [4],vii,178p,[6] leaves: ill,
facsim, music; 20cm.
Facsimile reprint of 1st ed., London: Cambridge University Press, 1915. —
Bibl. — Index.
ISBN 0 85409 917 4 : £2.10
Primary classification ADW/G(YD)

(B73-00881)

A/HG(X) — Afro-American music. History
Roberts, John Storm
Black music of two worlds/ [by] John Storm Roberts. — London:
Allen Lane, 1973. — x,286p: music; 23cm.
Originally published, New York: Praeger, 1972. — Bibl.p.261-267. — List of
records p.269-280. — Index.
ISBN 0 7139 0536 0 : £3.50

(B73-16795)

A/LZ — ELEMENTS OF MUSIC
A/R — Harmony
Ottman, Robert W
Advanced harmony: theory and practice/ [by] Robert W. Ottman.
— 2nd ed. — Englewood Cliffs; [Hemel Hempstead]:
Prentice-Hall, 1972. — ix,310p: music; 24cm.
Previous ed., Englewood Cliffs: Prentice-Hall, 1961. — Bibl.p.297-298. —
Index.
ISBN 0 13 012955 0 : £5.00

(B73-03715)

A/RM — Counterpoint
Rubio, Samuel
Classical polyphony/ [by] Samuel Rubio; translated [from the
Spanish] by Thomas Rive. — Oxford: Blackwell, 1972. — xvi,avi,
178p: ill, facsims, music; 23cm.
Translation of 'La Polifonía clásica'. Madrid: El Escorial, 1956. — Bibl.p.
163-170. — Index.
ISBN 0 631 11740 7 : £3.45

(B73-04219)

AB — MUSICAL LITERATURE. VOCAL MUSIC
AB/E(VC/P) — Singing. Teachers. White, Ernest George
Hewlett, Arthur Donald
Think afresh about the voice: a reappraisal of the teaching of
Ernest George White/ by Arthur D. Hewlett. — 2nd ed. —
[Deal] (Hillcrest, Ringwood, Deal, Kent): Ernest George White
Society, 1973. — v,60p,8 leaves: ill, form, music; 21cm.
Title page imprint: London. — Previous ed. 1970. — Index.
ISBN 0 9501610 1 2 Pbk: £0.75

(B73-19499)

AC — MUSICAL LITERATURE. OPERA
AC(C) — Encyclopaedias
Ewen, David
The new encyclopedia of the opera/ by David Ewen. — London:
Vision Press, 1973. — viii,759p; 24cm.
Originally published, New York: Hill and Wang, 1971.
ISBN 0 85478 033 5 : £7.20

(B73-32163)

Rosenthal, Harold
Concise Oxford dictionary of opera/ by Harold Rosenthal and
John Warrack. — [1st ed. reprinted with corrections]. — London:
Oxford University Press, 1973. — xv,446p; 20cm.
First ed. originally published 1964. — Also available in a boxed set with
'The concise Oxford dictionary of music'. — Bibl.p.ix-xii.
ISBN 0 19 311305 8 Pbk: £2.00
ISBN 0 19 311312 0 Pbk: £0.90

(B73-30857)

AC(XA1940) — Opera, to 1900
Graf, Herbert
The opera and its future in America/ by Herbert Graf. — Port
Washington; London: Kennikat Press, 1973. — 3-305p: ill, facsim,
music, plans; 26cm.
Originally published, New York: Norton, 1941. — Bibl.p.291-296. — Index.
ISBN 0 8046 1744 9 : £9.75

(B73-24202)

AC(XFYB201) — Opera. History, 1762-1972
Lang, Paul Henry
The experience of opera/ [by] Paul Henry Lang. — London:
Faber, 1973. — 331p; 23cm.
Index.
ISBN 0 571 10146 1 : £4.00

(B73-06590)

AC(YD/XEZQ102) — Opera. England, 1695-1796
Fiske, Roger
English theatre music in the eighteenth century/ [by] Roger Fiske.
— London: Oxford University Press, 1973. — xv,684,16p,leaf: ill,
music, ports; 24cm.
Bibl.p.641-645. — Index.
ISBN 0 19 316402 7 : £12.50

(B73-13015)

AC(YDN/XFE93) — Dublin, 1705-1797
Walsh, T J
Opera in Dublin, 1705-1797: the social scene/ [by] T.J. Walsh. —
Dublin: Allen Figgis, 1973. — xv,386,[16]p: ill, ports; 25cm.
Facsims. on lining papers. — Bibl.p.365-369. — Index.
ISBN 0 900372 74 5 : £5.00

(B73-30858)

AC/E(YC/Q) — Great Britain. Organisations
National Operatic and Dramatic Association
Year book/ National Operatic and Dramatic Association. —
London (1 Crestfield St., WC1H 8AU): National Operatic and
Dramatic Association.
1973. — [1973]. — [1],342p: ill, map; 19cm.
ISBN 0 901318 05 1 Pbk: £2.50
Also classified at 792'.0222'06242

(B73-08999)

ACF — MUSICAL LITERATURE. OPERETTA
ACFBN — Operetta. Libretto stories. Paraphrases
Drinkrow, John
    The vintage operetta book/ [by] John Drinkrow; illustrated from
    the Raymond Mander and Joe Mitchenson Theatre Collection. —
    Reading: Osprey Publishing, 1972. — 124,[16]p: ill, ports; 20cm.
    List of records p.112-124.
    ISBN 0 85045 102 7 : £1.95

(B73-03717)

ACLMBM — Ballad opera. The Grub Street opera. Libretto
Fielding, Henry
    The Grub-Street opera/ [by] Henry Fielding; edited by L.J.
    Morrissey. — Edinburgh: Oliver and Boyd, 1973. — [7],133p;
    22cm. — (The Fountainwell drama texts; 25)
    Bibl.p.129-130.
    ISBN 0 05 002755 7 : £2.00
    ISBN 0 05 002754 9 Pbk: £0.85

(B73-31566)

AD — MUSICAL LITERATURE. CHORAL MUSIC
AD(YDKRL/WB/XPG26) — Llangollen. International Musical
Eisteddfod, 1947-1972
Wright, Kenneth Anthony
    Gentle are its songs/ [by] Kenneth A. Wright; [with Welsh
    translation by] Urien Wiliam. — [London] (P.O. Box 775, W9
    1LN): Sir Gerald Nabarro (Publications) Ltd, 1973. — xii,232,
    [24]p: ill(some col), map, ports; 23cm.
    English and Welsh text, 2nd title page in Welsh. — Index.
    ISBN 0 903699 00 1 : £3.50

(B73-16140)

AD(YDKRL/WB/XPG3) — International Musical Eisteddfod,
Denbighshire, Llangollen. History, 1947-9
Tudor, Harold
    Making the nations sing: the birth of the Llangollen International
    Eisteddfod/ by Harold Tudor. — Birmingham (61 Lockwood Rd,
    Northfield, Birmingham): H. Tudor, 1973. — [5],49p; 21cm.
    Limited ed. of 100 copies.
    ISBN 0 9502935 0 4 Sd: Private circulation

(B73-19495)

AD/E — Performance
Holst, Imogen
    Conducting a choir: a guide for amateurs/ [by] Imogen Holst. —
    London: Oxford University Press, 1973. — xii,161p: ill, music;
    21cm.
    Bibl.p.150-152. — Index.
    ISBN 0 19 313407 1 Pbk: £1.30

(B73-16147)

Reynolds, Gordon
    The choirmaster in action/ [by] Gordon Reynolds. — Borough
    Green: Novello, 1972. — 62p: music; 19cm.
    Bibl.p.55-62.
    ISBN 0 85360 057 0 Pbk: £0.50

(B73-15415)

AD/LD(YD/D) — Church music. England. Essays
    English church music: a collection of essays. — Croydon
    (Addington Palace, Croydon, CR9 5AD): Royal School of Church
    Music.
    1973. — [1973]. — 3-66p,2 leaves: ports; 22cm.
    ISBN 0 85402 052 7 Pbk: £0.90

(B73-18105)

AD/LD(YDEUW/TE) — Church music. St George's Chapel, Windsor
Castle. Bibliographies of manuscripts
Windsor Castle. *St George's Chapel*
    The musical manuscripts of St George's Chapel, Windsor Castle: a
    descriptive catalogue/ by Clifford Mould. — Windsor (2 Victoria
    St., Windsor, Berks.): Oxley and Son (Windsor) Ltd for the Dean
    and Canons of St George's Chapel in Windsor Castle, 1973. — ix,
    74p: music; 28cm. — (Historical monographs relating to St
    George's Chapel, Windsor Castle; vol.14)
    ISBN 0 902187 16 3 Pbk: £1.25

(B73-09262)

AD/LE(YD/XDXJ341) — Cathedral music. England, 1549-1889
Bumpus, John Skelton
    A history of English cathedral music 1549-1889/ [by] John S.
    Bumpus. — [1st ed. reprinted]; with the addition of a new
    introduction by Watkins Shaw. — [Farnborough]: Gregg, 1972. —
    [6],ix,580p,24 leaves: ill, music, ports; 19cm.
    Facsimile reprint of 1st ed., London: T. Werner Laurie, 1908. —
    Bibl.p.571-573. — Index.
    ISBN 0 576 28244 8 : £10.80

(B73-13016)

ADG — Roman liturgy. Ordinary of the Mass
Animuccia, Giovanni
    Missarum liber primus/ [by] Giovanni Animuccia. — [1st ed.
    reprinted]; with the addition of an introduction by Thurston Dart.
    — Farnborough: Gregg, 1972. — [220]p: of music; 32cm.
    Latin text, English title page and introduction. — Facsimile reprint of 1st
    ed., Romae: Apud haeredes Valerii et Aloysii Doricorum, 1567.
    ISBN 0 576 28220 0 : £12.60

(B73-00361)

ADGM — Liturgical music. Anglican liturgy
Barnard, John, *fl.1641*
    First book of selected church musick/ [by] John Barnard. — [1st
    ed. reprinted]; with a new introduction by John Morehen. —
    [Farnborough]: Cregg, 1972. — 10v: chiefly music; 28cm.
    Facsimile reprint of 1st ed., London: Printed by Edward Griffin, 1641.
    ISBN 0 576 28200 6 : £72.00

(B73-16145)

ADTDS — Plainsong. Byzantine chant
Wellesz, Egon
    Studies in Eastern Chant/ general editors Egon Wellesz and Miloš
    Velimirović. — London: Oxford University Press.
    Vol.3/ edited by Miloš Velimirović. — 1973. — viii,187,[5]p: ill, facsims,
    music; 23cm.
    Index.
    ISBN 0 19 316320 9 : £6.00

(B73-22800)

ADW/G(YC) — Folk songs. Great Britain
Wales, Tony
    I'll sing you two o: words of more familiar folk songs for
    campfire, ceilidh and club/ edited by Tony Wales. — London:
    English Folk Dance and Song Society, 1973. — 60p: ill; 18cm.
    Index.
    ISBN 0 85418 089 3 Pbk: £0.40

(B73-22269)

ADW/G(YD) — Folk songs. England
Kidson, Frank
    English folk-song and dance/ by Frank Kidson and Mary Neal.
    — Wakefield: E.P. Publishing, 1972. — [4],vii,178p,[6] leaves: ill,
    facsim, music; 20cm.
    Facsimile reprint of 1st ed., London: Cambridge University Press, 1915. —
    Bibl. — Index.
    ISBN 0 85409 917 4 : £2.10
    Also classified at A/H/G/(YD)

(B73-00881)

Langstaff, John
    Soldier, soldier, won't you marry me?/ compiled by John
    Langstaff; illustrated by Anita Lobel. — Tadworth: World's Work,
    1973. — [31]p: chiefly col ill, music; 25cm.
    'John Langstaff has chosen his own favourite versions of the words and
    music. The music has been arranged for simple piano and guitar.' - book
    jacket. — Originally published, Garden City [N.Y.]: Doubleday, 1972.
    ISBN 0 437 54105 3 : £1.20

(B73-20978)

Sharp, Cecil James
    English folk song - some conclusions/ [by] Cecil J. Sharp. — 4th
    revised ed./ prepared by Maud Karpeles; with an appreciation of
    Cecil Sharp by Ralph Vaughan Williams. — Wakefield: E.P.
    Publishing, 1972. — xxv,199p: music; 22cm.
    Fourth revised ed. originally published, London: Heinemann, 1965. — Bibl.
    p.181-184. — Index.
    ISBN 0 85409 929 8 Pbk: £1.75

(B73-02067)

    Singers: a directory of freelance amateur singers in London and the
    Home Counties. — London (14 Barlby Rd, W10 6AR): Autolycus
    Publications.
    '73: 2nd ed./ [compiled by G.P. Humphreys]. — 1972 [i.e.1973]. — [15]p;
    21cm.
    ISBN 0 903413 10 8 Sd: £0.35

(B73-20239)

ADW/G(YDCR) — Folk songs. Sussex
Copper, Bob
    Songs and Southern breezes: country folk and country ways/ [by]
    Bob Copper; with drawings by the author; foreword by John
    Arlott. — London: Heinemann, 1973. — xv,297,[12]p: ill, map(on
    lining papers), music, ports; 23cm.
    ISBN 0 434 14456 8 : £3.50
    Primary classification ADW/G(YDCV)

(B73-27558)

ADW/G(YDCV) — Folk songs. Hampshire
Copper, Bob
    Songs and Southern breezes: country folk and country ways/ [by]
    Bob Copper; with drawings by the author; foreword by John
    Arlott. — London: Heinemann, 1973. — xv,297,[12]p: ill, map(on
    lining papers), music, ports; 23cm.
    ISBN 0 434 14456 8 : £3.50
    Also classified at ADW/G(YDCR); 784.4'9422'5; 784.4'9422'7

(B73-27558)

ADW/G(YMUL) — Folk songs. Lvov
Uhma, Stefan
Lwowskie piosenki/ Stefan Uhma; w opracowaniu i z
uzupelnieniami Mariana Wagnera. — Londyn [London] (240
King's St., W6 9JT): Kola Lwowian.
Część 1: Jak sie rodziły lwowskie piosenki. — 1971. — 43p; 23cm.
Sd: £0.50

(B73-31510)

Część 2: Kobieta i miłość. — 1971. — 60p; 23cm.
Sd: £0.50

(B73-31511)

Część 3: Pod znakiem Marsa/ [ilustracje Marek Gramski]. — 1973. — 74p:
ill, music, port; 23cm.
ISBN 0 9503005 0 0 Sd: £0.50

(B73-24206)

ADW/GB(XPK24) — Popular songs. History, 1950-1973
Barnes, Ken
Twenty years of pop/ by Ken Barnes. — Havant: K. Mason;
[London]: [Distributed by Barrie and Jenkins], 1973. — 96p:
ports; 21cm.
ISBN 0 85937 024 0 Pbk: £0.75

(B73-30278)

ADW/GB(XPN21) — Popular songs. History, 1953-1973
The **Radio** One story of pop: the first encyclopaedia of pop. —
London (49 Poland St., W1A 2LG): Phoebus Publishing Co.
Vol.1, no.1- ; 24th Sept 1973-. — 1973-. — ill(chiefly col), ports(chiefly
col); 30cm.
Weekly. — In 26 parts. — [2],29,[2]p(2fold) in 1st issue.
Sd: £0.25

(B73-29553)

ADW/GB/D — Popular songs. Composition
Harris, Rolf
Write your own pop song with Rolf Harris/ [illustrated by the
author]. — London: Wolfe: Keith Prowse Music Publishing Co.
Ltd, 1973. — 111p: ill, facsims, music, ports; 23cm.
ISBN 0 7234 0509 3 : £2.00

(B73-26165)

ADW/GNFF — Farm workers' songs
Palmer, Roy
The painful plough: a portrait of the agricultural labourer in the
nineteenth century from folk songs and ballads and contemporary
accounts/ selected and edited by Roy Palmer; foreword by
Edward Thompson. — London: Cambridge University Press,
1973. — 64p: ill, facsims, music, ports; 28cm.
Bibl. — Index.
ISBN 0 521 08512 8 Sd: £0.80(non-net)

(B73-02068)

ADW/GNGC(YT) — Coal mining songs. United States
Green, Archie
Only a miner: studies in recorded coal-mining songs/ [by] Archie
Green. — Urbana; London: University of Illinois Press, 1972. —
xv,504p: ill, facsims, music, ports; 26cm.
Bibl.p.453-478. — Index.
ISBN 0 252 00181 8 : £5.65

(B73-06593)

ADW/KG(XPE7) — Military songs, 1939-45
Page, Martin, *b.1938*
Kiss me goodnight, Sergeant Major: the songs and ballads of
World War II/ edited by Martin Page; illustrated by Bill Tidy;
introduction by Spike Milligan. — London: Hart-Davis,
MacGibbon, 1973. — 192p: ill; 25cm.
Index.
ISBN 0 246 10748 0 Pbk: £1.60

(B73-29557)

ADWBP — Songs. Concordances
Preston, Michael J
A complete concordance to the songs of the early Tudor court/ by
Michael J. Preston. — Leeds (Hudson Rd, Leeds LS9 7DL): W.S.
Maney and Son, 1972. — x,433p; 23cm. (Compendia:
computer-generated aids to literary and linguistic research; vol.4)
ISBN 0 901286 03 6 : £6.50

(B73-20977)

AEZDU(YJ) — Madrigals. Italy
Roche, Jerome
The madrigal/ [by] Jerome Roche. — London: Hutchinson, 1972.
— 167p: ill, music; 23cm.
Bibl.p.161-162. — Index.
ISBN 0 09 113260 6 : £2.60
ISBN 0 09 113261 4 Pbk: £1.35

(B73-02066)

AK — MUSICAL LITERATURE. VOCAL SOLOS
AK/E(M/XN53) — Singers. Biographies, 1920-1972
Simpson, Harold
Singers to remember/ [by] Harold Simpson. — [Lingfield]:
Oakwood Press, [1973]. — 223p; 23cm.
ISBN 0 85361 113 0 : £3.00

(B73-06591)

AKDW/G/E(P) — Trapp, Maria Augusta. Biographies
Trapp, Maria Augusta
Maria/ by Maria von Trapp. — London: Coverdale House;
London: Distributed ... [by] Hodder and Stoughton, 1973. — 188,
[16]p: ill(some col), ports(some col); 19cm.
Originally published, Carol Stream [Ill.]: Creation House, 1972.
ISBN 0 902088 42 4 : £1.75
ISBN 0 902088 43 2 Pbk: £0.40

(B73-25530)

AKDW/G/E(YDJHT/P) — Folk singers. Tyneside. Ridley, George
Ridley, George
George Ridley, Gateshead poet and vocalist/ [edited with an]
introduction by David Harker. — Newcastle upon Tyne: Graham,
1973. — 45p: ill, music; 22cm.
ISBN 0 902833 81 2 Sd: £0.40

(B73-19498)

AKDW/GB(P) — Beatles, The. Biographies
McCabe, Peter
Apple to the core: the unmaking of the Beatles/ [by] Peter
McCabe & Robert D. Schonfeld. — London (37 Museum St.,
W.C.1): Martin Brian and O'Keeffe Ltd, 1972. — 3-209p; 21cm.
ISBN 0 85616 090 3 : £2.00

(B73-05835)

AKDW/GB/E(M) — Popular songs. Singers
The **'Melody Maker'** file. — London (161 Fleet St., EC4P 4AA):
IPC Specialist and Professional Press Ltd.
1974/ [editor: Ray Coleman]. — [1973]. — [1],127p: ports(some col); 28cm.
ISBN 0 617 00093 x Pbk: £1.00

(B73-31505)

AKDW/GB/E(M/XN52) — Popular songs. Singers, 1920-1971
Barnes, Ken
Sinatra and the great song stylists/ [by] Ken Barnes with
contributions from...[others]. — Shepperton: Allan, 1972. — 192,
[48]p: ill, ports; 24cm.
Title page imprint: London. — Lists of recordings. — Index.
ISBN 0 7110 0400 5 : £3.00

(B73-00880)

AKDW/GB/E(P) — Beatles, The. Biographies
McCabe, Peter
Apple to the core/ [by] Peter McCabe and Robert D. Schonfeld.
— London: Sphere, 1973. — 3-209p; 20cm.
Originally published, New York: Pocket Books; London: Martin, Brian and
O'Keefe, 1972.
ISBN 0 7221 5899 8 Pbk: £0.40

(B73-05834)

AKDW/GB/E(P) — Popular songs. Humperdinck, Engelbert.
Biographies
Short, Don
Engelbert Humperdinck: the authorised biography/ by Don Short.
— London: New English Library, 1972. — 96,[12]p: ill, ports;
18cm.
ISBN 0 450 01453 3 Pbk: £0.40

(B73-02065)

AKDW/GB/E(P) — Simon, Paul. Biographies
Leigh, Spencer
Paul Simon - now and then/ by Spencer Leigh. — Liverpool (C52
The Temple, 24 Dale St., Liverpool L2 5RL): Raven Books, 1973.
— 110p: ports; 21cm.
ISBN 0 85977 008 7 Pbk: £0.60

(B73-28187)

AKDW/GCW/(P) — Country 'n' western singers. Cash, Johnny.
Biographies
Wren, Christopher, *b.1936*
Johnny Cash - winners got scars too/ by Christopher Wren. —
London: W.H. Allen, 1973. — [7],229,[16]p: ill, ports; 23cm.
Originally published as 'Winners got scars too'. New York: Dial Press, 1971.
ISBN 0 491 00794 9 : £2.00

(B73-09000)

AKDW/HHW(X) — Blues. History
Oliver, Paul
The story of the blues/ [by] Paul Oliver. — Harmondsworth:
Penguin, 1972. — [2],176,[2]p: ill, facsims, music, ports; 30cm.
Originally published, London: Barrie and Rockcliff, 1969. — Bibl.p.171-172.
— List of records p.172-174. — Index.
ISBN 0 14 003509 5 Pbk: £0.75

(B73-00879)

AKDW/HK(M//M) — Rock 'n' roll. Singers. Illustrations
Hirsch, Abby
The photography of rock/ edited by Abby Hirsch; designed by
George Delmerico. — Henley-on-Thames (Cobb House, Nuffield,
Henley-on-Thames, Oxon. RG9 5RU): Aidan Ellis Publishing Ltd,
1973. — 214,[24]p: of ill, ports; 28cm.
Originally published, Indianapolis: Bobbs-Merrill, 1972.
ISBN 0 85628 006 2 Pbk: £1.95

(B73-22267)

AKF/E(P) — Piaf, Edith. Biographies
Berteaut, Simone
Piaf/ [by] Simone Berteaut; translated from the French by
Ghislaine Boulanger. — Harmondsworth: Penguin, 1973. — 3-
434,[8]p: ports; 19cm.
This translation originally published, London: W.H. Allen, 1970. —
Translation of 'Piaf'. Paris: Laffont, 1969. — Index.
ISBN 0 14 003669 5 Pbk: £0.60

(B73-25529)

AKFDW/HHW/E(P) — Holiday, Billie. Biographies
Holiday, Billie
Lady sings the blues/ [by] Billie Holiday with William Dufty. —
London (24 Highbury Cres., N5 1RX): Barrie and Jenkins, 1973.
— [6],234,[4]p: ports; 23cm.
Also published, London: Sphere, 1973. — Originally published, Garden City
[N.Y.]: Doubleday, 1956; London: Barrie and Jenkins, 1958. — List of
gramophone records p.208-234.
ISBN 0 214 66872 x : £2.95

(B73-12435)

AKFDW/HHW/E(P) — Smith, Bessie. Biographies
Albertson, Chris
Bessie/ [by] Chris Albertson. — London: Barrie and Jenkins,
1972. — 253p: ill, facsims, ports; 24cm.
Originally published, New York: Random House, 1972. — Bibl.p.243-244.
— List of gramophone records p.239-242. — Index.
ISBN 0 214 65409 5 : £2.95

(B73-13017)

AKFDW/JV/E(P) — Music hall singers. Lloyd, Marie. Biographies
Farson, Daniel
Marie Lloyd & music hall/ by Daniel Farson. — London (28
Maiden La., WC2E 7JP): Tom Stacey Ltd, 1972. — 176,[16]p: ill,
facsims, ports; 24cm.
Index.
ISBN 0 85468 082 9 : £3.00

(B73-03721)

AKFL/E(P) — Melba, Dame Nellie. Biographies
Hetherington, John, b.1907
Melba: a biography/ by John Hetherington. — London: Faber,
1973. — 3-312p: 1 ill, facsim; 20cm.
Originally published 1967. — Bibl.p.299-303. — Index.
ISBN 0 571 10286 7 Pbk: £1.40

(B73-11782)

AKFQ/E(P) — Baker, Janet. Biographies
Blyth, Alan
Janet Baker/ [by] Alan Blyth. — [Shepperton]: Allan, 1973. —
64p: ill, ports; 25cm. — [Recordmasters; 3]
Title page imprint: London. — List of records p.61-64.
ISBN 0 7110 0424 2 : £1.75

(B73-21632)

AKG/E(P) — Chevalier, Maurice. Biographies
Chevalier, Maurice
Bravo Maurice!: a compilation from the autobiographical writings
of Maurice Chevalier/ translated from the French by Mary Fitton.
— London: Allen and Unwin, 1973. — 240,[12]p: ill, ports; 23cm.
Translation of 'Bravo Maurice!' Paris: Julliard, 1968.
ISBN 0 04 920037 2 : £3.50

(B73-24204)

AKG/E(P) — Lennon, John. Biographies
Wenner, Jann
Lennon remembers: the 'Rolling Stone' interviews [with John
Lennon and Yoko Ono]/ by Jann Wenner. — London: Talmy,
1972. — 190p: ill; 23cm.
Originally published, New York: Straight Arrow, 1971.
ISBN 0 900735 10 4 : £2.25

(B73-07792)

AKG/E(P) — MacRae, Kenny. Biographies
MacRae, Donald
A life of song: the story of Kenny MacRae/ by Donald MacRae.
— [Glasgow] (38 Lilybank Gardens, Glasgow G12 8SA): [D.
MacRae], 1972. — 55p: ill, ports; 19cm.
ISBN 0 9502730 0 7 Sd: £0.40

(B73-05260)

AKG/FD(P/WT) — Sinatra, Frank. Recorded music. Lists
Hainsworth, Brian
Songs by Sinatra, 1939-1970/ compiled by Brian Hainsworth. —
Bramhope (Little Timbers, Wyncroft Grove, Bramhope, Leeds
LS16 9DG): B. Hainsworth, 1973. — 2-92p; 21cm.
ISBN 0 9502861 0 9 Sd: £1.00

(B73-12708)

AKGDW/G/E(P) — Maguire, John. Biographies
Maguire, John
Come day, go day, God send Sunday: the songs and life story,
told in his own words, of John Maguire, traditional singer and
farmer from Co. Fermanagh/ collated by Robin Morton. —
London: Routledge and Kegan Paul, 1973. — xiv,188,[3]p: ill,
music, ports; 23cm.
Index.
ISBN 0 7100 7634 7 : £2.95

(B73-24205)

AKGH/E(P) — Kelly, Michael. Biographies
Kelly, Michael, b.1762
Solo recital: the reminiscences of Michael Kelly. — [Abridged
ed.]/ edited and with a biographical index by Herbert van Thal;
introduction by J.C. Trewin. — London: Folio Society, 1972. —
372p,12 leaves: ill, music, ports; 23cm.
Full ed. originally published in 2 vols as 'Reminiscences of M.K. of the
King's Theatre'/ edited by T.E. Hook. London: Colburn, 1826. — Index.
ISBN 0 85067 055 1 : £2.90 to members of the Society only

(B73-03213)

AL — MUSICAL LITERATURE. INSTRUMENTAL MUSIC
AL/B(X) — Instruments. History
Buchner, Alexander
Musical instruments: an illustrated history/ [by] Alexander
Buchner; [translated from the Czech MS. by Bořek Vančura]. —
London: Octopus Books, 1973. — 3-275p: chiefly ill(some col),
facsims; 34cm.
Ill. on lining papers. — Originally published in English translation as
'Musical instruments through the ages' / translated by Iris Urwin. London:
Spring Books, 1956.
ISBN 0 7064 0015 1 : £4.25

(B73-24887)

ALF(XFQ31) — Concertos. History, 1715-1745
Hutchings, Arthur
The baroque concerto/ by Arthur Hutchings. — 3rd revised ed.
— London: Faber, 1973. — 363p,10 leaves: ill, maps, music, port;
23cm.
Previous ed. 1964. — Bibl.p.351-356. — Index.
ISBN 0 571 04808 0 : £4.20

(B73-17452)

AM — MUSICAL LITERATURE. ORCHESTRAL MUSIC
AM/HMBN — Ballet music. Stories
Chappell, Warren
The sleeping beauty/ from the Tales of Charles Perrault; music by
Peter Ilyich Tschaikovsky; adapted and illustrated by Warren
Chappell. — London: Kaye and Ward, 1973. — [38]p: ill(chiefly
col), music; 20x26cm.
ISBN 0 7182 0949 4 : £1.25

(B73-24333)

**AMM/E(QB/XMN59) — Houston Symphony Orchestra. History,
1913-1971**
Roussel, Hubert
The Houston Symphony Orchestra, 1913-1971/ [by] Hubert
Roussel. — Austin; London: University of Texas Press, 1972. —
x,247,[16]p: ill, ports; 24cm.
Index.
ISBN 0 292 73000 4 : £3.40

(B73-10709)

AMM/HM — Ballet
Searle, Humphrey
Ballet music: an introduction/ by Humphrey Searle. — Second
revised ed. — New York: Dover Publications; London: Constable,
1973. — 256,[16]p: ill, ports; 22cm.
Previous ed.: London: Cassell, 1958. — Bibl.: p.232-233. — Index.
ISBN 0 486 22917 3 Pbk: £1.50

(B73-32165)

AMME — Symphonies
Rauchhaupt, Ursula von
The symphony/ edited by Ursula von Rauchhaupt; contributors
Hermann Beck ... [and others]; picture editor and design Franz
Heuss; translation [from the German] Eugene Hartzell. —
London: Thames and Hudson, 1973. — 324p: ill(some col),
facsims, map, music, ports(some col); 31x31cm.
'Part of this impression appears in conjunction with the record issue "The
Symphony", on the occasion of the 75th anniversary of the Deutsche
Grammophon Gesellschaft.' - title page verso. — Translation of 'Die Welt
der Symphonie'. Hamburg: Polydor International, 1972. — Bibl.p.304-308.
— List of records p.318-320. — Index.
ISBN 0 500 01099 4 : £8.50

(B73-26166)

AMT — MUSICAL LITERATURE. JAZZ
AMT(D/XPQ17) — Jazz. Essays, 1955-1971
Green, Benny
Drums in my ears/ [by] Benny Green. — London (10 Earlham
St., WC2H 9LP): Davis-Poynter, 1973. — 188p; 23cm.
ISBN 0 7067 0066 x : £2.50
ISBN 0 7067 0067 8 Pbk: £1.50

(B73-10167)

AMT(P) — Dorsey brothers. Biographies
Sanford, Herb
Tommy and Jimmy - the Dorsey years/ [by] Herb Sanford. — [Shepperton]: Allan, 1972. — 3-305p: ill, ports; 24cm.
Title page imprint: London. — Also published, New York: Arlington House, 1972. — Index.
ISBN 0 7110 0416 1 : £2.95

(B73-18107)

AMT/E(M) — Jazz musicians
Wilmer, Valerie
Jazz people/ by Valerie Wilmer; with photographs by the author. — 2nd ed. — London: Allison and Busby, 1971. — [8],167p: ports; 22cm. — (Alternative editions)
Previous ed. 1970. — Index.
ISBN 0 85031 085 7 Pbk: £1.00

(B73-00882)

AMT/E(M/XN21) — Jazz musicians, 1920-1940
Stewart, Rex
Jazz masters of the thirties/ by Rex Stewart. — New York: Macmillan; London: Collier-Macmillan, 1972. — 2-223,[8]p: ports; 22cm. — (The Macmillan jazz masters series)
ISBN 0 02 614690 8 : £1.90

(B73-08421)

AP — MUSICAL LITERATURE. INDIVIDUAL INSTRUMENTS & INSTRUMENTAL GROUPS
APV — Electronic music
Schwartz, Elliot
Electronic music: a listener's guide/ [by] Elliot Schwartz. — London: Secker and Warburg, 1973. — xii,306p: ill; 22cm.
Also published, New York: Praeger, 1973. — Bibl.p.287-292. — List of gramophone records p.293-298. — Index.
ISBN 0 436 44410 0 : £5.00

(B73-16150)

APV/B — Electronic music. Instruments
Douglas, Alan
Electronic music production/ [by] Alan Douglas. — London: Pitman, 1973. — ix,148p: ill, music; 23cm.
Bibl.p.143-144. — Index.
ISBN 0 273 31523 4 : £2.50

(B73-02643)

Judd, Frederick Charles
Electronics in music/ [by] F.C. Judd. — London: Spearman, 1972. — 169,[20]p: ill; 24cm.
Bibl.p.168.
ISBN 0 85435 301 1 : £3.15

(B73-05263)

APW — MUSICAL LITERATURE. KEYBOARD INSTRUMENTS
APW(X) — History
Gillespie, John
Five centuries of keyboard music: an historical survey of music for harpsichord and piano/ [by] John Gillespie. — New York: Dover Publications; London: Constable, 1972. — xiii,463,[22]p: ill, music; 24cm.
Originally published, Belmont [Calif.]: Wadsworth, 1965. — Bibl.p.442-446. — Index.
ISBN 0 486 22855 x Pbk: £2.50

(B73-13586)

APW(YD/XA1800) — England. History, to 1800
Caldwell, John
English keyboard music before the nineteenth century/ [by] John Caldwell. — Oxford: Blackwell, 1973. — xxi,328p,leaf: music; 24cm. — (Blackwell's music series)
Bibl.p.290-303. — Index.
ISBN 0 631 13770 x : £6.00

(B73-16149)

AQ(WT) — Piano. Lists
Hinson, Maurice
Guide to the pianist's repertoire/ [by] Maurice Hinson; edited by Irwin Freundlich. — Bloomington; London: Indiana University Press, 1973. — xlvii,831p; 24cm.
Bibl.p.769-795. — Index.
ISBN 0 253 32700 8 : £6.60

(B73-17042)

AQ/B(XA1910) — Piano. Instruments, to 1910
Dolge, Alfred
Pianos and their makers: a comprehensive history of the development of the piano from the monochord to the concert grand player piano/ by Alfred Dolge. — New York: Dover Publications; London: Constable, 1972. — 2-478p: ill, ports; 22cm.
Originally published in 2 vols, Covina: Covina Publishing Company, 1911-1913. — Index.
ISBN 0 486 22856 8 Pbk: £2.50

(B73-15416)

AQ/CY — Piano playing. Technique
Lhevinne, Josef
Basic principles in pianoforte playing/ [by] Josef Lhevinne. — [1st ed. reprinted]; with a new foreword by Rosa Lhevinne. — New York: Dover Publications; London: Constable, 1972. — xi,48p: ill, music, port; 22cm.
First ed. originally published, Philadelphia: Theo Presser Co., 1924.
ISBN 0 486 22820 7 Pbk: £0.60

(B73-23436)

AQ/E — Piano. Performance
Harrison, Sidney
The young person's guide to playing the piano/ [by] Sidney Harrison. — 2nd ed. — London: Faber, 1973. — 3-100p: ill, music; 22cm.
Previous ed. 1966. — Index.
ISBN 0 571 04787 4 : £1.50

(B73-20241)

Junkin, Harry
The piano can be fun/ [by] Harry Junkin & Cyril Ornadel. — London: Paul, 1973. — [7],107p: ill, music; 26cm.
'Based on the ATV television series'.
ISBN 0 09 115200 3 : £2.50
ISBN 0 09 115201 1 Pbk: £1.25

(B73-05262)

Neuhaus, Heinrich
The art of piano playing/ [by] Heinrich Neuhaus; translated [from the Russian] by K.A. Leibovitch. — [2nd ed.]. — London: Barrie and Jenkins, 1973. — xv,240p,leaf: music, port; 22cm.
Index.
ISBN 0 214 65364 1 : £3.50

(B73-14764)

AQ/E(P/XLG31) — Rubinstein, Arthur. Biographies, 1887-1917
Rubinstein, Arthur
My young years/ [by] Arthur Rubinstein. — London: Cape, 1973. — xiii,493,[24]p: ill, facsims, ports; 24cm.
Facsims. on lining papers. — Also published, New York: Knopf, 1973. — Index.
ISBN 0 224 00926 5 : £4.50

(B73-29558)

AQR/B(XA1900) — Harpsichord. Instruments. History, to 1900
Russell, Raymond
The harpsichord and clavichord: an introductory study/ by Raymond Russell. — 2nd ed./ revised by Howard Schott. — London: Faber, 1973. — [4],208,[103]p: ill; 26cm.
Previous ed., London: Faber, 1959. — Bibl.p.190-196. — Index.
ISBN 0 571 04795 5 : £7.50
Also classified at AQT/B(XA1900)

(B73-17453)

AQT/B(XA1900) — Clavichord. Instruments. History, to 1900
Russell, Raymond
The harpsichord and clavichord: an introductory study/ by Raymond Russell. — 2nd ed./ revised by Howard Schott. — London: Faber, 1973. — [4],208,[103]p: ill; 26cm.
Previous ed., London: Faber, 1959. — Bibl.p.190-196. — Index.
ISBN 0 571 04795 5 : £7.50
Primary classification AQR/B(XA1900)

(B73-17453)

AR(XCQ438) — Organ music. History, 1400-1837
Routh, Francis
Early English organ music from the Middle Ages to 1837/ by Francis Routh. — London: Barrie and Jenkins, 1973. — xi,305p: music; 23cm. — (Studies in church music)
Bibl.p.271-280. — Index.
ISBN 0 214 66804 5 : £6.75

(B73-04220)

AR(YC/VP/Q) — Organists. Great Britain. Royal College of Organists
Royal College of Organists
Year book/ Royal College of Organists. — London (Kensington Gore, SW7 2QS): Royal College of Organists.
1972-1973 — [1972] — [1],vi,175p: ill, port; 21cm.
Cover title.
ISBN 0 902462 03 2 Pbk: £0.75

(B73-04670)

ARW — MUSICAL LITERATURE. STRING INSTRUMENTS
AS/B(X) — Violin. Instruments. History
Wechsberg, Joseph
The violin/ [by] Joseph Wechsberg. — London: Calder and Boyars, 1973. — vi,314,[8]p: ill, ports; 25cm.
Published as 'The glory of the violin'. New York: Viking Press, 1973. — Index.
ISBN 0 7145 1020 3 : £5.00
Also classified at AS/E

(B73-29559)

AS/E — Violin. Performance
Wechsberg, Joseph
The violin/ [by] Joseph Wechsberg. — London: Calder and
Boyars, 1973. — vi,314,[8]p: ill, ports; 25cm.
Published as 'The glory of the violin'. New York: Viking Press, 1973. —
Index.
ISBN 0 7145 1020 3 : £5.00
Primary classification AS/B(X)

(B73-29559)

AS/E(P) — Menuhin, Yehudi. Biographies
Magidoff, Robert
Yehudi Menuhin: the story of the man and the musician/ by
Robert Magidoff. — 2nd ed./ with additional chapters by Henry
Raynor. — London: Hale, 1973. — [1],350,[24]p: ill, ports; 23cm.
Previous ed. 1956. — List of gramophone records p.324-340. — Index.
ISBN 0 7091 3351 0 : £3.00

(B73-24889)

AS/G/E — Violin. Folk music. Performance
Timpany, John
And out of his knapsack he drew a fine fiddle: an introduction to
the technique of English fiddling/ by John Timpany. — London:
English Folk Dance and Song Society, 1973. — 43p: ill, music;
22cm.
ISBN 0 85418 088 5 Sd: £0.50

(B73-19500)

AT — MUSICAL LITERATURE. PLUCKED STRING
INSTRUMENTS
ATQ/BC — Harp. Instrument making
Jaffrennou, Gildas
Folk harps/ [by] Gildas Jaffrennou. — Kings Langley (Book
Division, Station Rd, Kings Langley, Herts.): Model and Allied
Publications, 1973. — 103p: ill; 22cm.
Bibl.p.103.
ISBN 0 85242 313 6 : £2.50

(B73-30280)

ATQ/E(P) — Richards, Nansi. Biographies
Richards, Nansi
Cwpwrdd Nansi/ [gan] Nansi Richards (Telynores Maldwyn). —
Llandysul: Gwasg Gomer, 1972. — 126,[9]p: ill, ports; 22cm.
£0.75

(B73-19501)

ATS(TC) — Guitar. Bibliographies of scores
Exeter City Library
Music for guitar and lute/ Exeter City Library; compiled by
David Lindsey Clark. — Exeter (Castle St., Exeter, Devon EX4
3PQ): Exeter City Library, 1972. — [36]p; 22cm.
Index.
ISBN 0 904128 00 8 Sd: £0.10
Also classified at ATW(TC)

(B73-27122)

ATS/E — Guitar. Performance
Noad, Frederick McNeill
Playing the guitar: a self-instruction guide to technique and
theory/ by Frederick M. Noad. — Revised and expanded ed. —
New York: Collier Books; London: Collier-Macmillan, 1972. — 3-
145p: ill, music; 28cm.
Previous ed., New York: Crowell-Collier, 1963. — Bibl.p.144. — Index.
ISBN 0 02 080950 6 Pbk: £0.70

(B73-05836)

ATW(TC) — Lute. Bibliographies of scores
Exeter City Library
Music for guitar and lute/ Exeter City Library; compiled by
David Lindsey Clark. — Exeter (Castle St., Exeter, Devon EX4
3PQ): Exeter City Library, 1972. — [36]p; 22cm.
Index.
ISBN 0 904128 00 8 Sd: £0.10
Primary classification ATS(TC)

(B73-27122)

AU — MUSICAL LITERATURE. WIND INSTRUMENTS
AVR/CY — Flute playing. Technique
Chapman, Frederick Bennett
Flute technique/ by F.B. Chapman. — 4th ed. — London: Oxford
University Press, 1973. — viii,89p: music; 19cm.
Previous ed. 1958.
ISBN 0 19 318609 8 Pbk: £0.90

(B73-26821)

AVS/E(M) — Recorder players. Biographies
Thomson, John Mansfield
Recorder profiles/ [by] John M. Thomson. — London (48 Great
Marlborough St., W.1): Schott and Co. Ltd, 1972. — 77,[8]p:
ports; 22cm.
Index.
ISBN 0 901938 09 2 Pbk: £1.00

(B73-05837)

AVU/HX(P) — Parker, Charlie. Biographies
Russell, Ross
Bird lives!/ [by] Ross Russell. — London (27 Goodge St., W1P
1FD): Quartet Books Ltd, 1972. — ix,404,[16]p: ill, facsims;
23cm.
Also published, New York: Charterhouse Books, 1973. — Bibl.p.381-383. —
List of gramophone records p.384-388. — Index.
ISBN 0 7043 2007 x : £3.75
ISBN 0 7043 3005 9 Pbk: £1.75

(B73-22801)

AWM(B) — Brassband. Periodicals
Sounding Brass; and, The Conductor. — [Sevenoaks]: Novello.
Vol.1-, no.1- ; Apr. 1972-. — 1972-. — ill, ports; 25cm.
Quarterly. — 32p. in 1st issue. — Title page imprint: London. — 'The
Conductor' previously published separately.
Sd: £0.15

(B73-26820)

AWS(XA1721) — Trumpet, to 1721
Smithers, Don L
The music and history of the baroque trumpet before 1721/ [by]
Don L. Smithers. — London: Dent, 1973. — 323,[8]p: ill, music;
25cm.
Bibl.p.291-306. — Index.
ISBN 0 460 03991 1 : £8.00
Also classified at AWS/B(XA1721)

(B73-32170)

AWS/B — Trumpet. Instruments
Bate, Philip
The trumpet and trombone: an outline of their history,
development and construction/ [by] Philip Bate. — 2nd ed. —
[Tonbridge]: Benn, 1972. — xvi,272,[32]p: ill, music, 1 port; 23cm.
Title page imprint: London. — Previous ed. 1966. — Bibl.p.258-264. —
Index.
ISBN 0 510 36411 x : £3.00
Also classified at AWU/B

(B73-13587)

AWS/B(XA1721) — Trumpet. Instruments, to 1721
Smithers, Don L
The music and history of the baroque trumpet before 1721/ [by]
Don L. Smithers. — London: Dent, 1973. — 323,[8]p: ill, music;
25cm.
Bibl.p.291-306. — Index.
ISBN 0 460 03991 1 : £8.00
Primary classification AWS(XA1721)

(B73-32170)

AWT/B — Horn. Instruments
Morley-Pegge, Reginald
The French horn: some notes on the evolution of the instrument
and of its technique/ [by] R. Morley-Pegge. — 2nd ed. —
Tonbridge: E. Benn, 1973. — xvii,222,[17]p(1 fold): ill, music;
23cm. — (Instruments of the orchestra)
Title page imprint: London. — Previous ed. 1960. — Bibl.p.183-189. —
Index.
ISBN 0 510 36601 5 : £3.95

(B73-15417)

AWU — Trombone
Gregory, Robin
The trombone: the instrument and its music/ [by] Robin Gregory.
— London: Faber, 1973. — 3-328,[11]p: ill, music; 23cm.
Bibl.p.316-319. — Index.
ISBN 0 571 08816 3 : £6.50
Also classified at AWU/B

(B73-06594)

AWU/B — Instruments
Gregory, Robin
The trombone: the instrument and its music/ [by] Robin Gregory.
— London: Faber, 1973. — 3-328,[11]p: ill, music; 23cm.
Bibl.p.316-319. — Index.
ISBN 0 571 08816 3 : £6.50
Primary classification AWU

(B73-06594)

AWU/B — Trombone. Instruments
Bate, Philip
The trumpet and trombone: an outline of their history,
development and construction/ [by] Philip Bate. — 2nd ed. —
[Tonbridge]: Benn, 1972. — xvi,272,[32]p: ill, music, 1 port; 23cm.
Title page imprint: London. — Previous ed. 1966. — Bibl.p.258-264. —
Index.
ISBN 0 510 36411 x : £3.00
Primary classification AWS/B

(B73-13587)

**AX — MUSICAL LITERATURE. PERCUSSION
   INSTRUMENTS**
AX(QU) — Notation
Fink, Siegfried
Tablature 72/ [by] Siegfried Fink. — Hamburg; London: N.
Simrock; London (67 Belsize La., NW3 5AX): [Distributed by] R.
Schauer, 1972. — 8p: music; 30cm. — (Percussion studio) (Elite
edition; 2826)
ISBN 0 9502847 0 x Sd: £0.45

(B73-16796)

AX/BC — Instrument making
Dankworth, Avril
Make music fun/ [by] Avril Dankworth; illustrations by Leslie
Priestley. — Leicester: Dryad Press, 1973. — 32p: ill; 21cm.
Sd: £0.45

(B73-10168)

AXRQ/BC(YUH) — Steel drums. Instrument making. West Indies
Seeger, Peter
Steel drums, how to play them and make them: an instruction
manual/ by Peter Seeger. — New York: Oak Publications;
London (78 Newman St., W.1): Music Sales Ltd, [1972]. — [2],
40p: ill, map, music; 28cm.
Originally published, New York: Oak Publications, 1964. — Based on 'The
steel drums of Kim Loy Wong'. New York: Oak Publications, 1961.
ISBN 0 9502654 0 3 Pbk: £1.25
Also classified at 789'.6

(B73-03214)

AXSR(YDHR) — Church bells. *Herefordshire*
Sharpe, Frederick
The church bells of Herefordshire: their inscriptions and founders/
by Frederick Sharpe. — Launton ('Derwen', Launton, Oxon.): F.
Sharpe.
Vol.4: Putley-Yazor. — 1972. — xii p,p417-592: ill, facsims; 22cm.
ISBN 0 9500835 8 5 Pbk: £1.75

(B73-00362)

B — INDIVIDUAL COMPOSERS
BBCAN — Bach, Johann Sebastian. Musikalisches Opfer
David, Hans Theodore
J.S. Bach's 'Musical Offering': history, interpretation and analysis/
by Hans Theodore David. — New York: Dover Publications;
London: Constable, 1972. — iii-xi,190p: facsims, music; 22cm.
Originally published, New York: Schirmer, 1945. — Index.
ISBN 0 486 22768 5 Pbk: £1.25

(B73-05261)

BBE(N/XNH8) — Bantock, Sir Granville. Biographies, 1908-1915
Bray, Trevor
Bantock: music in the Midlands before the First World War/ [by]
Trevor Bray. — London (10e Prior Bolton St., N.1): Triad Press,
1973. — 36p: facsims, music, ports; 22cm.
Limited ed. of 275 numbered copies.
ISBN 0 902070 07 x Sd: £1.25

(B73-24885)

BBG(N) — Bartók, Béla. Biographies
Lesznai, Lajos
Bartók/ by Lajos Lesznai; translated from the German by Percy
M. Young. — London (26 Albemarle St., W1X 4QY): Dent, 1973.
— xii,219,[8]p: ill, music, ports; 20cm. — (The master musicians
series)
Translation of 'Béla Bartók: sein Leben, seine Werke'. Leipzig: Deutscher
Verlag für Musik, 1961. — Bibl.p.205-207. — Index.
ISBN 0 460 03136 8 : £2.50

(B73-24886)

BBH(N) — Bax, Sir Arnold. Biographies
Scott-Sutherland, Colin
Arnold Bax/ by Colin Scott-Sutherland. — London: Dent, 1973.
— xviii,214,[8]p: ill, music, ports; 24cm.
Index.
ISBN 0 460 03861 3 : £3.50

(B73-15413)

BBJ(N) — Beethoven, Ludwig van. Biographies
Arnold, Denis
The Beethoven companion/ edited by Denis Arnold and Nigel
Fortune. — London: Faber, 1973. — 3-542p: music; 22cm.
Originally published 1971. — Index.
ISBN 0 571 10318 9 Pbk: £2.50

(B73-17450)

Fischer, Hans Conrad
Ludwig van Beethoven: a study in text and pictures/ by Hans
Conrad Fischer and Erich Kock; [translated from the German]. —
London: Macmillan, 1972. — 205p: ill(some col), facsims(1 col),
map, music, ports(some col); 25cm.
Translation of 'Ludwig van Beethoven'. Salzburg: Residenz, 1970.
ISBN 0 333 12114 7 : £4.00

(B73-03211)

Knight, Frida
Beethoven and the age of revolution/ by Frida Knight. —
London: Lawrence and Wishart, 1973. — 206p,leaf: port; 23cm.
Bibl.p.193-195. — Index.
ISBN 0 85315 266 7 : £2.50

(B73-11184)

BBM — Berlioz, Hector
Dickinson, Alan Edgar Frederic
The music of Berlioz/ [by] A.E.F. Dickinson. — London: Faber,
1972. — 3-280,[9]p: ill, music, ports; 26cm.
Bibl.p.263-273. — List of works p.259-261. — Index.
ISBN 0 571 09618 2 : £8.00

(B73-00878)

Primmer, Brian
The Berlioz style/ [by] Brian Primmer. — London: Oxford
University Press, 1973. — [8],202p: music; 22cm. — (University of
Durham. Publications)
Index.
ISBN 0 19 713136 0 : £3.75

(B73-05259)

BBTAL — Brahms, Johannes. Instrumental music
Matthews, Denis
Brahms's three phases: an inaugural lecture-recital delivered before
the University of Newcastle upon Tyne on Monday 24 January
1972 and repeated on Wednesday 2 February 1972/ by Denis
Matthews. — Newcastle upon Tyne (Newcastle upon Tyne NE1
7RU): University of Newcastle upon Tyne, 1972. — 19p; 21cm. —
(University of Newcastle upon Tyne. Inaugural lectures)
ISBN 0 900565 79 9 Sd: £0.30

(B73-10166)

BBU(N) — Britten, Benjamin. Biographies
Kendall, Alan, *b.1939*
Benjamin Britten/ [by] Alan Kendall; introduction by Yehudi
Menuhin. — London: Macmillan, 1973. — 112p: ill(some col),
music, ports(some col); 28cm.
List of works: p.106-109. — Index.
ISBN 0 333 15226 3 : £2.95

(B73-31507)

BCBNACPF — Campion, Thomas. Masques
Campion, Thomas
The masque at the Earl of Somerset's marriage/ [by] Thomas
Campion. — Menston: Scolar Press, 1973. — [36]p: music; 23cm.
Facsimile reprint of 1st ed.: London: E. Allde for L. Lisle, 1614.
ISBN 0 85967 129 1 : £2.75
ISBN 0 85967 130 5 Pbk: £1.75

(B73-31563)

BCLSAC — Colasse, Pascal. Enée et Lavinie
Colasse, Pascal
Enée et Lavinie/ [par] Pascal Colasse. — [1st ed. reprinted]; with
the addition of an introduction by Graham Sadler. —
Farnborough: Gregg, 1972. — [16],lii,234p: of music; 28cm.
Facsimile reprint of 1st ed., Paris: Christophe Ballard, 1690.
ISBN 0 576 28236 7 : £12.00

(B73-16143)

BCMLADW(ZC) — Connally, James. Songs-expounding Socialism
Connolly, James
The James Connolly songbook. — Cork (9 St Nicholas Church
Place, Cove St., Cork): Cork Workers Club, [1973]. — [1],38p;
21cm.
'... based on a selection of songs and recitation which were performed at a
concert, given by James Connolly's comrades ... to commemorate the
anniversary of his birth ... on the 5th June, 1919 ...' - Introduction. —
Includes three songs not by Connolly.
ISBN 0 904086 00 3 Sd: £0.15

(B73-25527)

BDJ — Debussy, Claude
Nichols, Roger
Debussy/ [by] Roger Nichols. — London: Oxford University
Press, 1973. — 86p: music; 22cm. — (Oxford studies of
composers; 10)
Bibl.p.85-86.
ISBN 0 19 315426 9 Pbk: £1.20

(B73-24201)

BDL(XLD14/WJ) — Delius, Frederick 1884-1897. Exhibitions
Camden (*London Borough*). *Libraries and Arts Department. St
Pancras Library*
Delius and America: [catalogue of] an exhibition of photographs,
scores, letters and other material relating to Delius's visits to
America and illustrating the American background to 'Koanga'
and other works, [held] May 1-20 [at] St Pancras Library, London
[organised by the London Borough of Camden, Libraries and Arts
Department]. — London (St Pancras Library, 100 Euston Rd,
N.W.1): [London Borough of Camden, Libraries and Arts
Department], [1972]. — [1],15p; 30cm.
'This catalogue is published as a special issue of the Delius Society
Newsletter, London, May 1972'. — Bibl.p.15.
ISBN 0 9502653 0 6 Sd: £0.25

(B73-02642)

BEP(N) — Elgar, Sir Edward, bart. Biographies
Maine, Basil
Elgar, his life and works/ by Basil Maine. — Bath: Chivers, 1973.
— [1],ii-xv,287,ii-vii,323p,6 leaves(1 fol): 1 ill, music, ports; 23cm.
Originally published in 2 vols, London: Bell, 1933. — Bibl. — Index.
ISBN 0 85594 835 3 : £2.85(to members of the Library Association)

(B73-14761)

BEP(N/XMB33) — Elgar, Sir Edward, bart. Biographies, 1902-1934
Reed, William Henry
Elgar as I knew him/ by William H. Reed. — [2nd ed.]. —
London: Gollancz, 1973. — 223,[4]p: ill, facsims, ports; 22cm.
Previous ed. 1936.
ISBN 0 575 01641 8 : £2.60

(B73-16141)

BFK(N) — Field, John. Biographies
Piggott, Patrick
The life and music of John Field, 1782-1837, creator of the
nocturne/ [by] Patrick Piggott. — London: Faber, 1973. — iii-xvi,
287,[13]p: ill, facsims, music, ports; 26cm.
Bibl.p.271-275. — Index.
ISBN 0 571 10145 3 : £10.00

(B73-31512)

BFT(N) — Franck, César. Biographies
Davies, Laurence, b.1926
Franck/ by Laurence Davies. — London: Dent, 1973. — xviii,141,
[8]p: ill, facsim, music, ports; 20cm. — (The master musicians
series)
Bibl.p.132-134. — Index.
ISBN 0 460 03134 1 : £1.90

(B73-12434)

BGRN(N) — Gounod, Charles. Biographies
Harding, James
Gounod/ [by] James Harding. — London: Allen and Unwin,
1973. — 3-251,[15]p: ill, facsims, ports; 22cm.
Bibl.p.225-227. — List of music p.228-241. — Index.
ISBN 0 04 780021 6 : £4.75

(B73-20976)

BHC(WJ) — Handel, George Frideric. Exhibitions
Henry Watson Music Library
George Frideric Handel - the Newman Flower Collection in the
Henry Watson Music Library: a catalogue/ compiled by Arthur
D. Walker; with a foreword by Winton Dean. — [Manchester]
(Central Library, Manchester M2 5PD): Manchester Public
Libraries, 1972. — xiii,134p; 22cm.
Bibl.p.xiii. — Index.
ISBN 0 901315 18 4 : £3.50

(B73-00557)

BLT(N) — Lully, Jean Baptiste. Biographies
Scott, Ralph Henry Forster
Jean-Baptiste Lully/ [by] R.H.F. Scott. — London: Owen, 1973.
— 135,[4]p: facsim, ports; 23cm.
Bibl.p.135.
ISBN 0 7206 0432 x : £3.00

(B73-14125)

BLU(N) — Lutyens, Elisabeth. Biographies
Lutyens, Elisabeth
A goldfish bowl/ [by] Elisabeth Lutyens. — London: Cassell,
1972. — [6],330,[8]p: ill, facsims, ports; 22cm.
Index.
ISBN 0 304 93663 4 : £4.00

(B73-04669)

BME(N) — Mahler, Gustav. Biographies
Blaukopf, Kurt
Gustav Mahler/ [by] Kurt Blaukopf; translated [from the
German] by Inge Goodwin. — London: Allen Lane, 1973. — 279,
[8]p: ill, ports; 23cm.
Translation of 'Gustav Mahler oder der Zeitgenosse der Zukunft'. Wien
[Vienna]: Verlag Fritz Molden, 1969. — Bibl.p.265-266. — Index.
ISBN 0 7139 0464 x : £3.50

(B73-20237)

BMJ(N) — Mendelssohn, Felix. Biographies
Marek, George Richard
Gentle genius: the story of Felix Mendelssohn/ [by] George R.
Marek. — London: Hale, 1973. — xv,365: ill, facsim, ports; 26cm.
Originally published, New York: Funk and Wagnall, 1972. — Bibl.p.349-
353. — Index.
ISBN 0 7091 3900 4 : £4.50

(B73-16142)

BMN/FD(WT) — Monteverdi, Claudio. Recorded music. Lists
Westerlund, Gunnar
Music of Claudio Monteverdi: a discography/ [by] Gunnar
Westerlund & Eric Hughes. — London (29 Exhibition Rd, S.W.7):
British Institute of Recorded Sound, 1972. — viii,72p; 25cm.
ISBN 0 900208 05 8 : £2.00

(B73-01061)

BMNAC — Monteverdi, Claudio. Orfeo
Monteverdi, Claudio
L'Orfeo: favola in musica/ [da] Claudio Monteverde. — [2nd ed.
reprinted]; with the addition of an introduction by Denis Stevens.
— Farnborough: Gregg, 1972. — [8],100p: of music; 28cm.
Facsimile reprint of 2nd ed., Venezia [Venice]: Ricciardo Amadino, 1615.
ISBN 0 576 28177 8 : £7.20

(B73-16144)

BMS(N) — Mozart, Wolfgang Amadeus. Biographies
Levey, Michael
The life & death of Mozart/ [by] Michael Levey. — London (30
Gray's Inn Rd, WC1X 8JL): Cardinal, 1973. — 301,[16]p: ill,
facsims, music, ports; 20cm.
Originally published, London: Weidenfeld and Nicolson, 1971. — Bibl.p.291-
292. — Index.
ISBN 0 351 17178 9 Pbk: £0.90

(B73-22798)

Lingg, Ann M
Mozart: genius of harmony/ by Ann M. Lingg; illustrations by
Helen Frank. — Port Washington; London: Kennikat Press, 1973.
— xi,331p: ill; 24cm.
Originally published, New York: H. Holt, 1946. — Index.
ISBN 0 8046 1743 0 : £7.40

(B73-14126)

BPC/R — Palestrina, Giovanni Pierluigi da. Harmony
Boyd, Malcolm
Palestrina's style: a practical introduction/ [by] Malcolm Boyd. —
London: Oxford University Press, 1973. — [5],66p: music; 21cm.
Bibl.p.63.
ISBN 0 19 315224 x Pbk: £0.95

(B73-07791)

BRC(N) — Rakhmaninov, Sergei
Threlfall, Robert
Sergei Rachmaninoff: his life and music/ [by] Robert Threlfall. —
London: Boosey and Hawkes, 1973. — 74,[4]p: facsim, music,
port; 19cm.
List of music p.71-74.
ISBN 0 85162 009 4 Pbk: £0.75

(B73-22268)

BRGY(N/XA1921) — Raynor, John. Biographies, to 1921
Raynor, John, b.1909
A Westminster childhood/ [by] John Raynor; illustrations by
Dennis Flanders. — London: Cassell, 1973. — [7],213p: ill; 23cm.
ISBN 0 304 29183 8 : £3.25

(B73-24203)

BSF(N) — Schubert, Franz. Biographies
Hutchings, Arthur
Schubert/ by Arthur Hutchings. — Revised ed. — London: Dent,
1973. — vi,233,[8]p: ill, music, ports; 20cm. — (The master
musicians series)
Previous ed., London: Dent, 1945. — Bibl.p.216-218. — Index.
ISBN 0 460 03139 2 : £2.00

(B73-04216)

BSFADW — Schubert, Franz. Songs
Schubert and Schumann songs and translations/ [translated by]
Robert Randolph Garran. — Carlton: Melbourne University
Press; [London]: Distributed by Angus and Robertson], 1971. —
373p; 23cm.
Parallel German texts and English translations. — Originally published,
Carlton: Melbourne University Press, 1946.
ISBN 0 522 83999 1 : £4.15
Primary classification BSGADW

(B73-13019)

BSFAKDW — Schubert, Franz. Songs, etc
Capell, Richard
Schubert's songs/ [by] Richard Capell. — [3rd ed.]. — London:
Pan Books, 1973. — xi,292p: music; 20cm.
Previous ed., London: Duckworth, 1957. — Index.
ISBN 0 330 23775 6 Pbk: £0.95

(B73-29556)

BSG — Schumann, Robert
Walker, Alan, b.1930
Robert Schumann: the man and his music/ edited by Alan
Walker; [contributors] Frank Cooper... [and others]. — London:
Barrie and Jenkins, 1972. — xi,489,[12]p,leaf: ill, facsims, music,
ports; 24cm.
Bibl.p.442-445. — List of works p.447-483. — Index.
ISBN 0 214 66805 3 : £7.50

(B73-04217)

BSGADW — Schumann, Robert. Songs
Schubert and Schumann songs and translations/ [translated by]
Robert Randolph Garran. — Carlton: Melbourne University
Press; [London]: Distributed by Angus and Robertson], 1971. —
373p; 23cm.
Parallel German texts and English translations. — Originally published,
Carlton: Melbourne University Press, 1946.
ISBN 0 522 83999 1 : £4.15
Also classified at BSFADW

(B73-13019)

BSNKAC — Stoker, Richard. Johnson preserved. Librettos
Watt, Jill
Johnson preserv'd: opera in 3 acts/ libretto by Jill Watt; music by
Richard Stoker. — [London]: [Hinrichsen], [1972]. — [1],16p;
25cm.
Sd: Unpriced

(B73-09577)

BSO(N) — Stockhausen, Karlheinz. Biographies
Wörner, Karl Heinrich
Stockhausen: life and work/ [by] Karl Heinrich Wörner;
introduced, translated [from the German] by Bill Hopkins. —
London: Faber, 1973. — 3-270,[8]p: ill, ports; 23cm.
Revised translation of 'Karlheinz Stockhausen'. Rodenkirchen: P.J. Tonger
Musikverlag, 1963. — List of works p.257-258. — Index.
ISBN 0 571 08997 6 : £6.00
ISBN 0 571 10244 1 Pbk: £1.50

(B73-03714)

BSQB(N) — Strauss family. Biographies
Wechsberg, Joseph
The waltz emperors: the life and times and music of the Strauss
family/ [by] Joseph Wechsberg. — London: Weidenfeld and
Nicolson, 1973. — 272p: ill(some col), facsims, music, ports(some
col); 26cm.
Ill. on lining papers. — Index.
ISBN 0 297 76594 9 : £4.25

(B73-30279)

BSU(N) — Strauss, Richard. Biographies
Jefferson, Alan
The life of Richard Strauss/ [by] Alan Jefferson. — Newton
Abbot: David and Charles, 1973. — 240p: ill, geneal table, ports;
23cm.
Bibl.p.227-230. — Index.
ISBN 0 7153 6199 6 : £3.95

(B73-31509)

BSV(N/XLB39/EM) — Stravinsky, Igor. Biography, 1882-1920.
Illustrations
Stravinsky, Thedor
Catherine and Igor Stravinsky: a family album/ by Theodore
Stravinsky. — London: Boosey and Hawkes, 1973. — [126]p:
chiefly ill(5col), facsims, ports; 32cm.
Text in English, French, and German.
ISBN 0 85162 008 6 : £6.50

(B73-13584)

BSWACF — Sullivan, Sir Arthur Seymour. Savoy operas
Baily, Leslie
Gilbert and Sullivan and their world/ [by] Leslie Baily. —
London: Thames and Hudson, 1973. — 128p: ill, facsims, ports;
24cm.
Bibl.p.120. — Index.
ISBN 0 500 13046 9 : £2.25

(B73-27557)

BSXAPW — Sweelinck, Jan Pieterzoon. Keyboard music
Curtis, Alan
Sweelinck's keyboard music: a study of English elements in
seventeenth-century Dutch composition/ [by] Alan Curtis. — 2nd
ed. — Leiden: Leiden University Press for the Sir Thomas Browne
Institute, Leiden; London: Distributed by Oxford University Press,
1972. — xiv,243,[9]p: ill, facsims, music, ports; 22cm. — (Sir
Thomas Browne Institute. Publications: general series; no.4)
Previous ed. 1969. — Bibl.p.229-233. — Index.
ISBN 0 19 647470 1 : £7.75

(B73-09001)

BTD(N) — Tchaikovsky, Peter. Biographies
Garden, Edward
Tchaikovsky/ by Edward Garden. — London: Dent, 1973. — viii,
194,[8]p: ill, facsims, music, ports; 20cm. — (The master
musicians series)
Bibl.p.185-188. — List of works p.169-178. — Index.
ISBN 0 460 03105 8 : £1.95

(B73-11185)

Warrack, John
Tchaikovsky/ [by] John Warrack. — London: Hamilton, 1973. —
287p: ill(some col), facsims, geneal tables(on lining papers), music,
ports(some col); 26cm.
Bibl.p.280-281. — Index.
ISBN 0 241 02403 x : £5.00

(B73-26164)

BTF(N) — Theodorakis, Mikis. Biographies
Giannaris, George
Mikis Theodorakis: music and social change/ [by] George
Giannaris; foreward by Mikis Theodorakis. — London: Allen and
Unwin, 1973. — xix,322,[8]p: ill, music, ports; 22cm.
Originally published, New York: Praeger, 1972. — Bibl.p.301-8. — List of
records p.309-11. — Index.
ISBN 0 04 920038 0 : £3.95

(B73-20238)

BVB(N) — Varèse, Edgard. Biographies
Ouellette, Fernand
Edgard Varèse/ by Fernand Ouellette; translated from the French
by Derek Coltman. — London: Calder and Boyars, 1973. — xiii,
270,[16]p: ill, facsims, ports; 23cm.
This translation originally published, New York: Grossman, 1968. —
Translation of 'Edgard Varèse'. Paris: Seghers, 1966. — List of works
p.239-243. — Bibl.p.244-262. — Index.
ISBN 0 7145 0208 1 : £3.95

(B73-07096)

Varèse, Louise
Varèse: a looking-glass diary/ [by] Louise Varèse. — London:
Davis-Poynter.
In 2 vols.
Vol.1: 1883-1928. — 1973. — 3-290,[16]p: ill, facsims, ports; 24cm.
Originally published, New York: Norton, 1972. — Index.
ISBN 0 7067 0057 0 : £3.00

(B73-04218)

BVEAC — Verdi, Giuseppe. Opera
Budden, Julian
The operas of Verdi/ [by] Julian Budden. — London: Cassell.
In 2 vols.
1: From 'Oberto' to 'Rigoletto'. — 1973. — ix,524p: music; 24cm.
Index.
ISBN 0 304 93756 8 : £6.00

(B73-13585)

BWC(D) — Wagner, Richard. Essays
Wagner, Richard
Richard Wagner - stories and essays/ selected, edited and
introduced by Charles Osborne. — London: Owen, 1973. — 187p,
leaf: port; 23cm.
'The items in this book were originally published in German... [and] are
taken from 'Die gesammelten Schriften und Dictungen von Richard
Wagner.' - title page verso.
ISBN 0 7206 0122 3 : £3.25

(B73-13014)

BWCAC — Wagner, Richard. Opera
Magee, Bryan
Aspects of Wagner/ [by] Bryan Magee. — London: Panther, 1972.
— 109p; 18cm.
Originally published, London: Ross, 1968.
ISBN 0 586 03774 8 Pbk: £0.35

(B73-00360)

BWKRACM/LH — Webber, Andrew Lloyd. Jesus Christ Superstar
Forristal, Desmond
Superstar or son of God?/ [by] Desmond Forristal. — Dublin
(Pranstown House, Booterstown Ave., Booterstown, Dublin):
Veritas Publications; Dublin: Talbot Press, 1973. — 22p: col ill;
21cm.
ISBN 0 901810 60 6 Sd: £0.15
ISBN 0 85452 094 5 (Talbot Press) Sd: £0.15

(B73-25528)

BZ — LITERATURE ON NON-EUROPEAN MUSIC
BZHP(X) — Japan. History
Harich-Schneider, Eta
A history of Japanese music/ [by] Eta Harish-Schneider. —
London: Oxford University Press, 1973. — xxi,720,[33]p: ill(incl 1
col), facsims, map, music; 27cm.
Book and gramophone records (6 sides, 7 in., 33-1/3 rpm) in slip case. —
Bibl.p.598-617. — Index.
ISBN 0 19 316203 2 : £21.00

(B73-10162)

BZNDADW/G — Africa. Sudan. Dinka tribe. Folk songs
Deng, Francis Mading
The Dinka and their songs/ [by] Francis Mading Deng. —
Oxford: Clarendon Press, 1973. — viii,301p; 22cm. — (Oxford
library of African literature)
ISBN 0 19 815138 1 : £6.50
Also classified at 301.29'624

(B73-27559)

BZP — America
Collaer, Paul
Music of the Americas: an illustrated music ethnology of the Eskimo and American Indian peoples/ [edited by] Paul Collaer; with contributions by Willard Rhodes ... [and others]; [translated from the German by Irene R. Gibbons]. — London: Curzon Press, 1973. — 207p: ill(some col), maps, music; 35cm.
In slip case. — Translation of 'Amerika-Eskimo und indianische Bevölkerung'. Leipzig: VEB Deutscher Verlag für Musik, 1968. — Bibl.p. 177-196. — Index.
ISBN 0 7007 0004 8 : £6.50
Also classified at 781.7'1'17497

(B73-02064)

C/AY — GENERAL COLLECTIONS
C/AY (XA1750) — Collections, to 1750
Parrish, Carl
Masterpieces of music before 1750: an anthology of musical examples from Gregorian chant to J.S. Bach/ compiled and edited with historical and analytical notes by Carl Parrish and John F. Ohl. — London: Faber, 1973. — x,235p; 8vo.
A paperback version of the original edition published in 1952. (B52-11247).
ISBN 0 571 10248 4 : £2.25

(B73-50477)

C/AYD — England
Musica Britannica: a national collection of music. — London: Stainer and Bell.
Vol.34: Pelham Humfrey: Complete church music I; transcribed and edited by Peter Dennison. — 1972. — xix,142p; fol.
Unpriced
Also classified at CB/LD/AZ

(B73-50478)

Vol.37: Sterndale Bennett: piano and chamber music/ edited by Geoffrey Bush. — 1972. — xxiii,165p; fol.
Unpriced
Also classified at QP/AZ; N/AZ

(B73-50002)

C/AZ — Collected works of individual composers
Berlioz, Hector
New edition of the complete works of Hector Berlioz. — Cassel; London: Bärenreiter.
Duration of the whole work 206 mins.
Vol.2a: Les Troyens. Acts 1-2; edited by Hugh MacDonald. — 1969. — 8, 294p; fol.
Unpriced
Also classified at CQC

(B73-50479)

Vol.2b: Les Troyens. Acts 3-5; edited by Hugh Macdonald. — 1969. — 4, 295p-753p; fol.
Unpriced
Also classified at CQC

(B73-50480)

Vol.2c: Les Troyens; supplement, edited by Hugh Macdonald. — 1970. — 754p-947; fol.
Unpriced

(B73-50481)

Vol.5: Huit scenes de Faust; edited by Julian Rushton. — 1970. — xvii, 107p; fol.
Unpriced
Also classified at EMDX

(B73-50482)

Vol.16: Symphonie fantastique; edited by Nicholas Temperley. — 1972. — xxxv,221p; fol.
Unpriced
Also classified at MME

(B73-50483)

C/CY — COLLECTIONS, EXERCISES, ETC. , ILLUSTRATING TECHNIQUES OF PERFORMANCE
C/EF — Aural training
Associated Board of the Royal Schools of Music
Aural tests issued for the guidance of teachers and candidates/ Associated Board of the Royal Schools of Music. — London: Associated Board of the Royal Schools of Music.
Part 4 although advertised was not issued.
Part 1. Grades 1-5. — 1972. — 46p; 8vo.
£0.25

(B73-50930)

Part 2. Grades 6-7. — 1972. — 36p; 8vo.
£0.25

(B73-50931)

Part 3. Grade 8. — 1972. — 32p; 8vo.
£0.25

(B73-50932)

C/EG — Sight reading
Kodály, Zoltán
333 reading exercises/ by Zoltán Kodály. — Revised English ed. — London: Boosey and Hawkes, 1972. — 59p; obl. 8vo. — (Kodály, Zoltán. Choral method)
Tonic sol-fa notation.
£0.40

(B73-50003)

C/J — Music to accompany drama
Kagel, Mauricio
Staatstheater: szenische Komposition, 1967-70/ von Mauricio Kagel. — London: Universal, 1973. — 466p; obl 4to.
For different combinations of instruments.
Unpriced

(B73-50484)

CB — VOCAL MUSIC
CB/AY — Collections
Horton, John
The music group/ by John Horton. — London: Schott.
Book 4. — 1972. — 8vo.
Teacher's ed. (90p.); Pupil's ed. (79p.).
Unpriced

(B73-50004)

Book 5. — 1972. — 8vo.
£1.30

(B73-50485)

Book 6. — 1972. — 8vo.
£1.30

(B73-50486)

Richter, Clifford
Madrigals and motets of four centuries: a choral songbook of 18 European classics, for mixed voices/ edited by Clifford Richter, English version by John Colman. — New York; London: Associated Music, 1972. — 124p; 8vo.
Unpriced

(B73-50933)

CB/EG — Sight singing
London College of Music
Examinations in pianoforte playing and singing: sight reading tests, sight singing tests as set throughout 1972: grades 1-8 and diplomas/ London College of Music. — London: Ashdown, 1973. — 15p; 4to.
£0.30
Primary classification Q/EG

(B73-50289)

CB/LD/AZ — Church music. Collected works of individual composers
Musica Britannica: a national collection of music. — London: Stainer and Bell.
Vol.34: Pelham Humfrey: Complete church music I; transcribed and edited by Peter Dennison. — 1972. — xix,142p; fol.
Unpriced
Primary classification C/AYD

(B73-50478)

CC — OPERA. VOCAL SCORES
Beeson, Jack
[My heart's in the highlands. Vocal score]. My heart's in the highlands: chamber opera in two acts/ by Jack Beeson; libretto based on the play by William Saroyan. — New York; London: Boosey and Hawkes, 1973. — 285p; 4to.
Vocal score.
£10.00

(B73-50487)

Britten, Benjamin
[Owen Wingrave. Vocal score]. Owen Wingrave. Op 35: an opera in two acts/ by Benjamin Britten; libretto by Myfanwy Piper, based on the short story by Henry James, German translation by Claus Henneberg, vocal score by David Matthews. — London: Faber, 1973. — 213p; 4to.
£10.00

(B73-50488)

Delius, Frederick
[A village Romeo and Juliet. Vocal score]. A village Romeo and Juliet/ by Frederick Delius; lyric drama in six scenes after Gottfried Keller. — London: Boosey and Hawkes, 1973. — 179p; 8vo.
This edition is a reprint in reduced format of the full score originally published in Berlin, Harmonie, 1910.
£7.50

(B73-50005)

Humperdinck, Engelbert
[Hänsel und Gretel. Vocal score]. Hänsel und Gretel: Märchenspiel in drei Bildern/ von Engelbert Humperdinck; nach den Quellen herausgegeben von Horst Gurgel, Text von Adelheid Wette. — Leipzig: Peters; [London]: [Hinrichsen], 1972. — v, 218p; 8vo.
Unpriced

(B73-50006)

Orff, Carl
[Der Mond. Vocal score]. Der Mond = The moon: a little theatre of the world; English text by Maria Pelikan, vocal score by Hans Bergese. — Mainz; London: Schott, 1973. — 166p; 4to.
£9.60

(B73-50934)

Pergolesi, Giovanni Battista
[La Serva padrona. Vocal score]. La Serva padrona = From maid
to mistress/ by Giovanni Battista Pergolesi; libretto by G.A.
Federico, English version by Hamilton Benz. — New York;
London: Schirmer, 1972. — 87p; 8vo.
Unpriced

(B73-50935)

Rorem, Ned
[Bertha. Vocal score]. Bertha: one act opera/ by Ned Rorem; play
by Kenneth Koch. — New York; London: Boosey and Hawkes,
1973. — 44p; 4to.
£2.00

(B73-50936)

Williamson, Malcolm
[The Red Sea. Vocal score]. The Red Sea: opera in one act/ by
Malcolm Williamson; libretto by the composer. — London:
Weinberger, 1973. — 56p; 4to.
Unpriced

(B73-50007)

CF — OPERETTAS. VOCAL SCORES
Robinson, Stanford
[The Savoyards. Vocal score]. The Savoyards: a new operetta/
arranged from the music of Arthur Sullivan by Stanford
Robinson, musical arrangements, orchestration and vocal score by
Stanford Robinson, book and lyrics by Donald Madgwick. —
London: Boosey and Hawkes, 1973. — viii,247p; 4to.
£3.00

(B73-50489)

CM — MUSICAL PLAYS. VOCAL SCORES
Campbell, Norman
[Anne of Green Gables. Vocal score]. Anne of Green Gables/ by
Norman Campbell; a musical from the novel by L.M.
Montgomery, adapted by Donald Harron and Norman Campbell,
additional lyrics by Mavor Moore and Elaine Campbell. —
London: Chappell, 1973. — 156p; 4to.
£2.00

(B73-50937)

CN — Children's musical plays with keyboard accompaniment
Mozart, Wolfgang Amadeus
[Die Zauberflöte]. The golden flute: an opera for schools in two
acts based on Mozart's 'The magic flute'/ [edited by] Raymond
Walker and William Beaumont. — Sevenoaks: Novello, 1972. —
106p; 8vo.
Vocal score.
£1.00

(B73-50008)

Verrall, Pamela
[Around the world. Vocal score]. Around the world: songs with
chorus and accompaniment for recorders and percussion/ by
Pamela Verrall. — London: British and Continental, 1973. — 17p;
8vo.
£0.40

(B73-50938)

CQC — OPERA. FULL SCORES
Bach, Johann Christian
Amadis des Gaules/ by Johann Christian Bach. — Farnborough:
Gregg International, 1972. — [7],345p; 4to.
A facsimile reproduction of the original edition published Paris, Sieber,
1780.
ISBN 0 576 28235 9 : £12.60

(B73-50490)

Berlioz, Hector
New edition of the complete works of Hector Berlioz. — Cassel;
London: Bärenreiter.
Duration of the whole work 206 mins.
Vol.2a: Les Troyens. Acts 1-2; edited by Hugh MacDonald. — 1969. — 8,
294p; fol.
Unpriced
Primary classification C/AZ

(B73-50479)

Vol.2b: Les Troyens. Acts 3-5; edited by Hugh Macdonald. — 1969. — 4,
295-753p; fol.
Unpriced
Primary classification C/AZ

(B73-50480)

Elton, Antony
The Minister of Justice: opera/ by Antony Elton, libretto by the
composer. — Newton Hall [Durham]: Antony Elton, 1973. — v,
308p; 4to.
With a libretto inserted.
Unpriced

(B73-50939)

Goehr, Alexander
Triptych. Op.25/ by Alexander Goehr. — London: Schott.
No.1: Naboth's vineyard. — 1973. — 73p; 4to.
Part of the text in Latin.
£3.00

(B73-50940)

Mondonville, Joseph de
Titon et l'Aurore/ by Joseph de Mondonville. — Farnborough:
Gregg International, 1972. — [5],207p; 4to.
A facsimile reproduction of the original edition published Paris, 1753.
ISBN 0 576 28987 6 : £8.40

(B73-50491)

Piccini, Niccolò
Iphigénie en Tauride/ by Niccolò Piccini. — Farnborough: Gregg
International, 1972. — [12],264p; 4to.
A facsimile reproduction of the original edition published Paris, 1781.
ISBN 0 576 28239 1 : £12.00

(B73-50492)

Wagner, Richard
Tristan und Isolde/ by Richard Wagner. — New York: Dover;
London: Constable, 1973. — 655p; 4to.
Originally published Leipzig. Peters, circa 1911. This corresponds to the
original score except for instructions introduced by a 'B'. These reflect
details of Felix Mottl's performance.
ISBN 0 486 22915 7 : £3.75

(B73-50941)

CQM — MUSICAL PLAYS. FULL SCORES
Kagel, Mauricio
Tremens: szenische Montage eines Tests, für zwei Darsteller,
elektrische Instrumente, Schlagzeug, Tonbänder und Projektionen/
von Mauricio Kagel. — London: Universal, 1973. — 142p; fol.
Pages 57-81 with a new title page contain 'Variaktionen über Tremens'.
Unpriced

(B73-50493)

CQN — Children's musical plays. Full scores
Daubney, Brian
Ko-Ai and the dragon: a story to music/ by Brian Daubney. —
Croydon: Belwin-Mills Music, 1972. — obl 8vo & 4to.
Score (19p) & voices-part (24p).
£160

(B73-50494)

Paynter, John
The space-dragon of Galatar: an opera-workshop project for
schools, for voices, sound effects and piano/ by John Paynter;
words by Paul Townsend. — London: Universal, 1972. — viii,15p;
8vo.
Unpriced

(B73-50009)

DAC — OPERATIC CHORAL WORKS. CHORAL SCORES
Williamson, Malcolm
[The Red Sea. Chorus score]. The Red Sea: opera in one act/ by
Malcolm Williamson. — London: Weinberger, 1973. — 28p; 8vo.
£0.30

(B73-50010)

DD — ORATORIOS. VOCAL SCORES
Handel, George Frideric
[Messiah. Vocal score]. Der Messias = The Messiah: oratorio in
three parts/ by Georg Friedrich Händel; edited by John Tobin,
vocal score arranged by Max Schneider, German translation
Konrad Ameln. — Cassel, London: Bärenreiter, 1972. — vii,345p;
8vo.
£2.10

(B73-50495)

DE — RELIGIOUS CANTATAS WITH KEYBOARD
ACCOMPANIMENT
Flanders, Michael
[Captain Noah and his floating zoo. Vocal score]. Captain Noah
and his floating zoo: cantata in popular style/ by Michael
Flanders and Joseph Horovitz; arranged for male lead and SATB
with piano, optional bass and drums. — Sevenoaks: Novello, 1973.
— 69p; 8vo.
£0.69

(B73-50496)

Vale, Charles
[Even such is time. Vocal score]. Even such is time: cantata for
tenor solo, chorus and orchestra (or organ)/ by Charles Vale;
words by various poets. — London: Thames, 1972. — 18p; 8vo.
Unpriced

(B73-50011)

DE/LF — Christmas
Buxtehude, Dietrich
[Das neugebor'ne Kindelein. Vocal score]. The little newborn Jesus Child: for chorus of mixed voices (SATB) with organ or instrumental accompaniment/ by Dietrich Buxtehude; edited and arranged with keyboard reduction by Walter Ehret. — New York: Lawson-Gould; Wendover: Roberton, 1971. — 27p; 8vo.
£0.32
(B73-50942)

Tate, Phyllis
[Serenade to Christmas. Vocal score]. Serenade to Christmas: for mezzo-soprano solo mixed chorus and orchestra/ by Phyllis Tate. — London: Oxford University Press, 1973. — 48p; 8vo.
ISBN 0 19 338419 1 : Unpriced
(B73-50943)

DE/LL — Easter
Aston, Peter
Haec dies: dialogues and sonatas on the Resurrection of our Lord, for mixed voices and organ/ by Peter Aston. — Sevenoaks: Novello, 1972. — 44p; 4to.
£1.25
(B73-50944)

DFDM/LH — Liturgical music. Hymns. Holy Week
Ratcliffe, Desmond
The Passion of Christ: a devotional service of nine lessons and hymns (or chorales) based on the St Matthew Passion narrative/ [with] music selected by Desmond Ratcliffe; text compiled by Richard Tatlock. — Sevenoaks: Novello, 1973. — 35p; 8vo.
£0.35
(B73-50012)

DFF — ROMAN LITURGY
DFF/LH — Holy Week
Bevenot, Laurence
New music for Holy Week/ by Laurence Bevenot. — Wimbledon: Chapman, 1971. — 46p; 8vo.
£0.40
(B73-50013)

DGE — Ordinary of the Mass. Sanctus
Doe, Paul
Sanctus and Magnificat: anonymous 14th century/ transcribed and edited by Paul Doe. — Exeter: University of Exeter Press, 1973. — 16p; 8vo.
Unpriced
Also classified at DGKK
(B73-50497)

Haydn, Joseph
[Mass no.16 in B flat major, 'Theresa mass'.. Sanctus. Vocal score]. Sanctus/ by Joseph Haydn; edited for four-part chorus of mixed voices with organ or piano accompaniment by William Herrmann. — New York; London: Schirmer, 1971. — 7p; 8vo.
Unpriced
(B73-50014)

Mozart, Wolfgang Amadeus
[Mass. K.262.. Sanctus. Vocal score]. Sanctus = Holy holy holy/ by Wolfgang Amadeus Mozart; arranged and edited for four-part chorus of mixed voices with organ or piano accompaniment by Walter Ehret, English text by W.E. — New York; London: Schirmer, 1972. — 6p; 8vo.
Unpriced
(B73-50015)

DGKB — Divine Office
Mozart, Wolfgang Amadeus
[Dixit Dominus and Magnificat. Vocal score]. Dixit Dominus and Magnificat. K.193/ by Wolfgang Amadeus Mozart; edited for four-part chorus of mixed voices with piano accompaniment by Maynard Klein, piano reduction by Byron Hanson. — New York; London: Schirmer, 1972. — 43p; 8vo.
Unpriced
(B73-50498)

DGKK — Divine Office. Vespers. Magnificat
Buxtehude, Dietrich
[Magnificat. Vocal score]. Magnificat = My soul doth magnify the Lord: five-part chorus and organ (piano) or five-part string accompaniment (or only 2 violins) and thorough-bass/ by Dietrich Buxtehude; edited by Daniel Pinkham, English version by Jean Lunn. — New York: Peters; [London]: [Hinrichsen], 1971. — 19p; 8vo.
£0.45
(B73-50945)

Cavalli, Francesco
[Musiche sacre. Magnificat. Vocal score]. Magnificat for double chorus, cornetti (trumpets), trombones, strings, and keyboard continuo/ by Francesco Cavalli; realized by Raymond Leppard. — London: Faber Music, 1973. — 45p; 8vo.
Unpriced
(B73-50946)

Doe, Paul
Sanctus and Magnificat: anonymous 14th century/ transcribed and edited by Paul Doe. — Exeter: University of Exeter Press, 1973. — 16p; 8vo.
Unpriced
Primary classification DGE
(B73-50497)

DGM — ANGLICAN LITURGY
DGMKAD — Sentences
Thiman, Eric Harding
Six introductory sentences: for SATB and organ/ by Eric H. Thiman. — Sevenoaks: Novello, 1973. — 6p; 8vo.
£0.10
(B73-50947)

DGNP — Morning Prayer. Canticles
Farrant, John, b.1575
Te Deum and Jubilate: SATB/ by John Farrant the elder(?); edited by E.H. Fellowes, revised by Anthony Greening. — Revised ed.. — London: Oxford University Press, 1973. — 15p; 8vo.
ISBN 0 19 352106 7 : £0.30
(B73-50499)

DGNPV — Morning Prayer. Venite
Swann, Donald
[Festival Matins.. O come let us sing unto the Lord]. O come let us sing unto the Lord: for two-part chorus of female, male or mixed voices with piano accompaniment/ by Donald Swann; [text] Psalm 95. — Wendover: Roberton, 1970. — 7p; 8vo.
Unpriced
Also classified at FDGNPV; GDGNPV
(B73-50016)

DGNQ — Morning Prayer. Te Deum
Hall, Ian
Westminster Te Deum: for SATB and organ/ by Ian Hall. — London: Weinberger, 1972. — 23p; 8vo.
£0.25
(B73-50017)

DGNS — Morning Prayer. Benedictus
Swann, Donald
[Festival Matins.. Blessed be the Lord God of Israel]. Blessed be the Lord God of Israel: for two-part chorus of female, male or mixed voices with piano or organ accompaniment/ by Donald Swann; [text from] St. Luke 1. — Wendover: Roberton, 1970. — 7p; 8vo.
Unpriced
Also classified at FDGNS; GDGNS
(B73-50018)

DGNT — Morning prayer. Jubilate
Hedges, Hazel
Psalm of praise: for full chorus of mixed voices with organ or piano accompaniment/ by Hazel Hedges; text: Psalm 100. — New York; London: Schirmer, 1972. — 10p; 8vo.
Unpriced
(B73-50019)

Roe, Betty
Jubilate Deo: for SATB and organ/ by Betty Roe. — London: Thames, 1972. — 4p; 4to.
Unpriced
(B73-50500)

Walton, Sir William
Jubilate Deo: SSAATTBB and organ/ by William Walton. — London: Oxford University Press, 1973. — 11p; 8vo.
ISBN 0 19 351642 x : Unpriced
(B73-50501)

DGPP — Evening Prayer. Canticles
Aston, Peter
Magnificat and Nunc dimittis in F: for SATB and organ/ by Peter Aston. — London: Oxford University Press, 1973. — 14p; 8vo.
ISBN 0 19 351643 8 : £0.20
(B73-50948)

Hunt, Donald
Magnificat for treble solo, choir and organ, and, Nunc dimittis for bass solo, choir and organ/ by Donald Hunt. — London: Boosey and Hawkes, 1973. — 24p; 8vo.
£0.25
(B73-50502)

Leighton, Kenneth
The second service = Magnificat and Nunc dimittis. Op.62: SATB/ by Kenneth Leighton. — London: Oxford University Press, 1972. — 24p; 8vo.
ISBN 0 19 395236 x : £0.30
(B73-50021)

Mathias, William
  Magnificat and Nunc dimittis. Op.53: SATB/ by William Mathias.
  — London: Oxford University Press, 1973. — 18p; 8vo.
  ISBN 0 19 351636 5 : £0.30

(B73-50503)

Weelkes, Thomas
  [Magnificat and Nunc dimittis no.5, 'in medio chori']. Evening
  service no.5, 'in medio chori': for two altos, tenor, two basses,
  chorus and organ/ by Thomas Weelkes; reconstructed and edited
  by David Brown. — Sevenoaks: Novello, 1973. — 28p; 8vo.
  £0.34

(B73-50949)

Wise, Michael
  Magnificat and Nunc dimittis: SATBB/ by Michael Wise; edited
  by Christopher Dearnley, transcribed by Anthony Greening. —
  London: Oxford University Press, 1973. — 9p; 8vo.
  ISBN 0 19 351635 7 : £0.15

(B73-50950)

DGS — Communion
Aston, Peter
  Holy Communion, series 3: for SATB choir, congregation and
  organ/ by Peter Aston. — Croydon: Royal School of Church
  Music, 1973. — 8vo.
  Unpriced

(B73-50951)

Jackson, Francis
  Communion service, series 3, in the key of E. Op. 41: (treble, alto,
  tenor, bass)/ by Francis Jackson. — London: Oxford University
  Press, 1973. — 15p; 8vo.
  ISBN 0 19 395240 8 : £0.20

(B73-50952)

Kelly, Bryan
  Communion service, series 3: SATB/ by Bryan Kelly. — London:
  Oxford University Press, 1973. — 16p; 8vo.
  ISBN 0 19 395238 6 : £0.20

(B73-50953)

**DGT — LITURGIES OF DENOMINATIONS OTHER THAN
          ROMAN & ANGLICAN**
DGU — Jewish liturgy
Adler, Samuel
  Hinay yom hadin = Behold the day of judgment: four prayers
  from the High Holyday liturgy, for four-part chorus of mixed
  voices with soprano and tenor solo (cantor) with optional organ
  accompaniment/ by Samuel Adler. — New York; London:
  Schirmer.
  3: Uv'shofar gadol. — 1972. — 11p; 8vo. —
  Unpriced

(B73-50022)

DH — MOTETS, ANTHEMS, HYMNS, ETC.
Kechley, Gerald
  Drop slow tears: for mixed chorus and piano with optional
  instrumental accompaniment/ by Gerald Kechley; words by
  Phineas Fletcher. — New York: Galaxy Music; London: Galliard,
  1973. — 4to & 8vo.
  Score (6p.), chorus part (7p.) & 4 parts. — Duration 3 min.
  Unpriced

(B73-50954)

Brahms, Johnnes
  Lass dich nur nichts nicht dauren = Let not your heart be
  troubled: for four-part chorus of mixed voices with organ or piano
  accompaniment/ by Johannes Brahms; edited by Maynard Klein;
  text adapted from St John 14, English text by M.K. — New
  York; London: Schirmer, 1972. — 10p; 8vo.
  Unpriced

(B73-50955)

Brown, Frank Edwin
  Come, let us seek the Lord: anthem for general use, SATB/ words
  and music by Frank E. Brown. — London: F. Pitman, Hart,
  1972. — 8p; 8vo.
  Unpriced

(B73-50023)

Chapman, Edward
  Thou spirit of love divine: SATB accompanied/ words and music
  by Edward Chapman; based on a theme from Mahler's third
  symphony. — Wendover: Roberton, 1970. — 12p; 8vo.
  Unpriced

(B73-50024)

Harris, *Sir* William Henry
  Our day of praise is done: SATB/ by William H. Harris; words by
  J. Ellerton and E. Milner-White. — London: Oxford University
  Press, 1973. — 4p; 8vo.
  ISBN 0 19 351118 5 : Unpriced

(B73-50504)

Leighton, Kenneth
  Adventante Deo = Lift up your heads, gates of my heart: anthem
  for SATB and organ/ by Kenneth Leighton; words by John
  Addington Symonds. — Sevenoaks: Novello, 1972. — 20p; 8vo.
  £0.21

(B73-50025)

Naylor, Bernard
  Invitation to music: anthem for SATB and organ/ by Bernard
  Naylor; words by Richard Crashaw. — Wendover: Roberton,
  1973. — 11p; 8vo.
  £0.13

(B73-50026)

Reed, Phyllis Luidens
  I have a dream: for mixed chorus and piano with soprano solo/
  by Phyllis Luidens Reed; words by Martin Luther King, Jr. —
  New York: Galaxy Music; London: Galliard, 1973. — 5p; 8vo.
  Unpriced

(B73-50956)

Westbrook, Francis
  Faith of our fathers: anthem for a Dedication service/ by Francis
  Westbrook; words by Frederick William Faber. — Wendover:
  Roberton, 1972. — 8p; 8vo.
  £0.10

(B73-50027)

Wills, Arthur
  Let all men everywhere rejoice: anthem for SATB and organ (or
  brass, percussion and organ)/ by Arthur Wills; words by
  Raymond Gilbert. — Sevenoaks: Novello, 1972. — 11p; 8vo.
  £0.14

(B73-50028)

Wilson-Dickson, Andrew
  Jesu, send us peace: SATB/ by Andrew Wilson-Dickson; words
  anon. — York: Banks, 1973. — 4p; 8vo.
  Unpriced

(B73-50505)

DH/AY — Collections
Jackson, Francis
  Anthems for choirs/ edited by Francis Jackson. — London:
  Oxford University Press.
  Volume 1. — 1973. — 8p; 8vo.
  ISBN 0 19 353215 8 : £0.12

(B73-50506)

DH/AYE — Collections. Germany
Brodde, Otto
  Geistliche Zwiegesänge/ herausgegeben von Otto Brodde. —
  Cassel; London: Barenreiter.
  Band 2: Spruch-Bicinien. — 1971. — 141p; 8vo. —
  £2.10

(B73-50507)

DH/LF — Christmas
Gardner, John
  A Christmas hymn. Opus 109a: SATB (or S. only) and organ, by
  John Gardner: [words] hymn at First Vespers, Christmas Day;
  English translation by John Gardner. — London: Oxford
  University Press, 1971. — 6p; 8vo.
  ISBN 0 19 343016 9 : Unpriced
  Also classified at FDH/LF

(B73-50957)

Newbury, Kent A
  Gloria: a Christmas fanfare or introit, for four-part chorus of
  mixed voices with piano or organ accompaniment/ by Kent A.
  Newbury; words adapted from the Scriptures. — New York;
  London: Schirmer, 1971. — 6p; 8vo.
  Unpriced

(B73-50029)

DH/LGZ — Passiontide
Eldridge, Guy
  When I survey the wondrous cross: Passiontide anthem founded
  on the folk tune 'O waly waly', for SATB and organ/ by Guy
  Eldridge; words by Isaac Watts. — Sevenoaks: Novello, 1973. —
  7p; 8vo.
  £0.10

(B73-50030)

DH/LK — Good Friday
Leighton, Kenneth
  Solus ad victimam: SATB/ by Kenneth Leighton; words by Peter
  Abelard, translated by Helen Waddell. — London: Oxford
  University Press, 1973. — 5p; 8vo.
  ISBN 0 19 350349 2 : Unpriced

(B73-50958)

DH/LL — Easter
Lord, David
Most glorious Lord of lyfe!: SATB/ by David Lord; words by Edmund Spenser. — London: Oxford University Press, 1973. — 7p; 8vo.
ISBN 0 19 350346 8 : Unpriced

(B73-50959)

Scott, Anthony
Easter: a marriage anthem, SATB and organ/ by Anthony Scott; words by George Herbert. — London: Boosey and Hawkes, 1973. — 16p; 8vo.
£0.20

(B73-50031)

DH/LN — Whitsuntide
Naylor, Bernard
Come Holy Ghost, eternal God: set for SATBB and organ/ by Bernard Naylor; words by Francis Kinwelmersh. — Wendover: Roberton, 1973. — 8p; 8vo.
£0.10

(B73-50960)

DJ — MOTETS
Brunetti, Domenico
Cantemus Domino = Sing unto God: for 3-part chorus of mixed voices with organ/ by Domenico Brunetti; edited by Roger Wilhelm. — Wendover: Roberton, 1973. — 11p; 8vo.
£0.13

(B73-50508)

Gabrieli, Giovanni
[Sacrae symphoniae, bk.1. Plaudite. Vocal score]. Plaudite: for triple chorus of mixed voices/ by Giovanni Gabrieli; edited with organ accompaniment by Dale Jergenson and Daniel Wolfe. — New York; London: Schirmer, 1972. — iv,22p; 8vo.
Unpriced

(B73-50961)

Rameau, Jean Philippe
[Traité de l'harmonie, liv.3.. Laboravi clamans]. Laboravi clamans: motet for SSATB and organ/ by Jean-Philippe Rameau; edited by Daniel Pinkham [words from] Psalm 69. — New York; London: Peters, 1972. — 11p; 8vo.
Unpriced

(B73-50032)

DK — ANTHEMS
Amner, John
Lift up your heads: SSATB/ by John Amner; [text from] Psalm 24, edited by Anthony Greening. — London: Oxford University Press, 1972. — 7p; 8vo.
ISBN 0 19 350331 x : Unpriced

(B73-50033)

Griffin, Jack
The mountain of the Lord: anthem for SATB and organ/ by Jack Griffin; [text from] Isaiah 2. — Wendover: Roberton, 1973. — 8p; 8vo.
Duration 3 1/2 min.
£0.10

(B73-50034)

Hayes, William
[Cathedral music.. Bow down thine ear]. Bow down thine ear, O Lord: SATB (SS Soli)/ by William Hayes; edited by Bernard Rose, text from Psalm 86. — London: Oxford University Press, 1973. — 19p; 8vo.
ISBN 0 19 350334 4 : £0.25

(B73-50035)

Hayes, William
[Cathedral music. *Excerpts]*. Bow down thine ear, O Lord: SATB (SS Soli)/ by William Hayes; edited by Bernard Rose, text from Psalm 86. — London: Oxford University Press, 1973. — 19p; 8vo.
ISBN 0 19 350334 4 : £0.25

(B73-50035)

Mathias, William
Lift up your head, O ye gates. Op. 44, no.2/ by William Mathias: text from Psalm 24. — London: Oxford University Press, 1973. — 6p; 8vo.
ISBN 0 19 350344 1 : Unpriced

(B73-50962)

Milner, Anthony
Blessed art thou, O God of our fathers: anthem for SATB and organ/ by Anthony Milner. — London: Boosey and Hawkes, 1973. — 12p; 8vo.
£0.14

(B73-50036)

Newbury, Kent A
Break forth into joy: festival anthem, for four-part chorus of mixed voices with organ or piano accompaniment/ by Kent A. Newbury; [text] from the Psalms and Isaiah 52. — New York; London: Schirmer, 1971. — 12p; 8vo.
Unpriced

(B73-50037)

Rutter, John
O clap your hands: SATB/ by John Rutter, [text from] Psalm 47. — London: Oxford University Press, 1973. — 8p; 8vo.
ISBN 0 19 350347 6 : Unpriced

(B73-50963)

Sumsion, Herbert
Blessed are they that dwell in thy house: anthem for a dedication festival, or general use/ by Herbert Sumsion; text from Psalm 84. — South Croydon: Lengnick, 1973. — 16p; 8vo.
£0.18

(B73-50038)

Weelkes, Thomas
Christ rising again: verse anthem for two sopranos, two altos, chorus and organ/ by Thomas Weelkes; reconstructed and edited by David Brown, text: a version taken from Romans 6 and I Corinthians 15. — Sevenoaks: Novello, 1973. — 14p; 8vo.
£0.18

(B73-50509)

DK/LH — Passiontide
Pedrette, Edward
Is it nothing to you?: for four-part chorus of mixed voices with organ or piano accompaniment/ by Edward Pedrette; text from Lamentations of Jeremiah. — New York; London: Schirmer, 1972. — 4p; 8vo.
Unpriced

(B73-50039)

DK/LP — Harvest
Hare, Ian
Thou, O God, art praised in Sion: SATB anthem for harvest festival or general use/ by Ian Hare; verses from Psalm 65. — London: Oxford University Press, 1973. — 6p; 8vo.
ISBN 0 19 350340 9 : Unpriced

(B73-50510)

DM — HYMNS
Grieb, Herbert
O God of every race and creed: for four-part chorus of mixed voices with organ or piano accompaniment/ by Herbert Grieb; text by H G. — New York; London: Schirmer, 1972. — 6p; 8vo.
Unpriced

(B73-50040)

Houghton, Frank
Ten tunes/ with the words of hymns and choruses by Frank Houghton; harmonized by Stanley Houghton, Mrs R.V. Bazire and others. — London: OMF, 1973. — 7p; 8vo.
Unpriced

(B73-50511)

Taberer, Alfred A
[Dux animorum]. Leader of faithful souls/ by Alfred A. Taberer; words by Charles Wesley. — Chester: Bankhead Press, 1972. — s. sh; 8vo.
Prize-winning hymn tune at the Nantwich Circuit Eisteddfodd, 1972.
£0.01

(B73-50512)

DM/JS/AY — Television. Collections
Songs of celebration: a collection of new hymns featured in the Southern Television Hymn Competition 1973, appropriate for family service, communion service, wedding service, baptism service, harvest festival. — London: Weinberger, 1973. — 43p; 8vo.
£0.75

(B73-50513)

DP — CAROLS
Gardner, John
Solstice carol. Op. 115/ words and music (arranged for SATB) by John Gardner. — London: Chappell, 1973. — 7p; 8vo.
Unpriced

(B73-50964)

DP/AY — Collections
Swann, Donald
The rope of love. Around the earth in song: an anthology of contemporary carols/ partly written, composed and arranged by Donald Swann. — London: The Bodley Head, 1973. — 160p; 8vo.
ISBN 0 370 01272 0 : £2.50

(B73-50514)

DP/LF — Christmas
Cameron, Gordon
Voice of angels, steps of shepherds: carol for SATB and organ/ by Gordon Cameron; words by Canon Gilbert Williams. — Sevenoaks: Novello, 1973. — 3p; 8vo.
£0.07

(B73-50965)

Crawley, Christopher
The Sir Gawayn carols: SATB/ by Christopher Crawley; words selected and adapted by John Weeks. — London: Oxford University Press, 1973. — 7p; 8vo.
ISBN 0 19 343042 8 : Unpriced

(B73-50966)

Ellis, David
[Carols for an island Christmas. Vocal score]. Carols for an island Christmas: for SATB, trumpets, string orchestra and piano (with optional boys' voices, woodwind and percussion),/ by David Ellis. — Sevenoaks: Novello, 1973. — 12p; 8vo.
£0.23

(B73-50967)

Hughes, Edward
It's who you're with that counts: [SATB]/ by Edward Hughes; words by Peter Westmore. — London: British and Continental, 1973. — 6p; 8vo.
Unpriced

(B73-50968)

Kelly, Bryan
[Herod, do your worst. Sleep little baby: arr]. Sleep little baby: Christmas song/ by Bryan Kelly; arranged for SATB and piano or organ, words by John Fuller. — Sevenoaks: Novello, 1973. — 4p; 8vo.
£0.07

(B73-50969)

Roe, Betty
Away in a manger: carol for mixed choir and organ/piano/ by Betty Roe; words traditional. — London: Thames, 1973. — 4p; 8vo.
Unpriced

(B73-50041)

Rutter, John
Sing we to this merry company: SATB/ by John Rutter. — London: Oxford University Press, 1972. — 8p; 8vo.
ISBN 0 19 343037 1 : Unpriced

(B73-50042)

Thiman, Eric
[The shepherd's story. Vocal score]. The shepherd's story: Christmas chorus for mixed voice choir with piano or orchestra/ by Eric Thiman; words by K.M. Warburton. — Wendover: Roberton, 1973. — 7p; 8vo.
Staff & tonic sol-fa notation.
£0.10

(B73-50970)

Trant, Brian
The Virgin Mary had a baby boy: carol from the West Indies/ arranged SATB by Brian Trant. — London: Oxford University Press, 1973. — 7p; 8vo.
ISBN 0 19 343040 1 : Unpriced

(B73-50971)

DP/LF/AY — Christmas. Collections
Horder, Mervyn, *Baron*
The orange carol book/ arranged by Mervyn Horder. — London: Schott, 1973. — vii,88p; 8vo.
Originally published (B63-50063), London: Constable, 1962.
ISBN 0 901938 10 6 : £0.50

(B73-50972)

DPDE — CAROL CANTATAS
DPDF/LF — Carol services. Christmas
Ratcliffe, Desmond
The story of Christmas: a new presentation of the Festival of Nine Lessons/ music selected by Desmond Ratcliffe; text by Richard Tatlock. — Sevenoaks: Novello, 1973. — 41p; 8vo.
£0.40

(B73-50973)

DR — PSALMS
Mendelssohn, Felix
[Psalm 115. Op 31. Vocal score]. Not unto us, O Lord. Op 31: for chorus of mixed voices and soprano, tenor and baritone solos/ by Felix Mendelssohn; edited, with piano accompaniment and with English text, by Samuel Adler. — New York; London: Schirmer, 1972. — 24p; 4to.
Unpriced

(B73-50974)

DR/AY — Psalms. Collections
Psalm praise: for choir or congregation. — London: Falcon: Church Pastoral Aid Society, 1973. — 303p; 8vo.
Unpriced

(B73-50975)

DW — SONGS, ETC.
Ahrold, Frank
The courting of the deaf woman: American folk song/ arranged for 3-part (SAB) chorus of mixed voices by Frank Ahrold. — Wendover: Roberton, 1973. — 7p; 8vo.
£0.10

(B73-50515)

Beyer, Frederick
The man with the blue guitar: for four-part chorus of mixed voices with piano accompaniment/ by Frederick Beyer; words by Wallace Stevens. — New York; London: Schirmer, 1972. — 16p; 8vo.
Unpriced

(B73-50043)

Hughes, Robert
Five Indian poems: for mixed choir and small orchestra/ by Robert Hughes; poems by Sarojini Naidu. — London: Chappell, 1973. — 60p; 8vo.
Vocal score.
Unpriced

(B73-50516)

Jones, Daniel
Sea: for chorus and piano/ by Daniel Jones; words by Gwyn Thomas. — Rhuthun: Eisteddfod genedlaethol frenhinol Cymru, 1973. — 21p; 8vo.
Duration 6 mins.
Unpriced

(B73-50044)

Keel, Frederick
Lullaby/ by Frederick Keel; arranged for mixed chorus (SATB) and piano by Bernell W. Hales, words by Alfred Noyes. — New York: Galaxy; London: Galliard, 1973. — 7p; 8vo.
Unpriced

(B73-50976)

Mozart, Wolfgang Amadeus
Ecco quel fiero istante = Lo, now the hour of parting. K.436/ by Wolfgang Amadeus Mozart; nocturne, edited for three-part chorus of women's voices or three-part mixed voices with piano accompaniment by Maynard Klein, [words by] Pietro Metastasio, English text by M.K. — New York; London: Schirmer, 1973. — 8p; 8vo.
Unpriced
Primary classification FDW

(B73-50143)

Mozart, Wolfgang Amadeus
Luci care, luci bello = Eyes of beauty, eyes flashing bright. K.346: nocturne/ by Wolfgang Amadeus Mozart; edited for three-part chorus of mixed voices, SSA or SSB, with piano, or optional string or woodwind accompaniment, by Maynard Klein, words by Pietro Metastasio, English text by M.K. — New York; London: Schirmer, 1972. — 4p; 8vo.
Unpriced
Primary classification FDW

(B73-50144)

Mozart, Wolfgang Amadeus
Mi lagnero tacendo = Silent, I long for thy love. K.437: nocturne/ by Wolfgang Amadeus Mozart; edited for three-part chorus of women's voices or three-part mixed voices, with piano accompaniment by Maynard Klein; [words by] Pietro Metastasio, English text by M.K. — New York; London: Chappell, 1972. — 12p; 8vo.
Unpriced
Primary classification FDW

(B73-50145)

Pooler, Marie
The water is wide: Scottish folk song, arranged for four-part chorus of mixed voices with piano accompaniment/ by Marie Pooler. — New York; London: Schirmer, 1971. — 12p; 8vo.
Unpriced

(B73-50977)

Rutter, John
[Fancies. Riddle song]. Riddle song: SATB/ by John Rutter; words, 15th century. — London: Oxford University Press, 1973. — 6p; 8vo.
Vocal score.
ISBN 0 19 343031 2 : Unpriced

(B73-50517)

Rutter, John
[Fancies. Vocal score]. Fancies: a cycle of choral settings with small orchestra/ by John Rutter. — London: Oxford University Press, 1973. — 40p; 8vo.
Vocal score. Duration 16 min.
ISBN 0 19 338071 4 : Unpriced
(B73-50045)

Simpson, John
Wi'a hundred pipers an' a': SAB/ arranged by John Simpson. — London: British and Continental, 1973. — 15p; 8vo.
Unpriced
(B73-50978)

DW/AY — Collections
Fussan, Werner
Swing and sing: Tanzsuite für gemischten Chor (auch Kammerchor) und Rhythmusgruppe/ [compiled by] Werner Fussan. — Mainz; London: Schott, 1973. — 35p; 4to.
Unpriced
(B73-50518)

Lethbridge, Lionel
Opera song book/ arranged by Lionel Lethbridge. — London: Oxford University Press.
2: Eight operatic choruses for unison, two-part, or SAB voices and piano. — 1973. — 47p; 8vo. —
ISBN 0 19 330521 6 : £0.50
(B73-50046)

DW/LC — Spirituals
Barthelson, Joyce
Somebody's knockin' at your door: spiritual, for 4-part chorus of mixed voices with piano/ arranged by Joyce Barthelson. — Wendover: Roberton, 1967. — 8p; 8vo.
Unpriced
(B73-50519)

DX — SECULAR CANTATAS
DX/X — Secular cantatas. Canons
Tippett, *Sir* Michael
[The Shires suite.. Come, let us sing you a song in canon. Vocal score]. Come, let us sing you a song in canon: cantata/ by Michael Tippett. — London: Schott, 1972. — 20p; 8vo.
£0.50
(B73-50047)

E — CHORAL WORKS WITH ACCOMPANIMENT OTHER THAN KEYBOARD
ELDGNT — With instruments. Anglican liturgy. Morning Prayer. Jubilate
Sansom, Clive A
Jubilate jazz: for SATB with instrumental accompaniment/ by Clive A. Sansom. — London: Paterson, 1973. — 15p; 8vo.
A free translation.
Unpriced
(B73-50048)

EMDG — With orchestra. Ordinary of the Mass
Haydn, Joseph
[Mass no.3 in D minor, 'Nelson Mass']. Messe D-moll, (Nelson-Messe): für vierstimmigen Chor, Soli, Orchester und Orgel/ von Joseph Haydn; [edited by Wilhelm Weismann]. — Leipzig: Peters; [London]: [Hinrichsen], 1971. — 118p; 8vo.
Unpriced
(B73-50049)

EMDR — With orchestra. Psalms
Vaughan Williams, Ralph
Fantasia (quasi variazione) on the 'Old 104th' psalm tune: for solo piano, mixed chorus and orchestra/ by R. Vaughan Williams; words from the metrical version by Thomas Sternhold and John Hopkins. — London: Oxford University Press, 1973. — 28p; 8vo.
Duration 12 mins.
ISBN 0 19 338922 3 : £1.75
(B73-50050)

EMDX — With orchestra. Secular cantatas
Berlioz, Hector
New edition of the complete works of Hector Berlioz. — Cassel; London: Bärenreiter.
Vol.5: Huit scenes de Faust; edited by Julian Rushton. — 1970. — xvii, 107p; fol.
Unpriced
Primary classification C/AZ
(B73-50482)

Birtwistle, Harrison
The fields of sorrow: for 2 solo sopranos, chorus and orchestra/ by Harrison Birtwistle; words by Ausonius. — London: Universal, 1973. — 19p; 4to.
Unpriced
(B73-50979)

Stockhausen, Karlheinz
Nr 10 = Carré: für 4 orchester und Chöre/ von Karlheinz Stockhausen. — London: Universal.
Nr.1. — 1973. — xiv,118p; fol. —
Unpriced
(B73-50523)

Nr.2. — 1973. — xiv,116p; fol. —
Unpriced
(B73-50521)

Nr.3. — 1973. — xiv,118p; fol. —
Unpriced
(B73-50520)

Nr.4. — 1973. — xiv,116p; fol. —
Unpriced
(B73-50522)

ENYJDW — With strings & percussion. Songs, etc
Feldman, Morton
Rothko chapel/ by Morton Feldman. — London: Universal, 1973. — 39p; 8vo.
Duration 30 min.
Unpriced
(B73-50524)

ENYLDE/LL — With keyboard & percussion. Religious cantatas. Easter
Gardner, John
Cantata for Easter, Op.105: for soloists, mixed chorus, organ and percussion/ by John Gardner. — London: Oxford University Press, 1973. — 119p; 8vo.
Duration 30 mins.
ISBN 0 19 336214 7 : Unpriced
(B73-50051)

ERXMDH — With string orchestra. Motets, Anthems, Hymns, etc
Esterházy, Pál
Harmonia caelestis: für Sopran, vierstimmigen gemischten Chor und Instrumente/ von Pál Esterházy; herausgegeben von Ferenc Bónis. — Cassel; London: Bärenreiter.
Heft 1: Weihnachtskantaten. — 1972. — 36p; 8vo.
£1.35
(B73-50525)

EVQNTQDW/G/AYH — With two piccolos & piano. Folk songs. Collections. France
Moyse, Louis
Three French songs: music, based on French melodies/ [arranged] for five-part chorus of mixed voices with two piccolos (or two flutes) and piano by Louis Moyse, English text by Edmond Brelaford. — New York; London: Schirmer, 1972. — 41p; 4to.
Contents: 1 Joli tambour. Pretty drum boy. — 2 O ma tendre musette. O, my gentle musette. — 3 Gentille alouette. Pretty skylark.
Unpriced
(B73-50053)

EVRDH/LF — With flute. Motets, Anthems, Hymns, etc. Christmas
Rudland, Malcolm
Mary of the wilderness: carol for SATB and flute/ by Malcolm Rudland; words by Hamish B. Whyte. — London: Thames, 1972. — 3p; 8vo.
Unpriced
(B73-50054)

EWNPDGNT — With brass septet. Anglican liturgy. Morning Prayer. Jubilate
Cruft, Adrian
Jubilate Deo (St Peter ad Vincula): canticle or anthem for SATB chorus and brass ensemble. Op.51/ by Adrian Cruft. — London: Boosey and Hawkes, 1972. — 4to.
Score (10p.) & 7 parts.
£1.15
(B73-50055)

EWSNTDP/LF — With trumpet trio. Carols. Christmas
Copley, ian
The trumpet carol: for mixed voices and trumpets/ by Ian Copley; words by Barbara Kluge. — London: Thames, 1973. — 8vo.
Score (2p.) & part. — The parts for 3 trumpets are printed in score.
Unpriced
(B73-50526)

EWUNPPWDH — With six trombones & keyboard. Motets, Anthems, Hymns, etc
Schütz, Heinrich
[Psalmen Davids, 1619. Die mit Tränen säen]. Die mit Tränen säen: motet for two five-part choirs and basso continuo/ by Heinrich Schütz; edited by Wilhelm Ehmann, continuo realization by Heinrich Ehmann, text from Psalm 126. — Cassel; London: Bärenreiter, 1972. — iv,28p; 8vo.
£1.50

(B73-50527)

EZ — UNACCOMPANIED CHORAL WORKS
EZ/AF — Exercises
Eberhardt, Carl
Praxis der Chorprobe: Arbeitsheft für die Choreinstudierung/ von Carl Eberhardt. — Frankfurt; London: Peters, 1973. — 40p; 4to.
£2.50

(B73-50528)

Regner, Hermann
Chorstudien: for mixed choir/ by Hermann Regner. — Mainz; London: Schott, 1972. — 15p; 4to.
Unpriced

(B73-50056)

EZDE — Religious cantatas
Burgon, Geoffrey
The fire of heaven: for unaccompanied triple choir/ by Geoffrey Burgon; text by Thomas Traherne. — London: Stainer and Bell, 1973. — 36p; 4to.
Duration 12 mins.
Unpriced

(B73-50529)

Halffter, Cristobal
Gaudium et spes: Beunza: para 32 voces y cinta por Cristobal Halffter. — London: Universal, 1973. — 54p; fol.
Accompanied by various sounds from a tape recorder.
Unpriced

(B73-50980)

EZDG — Roman liturgy. Ordinary of the Mass
Byrd, William
Mass for five voices, (S A T T B)/ by William Byrd; transcribed and edited by Philip Brett. — London: Stainer and Bell, 1973. — 55p; 8vo.
Unpriced

(B73-50530)

Dufay, Guillaume
Missa 'L'Homme armé': for mixed choir (SATB) a cappella/ by Guillaume Dufay; edited by Gabor Darvas. — London: Boosey and Hawkes, 1971. — 56p; 8vo.
£1.00

(B73-50981)

Martin, Frank
[Mass]. Messe für zwei vierstimmige Chöre/ von Frank Martin. — Cassel; London: Bärenreiter, 1972. — 56p; 8vo.
£1.80

(B73-50057)

Naylor, Bernard
Missa sine credo a 4/ by Bernard Naylor. — Wendover: Roberton, 1973. — 15p; 8vo.
£0.18

(B73-50531)

Okeghem, Jean
[Mass, 'L'homme armé']. Missa 'L'homme armé': for mixed choir (S.Ms.A.T., Bar, B) a cappella/ by Johannes Ockeghem; edited by Gábor Darvas. — London: Boosey and Hawkes, 1972. — 51p; 8vo.
£1.00

(B73-50058)

EZDGKAD/LEZ — Roman liturgy. Proper of the Mass. Graduals, Tracts, Alleluias. Advent
Byrd, William
[Gradualia, Lib 1.. Rorate coeli desuper]. Rorate coeli desuper = Drop down, ye heavens: SAATB/ by William Byrd; edited with English words by Anthony Greening. — London: Oxford University Press, 1973. — 10p; 8vo.
ISBN 0 19 352062 1 : Unpriced

(B73-50059)

EZDGKH/LHLN — Roman liturgy. Divine Office. Matins. Holy Week (last three days). Miserere
Byrd, William
[Liber secundus sacrarum cantionum. Miserere]. Miserere mei = Look on me in mercy: SATBB/ by William Byrd; edited by S. Townsend Warner, revised edition by John Morehen. — Revised ed.. — London: Oxford University Press, 1973. — 7p; 8vo.
ISBN 0 19 352053 2 : Unpriced

(B73-50532)

EZDGKH/LK — Roman liturgy. Divine office. Matins. Good Friday
Biber, Carl Heinrich
Tenebrae factae sunt = Darkness was over all: for four-part chorus of mixed voices a cappella/ by C.H. Biber; edited by Reinhard G. Pauly, English text by R.G.P. — New York; London: Schirmer, 1972. — 8p; 8vo.
Unpriced
Also classified at EZDJ/LK

(B73-50060)

EZDGMM — Anglican liturgy. Preces & responses
Naylor, Bernard
The preces and responses: SSATB unacc./ by Bernard Naylor. — London: Oxford University Press, 1972. — 7p; 8vo.
ISBN 0 19 351641 1 : Unpriced

(B73-50061)

Reading, John
The preces and responses. Responses in A Sharpe: SATB unacc./ by John Reading; edited by Michael Walsh. — London: Oxford University Press, 1972. — 4p; 8vo.
ISBN 0 19 351637 3 : Unpriced

(B73-50062)

EZDGNT — Anglican liturgy. Morning Prayer. Jubilate
Hoag, Charles K
O be joyful: for six-part chorus of mixed voices, SSA-TBB a cappella/ by Charles K. Hoag; text, Psalm 100. — New York; London: Schirmer, 1972. — 9p; 8vo.
Unpriced

(B73-50063)

EZDGU — Jewish liturgy
Adler, Samuel
Hinay yom hadin - Behold the day of judgment: four prayers from the High Holyday liturgy, for four-part chorus of mixed voices with soprano and tenor solo (cantor) with optional organ accompaniment/ by Samuel Adler. — New York; London: Schirmer.
1: Hayom harat olam. — 1972. — 6p; 8vo. —
Unpriced

(B73-50064)

2: Ayl melech yoshayr. — 1972. — 9p; 8vo. —
Unpriced

(B73-50065)

4: Avinu malkaynu chanayno. — 1972. — 9p; 8vo. —
Unpriced

(B73-50066)

EZDH — Motets, Anthems, Hymns, etc
Aston, Peter
Alleluya psallat: sequence for SATB unaccompanied/ by Peter Aston; words anonymous, from the 'Worcester fragments', English words by Peter Aston. — Sevenoaks: Novello, 1972. — 12p; 8vo.
£0.14

(B73-50068)

Baudach, Ulrich
Furchte dich nicht: [SSAB, with] Christus spricht: wer mich liebt: [SSAB, with] Herr, wer festen Herzens ist, dem bewahrst du Frieden: [SSA]/ von Ulrich Baudach. — Cassel; London: Bärenreiter, 1972. — 6p; 8vo.
£0.15

(B73-50069)

Bernstein, Leonard
[Mass.. Almighty Father]. Almighty Father: chorale for four part chorus of mixed voices a cappella/ by Leonard Bernstein; words by Stephen Schwartz and Leonard Bernstein. — New York; London: Amberson: Schirmer, 1971. — 3p; 8vo.
Unpriced

(B73-50070)

Brahms, Johannes
[Ach arme Welt. Op. 110, no.2]. Ach arme Welt = Alas, poor world: motet for four part chorus of mixed voices a cappella/ by Johannes Brahms; edited by Maynard Klein, English text by M.K. — New York; London: Schirmer, 1972. — 7p; 8vo.
Unpriced

(B73-50982)

Brahms, Johannes
[Ich aber bin elend. Op. 110, no.1]. Ich aber bin elend = Lord God, I am weary: motet for eight part double chorus of mixed voices a cappella/ by Johannes Brahms; edited by Maynard Klein, English text by M.K. — New York; London: Schirmer, 1972. — 15p; 8vo.
Unpriced

(B73-50983)

Chorbajian, John
And did those feet in ancient time: for full chorus of mixed voices a cappella/ by John Chorbajian; words by William Blake. — New York; London: Schirmer, 1972. — 8p; 8vo.
Unpriced

(B73-50071)

Crotch, William
Methinks I hear the full celestial choir: for 5-part chorus of mixed voices unaccompanied/ by William Crotch; edited by Russell A. Hammar. — Wendover: Roberton, 1973. — 12p; 8vo.
£0.13
(B73-50533)

Fast, Willard S
Alleluia to the Lord of being: for full chorus of mixed voices a cappella/ by Willard S. Fast; words by Trudy Ernst. — New York; London: Schirmer, 1972. — 14p; 8vo.
Unpriced
(B73-50072)

Fast, Willard S
To mercy, pity, peace and love: for four-part chorus of mixed voices a cappella/ by Willard S. Fast; words by William Blake. — New York; London: Schirmer, 1971. — 8p; 8vo.
Unpriced
(B73-50073)

Ford, Virgil T
All as God wills: for four-part chorus of mixed voices a cappella/ by Virgil T. Ford; words by John G. Whittier. — New York; London: Schirmer, 1972. — 6p; 8vo.
Unpriced
(B73-50074)

Ford, Virgil T
Come, sound his praise abroad: for four-part chorus of mixed voices a cappella/ by Virgil T. Ford; words by Isaac Watts. — New York; London: Schirmer, 1971. — 4p; 8vo.
Unpriced
(B73-50075)

Reda, Siegfried
Fünf Madrigale: für gemischten Chor/ von Siegfried Reda; [text] über die alte Epistel zum . Sonntag nach Epiphanias. — Cassel; London: Bärenreiter, 1972. — 8p; 8vo.
£0.40
(B73-50067)

Rose, Gregory
God's strange ways: SATB a cappella/ words and music by Gregory Rose. — London: Boosey and Hawkes, 1973. — 11p; 8vo.
£0.14
(B73-50984)

Rubbra, Edmund
This spiritual house almighty God shall inhabit. Op 146: motet for unaccompanied 4-part choir/ by Edmund Rubbra; words from Rahere's Vision of St Bartholomew. — South Croydon: Lengnick, 1973. — 8p; 8vo.
£0.12
(B73-50534)

Schein, Johann Hermann
[Israelsbrünnlein. Zion spricht: arr]. Zion spricht = Zion speaks/ by J. H. Schein; edited and arranged for six-part chorus of mixed voices unaccompanied, by Morris D. Hayes; English text by Richard C. Clark. — Wendover: Roberton, 1972. — 16p; 8vo.
Unpriced
(B73-50535)

Statham, Heathcote
O come, thou spirit divinest: introit for SATB/ by Heathcote Statham; [words] anon. — London: Cramer, 1972. — 4p; 8vo.
£0.06
(B73-50076)

EZDH/LF — Motets, Anthems, Hymns, etc. Christmas
Sprague, Richard L
Gloria in excelsis Deo: for four-part chorus of mixed voices a cappella/ by Richard L. Sprague. — New York; London: Schirmer, 1971. — 8p; 8vo.
Unpriced
(B73-50077)

EZDH/LL — Motets, Anthems, Hymns, etc. Easter
Johnson, Robert Sherlaw
Christus resurgens: SATB unacc./ by Robert Sherlaw Johnson. — London: Oxford University Press, 1973. — 10p; 8vo.
Duration 3 min (shorter version) to 5 1/2 min (full version).
ISBN 0 19 343036 3 : £0.20
(B73-50985)

EZDJ — Motets
Byrd, William
[Liber primus sacrarum cantionum. Laetentur coeli]. Laetentur coeli = Be glad ye heavens: SATBB by William Byrd/ edited by A. Ramsbotham, revised with English text by Roger Bray. — Revised ed.. — London: Oxford University Press, 1973. — 10p; 8vo.
ISBN 0 19 352058 3 : Unpriced
(B73-50536)

Giorgi, Giovanni
[Gloria et honore: arr]. Glory and honor: for four-part chorus of mixed voices a cappella/ by Giovanni Giorgi; edited and arranged by Walter Ehret. — New York; London: Schirmer, 1972. — 12p; 8vo.
Unpriced
(B73-50986)

Haydn, Michael
[Exultabunt sancti: arr]. Thou art mighty: for four-part chorus of mixed voices/ by Michael Haydn; arranged with organ or piano accompaniment (optional) by Reinhard Pauly. — New York; London: Schirmer, 1972. — 12p; 8vo.
Unpriced
(B73-50987)

Lasso, Orlando di
Adoramus te, Christe: SATB unacc./ by Orlandus Lassus; edited by Andrew Parker. — London: Oxford University Press, 1973. — 3p; 8vo.
ISBN 0 19 350332 8 : Unpriced
(B73-50537)

Parsons, Robert
Ave Maria: SAAT Bar B/ by Robert Parsons; edited by Nicholas Steinitz. — London: Oxford University Press, 1973. — 10p; 8vo.
ISBN 0 19 350335 2 : £0.15
(B73-50988)

EZDJ/AYD — Motets. Collections. England
Bent, Margaret
Five sequences for the Virgin Mary/ edited by Margaret Bent, anonymous text (English 14th century). — London: Oxford University Press, 1973. — 8p; 8vo.
ISBN 0 19 341207 1 : Unpriced
(B73-50989)

EZDJ/AYE — Motets. Collections. Germany
Ameln, Konrad
[Biblische Motetten für das Kirchenjahr, Band 1: Spruchmotetten]. Spruchmotetten/ herausgegeben von Konrad Ameln und Harald Kümmerling. — Cassel; London: Bärenreiter.
1: [Motets by] Wolfgang Carl Briegel, Andreas Raselins [and anonymous works]. — 1972. — 24p; 8vo.
£0.90
(B73-50078)
2: [Motets by] Johann Christenius [and others]. — 1972. — 24p; 8vo.
£0.90
(B73-50079)

EZDJ/LF — Motets. Christmas
Handl, Jacob
[Tomus primus operis musici.. Pueri concinite]. Pueri concinite: for four equal voices SSSA or SSAA a cappella/ by Jacob Handl; transcribed and edited by Cyril F. Simkins, English and German adapted M.J. — Wendover: Roberton, 1972. — 7p; 8vo.
Unpriced
(B73-50080)

Handl, Jacob
[Tonus primus operis musici. Regem natum]. Regem natum = Our king is born: for 4-part chorus of mixed voices unaccompanied/ by Jacob Handl; edited by James McCullough, English text by J. McC. — Wendover: Roberton, 1970. — 7p; 8vo.
Unpriced
(B73-50538)

Panufnik, Andrzej
Song to the Virgin Mary: for mixed chorus a cappella or 6 solo voices/ by Andrzej Panufnik; words anonymous. — Revised edition. — London: Boosey and Hawkes, 1973. — 24p; 8vo.
£0.40
Also classified at JNEZAZDJ/LF
(B73-50081)

Victoria, Tomas Luis de
[Motecta. O regem coeli]. In festo natalis Domini: for 4-part chorus of mixed voices unaccompanied/ by Tomàs Victoria; edited by Harold Schmidt. — Wendover: Roberton, 1973. — 15p; 8vo.
Unpriced
(B73-50539)

EZDJ/LK — Motets. Good Friday
Biber, Carl Heinrich
Tenebrae factae sunt = Darkness was over all: for four-part chorus of mixed voices a cappella/ by C.H. Biber; edited by Reinhard G. Pauly, English text by R.G.P. — New York; London: Schirmer, 1972. — 8p; 8vo.
Unpriced
Primary classification EZDGKH/LK
(B73-50060)

EZDK — Anthems
Mathias, William
The law of the Lord. Op.61, no.2: an introit, SATB unacc./ by
William Mathias; text from Psalm 19. — London: Oxford
University Press, 1973. — [2]p; 8vo.
ISBN 0 19 350341 7 : £0.05

(B73-50990)

Newbury, Kent A
Give ear to my words: general anthem, for four-part chorus of
mixed voices a cappella/ by Kent A. Newbury; text from Psalms
4 and 5. — New York; London: Schirmer, 1972. — 4p; 8vo.
Unpriced

(B73-50082)

Newbury, Kent A
How lovely is thy dwelling place: for four-part chorus of mixed
voices a cappella/ by Kent A. Newbury; text from Psalm 84. —
New York; London: Schirmer, 1971. — 8p; 8vo.
Unpriced

(B73-50083)

Newbury, Kent A
I long for thy salvation: general anthem, for four-part chorus of
mixed voices a cappella/ by Kent A. Newbury; text from Psalm
119. — New York; London: Schirmer, 1972. — 6p; 8vo.
Unpriced

(B73-50084)

Newbury, Kent A
Let the word of Christ dwell in you richly: general anthem, for
four-part chorus of mixed voices a cappella/ by Kent A.
Newbury; text from Colossians 4. — New York; London:
Schirmer, 1972. — 8p; 8vo.
Unpriced

(B73-50085)

Rose, Bernard
Praise ye the Lord: anthem for double choir (unaccompanied)/ by
Bernard Rose; Psalm 149. — Sevenoaks: Novello, 1973. — 16p;
8vo.
£0.18

(B73-50540)

Vernon, Knight
Swords into plowshares: for four-part chorus of mixed voices a
cappella/ by Vernon Knight; text from Isaiah 2. — New York;
London: Schirmer, 1972. — 10p; 8vo.
Unpriced

(B73-50086)

EZDK/LGZ — Anthems. Passiontide
Barlow, David
Behold and see: Passiontide introit, for SATB (unaccompanied)/
by David Barlow; text from Lamentations 1. — Sevenoaks:
Novello, 1973. — 3p; 8vo.
£0.07

(B73-50087)

EZDM — Hymns
De Cormier, Robert
Wayfaring stranger: for 4-part chorus of mixed voices
unaccompanied/ arranged by Robert De Cormier; words from
Sacred Harp. — Wendover: Roberton, 1971. — 7p; 8vo.
£0.10

(B73-50541)

Ford, Virgil T
Lord dismiss us with thy blessing: a choral benediction, for
four-part chorus of mixed voices a cappella/ by Virgil T. Ford. —
New York; London: Schirmer, 1971. — 4p; 8vo.
Unpriced

(B73-50088)

Hassler, Hans Leo
[Kirchengesäng: Psalmen und geistliche Lieder.. Selections].
Kirchengesänge, Psalmen und geistliche Lieder: Choralsätz für
gemischten Chor/ von Hans Leo Hassler; zusammengestellt von
Ulrich W. Zimmer. — Cassel; London: Bärenreiter, 1972. — 44p;
8vo.
£1.35

(B73-50089)

Lynn, George
Two chorales/ edited for four-part chorus of mixed voices with
optional piano accompaniment by George Lynn. — New York;
London: Schirmer, 1972. — 7p; 8vo.
Contents: 1. Komm heiliger Geist, Herre Gott. Come, O Holy Ghost God
and Lord, by Lucas Osiander; text by Lucas Osiander - 2. Psalm 121, by
Heinrich Schutz: freely translated by Cornelius Becker.
Unpriced

(B73-50090)

[Sacred harp]. Three hymns: arranged for four-part chorus of mixed
voices with tenor solo a cappella/ by James D. Cram. — New
York; London: Chappell.
1: Paradise. — 1972. — 8p; 8vo.
Unpriced

(B73-50091)

2: The morning trumpet. — 1972. — 12p; 8vo.
Unpriced

(B73-50092)

3: Sweet rivers. — 1972. — 8p; 8vo.
Unpriced

(B73-50093)

EZDP — Carols
Evans, E L
The young child's carol/ by E.L. Evans; words by O.M. Spurgeon.
— London: British and Continental, 1973. — [2]p; 8vo.
Unpriced

(B73-50095)

Naylor, Bernard
Exultet mundus gaudio: introduction and sequence of nine carols
for the Christian year, for SSAATTBB chorus, SATB soli and
two-part chorus of trebles/ by Bernard Naylor; text assembled and
adapted by Anita Freeland. — Wendover: Roberton, 1972. — 43p;
8vo.
Duration 18 min.
£0.50

(B73-50094)

EZDP/LF — Carols. Christmas
Beechey, Gwilym
Ave Maria, gracia Dei plena: SATB unacc/ by Gwilym Beechey;
medieval works. — York: Banks, 1973. — 2p; 8vo.
£0.04

(B73-50991)

Bradley, John
The Christ-child lay on Mary's lap: for SATB unaccompanied/ by
John Bradley; words by G.K. Chesterton. — Sevenoaks: Novello,
1973. — 4p; 8vo.
£0.07

(B73-50992)

Czajanek, Victor
Weihnacht wie bist so schon = Christmas so wondrous fair: carol
from Upper Austria, for four-part chorus of mixed voices a
cappella/ by Victor Czajanek; arranged by Maynard Klein,
English text by M.K. — New York; London: Schirmer, 1972. —
8p; 8vo.
Unpriced

(B73-50096)

Deale, Edgar Martin
O men from the fields: SATB unacc./ by Edgar M. Deale; words
by Padraic Colum. — London: Oxford University Press, 1973. —
4p; 8vo.
ISBN 0 19 343038 x : Unpriced

(B73-50993)

Dickson, Andrew
The nativity: SATB unacc/ by Andrew Dickson; works by Henry
Vaughan. — York: Banks, 1973. — 4p; 8vo.
£0.05

(B73-50994)

Douglas, James
A Christmas fable/ by James Douglas; words by Alice V. Stuart.
— Wendover: Roberton, 1972. — 4p; 8vo.
Staff & tonic sol-fa notation.
£0.07

(B73-50097)

Gardner, Ward
Lullay, lullay, thou lytil child: SATB unacc/ by Ward Gardner;
words anon. — York: Banks, 1973. — s.sh; 8vo.
£0.03

(B73-50995)

Handl, Jacob
Resonet in laudibus = Joseph dearest, Joseph mine: for four-part
chorus of mixed voices/ by Jacob Handl; transcribed and edited
by C.F. Simkins, with English, German and Latin text adapted
equi-syllabically by Maurice Jacobson. — Wendover: Roberton,
1972. — 7p; 8vo.
Unpriced

(B73-50098)

Hedges, Anthony
A manger carol: for soli and SATB unaccompanied/ words and
music by Anthony Hedges. — Sevenoaks: Novello, 1973. — 3p;
8vo.
£0.07

(B73-50996)

Joubert, John
Coverdale's carol. Opus 75: for SATB unaccompanied/ by John
Joubert; words by Miles Coverdale. — Sevenoaks: Novello, 1973.
— 4p; 8vo.
£0.07

(B73-50542)

Kelly, Bryan
Abingdon carols: six carols for SATB/ by Bryan Kelly. —
Sevenoaks: Novello, 1973. — 26p; 8vo.
£0.35

(B73-50997)

Monelle, Raymond
Lullay myn lykyng: for mixed voice choir with soprano solo,
unaccompanied/ by Raymond Monelle; words: 15th century. —
Wendover: Roberton, 1973. — 7p; 8vo.
Staff & tonic sol-fa notation.
£0.10

(B73-50998)

Neander, Valentin
[Uns ist geborn ein Kindelein]. Cradle: SSATB unacc/ by V.
Neandri; ed Ward Gardner, English words by Ward Gardner. —
York: Banks, 1973. — 2p; 8vo.
£0.04

(B73-50999)

Rastall, Richard
Two Coventry carols: for 3 voices (S/ATB) with optional
instruments/ edited by Richard Rastall. — Lustleigh: Antico,
1973. — 4to.
Score (5p.) & 3 parts.
Unpriced

(B73-51000)

Roe, Betty
Away in a manger: carol for mixed choir and organ/piano/ by
Betty Roe; words traditional. — London: Thames, 1973. — 4p;
8vo.
Unpriced
Primary classification JDP/LF

(B73-50604)

Roe, Betty
Deck the hall: carol for mixed voices/ arranged by Betty Roe. —
London: Thames, 1973. — 3p; 8vo.
Unpriced

(B73-50543)

Rudland, Malcolm
Carol of Joseph: for SATB choir/ by Malcolm Rudland; words by
Hamish B. Whyte. — London: Thames, 1973. — 2p; 8vo.
Unpriced

(B73-50099)

Spencer, Williametta
Wassail wassail all over the town: a madrigal for Christmas time,
for four-part chorus of mixed voices a cappella/ by Williametta
Spencer; words traditional. — New York; London: Associated
Music, 1971. — 8p; 8vo.
Unpriced

(B73-50100)

Vale, Charles
Christ's carol: SATB unaccompanied/ by Charles Vale; words by
E.J. Falconer. — Wendover: Roberton, 1973. — 4p; 8vo.
Staff & tonic sol-fa notation.
£0.07

(B73-51001)

Walker, Robert
Adam lay ybounden: carol for SATB unaccompanied/ by Robert
Walker; words anonymous. — Sevenoaks: Novello, 1973. — 4p;
8vo.
£0.07

(B73-51002)

Walker, Robert
In the bleak mid winter: carol for SATB unaccompanied/ by
Robert Walker; words by Christina G. Rossetti. — Sevenoaks:
Novello, 1973. — 4p; 8vo.
£0.07

(B73-51003)

Wesley, Samuel Sebastian
[An air composed for Holsworthy Church bells]. It came upon the
midnight clear/ by S.S. Wesley; arr. for SATB unacc by E.
Tostevin, words by E.H. Sears. — London: Oxford University
Press, 1973. — 3p; 8vo.
ISBN 0 19 343041 x : Unpriced

(B73-50544)

EZDP/LFP — Carols. Epiphany
Smith, Peter Melville
Eastern monarchs: SATB unacc/ by Peter Melville Smith; 15th
century Latin words, translation anonymous. — York: Banks,
1973. — 8vo.
Unpriced

(B73-51004)

EZDR — Psalms
Betts, Donald
As the hart panteth after the water brooks: for four-part chorus of
mixed voices a cappella/ by Donald Betts; text, Psalm 42. — New
York; London: Associated Music, 1972. — 10p; 8vo.
Unpriced

(B73-50101)

Najera, Edmund
Ad flumina Babylonis: for double chorus of mixed voices a
cappella/ by Edmund Najera; text Psalm 136 (Liber nova). —
New York; London: Schirmer, 1972. — 16p; 8vo.
Unpriced

(B73-50102)

Vecchi, Horatio
[Moteca. Cantate Domino]. Cantate Domino. Sing unto the Lord:
for 4-part chorus of mixed voices with optional organ/ by Orazio
Vecchi; edited by Roger Wilhelm. — Wendover: Roberton, 1972.
— 10p; 8vo.
Unpriced

(B73-50545)

EZDR/AZ — Psalms. Collected works of individual composers
Dowland, John
[Works, psalms]. Complete psalms for SATB/ by John Dowland;
edited by Diana Poulton. — London: Stainer and Bell, 1973. —
28p; 4to.
ISBN 0 85249 168 9 : Unpriced

(B73-51005)

EZDTF — Lord's Prayer
Stone, Robert
The Lord's Prayer: SATB unacc./ by Robert Stone; edited by
Anthony Greening. — London: Oxford University Press, 1973. —
7p; 8vo.
ISBN 0 19 350345 x : £0.05

(B73-51006)

EZDU — Madrigals
Brudieu, Joan
[Madrigales. Las Canas]. Las Canas = The lancers: for four-part
chorus of mixed voices a cappella/ by Joan Brudieu; edited by
Marlin Merrill, translation M.M.. — Wendover: Roberton, 1966.
— 12p; 8vo.
Unpriced

(B73-50546)

Busnois, Antoine
Faites de moy toute qu'il vous plaira/ by Antoine Busnois; edited
by H.M. Brown. — London: Oxford University Press, 1973. —
3p; 8vo.
ISBN 0 19 341201 2 : Unpriced

(B73-50103)

Jacopo da Bologna
Three madrigals: for 3 voices and/or instruments/ by Jacopo da
Bologna; edited by Nigel Wilkins. — Lustleigh: Antico, 1973. —
4to.
Score (16p.) & 3 parts. — Contents: 1.Sotto l'imperio - 2.Si com'al canto -
3.Aquil'altera/Creatura gentil'/Uccel di Dio.
Unpriced
Also classified at LNT

(B73-50104)

Jacopo da Bologna
Three madrigals: for 3 voices and/or instruments/ by Jacopo da
Bologna; edited by Nigel Wilkins. — Lustleigh: Antico, 1973. —
4to.
Score (16p.) & 3 parts. — Contents: 1.Sotto l'imperio - 2.Si com'al canto -
3.Aquil'altera/Creatura gentil'/Uccel di Dio.
Unpriced
Also classified at LNT

(B73-50105)

Josquin Des Prés
Faultte d'argent = Life without money: for five-part chorus of
mixed voices a cappella/ by Josquin des Prez; edited by James P.
Dunn, English text by J.P.D. — New York; London: Schirmer,
1972. — 11p; 8vo.
Unpriced

(B73-50106)

Le Jeune, Claude
[Meslanges liv 2. S'ebahit-on si je vous aime]. How can my love:
chanson for SATB/ by Claude Le Jeune; edited by John A.
Parkinson, edited by Stephen R. Parkinson. — 130 Farley Rd,
Selsdon, Croydon: J.A. Parkinson, 1973. — 4p; 8vo.
Unpriced

(B73-50547)

Marenzio, Luca
[Madrigali a quattro voci.. Non vidi mai]. Non vidi mai = After
a rainy evening: for four-part chorus of mixed voices a cappella/
by Luca Marenzio; edited by James P. Dunn, English text by
J.P.D. — New York; London: Schirmer, 1972. — 11p; 8vo.
Unpriced

(B73-50107)

Marenzio, Luca
[Il quinto libro de madrigale a sei voci. Leggiadre ninfe].
Leggiadre ninfe = You graceful nymphs: for six-part chorus of
mixed voices a cappella/ by Luca Marenzio; edited by James P.
Dunn, English text by James P. Dunn. — New York; London:
Schirmer, 1972. — 10p; 8vo.
Unpriced

(B73-50548)

Marenzio, Luca
[Il secondo libro de madrigali a sei voce.. In un bel bosco]. In un
bel bosco = In a fair greenwood: for six-part chorus of mixed
voices a cappella/ by Luca Marenzio; edited by James P. Dunn,
English text by J.P.D. — New York; London: Schirmer, 1972. —
16p; 8vo.
Unpriced

(B73-50109)

Marenzio, Luca
[Il terzo libro de madrigali a cinque voci.. Togli, dolce ben mio].
Togli, dolce ben mio = Take thou, my sweetheart, these lovely
flow'rs: for five-part chorus of mixed voices a cappella/ by Luca
Marenzio; edited by James P. Dunn, English text by J.P.D. —
New York; London: Chappell, 1972. — 7p; 8vo.
Unpriced

(B73-50110)

Merril, Marlin
Di pera mora = Cruel they beauty: 16th century Spanish dance
song, for 4-part chorus of mixed voices unaccompanied/ edited by
Marlin Merril, English version by M.M. — Wendover: Roberton,
1966. — 7p; 8vo.
Unpriced

(B73-50549)

Vecchi, Horatio
[Madrigali a cinque voci. Pastorella gratiosella]. Shepherd maiden,
fair and graceful: for 5-part chorus of mixed voices
unaccompanied/ by Orazio Vecchi; arranged by Walter Ehret,
English text by W. E.. — Wendover: Roberton, 1968. — 7p; 8vo.
Unpriced

(B73-50550)

EZDU/AY — Madrigals. Collections
Dart, Thurston
Invitation to madrigals/ devised and begun by Thurston Dart. —
London: Stainer and Bell.
6: for SSATB and SSAT Ba B; transcribed and edited by David Scott. —
1972. — 59p; 8vo.
ISBN 0 903000 02 4 : Unpriced

(B73-50551)

Scott, David
Invitation to madrigals: for S S A T B & S S A T B a B/ newly
transcribed and edited by David Scott. — London: Stainer and
Bell.
Previous volumes entered under the name of Thurston Dart.
Volume 7. — 1973. — 59p; 8vo.
ISBN 0 85249 167 0 : Unpriced

(B73-51007)

EZDW — Songs, etc
Brown, Christopher
Four madrigals. Op. 29: for unaccompanied mixed voices/ by
Christopher Brown. — London: Oxford University Press, 1973. —
48p; 8vo.
ISBN 0 19 343521 7 : Unpriced

(B73-50552)

Chorbajian, John
For lo the winter is past: for full chorus of mixed voices a
cappella/ by John Chorbajian; words by John Ruskin. — New
York; London: Schirmer, 1972. — 4p; 8vo.
Unpriced

(B73-50111)

Chorbajian, John
There is a silence: for full chorus of mixed voices a cappella/ by
John Chorbajian; words by Thomas Hood. — New York; London:
Schirmer, 1971. — 10p; 8vo.
Unpriced

(B73-50112)

Dare, Marie
A widow bird sate mourning: SATB unaccompanied/ by Marie
Dare; words by Shelley. — Wendover: Roberton, 1973. — 4p;
8vo.
£0.07

(B73-50113)

Droste, Doreen
The song of wandering Aengus: SATB a cappella by Doreen
Droste/ poem by W.B. Yeats. — New York: Galaxy; London:
Galliard, 1973. — 11p; 8vo.
Unpriced

(B73-50553)

Fast, Willard S
Be not afraid because the sun goes down: for four-part chorus of
mixed voices a cappella/ by Willard S. Fast; words by Robert
Nathan. — New York; London: Schirmer, 1972. — 8p; 8vo.
Unpriced

(B73-50114)

Fast, Willard S
Go, lovely rose: for full chorus of mixed voices a cappella/ by
Willard S. Fast; words by Edmund Waller. — New York;
London: Schirmer, 1972. — 7p; 8vo.
Unpriced

(B73-50115)

Fast, Willard S
When I was one-and-twenty: for four-part chorus of mixed voices
a cappella/ by Willard S. Fast; words by A.E. Houseman. — New
York; London: Schirmer, 1972. — 4p; 8vo.
Unpriced

(B73-50116)

Feld, Jindrich
Inventionen: für gemischten Chor/ von Jindrich Feld. — Cassel,
London: Bärenreiter, 1973. — 32p; 8vo.
£1.35

(B73-50554)

Gay, John
[Beggar's opera. Selections]. Four songs/ [selected by Johann
Christoph Pepusch] arranged for unaccompanied mixed chorus by
Gregor Medinger. — London: Oxford University Press, 1973. —
8p; 8vo.
ISBN 0 19 343673 6 : £0.12

(B73-50555)

Heath, Fenno
Love-song: for four-part chorus of mixed voices a cappella/ by
Fenno Heath; words by Rainer Maria Rilke. — New York;
London: Schirmer, 1972. — 7p; 8vo.
Unpriced

(B73-50117)

Laloux, Fernand
Two national songs: SATB unaccompanied/ arranged by Fernand
Laloux. — London: Boosey and Hawkes.
1: The robin's last will. — 1971. — 20p; 8vo.
Unpriced

(B73-51008)

Lekberg, Sven
Far away across the mountain: for four-part chorus of mixed
voices a cappella/ by Sven Lekberg; text by S.L. — New York;
London: Schirmer, 1972. — 8p; 8vo.
Unpriced

(B73-50118)

Lekberg, Sven
She walks in beauty: for three-part chorus of mixed voices a cappella/ by Sven Lekberg; words by Lord Byron. — New York; London: Schirmer, 1972. — 7p; 8vo.
Unpriced

(B73-50119)

Lekberg, Sven
The trees stand silent: for five-part chorus of mixed voices SSATB a cappella/ by Sven Lekberg; words by Thomas Keohler. — New York; London: Schirmer, 1972. — 8p; 8vo.
Unpriced

(B73-50120)

Lekberg, Sven
We are the music-makers: for four-part chorus of mixed voices with descant a cappella/ by Sven Lekberg; words by Arthur O'Shaughnessy. — New York; London: Schirmer, 1972. — 8p; 8vo.
Unpriced

(B73-50121)

Lekberg, Sven
Weep, you no more, sad fountains: for four-part chorus of mixed voices a cappella/ by Sven Lekberg; words anonymous. — New York; London: Schirmer, 1972. — 8p; 8vo.
Unpriced

(B73-50122)

Maw, Nicholas
Five Irish songs: for mixed chorus a cappella/ by Nicholas Maw. — London: Boosey and Hawkes.
1: I shall not die for thee; words by Douglas Hyde. — 1973. — 8p; 8vo.
£0.09

(B73-50556)
2: Dear dark head; words by Samuel Ferguson. — 1973. — 6p; 8vo.
£0.09

(B73-50557)
3: Popular song; words anon. — 1973. — 6p; 8vo. —
£0.09

(B73-50558)
4: Ringleted youth of my love; words by Douglas Hyde. — 1973. — 8p; 8vo.
£0.14

(B73-50559)
5: Jig; words by Cecil Day-Lewis. — 1973. — 16p; 8vo.
£0.20

(B73-50560)

Mendelssohn, Felix
[Fruhlingsfeier. Op.48, no.3]. Spring repose: for four-part chorus of mixed voices a cappella/ by Felix Mendelssohn; edited by Robert S. Hines, words by L. Uhland, English text by R.S.H. — New York; London: Schirmer, 1971. — 4p; 8vo.
Unpriced

(B73-50123)

Naylor, Bernard
Six poems from 'Miserere'/ set to music for double mixed chorus and two soprano soloists by Bernard Naylor; [words by] David Gascoyne. — Wendover: Roberton, 1972. — 24p; 8vo.
£0.30

(B73-50124)

Ophenbeidt
Fugue on 'Hey diddle diddle': for SATB unaccompanied/ by Profeffor Ophenbeidt; transcribed by Charles Vale. — London: Thames, 1972. — 8p; 8vo.
The composer was an eclectic once compared favourably to Offenbach. Glade's Supp. states 'His (Offen)bach is worse than his...' - Publisher's note.
Unpriced

(B73-50125)

Paynter, John
The high school band: SSATB (S. solo) unacc./ by John Paynter; poem by Reed Whittemore. — London: Oxford University Press, 1973. — 10p; 8vo.
Duration 4 min.
ISBN 0 19 343039 8 : Unpriced

(B73-51009)

Paynter, John
May Magnificat: three choruses for mixed voices by John Paynter/ poems by Gerard Manley Hopkins. — London: Oxford University Press, 1973. — 13p; 8vo.
ISBN 0 19 343692 2 : £0.35

(B73-50126)

Radford, Anthony
And wilt thou leave me thus?: For SSATBB unaccompanied/ by Anthony Radford; words by Sir Thomas Wyatt. — London: Thames, 1972. — 5p; 4to.
Unpriced

(B73-50561)

Rose, Gregory
It's snowing: S.A.T.B./ words and music by Gregory Rose. — London: Boosey and Hawkes, 1973. — 5p; olb.4to.
£0.15

(B73-51010)

Schnebel, Dieter
Für Stimmen (... missa est)!. — Mainz; London: Schott.
Nos 1 and 2 are classified at NYFXP.
Nr. 3: Madrisha II; fur 3 Chorgruppen. — 1973. — 12ff, 25p; fol.
£4.80

(B73-51011)

Sculthorpe, Peter
Autumn song: for unaccompanied chorus (SAT Bar B)/ by Peter Sculthorpe; words by Roger Corell. — London: Faber Music, 1972. — 4p; 8vo.
Unpriced

(B73-50127)

Steinfeld, Karl-Heinz
Draussen am Rain = Uti var hage: Schwedisches Volkslied, für gemischten Chor a cappella/ Chorsatz von Karl-Heinz Steinfeld; deutscher Text von Gustav Schulten. — Cologne; London: Bosworth, 1972. — 2p; 8vo.
£0.10

(B73-50562)

EZDW/AYD — Songs. Collections. England
Bush, Geoffrey
Invitation to the partsong/ edited by Geoffrey Bush and Michael Hurd. — London: Stainer and Bell.
Volume 1. — 1973. — 44p; 8vo. —
ISBN 0 85249 165 4 : Unpriced
Also classified at EZDW/XC/AYD

(B73-51012)

EZDW/G/AY — Folk songs. Collections
Ives, Grayston
Three folk songs: for unaccompanied mixed choir/ arranged by Grayston Ives. — Wendover: Roberton.
Staff & tonic sol-fa notation.
No.1: Buy broom besoms: North country street song. — 1973. — 8p; 8vo.
£0.10

(B73-50129)
No.2: The lark in the clear air: Irish folk song; words by Sir Samuel Ferguson. — 1973. — 8p; 8vo.
£0.10

(B73-50130)
No.3: The tailor and the mouse: English folk song. — 1973. — 12p; 8vo.
£0.13

(B73-50563)

EZDW/LC — Songs, etc. Spirituals
Hopkins, Ewart
All my trials, Lord: West Indian folk song/ arranged for mixed choir (unaccompanied) by Ewart Hopkins. — Wendover: Roberton, 1972. — 7p; 8vo.
£0.10

(B73-50131)

EZDW/XC/AYD — Rounds. Collections. England
Bush, Geoffrey
Invitation to the partsong/ edited by Geoffrey Bush and Michael Hurd. — London: Stainer and Bell.
Volume 1. — 1973. — 44p; 8vo. —
ISBN 0 85249 165 4 : Unpriced
Primary classification EZDW/AYD

EZDX — Secular cantatas
Wilson, Richard
Home from the range: for full chorus of mixed voices a cappella/ by Richard Wilson; text from Stephen Sandy. — New York; London: Schirmer, 1971. — 30p; 8vo.
Unpriced

(B73-50132)

F — FEMALE VOICES, CHILDREN'S VOICES
FDE — Religious cantatas
Britten, Benjamin
[Rejoice in the Lamb. Op.30. Vocal score: arr]. Rejoice in the Lamb. Op 30: festival cantata/ by Benjamin Britten; arranged for S.S.A.A. choir and organ by Edmund Walters, words by Christopher Smart, ins Deutsche übersetzt von Harold Wolff. — London: Boosey and Hawkes, 1973. — 40p; 8vo.
£1.00

(B73-50564)

Hurd, Michael
Swingin' Samson: a cantata in popular style for unison voices (with divisions) and piano with guitar chord-symbols/ words and music by Michael Hurd. — Sevenoaks: Novello, 1973. — 22p; 8vo.
£0.35

(B73-51013)

FDE/LF — Religious cantatas. Christmas
Williamson, Malcolm
[The winter star. Vocal score]. The winter star: a cassation for audience and instruments/ by Malcolm Williamson; words by the composer. — London: Weinberger, 1973. — 19p; 4to.
Unpriced

(B73-51014)

FDGE — Roman liturgy. Ordinary of the Mass. Sanctus
Haydn, Joseph
[Mass. no.16 in B flat major, 'Theresa mass'.. Sanctus. Vocal score: arr]. Sanctus/ by Joseph Haydn; arranged and edited for three-part chorus of women's voices with organ or piano accompaniment by William Herrmann. — New York; London: Schirmer, 1972. — 7p; 8vo.
Unpriced

(B73-50133)

FDGNPV — Anglican liturgy. Morning Prayer. Venite
Swann, Donald
[Festival Matins.. O come let us sing unto the Lord]. O come let us sing unto the Lord: for two-part chorus of female, male or mixed voices with piano accompaniment/ by Donald Swann; [text] Psalm 95. — Wendover: Roberton, 1970. — 7p; 8vo.
Unpriced
Primary classification DGNPV

(B73-50016)

FDGNQ — Anglican liturgy. Morning Prayer. Te Deum
Swann, Donald
A modern Te Deum: We praise thee, O God: for equal voices with piano or organ accompaniment/ by Donald Swann. — Wendover: Roberton, 1971. — 16p; 8vo.
Duration 5 mins.
£0.18

(B73-50134)

FDGNS — Anglican liturgy. Morning Prayer. Benedictus
Swann, Donald
[Festival Matins.. Blessed be the Lord God of Israel]. Blessed be the Lord God of Israel: for two-part chorus of female, male or mixed voices with piano or organ accompaniment/ by Donald Swann; [text from] St. Luke 1. — Wendover: Roberton, 1970. — 7p; 8vo.
Unpriced
Primary classification DGNS

(B73-50018)

FDH — Motets, Anthems, Hymns, etc
Agnes Cecilia, *Sister*
Suantraí: S S A/ gléasta ag Sr M. Agnes Cecilia. — Dublin: McCullough, Pigott, 1971. — 4p; 8vo.
Unpriced

(B73-51015)

Cobb, Donald
Heaven conserve thy course in quietness: for women's chorus and viola, or piano/ by Don Cobb; words by Ezra Pound. — New York: Galaxy Music; London: Galliard, 1973. — 8p; 8vo.
Duration 2 3/4 min.
Unpriced
Primary classification FE/SQDH

Harris, *Sir* William Henry
He that is down needs fear no fall: SSA/ by William H. Harris; words by John Bunyan. — London: Oxford University Press, 1973. — 3p; 8vo.
ISBN 0 19 351117 7 : Unpriced

(B73-50565)

Rose, Michael
Mirth: anthem for female or boy's voices and organ/ by Michael Rose, words by Christopher Smart. — Sevenoaks: Novello, 1973. — 9p; 8vo.
£0.14

(B73-51016)

Green, Philip
[Let me bring love. Suffer little children]. Suffer little children/ by Philip Green. — Croydon: Belwin-Mills, 1972. — 4p; 4to.
£0.20

(B73-51017)

FDH/LF — Motets, Anthems, Hymns, etc. Christmas
Gardner, John
A Christmas hymn. Opus 109a: SATB (or S. only) and organ, by John Gardner: [words] hymn at First Vespers, Christmas Day; English translation by John Gardner. — London: Oxford University Press, 1971. — 6p; 8vo.
ISBN 0 19 343016 9 : Unpriced
Primary classification DH/LF

FDJ — Motets
Donati, Ignazio
[Concerti ecclesiastici. Op.4. *Excerpts]*. Non vos relinquam orphanos = I will not leave you fatherless: SSA or T.T. Bar./ by Ignazio Donati; edited by Jerome Roche, [text from] St. John 14, translated by Elizabeth Roche. — London: Oxford University Press, 1972. — 8p; 8vo.
ISBN 0 19 350336 0 : Unpriced
Also classified at GDJ

(B73-50135)

Donati, Ignazio
[Concerti ecclesiastici. Op.4. Nun vos relinquam orphanos]. Non vos relinquam orphanos = I will not leave you fatherless: SSA or T.T. Bar./ by Ignazia Donati; edited by Jerome Roche, [text from] St John 14, translated by Elizabeth Roche. — London: Oxford University Press, 1972. — 8p; 8vo.
ISBN 0 19 350336 0 : Unpriced
Also classified at GDJ

(B73-51035)

FDK — Anthems
Purcell, Henry
Hear my prayer, O Lord/ by Henry Purcell; arranged for two equal voices by Laurence H. Davies, [text from] Psalm 102. — Wendover: Roberton, 1972. — 4p; 8vo.
Staff & tonic sol-fa notation.
£0.07

(B73-50136)

FDM — Hymns
Cookridge, John Michael
Unless love prevails: a modern spiritual for SA with pianoforte accompaniment/ words and music by John M. Cookridge. — Dublin: McCullough, Pigott, 1973. — 4p; 8vo.
£0.10

(B73-51018)

Sansom, Clive A
O sinner man/ arranged for two part singing by Clive A. Sansom. — London: Studio Music, 1973. — 4p; 8vo.
Unpriced

(B73-51019)

Tomlins, Greta
Who would true valour see: S.S.A. with piano or organ/ by Greta Tomlins; words by Percy Dearmer after John Bunyan, verse by John Bunyan. — Wendover: Roberton, 1970. — 7p; 8vo.
£0.09

(B73-50137)

FDP/LF — Carols. Christmas
Adams, Jean
A ring of carols: for female or boys' voices and piano/ words and music by Jean Adams. — Sevenoaks: Paxton, 1973. — 12p; 8vo.
£0.27

(B73-51020)

Bacon, Ernst
In that poor stable: carol for voice(s) and piano or organ/ by Ernst Bacon; words by Beatrice Quickenden. — Sevenoaks: Novello, 1973. — 6p; 8vo.
£0.10

(B73-51021)

Carter, Andrew
Tomorrow shall be my dancing day: English traditional carol/ arr. two-part by Andrew Carter. — York: Banks, 1973. — 4p; 8vo.
£0.05

(B73-51022)

Drayton, Paul
Corpus Christi carol: for unison voices with optional divisions, and piano or organ/ by Paul Drayton; words anonymous, 16th century. — Sevenoaks: Novello, 1973. — 6p; 8vo.
£0.10

(B73-51023)

Hugh-Jones, Elaine
Chanticleer: SSA/ Elaine Hugh-Jones; words by W. Austin. — London: Oxford University Press, 1973. — 7p; 8vo.
ISBN 0 19 342596 3 : Unpriced

(B73-51024)

Moore, Philip

Immortal babe: carol for accompanied two-part chorus/ by Philip Moore; words by Bishop Joseph Hall. — London: Thames, 1973. — 4p; 8vo.

Unpriced

(B73-50566)

Nicholson, Ralph

Herrick's carol: for women's voices and piano/ by Ralph Nicholson; words by Robert Herrick. — London: Weinberger, 1973. — 4p; 8vo.

Staff & tonic sol-fa notation.

£0.08

(B73-50138)

Parker, Alice

Fum fum fum!: Traditional Spanish carol/ arranged for three-part chorus of women's voices by Alice Parker and Robert Shaw, English version by Alice Parker and Robert Shaw. — New York; London: Schirmer, 1971. — 7p; 8vo.

Unpriced

(B73-50139)

Spearing, Robert

A hymn to the Virgin. Opus 20: Christmas anthem for two part female, or boys, voices, trumpet (optional) and organ/ by Robert Spearing; words anonymous, translated by Brian Stone. — Sevenoaks: Novello, 1973. — 4p; 8vo.

£0.07

(B73-51025)

Thiman, Eric Harding

Pilgrims to Bethlehem: two-part song with piano/ by Eric Thiman; words by Kathleen Warburton. — Wendover: Roberton, 1972. — 7p; 8vo.

Staff & tonic sol-fa notation.

£0.10

(B73-50140)

Weston, Gordon

Gorwyd Iesu Grist = Christus natus est: two part carol by Gordon Weston; traditional words, Welsh version by Ivor Owen. — Cardiff: University of Wales Press, 1973. — 5p; 4to.

£0.15

(B73-51026)

FDPDE/LF/JN — Carol cantatas. Christmas. Mime

Fenton, Lesley

A children's nativity: a nativity mime with narrative and carols (with ad lib. percussion, recorders, etc.)/ by Leslie Fenton and Pauline Andrew. — London: Keith Prowse Music, 1973. — iv, 28p; 8vo.

£0.40

(B73-51027)

FDR — Psalms

Williamson, Malcolm

I will lift up mine eyes. Psalm 121: anthem for chorus, echo chorus and organ/ by Malcolm Williamson. — London: Weinberger, 1970. — 4p; 8vo.

£0.05

(B73-50567)

FDW — Songs, etc

Binge, Ronald

The watermill/ by Ronald Binge; arranged for S.S.C. by the composer, words by Jo Manning Wilson. — London: Inter-Art, 1973. — 8p; 8vo.

£0.12

(B73-50141)

Gardner, John

[A Shakespeare sequence. Op.66.. Who is Sylvia?]. Who is Sylvia?: SSAA/ by John Gardner; [words by] Shakespeare. — London: Oxford University Press, 1972. — 6p; 8vo.

ISBN 0 19 342594 7 : Unpriced

(B73-50142)

Le Fleming, Christopher

Trees in the valley. Op. 40/ by Christopher le Fleming; words by Grace Armitage. — London: Boosey and Hawkes.

1: The plane: unison and piano. — 1973. — 3p; 8vo.

£0.05

Also classified at JFDW

(B73-51029)

2: Beeches (copper and green): two part or unison and piano. — 1973. — 4p; 8vo.

£0.05

Also classified at JFDW

(B73-51028)

3: The holly: SSA and piano. — 1973. — 4p; 8vo.

£0.05

Also classified at JFDW

(B73-51030)

4: The willow: unison and piano. — 1973. — 3p; 8vo.

£0.05

Also classified at JFDW

(B73-51031)

5: The yew: SA and piano. — 1973. — 4p; 8vo.

£0.05

Also classified at JFDW

(B73-51032)

6: The elm: SSA and piano. — 1973. — 4p; 8vo.

£0.05

Also classified at JFDW

(B73-51033)

7: Poplars: unison and piano. — 1973. — 3p; 8vo.

£0.05

Also classified at JFDW

(B73-51034)

8: The oak: two part or unison and piano. — 1973. — 3p; 8vo.

£0.05

Also classified at JFDW

(B73-51035)

Mozart, Wolfgang Amadeus

Ecco quel fiero istante = Lo, now the hour of parting. K.436/ by Wolfgang Amadeus Mozart; nocturne, edited for three-part chorus of women's voices or three-part mixed voices with piano accompaniment by Maynard Klein, [words by] Pietro Metastasio, English text by M.K. — New York; London: Schirmer, 1973. — 8p; 8vo.

Unpriced

Also classified at DW

(B73-50143)

Mozart, Wolfgang Amadeus

Luci care, luci bello = Eyes of beauty, eyes flashing bright. K.346: nocturne/ by Wolfgang Amadeus Mozart; edited for three-part chorus of mixed voices, SSA or SSB, with piano, or optional string or woodwind accompaniment, by Maynard Klein, words by Pietro Metastasio, English text by M.K. — New York; London: Schirmer, 1972. — 4p; 8vo.

Unpriced

Also classified at DW

(B73-50144)

Mozart, Wolfgang Amadeus

Mi lagnero tacendo = Silent, I long for thy love. K.437: nocturne/ by Wolfgang Amadeus Mozart; edited for three-part chorus of women's voices or three-part mixed voices, with piano accompaniment by Maynard Klein; [words by] Pietro Metastasio, English text by M.K. — New York; London: Chappell, 1972. — 12p; 8vo.

Unpriced

Also classified at DW

(B73-50145)

Price, Beryl

A cycle of cats: three songs for soprano and alto voices with piano/ by Beryl Price. — London: Oxford University Press, 1972. — 32p; 8vo.

Contents: 1. The matron cat's song; words by Ruth Pitter - 2. My cat Jeoffry; words by Christopher Smart - 3. The song of the Jellicles; words by T.S. Eliot.

ISBN 0 19 337853 1 : £0.60

(B73-50146)

Russell-Smith, Geoffry

The wedding ring: SSAA and piano/ words and music by Geoffry Russell-Smith. — London: Boosey and Hawkes, 1973. — 8p; 8vo.

£0.09

(B73-50568)

Thiman, Eric Harding

Listening: three-part song for female voices and piano/ by Eric H. Thiman; words by Madeline Thomas. — Wendover: Roberton, 1972. — 7p; 8vo.

Staff & tonic sol-fa notation.

£0.10

(B73-50147)

FDW/LC — Spirituals

Arch, Gwyn

This train: folk spiritual, SSA/ arr. by Gwyn Arch. — London: British and Continental, 1973. — 11p; 8vo.

Unpriced

(B73-51036)

Nelson, Havelock

You must have that true religion: negro spiritual, for soprano and alto accompanied/ arranged by Havelock Nelson. — London: Keith Prowse Music, 1973. — 4p; 8vo.

Unpriced

(B73-51037)

FDW/LC/AY — Spirituals. Collections
Brown, Sebastian
   30 negro spirituals: arranged, for unison (or two-part) singing with
   piano or guitar accompaniment/ by Sebastian Brown. — Piano
   edition. — London: Oxford University Press.
   A unison version of this publication is to be classified at JDW/LC/AY.
   Book 1: Two-part versions. — 1973. — 8vo.
   ISBN 0 19 330186 5 : Unpriced

(B73-50148)

FDX — Secular cantatas
Kagel, Mauricio
   [Achtzehn acht und neunzig]. 1898: für Kinderstimmen und
   Instrumente/ von Mauricio Kagel. — London: Universal, 1973. —
   93p; 4to.
   Unpriced

(B73-51038)

FE/LDW — With instruments. Songs, etc
Paynter, John
   Fog: for voices and instruments/ by John Paynter; text by
   Elizabeth Paynter. — London: Universal, 1973. — s.sh; obl.fol.
   Unpriced

(B73-50569)

Rees, Howard
   Honeywell: for three groups of instruments and/or voices/ by
   Howard Rees. — London: Universal, 1973. — s.sh; obl.fol.
   Unpriced
   Primary classification LJ

(B73-50656)

FE/NYLDX — With keyboard & percussion. Secular cantatas
Desch, Rudolf
   Von allerlei Hunden: eine frohliche Kantate, für Kinderchor,
   Klavier, Glockenspiel, Zupfbass, und Schlagwerk, (grosse und
   kleine Trommel, Holztrommel, Tamburin, Becken, Triangel)/ von
   Rudolf Desch; nach Texten von Karl Vetter. — Mainz; London:
   Schott, 1973. — 21p; 8vo.
   £1.40

(B73-50570)

FE/SQDH — With viola. Motets, Anthems, Hymns, etc
Cobb, Donald
   Heaven conserve thy course in quietness: for women's chorus and
   viola, or piano/ by Don Cobb; words by Ezra Pound. — New
   York: Galaxy Music; London: Galliard, 1973. — 8p; 8vo.
   Duration 2 3/4 min.
   Unpriced
   Also classified at FDH

(B73-51039)

FE/XRUDP/LF — With bass drum. Carols. Christmas
Paget, Michael
   Adam and the apple: an occasional carol for various combinations
   of voices percussion and optional trumpets/ by Michael Paget;
   15th century words. — New York; London: Schirmer, 1971. —
   6p; 8vo.
   £0.15

(B73-50571)

FEZ/XC/AY — Unaccompanied voices. Rounds. Collections
Henriksen, Josef
   Jack be nimble: a collection of rounds for choral societies, choirs
   and schools/ by Josef Henriksen. — Hoddesdon: St. Gregory,
   1972. — 21p; obl.4to.
   £0.45

(B73-50572)

**FEZDGE — Unaccompanied voices. Roman liturgy. Ordinary of the
   Mass. Sanctus**
Victoria, Tomás Luis de
   [Missae totius anni: Missa O magnum mysterium. Santus: arr].
   Sanctus = Holy holy holy/ by Tomás Luis de Victoria; edited
   and arranged for three-part chorus of women's voices a cappella
   by Jerry Weseley Harris, English version by J.W.H. — New York;
   London: Schirmer, 1972. — 7p; 8vo.
   Unpriced

(B73-50149)

FEZDH — Unaccompanied voices. Motets, Anthems, Hymns, etc
Lekberg, Sven
   Let all the world in every corner sing: for four-part chorus of
   women's voices a cappella/ by Sven Lekberg; words by George
   Herbert. — New York; London: Schirmer, 1971. — 8p; 8vo.
   Unpriced

(B73-50150)

**FEZDH/LGZ — Unaccompanied voices. Motets, Anthems, Hymns,
   etc. Passiontide**
Trevor, Caleb Henry
   Two Passiontide anthems/ arranged for SSAA (unaccompanied)
   by C.H. Trevor. — Sevenoaks: Novello, 1972. — 3p; 8vo.
   Contents: O salutaris hostia = O saving victim/ by Gounod - For our
   offences/ by Mendelssohn.
   £0.07

(B73-50151)

FEZDM — Unaccompanied voices. Hymns
De Cormier, Robert
   Wayfaring stranger: for 2/3 part chorus of female or children's
   voices unaccompanied/ arranged by Robert De Cormier. —
   Wendover: Roberton, 1971. — 4p; 8vo.
   £0.07

(B73-50573)

FEZDP/LF — Unaccompanied voices. Carols. Christmas
Gruber, Franz
   [Stille Nacht, heilige Nacht: arr]. Silent night/ by Franz Gruber;
   arranged for women's or boy's voices by Ian T. Hunter, words by
   Joseph Mohr. — London: Thames, 1973. — 3p; 8vo.
   Unpriced

(B73-50152)

Hunter, Ian
   The birds: Czech carol/ arranged for women's or boy's voices
   (SSA) by Ian T. Hunter. — London: Thames, 1973. — 3p; 8vo.
   Unpriced

(B73-50153)

FEZDU — Unaccompanied voices. Madrigals
East, Michael
   [First set of madrigals.. Corydon would kiss her then: arr].
   Corydon would kiss her then/ by Michael East; arranged for
   3-part chorus of female voices unaccompanied by Mary Jane
   Shipp; words by Nicholas Breton. — Wendover: Roberton, 1973.
   — 7p; 8vo.
   £0.10

(B73-50154)

East, Michael
   [First set of madrigals. In the merry month of May: arr]. In the
   merry month of May/ by Michael East; arranged for 3-part
   chorus of female voices unaccompanied by Mary Shipp; words by
   Nicholas Breton. — Wendover: Roberton, 1973. — 7p; 8vo.
   £0.10

(B73-50155)

Youll, Henry
   [Canzonets to three voyces.. Come merry lads, let us away: arr].
   Come merry lads, let us away/ by Henry Youll; arranged for
   3-part chorus of female voices unaccompanied by Clifford Shipp.
   — Wendover: Roberton, 1973. — 7p; 8vo.
   £0.10

(B73-50156)

FEZDW — Unaccompanied voices. Songs, etc
Brahms, Johannes
   [German folksongs for four-part chorus, bk,2, no.1. In stiller
   Nacht]. In stiller Nacht = In still of night: for four-part chorus of
   women's voices a cappella/ arranged by Johannes Brahms, edited
   by Maynard Klein, English text by M.K. — New York; London:
   Schirmer, 1972. — 7p; 8vo.
   Unpriced

(B73-51042)

Carter, John
   Weep you no more, sad fountains: for four-part chorus of women's
   voices a cappella/ by John Carter; words by John Dowland. —
   New York; London: Schirmer, 1972. — 6p; 8vo.
   Unpriced

(B73-50157)

Kodály, Zoltán
   Fiddle-dee: SSAA unaccompanied/ by Zoltán Kodály; English
   translation by Geoffry Russell-Smith. — London: Boosey and
   Hawkes, 1972. — 3p; 8vo.
   £0.05

(B73-51041)

Kodály, Zoltán
   Have good courage: SSA unaccompanied/ transcribed from a
   contemporary tune by Zoltán Kodály, words by Andrew Horvath
   de Szkharos, English translation by Geoffry Russell-Smith. —
   London: Boosey and Hawkes, 1973. — 11p; 8vo.
   £0.14

(B73-50574)

FEZDW/G/AYDK — Unaccompanied voices. Folk songs. Collections.
Wales
Williams, Bryn
Three Welsh folk songs = Tair cânwerin: for female voices with
piano/ arranged by Bryn Williams, Welsh [words] traditional,
English text by Bryn Williams. — Wendover: Roberton, 1972. —
16p; 8vo.
Staff & tonic sol-fa notation.
£0.18
(B73-50158)

FLDGB — Treble voices. Roman liturgy. Ordinary of the Mass.
Kyrie
Pehkonen, Elis
Kyries: for treble voices in 2 or 4 parts with soli and organ with
optional side drum/ by Elis Pehkonen. — London: Chappell,
1973. — 16p; 8vo.
Unpriced
Primary classification FLDH
(B73-50161)

FLDGPP — Treble voices. Anglican liturgy. Evening Prayer.
Canticles
Holman, Derek
Magnificat & Nunc dimittis in A: for treble voices and organ/ by
Derek Holman. — South Croydon: Lengnick, 1973. — 13p; 8vo.
£0.18
(B73-50159)

FLDH — Treble voices. Motets, Anthems, Hymns, etc
Lloyd, Richard
A prayer: for treble voices and organ/ by Richard Lloyd; words:
Irene Cavenaugh. — South Croydon: Lengnick, 1973. — 4p; 8vo.
£0.06
(B73-50160)

Pehkonen, Elis
Kyries: for treble voices in 2 or 4 parts with soli and organ with
optional side drum/ by Elis Pehkonen. — London: Chappell,
1973. — 16p; 8vo.
Unpriced
Also classified at FLDGB
(B73-50161)

FLDJ — Treble voices. Motets
Crivelli, Giovanni Battista
[Il Primo libro delli motetti concertati.. Ut flos, ut rosa]. Ut flos,
ut rosa. = Like flowers, like roses bloom the crowns: S.S. or
T.T./ by Giovanni Battista Crivelli; edited by Jerome Roche,
English translated by Elizabeth Roche. — London: Oxford
University Press, 1973. — 8p; 8vo.
ISBN 0 19 350337 9 : Unpriced
Also classified at GHDJ
(B73-50162)

FLDP/LF — Treble voices. Carols. Christmas
Platts, Kenneth
A shepherd's carol. Opus 12: for treble voices and piano/ by
Kenneth Platts; mediaeval text adapted by the composer. —
London: Ashdown, 1973. — 4p; 8vo.
£0.05
(B73-51043)

Wood, Charles
[Mater ora filium: arr]. Mater ora filium: Irish folk song/
arranged as a carol to anonymous 15th-century words by Charles
Wood, re-arranged for treble voices (two-part with optional solo)
and organ by Harrison Oxley. — Sevenoaks: Novello, 1973. — 6p;
8vo.
£0.10
(B73-50575)

FLDR — Treble voices. Psalms
Coombes, Douglas
Psalm 96: S.S. accompanied/ by Douglas Coombes. — London:
Keith Prowse, 1973. — 16p; 8vo.
Unpriced
(B73-50163)

FLDW — Soprano voices. Songs, etc
Pasfield, William Reginald
At the mid hour of night, (from Moore's Irish melodies)/
arranged for S. S. (or S.A.) and piano by W.R. Pasfield. —
London: Ashdown, 1973. — 3p; 8vo.
£0.05
(B73-50576)

Pasfield, William Reginald
The last rose of summer, (from Moore's Irish melodies)/ arranged
for S.S. (or S.A.) and piano by W.R. Pasfield. — London:
Ashdown, 1973. — 3p; 8vo.
£0.05
(B73-50577)

Pasfield, William Reginald
The young may moon, (from Moore's Irish melodies)/ arranged
for S.S. (or S.A.) and piano by W.R. Pasfield. — London:
Ashdown, 1973. — 3p; 8vo.
£0.05
(B73-50578)

FLDW/LC — Treble voices. Spirituals
Barthelson, Joyce
Rock-a my soul: negro spiritual, for 3-part chorus of treble voices
with piano accompaniment/ by Joyce Barthelson. — Wendover:
Roberton, 1970. — 11p; 8vo.
£0.13
(B73-50579)

FLEZDP/LF — Unaccompanied treble voices. Carols. Christmas
Wood, John
Yeoman's carol: for SSS unaccompanied/ by John Wood; words
from a Dorset church-gallery book. — Sevenoaks: Novello, 1973.
— 4p; 8vo.
£0.07
(B73-50580)

FTDW/X — High voices. Canons
Stoker, Richard
Requiescat: canon for two-part high voices (or children's two-part
choir)/ by Richard Stoker; words by Matthew Arnold. —
London: Ashdown, 1973. — 5p; 8vo.
£0.10
(B73-50581)

G — MALE VOICES
GDGNPV — Anglican liturgy. Morning Prayer. Venite
Swann, Donald
[Festival Matins.. O come let us sing unto the Lord]. O come let
us sing unto the Lord: for two-part chorus of female, male or
mixed voices with piano accompaniment/ by Donald Swann; [text]
Psalm 95. — Wendover: Roberton, 1970. — 7p; 8vo.
Unpriced
Primary classification DGNPV
(B73-50016)

GDGNS — Anglican liturgy. Morning Prayer. Benedictus
Swann, Donald
[Festival Matins.. Blessed be the Lord God of Israel]. Blessed be
the Lord God of Israel: for two-part chorus of female, male or
mixed voices with piano or organ accompaniment/ by Donald
Swann; [text from] St. Luke 1. — Wendover: Roberton, 1970. —
7p; 8vo.
Unpriced
Primary classification DGNS
(B73-50018)

GDH/LF — Motets, Anthems, Hymns, etc. Christmas
Berlioz, Hector
[L'Enfance du Christ. L'Adieu des bergers. Vocal score: arr].
Thou must leave thy lowly dwelling. The shepherds farewell to the
Holy Family/ by Hector Berlioz; arranged for T T Bar B by K.J.
Dinham, English words by Paul England. — Sevenoaks: Novello,
1973. — 8p; 8vo.
£0.10
(B73-51044)

GDJ — Motets
Donati, Ignazio
[Concerti ecclesiastici. Op.4. *Excerpts*]. Non vos relinquam
orphanos = I will not leave you fatherless: SSA or T.T. Bar./ by
Ignazio Donati; edited by Jerome Roche, [text from] St. John 14,
translated by Elizabeth Roche. — London: Oxford University
Press, 1972. — 8p; 8vo.
ISBN 0 19 350336 0 : Unpriced
Primary classification FDJ
(B73-50135)

Donati, Ignazio
[Concerti ecclesiastici. Op.4. Nun vos relinquam orphanos]. Non
vos relinquam orphanos = I will not leave you fatherless: SSA or
T.T. Bar./ by Ignazia Donati; edited by Jerome Roche, [text from]
St John 14, translated by Elizabeth Roche. — London: Oxford
University Press, 1972. — 8p; 8vo.
ISBN 0 19 350336 0 : Unpriced
Primary classification FDJ
(B73-51035)

GDW — Songs, etc
Harry, Lynn
En route/ by Lynn Harry; arranged for men's voices, TTBB and
piano; words by David Davies. — London: K.P.M, 1973. — 4p;
8vo.
Staff & tonic sol-fa notation.
Unpriced
(B73-50164)

Miller, Lewis M
The faucet: for four-part chorus of men's voices with piano
accompaniment/ by Lewis M. Miller; words by S.J. Sackett. —
New York; London: Schirmer, 1972. — 4p; 8vo.
Unpriced
(B73-50165)

Sykes, Harold Hinchcliff
As we sailed out of London river: male voice chorus (TTBB) and
piano/ by Harold H. Sykes; arranged by Trevor Widdicombe,
words by Walter de la Mare. — Wendover: Roberton, 1972. —
6p; 8vo.
Staff & tonic sol-fa notation. — Duration 2 mins.
£0.10
(B73-50166)

**GEZDG — Unaccompanied voices. Roman liturgy. Ordinary of the
Mass**
Wright, Paul
Missa brevis: for men's voices/ by Paul Wright. — London:
Thames, 1973. — 11p; 8vo.
"It is suggested that the Gloria and Credo should either be sung to
plainsong or said" - Composer's note.
Unpriced
(B73-50582)

**GEZDGMM — Unaccompanied voices. Anglican liturgy. Preces &
responses**
Marlow, Richard
The preces and responses: T.T.B.B. unacc./ by Richard Marlow.
— London: Oxford University Press, 1972. — 4p; 8vo.
ISBN 0 19 351640 3 : Unpriced
(B73-50167)

GEZDP/LF — Unaccompanied voices. Carols. Christmas
Weston, Gordon
Seren Bethlehem = Star of Bethlehem: TTBB/ gan Gordon
Weston; words, J.J. Williams, addiasied Ivor Owen. — Cardiff:
University of Wales Press, 1973. — 7p; 4to.
£0.15
(B73-51045)

GEZDW — Unaccompanied voices. Songs, etc
Dexter, Harry
The constant lover: early 18th century songs/ arranged for
unaccompanied TTBB by Harry Dexter; words, anon. — London:
Ashdown, 1973. — 8p; 8vo.
Unpriced
(B73-50168)

Hanby, B R
[Darling Nelly Gray: arr]. Nelly Gray: plantation song/ von B.R.
Hanby; Satz und Textfassung von Rudolf Desch. — Mainz;
London: Schott, 1973. — 7p; 8vo.
Not attributed to the composer in this publication.
£0.30
(B73-50583)

Parker, Alice
The parting glass: Irish folk song/ arranged for 4-part chorus of
male voices by Alice Parker. — Wendover: Roberton, 1969. — 7p;
8vo.
£0.10
(B73-50584)

GEZDW/LC — Unaccompanied voices. Spirituals
Heath, Fenno
In that great gettin' up morning: spiritual/ arranged for four-part
chorus of men's voices a cappella by Fenno Heath. — New York;
[London]: Schirmer, 1971. — 16p; 8vo.
Unpriced
(B73-50169)

GHDJ — Tenor voices. Motets
Crivelli, Giovanni Battista
[Il Primo libro delli motetti concertati.. Ut flos, ut rosa]. Ut flos,
ut rosa. = Like flowers, like roses bloom the crowns: S.S. or
T.T./ by Giovanni Battista Crivelli; edited by Jerome Roche,
English translated by Elizabeth Roche. — London: Oxford
University Press, 1973. — 8p; 8vo.
ISBN 0 19 350337 9 : Unpriced
Primary classification FLDJ
(B73-50162)

J — VOICES IN UNISON
JDGKAD/AY — Graduals. Collections
Responsorial psalms for the Sundays of the year, year 1. —
London: St Thomas More Centre for Pastoral Liturgy.
22nd to 34th Sunday of the yearly cycle. — 1971. — 35p; 8vo. —
Unpriced
(B73-50585)
Advent to the Baptism of our Lord. — 1971. — 27p; 8vo. —
Unpriced
(B73-50586)
Second Sunday of Easter to Pentecost. — 1971. — 22p; 8vo. —
Unpriced
(B73-50587)
Second Sunday of the yearly cycle to Fifth Sunday of Lent. — 1971. — 37p;
8vo. —
Unpriced
(B73-50588)
Trinity Sunday to 21st Sunday of the year. — 1971. — 40p; 8vo. —
Unpriced
(B73-50589)

Responsorial psalms for the Sundays of the year, year 2. —
London: St Thomas More Centre for Pastoral Liturgy.
26th-34th Sundays. — 1971. — 13p; 8vo. —
Unpriced
(B73-50590)
Advent to the Baptism of our Lord. — 1971. — 29p; 8vo. —
Unpriced
(B73-50591)
Second Sunday of Easter to Pentecost. — 1971. — 22p; 8vo. —
Unpriced
(B73-50592)
Second Sunday of the yearly cycle to Fifth Sunday of Lent. — 1971. — 34p;
8vo. —
Unpriced
(B73-50593)
Trinity Sunday to 21st Sunday of the year. — 1971. — 40p; 8vo. —
Unpriced
(B73-50594)
Twenty second Sunday of the yearly cycle to the thirty-fourth Sunday. —
1971. — 28p; 8vo. —
Unpriced
(B73-50595)

Responsorial psalms for the Sundays of the year, year 3. —
London: St Thomas More Centre for Pastoral Liturgy.
2nd Sunday of Easter to Pentecost. — 1971. — 21p; 8vo. —
Unpriced
(B73-50596)
23rd Sunday of the year to 34th Sunday of the year. — 1971. — 37p; 8vo.
—
Unpriced
(B73-50597)
Advent to Epiphany. — 1971. — 20p; 8vo. —
Unpriced
(B73-50598)
Trinity Sunday to 22nd Sunday of the year. — 1971. — 33p; 8vo. —
Unpriced
(B73-50599)

JDGS — Anglican liturgy. Communion
Appleford, Patrick
New English Mass, series 3/ by Patrick Appleford. — London:
Weinberger, 1973. — 10p; 8vo.
£0.25
(B73-50170)

Dearnley, Christopher
Communion service, series 3: unison (and optional SATB)/ by
Christopher Dearnley and Alan Wicks. — London: Oxford
University Press, 1973. — 8p; 8vo.
ISBN 0 19 351645 4 : Unpriced
(B73-50600)

Gibbs, Alan
St. Margaret's Communion, Series 3: for congregation and choir in
unison (optional SATB) with organ or piano/ by Alan Gibbs. —
Croydon: Royal School of Church Music, 1973. — 8vo.
Score (8p.) & congregational copy (4p.).
Unpriced
(B73-51047)

Rowe, Winston Hugh
Communion service, Series 3: for congregation and choir/ by
W.H. Rowe. — London: Cramer, 1973. — 8p; 8vo.
£0.09
(B73-51048)

Shephard, Richard
The Addington service: Holy Communion, Series 3/ by Richard
Shephard. — Croydon: Royal School of Church Music, 1973. —
8vo.
Score (8p.) & congregational copy (4p.). — The Agnus Dei may be sung by
voices in SATB.
Unpriced
(B73-51049)

JDH — Motets, Anthems, Hymns, etc
Chapman, Edward
Thou spirit of love divine: unison song/ words and music by Edward Chapman; based on a theme from Mahler's third symphony. — Wendover: Roberton, 1970. — 7p; 8vo.
£0.09

(B73-50171)

JDM — Hymns
Oswin, Mary
A grain of wheat: 12 songs of grouping and growing/ by Mary Oswin; piano accompaniments by John Rombaut. — Southend: Mayhew-McCrimmon, 1972. — 23p; 8vo.
£0.47

(B73-50601)

JDM/AY — Hymns. Collections
Maynard, John
In tune: over 60 hymns and songs, for churches schools and groups/ compiled by John Maynard and Cecily Taylor. — London: Vanguard, 1973. — 78p; 4to.
Unpriced

(B73-50172)

Teach me how to look: a collection of new hymns. — London: Weinberger, 1973. — 26p; 8vo.
£0.50

(B73-50602)

JDP/LF — Carols. Christmas
Copley, Ian
The waifs' carol: for unison voices (optional second part) and piano/ by Ian Copley; words by Barbara Kluge. — London: Thames, 1973. — 3p; 8vo.
Unpriced

(B73-50603)

Kelly, Bryan
[Herod, do your worst. Sleep little baby]. Sleep little baby: Christmas song for unison voices and piano/ by Bryan Kelly, words by John Fuller. — Sevenoaks: Novello, 1968. — 3p; 8vo.
£0.07

(B73-51050)

Noble, Harold
Love came down at Christmas: carol/ music by Harold Noble, words by Christina Rosetti. — London: Studio Music, 1973. — 3p; 8vo.
Unpriced

(B73-51051)

Roe, Betty
Away in a manger: carol for mixed choir and organ/piano/ by Betty Roe; words traditional. — London: Thames, 1973. — 4p; 8vo.
Unpriced
Also classified at EZDP/LF

(B73-50604)

JDP/LF/AY — Carols. Christmas. Collection
CHRISTMAS magic: your own favourite songs and carols. — London: Chappell, 1973. — 56p; 4to.
Unpriced
Primary classification JDW/LF/AY

JDP/LF/AY — Carols. Christmas. Collections
Burdett, Brian V
The Christmas carol book: words and music of 24 popular carols chosen and arranged by Brian V. Burdett in collaboration with Shirley M. Sturgeon. — Norwich: Jarrold, 1973. — 62p; 8vo.
ISBN 0 85306 437 7 : Unpriced

(B73-51052)

CHAPPELL'S book of Christmas carols. — London: Chappell, 1973. — 28p; 4to.
£0.75

(B73-51053)

Three carols for Christmas. — London: Chappell, 1973. — 19p; 8vo.
Contents: Coventry carol: unison song/music by Terence Greaves; words anon - Torches: for treble voices and organ/music by Elis Pehkonen; words translated by J.B. Trend - Dawn carol: for unison voices and organ (or piano), by Malcolm Williamson.
Unpriced

(B73-51054)

JDR — Psalms
Graves, Richard
In pastures green: unison, 2nd part ad lib/ by Richard Graves; words rational version of Psalm 23. — London: Bosworth, 1972. — 4p; 8vo.
Duration 2-1/2 min - Staff & tonic sol-fa notation.
£0.07

(B73-51055)

Williamson, Malcolm
Carols of King David: for unison choir, congregation and organ/ by Malcolm Williamson. — London: Weinberger.
No.3: Together in unity: Psalm 133. — 1972. [4p; 8vo. — £0.05

(B73-51056)

JDW — Songs, etc
Cookridge, John Michael
Gonna alter m'ways/ words and music by John M. Cookridge. — Chichester: Janay, 1973. — 4p; 8vo.
£0.06

(B73-50173)

Cookridge, John Michael
The seasons of love/ words and music by John M. Cookridge. — Chichester: Janay, 1973. — 4p; 8vo.
£0.06

(B73-50174)

Wilcock, Frank
Show album: songs and sketches/ with music by Frank Wilcock; written by Robert Rutherford. — Glasgow: Brown, Son and Ferguson, 1973. — 35p; 4to.
£0.75

(B73-51057)

JDW/G/AYPE — Folk songs. Collections. Greece
Frye, Ellen
The marble threshing floor: a collection of Greek folksongs/ collected and transcribed by Ellen Frye. — Austin; London: Texas University Press for the American Folklore Society, 1973. — xvi, 327p; 8vo.
ISBN 0 292 75005 6 : Unpriced

(B73-51058)

JDW/KJ/AY — Political songs. Collections
Fowke, Edith
[Songs of work and freedom]. Songs of work and protest/ selected and edited by Edith Fowke and Joe Glazer; music arrangements, Kennneth Brag. — New York: Dover; London: Constable, 1973. — 209p; 4to.
Originally published as Songs of work and freedom, Chicago, Labour Education Division of Roosevelt University, 1960.
ISBN 0 486 22899 1 : £1.75

(B73-51059)

JDW/LF/AY — Songs. Christmas. Collections
CHRISTMAS magic: your own favourite songs and carols. — London: Chappell, 1973. — 56p; 4to.
Unpriced
Also classified at JDP/LF/AY

(B73-51060)

JE/LDW/G/AYDG — With instruments. Folk songs. Collections. Midlands
Palmer, Roy
Songs of the Midlands/ edited by Roy Palmer, music editors: Pamela Bishop and Katherine Thomson. — Wakefield: E.P. Publishing, 1972. — 115p; 4to.
ISBN 0 7158 0377 8 : Unpriced

(B73-50175)

JE/TSDW/AY — With guitar. Songs, etc. Collections
Elsworth, Cecilie
The family motoring book/ compiled by Cecilie Elsworth and Lerona Newsom. — London: Tom Stacey, 1973. — 144p; obl 8vo.
ISBN 0 85468 025 x : £1.00

(B73-50605)

JE/TSDW/G/AY — With guitar. Folk songs. Collections
Sounds like folk. — London: E F D S.
No.2: The railways in song. — 1973. — 28p; 8vo. — £0.30

(B73-50606)

Sounds like folk. — London: EFDS Publications.
No.3: Growing up songs. — 1973. — 30p; 8vo. — £0.30

(B73-51061)

JE/TSDW/G/AYC — With guitar. Folk songs. Collections. Great Britain
Hill, Margaret
Floroj sen kompar: Britaj popolkantoj/ [compiled by] Margaret Hill kaj William Auld. — London: British Esperanto Association, 1973. — 87p; 8vo.
Unpriced

(B73-50176)

JE/TSDW/G/AYDJJ — With guitar. Folk songs. Collections.
Northumberland
Polwarth, Gwen
    Folk songs and dance tunes from the North with fiddle tunes,
    pipe tunes and street cries/ compiled by Gwen and Mary
    Polwarth. — Newcastle upon Tyne: Frank Graham, 1970. — 62p;
    8vo.
    ISBN 0 900409 93 2 : £0.60
    Also classified at SPMH/G/AYDJJ
                                                                (B73-51062)

JE/TSDW/G/AYDL — With guitar. Folk songs. Collections.
Scotland
Buchan, Norman
    The Scottish folksinger: 118 modern and traditional folksongs/
    collected and edited by Norman Buchan and Peter Hall. —
    Glasgow; London: Collins, 1973. — 159p; 8vo.
    ISBN 0 00 411115 x : £0.95
                                                                (B73-50607)

JE/TSDW/G/AYH — With guitar. Folk songs. Collections. France
Mills, Alan
    Favorite French folk songs: sixty-five traditional songs of France
    and Canada/ selected, translated and adapted by Alan Mills; with
    guitar accompaniments by Jerry Silverman. — New York: Oak
    Publications; London: Music Sales, 1972. — 95p; 8vo.
    £0.95
    Primary classification JE/TSDW/G/AYSXH
                                                                (B73-50178)

Scott, Barbara
    Folk songs of France: 25 traditional French songs with guitar
    chords, in both French and English/ compiled and edited by
    Barbara Scott. — New York: Oak Publications; London: Music
    Sales, 1972. — 72p; 8vo.
    £0.95
                                                                (B73-50177)

JE/TSDW/G/AYK — With guitar. Folk songs. Collections. Spain
Paz, Elena
    Favorite Spanish folksongs: traditional songs from Spain and Latin
    America/ compiled and edited by Elena Paz. — New York: Oak
    Publications; London: Music Sales, 1972. — 96p; 8vo.
    £0.95
    Primary classification JE/TSDW/G/AYU
                                                                (B73-50179)

JE/TSDW/G/AYSXH — With guitar. Folk songs. Collections.
Quebec Province
Mills, Alan
    Favorite French folk songs: sixty-five traditional songs of France
    and Canada/ selected, translated and adapted by Alan Mills; with
    guitar accompaniments by Jerry Silverman. — New York: Oak
    Publications; London: Music Sales, 1972. — 95p; 8vo.
    £0.95
    Also classified at JE/TSDW/G/AYH
                                                                (B73-50178)

JE/TSDW/G/AYU — With guitar. Folk songs. Collections. Latin
America
Paz, Elena
    Favorite Spanish folksongs: traditional songs from Spain and Latin
    America/ compiled and edited by Elena Paz. — New York: Oak
    Publications; London: Music Sales, 1972. — 96p; 8vo.
    £0.95
    Also classified at JE/TSDW/G/AYK
                                                                (B73-50179)

JE/TSDW/G/AYULL — With guitar. Folk songs. Collections.
Tobago
Harvey, John
    Buddy Lindo: folk songs of Trinidad and Tobago, for unison
    voices and guitar/ compiled by John Harvey, collected by John
    Harvey and J.D. Elder, edited by Denise Narcisse-Mair. —
    London: Oxford University Press, 1973. — 24p; 8vo.
    ISBN 0 19 330450 3 : £0.25
    Primary classification JE/TSDW/G/AYULM
                                                                (B73-50608)

JE/TSDW/G/AYULM — With guitar. Folk songs. Collections.
Trinidad
Harvey, John
    Buddy Lindo: folk songs of Trinidad and Tobago, for unison
    voices and guitar/ compiled by John Harvey, collected by John
    Harvey and J.D. Elder, edited by Denise Narcisse-Mair. —
    London: Oxford University Press, 1973. — 24p; 8vo.
    ISBN 0 19 330450 3 : £0.25
    Also classified at JE/TSDW/G/AYULL
                                                                (B73-50608)

JE/TSDW/G/AYXR — With guitar. Folk songs. Collections. New
Zealand
Colquhoun, Neil
    New Zealand folksongs: song of a young country/ edited by Neil
    Colquhoun. — Folkestone: Bailey and Swinfen, 1972. — 64p; 4to.
    ISBN 0 561 00189 8 : £1.35
                                                                (B73-50609)

˙ JE/TSDW/GCG/AY — With guitar. Bluegrass songs. Collections
Cyporyn, Dennis
    The bluegrass songbook: eighty-eight original folk and old-time
    mountain tunes/ compiled by Dennis Cyporyn. — New York:
    Collier; London: Collier-Macmillan, 1973. — 159p; 4to.
    ISBN 0 02 060380 0 : £1.25
                                                                (B73-50610)

JE/TSDW/GM/AYC — With guitar. Occupational songs.
Collections. Great Britain
Raven, Jon
    Songs of a changing world/ by Jon Raven. — London: Ginn,
    1972. — 63p; 8vo.
    ISBN 0 602 21848 9 : Unpriced
                                                                (B73-50180)

JE/TSDW/KC/AYD(XFYK36) — With guitar. Sea songs.
Collections. England, 1770-1805
Palmer, Roy
    The valiant sailor: sea songs and ballads and prose passages
    illustrating life on the lower deck in Nelson's navy/ selected and
    edited by Roy Palmer. — Cambridge: Cambridge University Press,
    1973. — 64p; 4to.
    ISBN 0 521 20101 2 : Unpriced
                                                                (B73-50611)

JE/TSDW/KG/AYC — With guitar. Military songs. Collections.
Great Britain
Dallas, Karl
    The cruel wars: 100 soldiers' songs from Agincourt to Ulster/
    compiled by Karl Dallas. — London: Wolfe, 1972. — 272p; 8vo.
    ISBN 0 7234 0493 3 : £1.60
                                                                (B73-50612)

JEZDW/AYDJD — Unaccompanied voices. Songs, etc. Collections.
Lancashire
Boardman, Harry
    Folk songs and ballads of Lancashire/ compiled and edited by
    Harry Boardman and Lesley Boardman. — London: Oak
    Publications Music Sales, 1973. — 44p; 8vo.
    A large proportion of the tunes are composed by Harry Boardman.
    Unpriced
                                                                (B73-50613)

JEZDW/G/AY — Unaccompanied voices. Folk songs. Collections
Wales, Tony
    Folk song to-day/ edited by Tony Wales. — London: E F D S.
    Vol 1 (B66-50246) was entered under the name of Kennedy.
    Vol.2. — 1969. — 29p; 8vo.
    £0.20
                                                                (B73-50614)
    Vol.4. — 1970. — 36p 8vo.
    £0.20
                                                                (B73-50615)

Wales, Tony
    Folk song today/ edited by Tony Wales. — London: E F D S.
    Vol 1 (B66-50246) was entered under the name of Kennedy.
    Vol.5. — 1971. — 33p; 8vo.
    £0.20
                                                                (B73-50616)

JEZDW/G/AYDLZN — Unaccompanied voices. Folk songs.
Collections. Shetlands
Robertson, Thomas Alexander
    Da sangs at a'll sing ta dee: a book of Shetland songs/ edited by
    T.A. Robertson, the music edited by M. Robertson. — Lerwick:
    Shetland Folk Society, 1973. — 119p; 8vo.
    Unpriced
                                                                (B73-51063)

JFDM — Female voices, Children's voices. Hymns
Cookridge, John Michael
    The other man's shoes: a modern spiritual/ words and music by
    John M. Cookridge. — Chichester: Janay, 1973. — 4p; 8vo.
    £0.06
                                                                (B73-50181)

JFDM/AY — Female voices, Children's voices. Hymns. Collections
Harrop, Beatrice
    Someone's singing, Lord: hymns and songs for children with piano
    accompaniments, with chords for guitar, and with parts for
    descant recorders, glockenspiel, chime bars and percussion/
    general editor: Beatrice Harrop. — London: Black, 1973. — 86p;
    obl.4to.
    ISBN 0 7136 1355 6 : Unpriced
                                                                (B73-50182)

JFDM/AY — Female voices. Children's voices. Hymns. Collections
Lewis, Pete
    Sing life, sing love: songs/ edited by Pete Lewis, Roy Lawrence,
    Gordon Simpson; arranged for schools by William M. McIntyre.
    — Edinburgh: Holmes McDougall, 1971. — 8vo.
    Pianoforte ed. (55p.) & melody ed. (55p.).
    ISBN 0 7157 1005 2 : Unpriced
                                                                (B73-51064)

JFDM/GJ — Female voices, Children's voices. Children's hymns
Coyle, Margaret
Sing for joy: twenty seven songs for infants/ by Margaret Coyle. — Southend: Mayhew-McGrimmon, 1972. — 31p; 8vo.
ISBN 0 85597 019 7 : £0.50

(B73-50617)

JFDM/GJ/AY — Female voices. Children's voices. Children's hymns. Collections
Buzzing, Pauline
New child songs: Christian songs for under-eights/ compiled by Pauline Buzzing; words compiler: Dorothy Wilton, general editor: Aubrey George Smith. — Nutfield: Denholme House Press, 1973. — 128p; 8vo.
ISBN 0 85213 074 0 : £1.50

(B73-51065)

JFDM/GJ/AY — Female voices, Children's voices. Children's hymns. Collections
Maynard, John
It's all in the book: 20 hymns and songs for young people/ compiled by John Maynard. — London: Vanguard Music, 1973. — 39p; 8vo.
Unpriced

(B73-50618)

JFDP/LF — Female voices, Children's voices. Carols. Christmas
Bennett, F Roy
Welcome the Christ-child: seven carols for junior voices/ words and music by F. Roy Bennett. — London: Ashdown, 1973. — 15p; 8vo.
£0.18

(B73-50619)

Graves, Richard
As I went riding by: carol for unison voices with optional descant, and piano/ by Richard Graves; words by Cecily Taylor. — Sevenoaks: Novello, 1973. — 4p; 8vo.
£0.07

(B73-51066)

Greaves, Terence
Coventry carol: unison song/ by Terence Greaves; words anon. — London: Chappell, 1972. — 6p; 8vo.
Unpriced

(B73-50183)

Roe, Betty
Come all ye children: carol for unison voices and piano (organ)/ by Betty Roe; words by Barbara Softly. — London: Thames, 1971. — 2p; 8vo.
Unpriced

(B73-50184)

Roe, Betty
Sing for Christmas: 6 songs for unison voices (optional 2nd part)/ by Betty Roe; words by Jean Kenward. — London: Thames, 1973. — 19p; 8vo.
Unpriced

(B73-50620)

Rose, Michael
Now the most high is born = Nunc natus est altissimus: carol for female or boys' voices and organ/ by Michael Rose; words by James Ryman. — Sevenoaks: Novello, 1973. — 11p; 8vo.
The voices are very occasionally divided.
£0.14

(B73-51067)

JFDW — Female voices, Children's voices. Songs, etc
Bullard, Alan
Charles Augustus Fortescue: for unison or two-part voices and piano/ by Allan Bullard; words by Hilaire Belloc. — Sevenoaks: Novello, 1972. — 7p; 8vo.
£0.10

(B73-50185)

Cook, Roger
Children of the world unite/ by Roger Cook and Roger Greenaway. — London: Cookaway Music: [Distributed by] Music Sales, 1972. — 4p; 4to.
£0.20

(B73-50189)

Cookridge, John Michael
Carlo mio/ words and music by John M. Cookridge. — Chichester: Janay, 1973. — 4p; 8vo.
£0.06

(B73-50186)

Cookridge, John Michael
Don't look down/ words and music by John M. Cookridge. — Glasgow: Bayley and Ferguson, 1973. — 4p; 8vo.
£0.10

(B73-50621)

Cookridge, John Michael
Gypsy Marie/ words and music by John M. Cookridge. — Glasgow: Bayley and Ferguson, 1973. — 4p; 8vo.
£0.10

(B73-50622)

Cookridge, John Michael
I'll ask the Lord/ words and music by John M. Cookridge. — Chichester: Janay, 1972. — 4p; 8vo.
£0.06

(B73-50187)

Craxton, Harold
The snowdrop: unison song/ by Harold Craxton; words by Norman Gale. — London: Cramer, 1973. — 4p; 8vo.
Unpriced

(B73-50623)

Hunt, Reginald
O good ale: unison song with piano accompaniment (and ad lib. parts for violins, descant recorders, guitars, tambourine, glockenspiel, cymbals and drums)/ by Reginald Hunt; words traditional. — London: Ashdown, 1973. — 8p; 8vo.
£0.10

(B73-51068)

King, Audrey
My little garden plot: unison children's voices/ by Audrey King. — London: Bosworth, 1973. — 3p; 8vo.
Staff & tonic sol-fa notation.
£0.10

(B73-51069)

Le Fleming, Christopher
Trees in the valley. Op. 40/ by Christopher le Fleming; words by Grace Armitage. — London: Boosey and Hawkes.
1: The plane: unison and piano. — 1973. — 3p; 8vo.
£0.05
Primary classification FDW
2: Beeches (copper and green): two part or unison and piano. — 1973. — 4p; 8vo.
£0.05
Primary classification FDW
3: The holly: SSA and piano. — 1973. — 4p; 8vo.
£0.05
Primary classification FDW
4: The willow: unison and piano. — 1973. — 3p; 8vo.
£0.05
Primary classification FDW
5: The yew: SA and piano. — 1973. — 4p; 8vo.
£0.05
Primary classification FDW
6: The elm: SSA and piano. — 1973. — 4p; 8vo.
£0.05
Primary classification FDW
7: Poplars: unison and piano. — 1973. — 3p; 8vo.
£0.05
Primary classification FDW
8: The oak: two part or unison and piano. — 1973. — 3p; 8vo.
£0.05
Primary classification FDW

Noble, Harold
The fairy tailor: unison song/ by Harold Noble; words by Edward Lockton. — London: Bosworth, 1973. — 4p; 8vo.
Staff & tonic sol-fa notation.
£0.10

(B73-51070)

Noble, Harold
The harebell: unison song/ music by Harold Noble, words by Rebecca Todhunter. — London: Studio Music, 1973. — 8vo.
Unpriced

(B73-51071)

Parry, William Howard
Four winds: unison, with optional second part/ by W.H. Parry; words by Berta Lawrence. — South Croydon: Lengnick, 1973. — 4p; 8vo.
£0.06

(B73-50188)

Reaks, Brian
As fit as a fiddle: six health education songs for younger children/ words and music by Brian Reaks. — London: British and Continental, 1973. — 11p; 4to.
Unpriced

(B73-50624)

JFDW/AY — Female voices, Children's voices. Songs, etc.
Collections
Harewood, Marion
[Classical songs for children]. The Penguin book of accompanied songs/ edited by Marion Harewood and Ronald Duncan, arrangements by Percy Young. — Harmondsworth: Penguin Books, 1973. — 248p; 8vo.
Originally catalogued (B65-50194) under the name Maria Donata Lascelles, Countess of Harewood.
ISBN 0 14 070839 1 : £0.75

(B73-50190)

JFDW/G/AYF — Female voices, Children's voices. Folk songs.
Collections. Czechoslovakia
Tausky, Vilem
Up and down the River Danube: twelve Czecholsovak folk songs/ arranged by Vilem Tausky; English words by C.K. Offer. — Wendover: Roberton, 1969. — 24p; 4to.
Unpriced

(B73-50191)

JFDW/G/JT/AY — Female voices. Children's voices. Folk songs.
Radio. Collections
Coombes, Douglas
Songs for singing together: fifty songs from around the world, taken from the B B C's music programme for schools 'Singing together'/ compiled and arranged by Douglas Coombes. — London: British Broadcasting Corporation, 1973. — 91p; 4to.
£1.25

(B73-51072)

JFDW/GR — Female voices, Children's voices. Songs, etc. Activities
McNess-Eames, Vera
Rhythm and action songs for tiny tots/ by Vera McNess-Eames. — Ilfracombe: Stockwell, 1973. — 30p; obl.8vo.
ISBN 0 7223 0403 x : £0.25

(B73-51073)

JFDX — Female voices, Children's voices. Secular cantatas
Williamson, Malcolm
Ode to music/ by Malcolm Williamson; words, Ursula Vaughan Williams. — London: Weinberger, 1973. — 8p; 4to.
Duration 5 min.
Unpriced

(B73-50192)

JFDX/GJ — Female voices, Children's voices. Children's secular
cantatas
Meryll, Jane
[Vocabulary ramblebuggies and educational wordopolis. Vocal score]. Vocabulary ramblebuggies and educational wordopolis/ by Jane Meryll; arranged and edited by Malcolm Binney, words by Arthur King. — Croydon: Belwin-Mills, 1973. — 15p; 8vo.
£0.40

(B73-50625)

JFE/LPDX/GR — Female voices, Children's voices with instruments
& piano. Secular cantatas. Activities
Chatterley, Albert
Sticks and stones: a classroom music project for young children and audience/ by Albert Chatterley. — Sevenoaks: Novello, 1973. — 38p; 8vo.
£0.64

(B73-50626)

JFE/NYDPDP/LF/AY — Female voices, Children's voices with
woodwind, strings, keyboard & percussion. Carols.
Christmas. Collections
Rutter, John
Carols for schools: twelve carols for unison voices, recorders or flutes, percussion, guitar and piano/ edited by John Rutter. — London: Oxford University Press, 1972. — 64p; 8vo.
ISBN 0 19 330665 4 : £1.60

(B73-50193)

JFE/NYDSDP — Female voices, Children's voices with recorders,
strings, keyboard & percussion. Carols
Tate, Phyllis
Ring out, sing out: a festival carol for spring and summer, for unison voices, recorders, percussion, violins, cellos and piano/ by Phyllis Tate; words anon. — Lonon: Oxford University Press, 1973. — 4to.
Score (20p.) & 6 parts. — Duration 3 1/4 min.
ISBN 0 19 344943 9 : Unpriced

(B73-51074)

JFE/NYESDP/LF/AY — Female voices. Children's voices with
recorders, strings & percussion. Christmas carols.
Collections
Harrop, Beatrice
Carol gaily carol: Christmas songs for children with piano accompaniments, with chords for guitar and with parts for descant recorders, glockenspiel, chime bars and percussion/ chosen by Beatrice Harrop. — London: Black, 1973. — 80p; obl 4to.
ISBN 0 7136 1407 2 : Unpriced

(B73-51075)

JFE/NYESDP/LF/AYD — Female voices, Children's voices with
recorder, strings & percussion. Christmas carols.
Collections. England
Murray, Margaret
Nine carols/ arranged for Orff instruments by Margaret Murray. — London: Schott, 1973. — 20p; obl. 8vo. — (Orff-Schulwerk; no.6)
£0.25

(B73-51076)

JFE/NYFSDW/LC/AY — Female voices, Children's voices with
recorders, keyboard & percussion. Spirituals.
Collections
Atkins, John G
In his hands: a cycle of spiritual and work songs/ compiled by John G. Atkins. — London: British and Continental Music, 1973. — 32p; 8vo.
£0.50

(B73-50627)

JFE/NYLDW/GJ/AY — Female voices, Children's voices with
percussion & keyboard, Children's songs. Collections
Wilson, Mabel
More songs for music time: for unison voices, with tuned and rhythmic percussion accompaniments/ arranged by Mable Wilson. — London: Oxford University Press, 1973. — 33p; obl. 8vo.
ISBN 0 19 330876 2 : £0.50

(B73-50194)

JFE/XMDW/G/AYDK — Female voices, Children's voices, with
percussion band. Folk songs. Collections. Wales
Jones, E Olwen
Chwe can werin gymreig = Six Welsh folk songs/ voices and percussion arranged by E. Olwen Jones. — London: Schott, 1973. — obl.8vo. — (Orff. Schulwerk)
Score (15p.) & voice-part (7p.).
£1.00

(B73-51077)

JFEZDM/GJ/AY — Unaccompanied female voices, children's voices.
Children's hymns. Collections
Behr, Heinz Otto
Neue Kinderlieder: für Kinder - und Familiengottesdienst/ herausgegeben von Heinz-Otto Behr, Uwe Seidel, Diethard Zils. — Regensburg: Bosse; [London]: [Bärenreiter], 1972. — 60p; 8vo.
£0.60

(B73-50195)

JFEZDW/GS/AYT — Unaccompanied female voices, children's
voices. Singing games. Collections. United States
Chase, Richard
Old songs and singing games/ collected and edited by Richard Chase. — New York: Dover; London: Constable, 1973. — xii,49p; 8vo.
Originally published Chapel Hill, University of North Carolina Press, 1937. A brief list of folk song publications, many of them now unavailable, has been omitted.
ISBN 0 486 22879 7 : Unpriced

(B73-51078)

JFEZDW/PP/AY — Unaccompanied female voices, children's voices.
Songs, etc. Pentatonic music. Collections
Kodály, Zoltán
Pentatonic music/ by Zoltán Kodály; [edited by Geoffry Russell-Smith]. — London: Boosey and Hawkes. — (Kodály, Zoltán. Choral method)
Tonic sol-fa notation.
Vol.4: 140 Churash melodies. — 1972. — 48p; obl. 8vo.
£0.30

(B73-50196)

JGDW — Male voices. Songs, etc
Milner, John
The scout show book/ by John Milner; sketches and lyrics by Hazel Addis. — Glasgow: Brown Son and Ferguson, 1973. — 52p; 8vo.
£0.75

(B73-51079)

JN — SINGLE VOICES IN COMBINATION
JNAYME/MDX — Vocal septets with orchestra. Secular cantatas
Fortner, Wolfgang
Versuch eines Agon um ...?: for 7 vocalists and orchestra/ by Wolfgang Fortner. — Mainz; London: Schott, 1973. — 75p; 4to.
Study score. — Duration 17 min.
£3.84

(B73-51080)

JNDDE/LF — Vocal trios. Religious cantatas. Christmas
Britten, Benjamin
Canticle 4. Journey of the Magi: for counter-tenor, tenor, baritone and piano/ by Benjamin Britten;; poem by T.S. Eliot. — London: Faber Music, 1972. — 28p; 4to.
Unpriced

(B73-50197)

JNEZAZDJ/LF — Unaccompanied vocal sextets. Motets. Christmas
Panufnik, Andrzej
Song to the Virgin Mary: for mixed chorus a cappella or 6 solo voices/ by Andrzej Panufnik; words anonymous. — Revised edition. — London: Boosey and Hawkes, 1973. — 24p; 8vo.
£0.40
Primary classification EZDJ/LF

(B73-50081)

JNFEDW — Female voice, Child's voice duets. Songs, etc
Berthold, G
Duetto for two cats with an accompaniment for the pianoforte/ composed and dedicated to social circles by G. Berthold. — London: Schott, 1973. — [2],3p; 4to.
Sometimes attributed to Rossini, but probably the work of Robert Lucas Pearsall. A facsimile of the edition published London, Ewer & Johanning, 1823.
£0.50

(B73-50628)

JNFTEDJ — Vocal trios. High voices. Motets
Locke, Matthew
Two motets: for two high voices and keyboard/ by Matthew Locke; edited by Maurice Bevan. — London: Thames, 1972. — 12p; 8vo.
Contents: Cantate Domino - O Domine Jesu Christe.
Unpriced

(B73-50198)

JNGEDW — Vocal male duets. Songs, etc
Bizet, Georges
[Les Pêcheurs de perles. Au fond du temple saint: arr]. Au fond du temple saint: duet/ by Georges Bizet; English words by Diana and David Ellenberg, French words by M. Carré et Cormon. — London: United Music, 1973. — 12p; 4to.
Unpriced

(B73-51081)

KDH — MOTETS, ANTHEMS, HYMNS, ETC. SOLOS
Lawes, Henry
[Ayres and dialogues, bk.2. Hymns to the Holy Trinity]. Hymns to the Holy Trinity: for solo voice and keyboard continuo/ by Henry Lawes; edited by Gwilym Beechey, words by John Crofts. — London: Oxford University Press, 1973. — 8p; 4to.
ISBN 0 19 345493 9 : £0.75

(B73-51082)

KDJ — MOTETS. SOLOS
Green, Philip
Hail Mary/ by Philip Green. — Croydon: Belwin-Mills, 1973. — 4p; 4to.
£0.20

(B73-51083)

KDK — ANTHEMS. SOLOS
Lekberg, Sven
O Lord, thou hast searched me/ music by Sven Lekberg; text from Psalm 139. — New York; London: Schirmer, 1972. — 5p; 4to.
Unpriced

(B73-50199)

KDP — CAROLS. SOLOS
KDP/LF — Christmas
Fulton, Norman
Two Christmas songs. Opus 37/ by Norman Fulton. — London: Oxford University Press, 1973. — 6p; 4to.
Contents: 1.No room at the inn (Robert) - 2.Make we merry (Hill).
ISBN 0 19 345341 x : £0.50

(B73-51084)

Green, Philip
The first Christmas/ by Philip Green: words Norman Newell. — Croydon: Belwin-Mills, 1973. — 4p; 4to.
£0.20

(B73-51085)

KDW — SONGS, ETC. SOLOS
Bernstein, Leonard
[Mass.. A simple song]. A simple song/ by Leonard Bernstein; words by Stephen Schwartz and Leonard Bernstein. — New York; London: Amberson: Schirmer, 1972. — 6p; 4to.
Unpriced

(B73-50200)

Bernstein, Leonard
[Mass. The word of the Lord]. The word of the Lord/ by Leonard Bernstein; words by Stephen Schwartz and Leonard Bernstein. — New York; London: Amberson: Schirmer, 1972. — 14p; 4to.
Unpriced

(B73-50201)

Binge, Ronald
The jolly swagman/ by Ronald Binge; words by Jo Manning Wilson. — London: Mozart Edition, 1972. — 4p; 4to.
Unpriced

(B73-50202)

Binge, Ronald
Sailing by: words and music by Ronald Binge. — London: Mozart Edition, 1972. — 4p; 4to.
Unpriced

(B73-50203)

Bricusse, Leslie
'The good old bad old days!': a new musical/ vocal selections by Leslie Bricusse and Anthony Newley. — London: Peter Maurice Music, (KPM Music Group), 1972. — 40p; 4to.
£0.75

(B73-50204)

Campra, André
[Operas. Selections]. Operatic airs/ by André Campra; edited by Graham Sadler. — London: Oxford University Press, for the University of Hull, 1972. — 94p; 4to.
£3.50

(B73-50629)

Dale, Mervyn
Eight nonsense songs/ by Mervyn Dale; words by Edward Lear. — London: Ashdown, 1973. — 4to.
Score (16p.) & words ed., (7p.).
£0.40

(B73-51086)

Debussy, Claude
Cinq poèmes de Charles Baudelaire: songs for solo voice and piano/ by Claude Debussy; edited, based on the sources, by Reiner Zimmermann. — Leipzig; London: Peters, 1972. — vi,38p; 8vo.
With a leaflet inserted containing the French words with a German translation.
Unpriced

(B73-50631)

Debussy, Claude
Trois ballads de François Villon: songs for solo voice and piano/ by Claude Debussy; edited, based on the sources, by Reiner Zimmermann. — Leipzig; London: Peters, 1972. — v,25p; 8vo.
With a leaflet containing the French words with a German translation.
Unpriced

(B73-50632)

Debussy, Claude
Trois chansons de France, [and] Trois poèmes de Tristan l'Hermite: songs for solo voice and piano/ by Claude Debussy; edited, based on the sources, by Reiner Zimmermann. — Leipzig; London: Peters, 1972. — vi,17p; 8vo.
With a separate leaf inserted bearing the French words with German translation.
Unpriced

(B73-50633)

Debussy, Claude
Trois poèmes de Stéphane Mallarmé: songs for solo voice and piano/ by Claude Debussy; edited, based on the sources, by Reiner Zimmermann. — Leipzig; London: Peters, 1972. — vi,14p; 8vo.
With a separate leaf inserted bearing the French words with German translation.
Unpriced

(B73-50634)

Delius, Frederick
[Songs. Selections]. Ten songs/ by Frederick Delius; edited with an introduction by Robert Threlfall. — London: Galliard, 1973. — 32p; 8vo.
Contents: Five songs from the Norwegian and the first publication of Five songs from the Danish comprising 1. The page sat in the lofty tower; words by J.P. Jacobsen - 2. Dreamy nights; words by Holger Drachmann - 3. Summer nights; words by Holger Drachmann - 4. Through long long years; words by J.P. Jacobsen - 5. Wine roses; words by J.P. Jacobsen.
Unpriced

(B73-50635)

Gershwin, George
[Songs. Selections]. The Gershwin years: songs. — London: Chappell, 1973. — 63p; 4to.
£1.50

(B73-51087)

Gibson, Isabella Mary
Lochnagar/ by Gibson; words by Byron; arranged by James Masterton. — Glasgow: Kerr, 1971. — 4p; 4to.
Unpriced

(B73-50205)

Lehár, Franz
The Czarevitch: songs from the operetta/ by Franz Lehár; original lyrics by Heinz Reichert and Bela Jenbach, English by Adam Carstairs. — London: Glocken Verlag, 1973. — 26p; 4to.
Unpriced

(B73-50206)

Macleod, Kenneth Iain Eachainn
Music from the heart: a memorial tribute being 15 selected songs/ by Kenneth I.E. Macleod; composed to poems by his mother Christina Macleod and others. — Leeds: John Blackburn, 1972. — 32p; 4to.
Unpriced
(B73-50207)

Niles, John Jacob
Evening: for voice and piano/ by John Jacob Niles; words by Thomas Merton. — New York; London: Schirmer, 1972. — 5p; 4to.
Unpriced
(B73-50208)

Reutter, Hermann
Neun Lieder: für eine Manner oder Frauenstimme (mittel bis hoch) und Klavier/ von Hermann Reutter; Gedichte von Ricarda Huch. — Mainz; London: Schott, 1973. — 31p; 4to.
Nos. 1,5.6 and 8 may be sung by a woman, and the remaining songs sung by a man.
£1.50
(B73-50636)

Simon, Paul
The songs of Paul Simon. — London: Joseph, 1972. — xii,331p; 4to.
With lyrics appearing on pages 301-331.
£2.95
(B73-50209)

Strouse, Charles
'Applause' song book: [songs from] a new musical by Charles Strouse/ lyrics by Lee Adams. — London: Edwin H. Morris, 1972. — 71p; 4to.
£1.25
(B73-50210)

Theodorakis, Mikis
The love in your eyes/ by Mikis Theodorakis; lyrics by Norman Newell. — London: Dick James Music, 1973. — 4p; 4to.
£0.20
(B73-50211)

Wilson, Robert Barclay
Heard ye the mighty roar?: [Song]/ music by Robert Barclay Wilson; words by Martin Dickson. — London: Cramer, 1972. — 7p; 4to.
Unpriced
(B73-50212)

KDW/AZ — Collected works of individual composers
Coward, *Sir* Noel
[Works, songs]. The Noel Coward collection: songs. — London: Chappell.
Volume 1. — 1972. — 39p; 4to. —
£0.60
(B73-50630)

KDW/G/AYC — Folk songs. Collections. Great Britain
Stuart, Forbes
Stories of Britain in song/ compiled with commentaries by Forbes Stuart; musical arrangements by Geoffrey Winters, illustrated by Janet Archer. — London: Longman Young Books, 1972. — 2-208p: ill(1 col); 4to.
ISBN 0 582 15330 1 : £2.75
(B73-50213)

KDW/G/AYDK — Folk songs. Collections. Wales
Beaumont, Adrian
Dwy gan werin = Two Welsh folk songs/ compiled by Adrian Beaumont. — Cardiff: University of Wales Press, 1973. — 9p; 4to.
Contents: 1.Clychau Aberdyfi - 2.Wrth fynd hefo Deio i Dywyn.
Unpriced
(B73-51088)

KDW/GB/AY(XPKIO) — Popular songs. Collections, 1950-1959
Great songs of the fifties. — New York; London: Wise, Music Sales, 1973. — 111p; 4to.
£1.50
(B73-51089)

KDW/GCW/AY — Country 'n' western. Collections
American country music. — London: Wise, Music Sales, 1973. — 144p; 4to.
Unpriced
(B73-50637)

KDW/JR — Songs, etc. Films
Arlen, Harold
The wizard of Oz: song album from the film/ with music by Harold Arlen; lyrics by E.Y. Harburg. — London: Robbins Music, Francis, Day & Hunter, 1973. — 36p; 4to.
£0.75
(B73-50639)

Barry, John
Alice's adventures in Wonderland: song book/ with music by John Barry; lyrics by Don Black. — London: Edwin H. Morris, 1972. — 36p; 4to.
£1.00
(B73-50214)

Leitch, Donovan
The pied piper: songs from the film/ words and music by Donovan Leitch. — London: Donovan Music, 1973. — 12p; 4to.
Contents: Sailing homeward - People call me the pied piper - The piper's theme.
£0.30
(B73-50215)

Schwartz, Stephen
Godspell: film souvenir song book/ words and music by Stephen Schwartz. — London: Valando Music, 1973. — 51p; 4to.
£1.00
(B73-50638)

KE — VOCAL SOLOS WITH ACCOMPANIMENT OTHER THAN KEYBOARD
KE/LNTDW/AYJ — With instrumental trio. Songs, etc. Collections. Italy
Boorman, Stanley
Four frottole: for voice and 3 instruments or 4 instruments/ edited by Stanley Boorman. — Newton Abbot: Antico, 1972. — 10p; 4to.
Unpriced
(B73-50216)

KE/NYDNQDX — With woodwind, strings, keyboard & percussion sextet. Secular cantatas
Feldman, Morton
I met Heine on the Rue Furstenberg/ by Morton Feldman. — New York; London: Universal, 1973. — 12p; 8vo.
Duration 10 min..
Unpriced
(B73-50640)

KE/TSDW/G/AY — With guitar. Folk songs. Collections
Evans, Roger
Roger Evans book of folk songs and how to play them: all guitar chords, melody, lyrics & easy to understand guitar accompaniments. — London: Robbins, Francis, Day & Hunter, 1972. — 56p; 4to.
£0.60
(B73-50217)

KE/TSDW/G/AYD — With guitar. Folk songs. Collections. England
Hamer, Fred
Green groves: more English folk songs/ collected by Fred Hamer, transcribed by Christopher Wilson. — London: EFDS, 1973. — 79p; 4to.
£0.75
(B73-50218)

KE/TSDW/JV/AY — With guitar. Music hall songs. Collections
Davison, Peter
Songs of the British music hall/ compiled and edited with a critical history of the songs and their times by Peter Davison. — New York: Oak Publications; London: Music Sales, 1973. — 244p; 4to.
ISBN 0 8256 0099 5 : Unpriced
(B73-50219)

KF — FEMALE VOICE, CHILD'S VOICE
KFDW/AY — Songs, etc. Collections
Children's favourites. — London: Southern Music: Music Sales, 1972. — 25p; 4to.
£0.40
(B73-50220)

KFE/TSDW/AY — With guitar. Songs, etc. Collections
Perkins, Polly
Songs for the liberated woman/ compiled with guitar chords by Polly Perkins. — London: Kahn and Averill, 1973. — 128p; 8vo.
ISBN 0 900707 24 0 : £0.70
(B73-51090)

KFEZDW — Unaccompanied female voice. Songs, etc
Lefanu, Nicola
But stars remaining: for female voice (unaccompanied) by Nicola Lefanu/ words adapted from two poems by C. Day Lewis. — Sevenoaks: Novello, 1973. — 4p; 4to.
£0.35
(B73-50641)

Lefanu, Nicola
Il Cantico dei cantici II = The song of songs. Ch. 2: dramatic scena for female voice (unaccompanied)/ by Nicola LeFanu. — Sevenoaks: Novello, 1973. — 4p; 4to.
£0.35
(B73-50642)

KFLDH — Soprano voice. Motets, Anthems, Hymns, etc
Johnson, Robert Sherlaw
The praises of heaven and earth: for solo soprano piano, and electronic tape/ by Robert Sherlaw Johnson; text derived from Psalm 148. — London: Oxford University Press, 1972. — 12p; 4to and obl 4to.
Printed on one side of the leaf only, with a separate leaf containing notes on the notation and interpretation.
ISBN 0 19 345480 7 : £1.20

(B73-50221)

KFLDX — Soprano voice. Secular cantatas
Handel, George Frideric
Airs francais = Cantate francaise: for soprano and basso continuo/ by Georg Friedrich Händel; edited by Percy Young, continuo realization, Walter H. Bernstein, English words Percy M. Young, German words, Peter Schmidt. — First ed.. — Cassel; London: Bärenreiter, 1972. — 4to.
Score (15p.) & 2 parts.
£1.50

(B73-50643)

Scarlatti, Alessandro
Io son pur solo: solo cantata for soprano and basso continuo/ by Alessandro Scarlatti; edited by Malcolm Boyd, Ubertragung ins Deutsche Walther Durr. — First edition. — Cassel; London: Bärenreiter, 1972. — 4to.
Score (12p.) & 2 parts.
£1.20

(B73-50222)

Scarlatti, Alessandro
Luntan dalla suna Clori: solo cantata for soprano and basso continuo/ by Alessandro Scarlatti; edited by Malcolm Boyd, Ubertragung ins Deutsche Walther Dürr. — First edition. — Cassel; London: Bärenreiter, 1972. — 4to.
Score (12p.) & 2 parts.
£1.20

(B73-50223)

KFLE/MDW — Soprano voice with orchestra. Songs, etc
Dallapiccola, Luigi
Liriche greche: per soprano e diverso gruppi strumentali/ di Luigi Dallapiccola. — London: Eulenberg, 1973. — 76p; 8vo.
Contents: 1. Cinque frammenti di Saffo - 2. Due liriche di Anacreonte - 3. Sex carmina Alcaei.
£2.80

(B73-50224)

KFLE/MDX — Soprano voice with orchestra. Secular cantatas
McCabe, John
Notturni ed alba: for soprano and orchestra/ by John McCabe; words, medieval latin. — Sevenoaks: Novello, 1973. — 117p; 4to.
£2.50

(B73-50644)

KFLE/NVNTDW — Soprano voice with wind & string trio. Songs, etc
Walker, Eldon
Elegy: soprano, flute horn, cello/ by Eldon Walker; text by John Webster. — London: Thames, 1972. — fol.
Unpriced

(B73-50645)

KFLE/NYGNRDW — Soprano voice with strings, keyboard & percussion quintet. Songs, etc
Takemitsu, Toru
Stanza 1: per chitarra, arpa, pianoforte, celesta, vibrafono e voce feminile (soprano)/ de Toru Takemitsu, teste di Ludwig von Wittgenstein. — London: Universal, 1973. — 14p; fol.
Unpriced

(B73-51091)

KFLE/NYLNQDW — Soprano voice with keyboard & percussion sextet. Songs, etc
Geviksman, Vitali
Japanische Elegien: Vokal-instrumental-Zyklus in sieben Teilen nach Worten altjapanischer Dichter, fur Soprano und Kammerensemble/ von Vitali Geviksman. — Leipzig; London: Peters, 1972. — 43p; 4to.
£3.50

(B73-50646)

KFLE/NYLNUDE — Soprano voice with keyboard & percussion duet. Religious cantatas
Halffter, Cristóbal
Noche pasiva del sentido, (San Juan de la Cruz)/ de Cristóbal Halffter. — London: Universal, 1973. — 19p; obl fol.
The two instrumentalists play a wide variety of percussion instruments.
Unpriced

(B73-50647)

KFLE/RXMDW — Soprano voice with string orchestra. Songs, etc
Stiles, Frank
Sonnet: for soprano voice and string orchestra/ by Frank Stiles. — London: Mixolydian Press, 1970. — 27p; 8vo.
Miniature score.
Unpriced

(B73-50648)

KFLE/SNTPWDE — Soprano voice with two violins & keyboard. Religious cantatas
Weiland, Julius Johann
[Erstlinge musicalischer Andachten.. Jauchzet Gott, alle Lande]. Jauchzet Gott, alle Lande = Make a joyful noise unto God: sacred concerto for soprano, two violins and basso continuo/ by Julius Johann Weiland; edited by Ferdinand Saffe. — Cassel; London: Bärenreiter, 1972. — 4to.
Score (8p.) & 4 parts.
£1.50

(B73-50225)

KFLE/VRPLVVDW — Soprano voice with flute & clarinet. Songs, etc
Walker, Eldon
This bird ...: soprano, flute, clarinet/ by Eldon Walker. — London: Thames, 1973. — 14p; fol.
Unpriced

(B73-50649)

KFLE/VRPLXTRTDR — Soprano voice with flute & vibraphone. Psalms
Wernert, Wolfgang
Psalm 116: für Sopran, Flöte, Vibraphon/ von Wolfgang Wernert. — Regensburg: Bosse; [London]: [Bärenreiter], 1971. — 6p; 4to.
£1.50

(B73-50226)

KFNDX — Mezzo-soprano voice. Secular cantatas
Horovitz, Joseph
Lady Macbeth: a scena for mezzo-soprano and piano/ by Joseph Horovitz; [words by William Shakespeare]. — Sevenoaks: Novello, 1973. — 16p; 4to.
£0.65

(B73-50227)

KFNE/MDX — Mezzo-soprano voice with orchestra. Secular cantatas
Crosse, Gordon
Memories of morning. Night: a monodrama for mezzosoprano and orchestra/ by Gordon Crosse; text drawn from Jean Rhys's novel Wide Sargasso Sea. — London: Oxford University Press, 1973. — 107p; 8vo.
ISBN 0 19 362487 7 : £3.00

(B73-50650)

KFNE/RXNSDW — Mezzo-soprano voice with string quartet. Songs, etc
Binkerd, Gordon
Three songs for mezzo soprano and string quartet/ by Gordon Binkerd. — New York; London: Boosey and Hawkes, 1973. — 8vo.
Miniature score (32p.) & 4 parts. — Contents 1. Never the nightingale; poem by Adelaide Craspey - 2. How lillies come white; poem by Robert Herrick. — 3. Upon parting; poem by Robert Herrick.
£6.25

(B73-50651)

KFNE/SPLSRDW — Mezzo-soprano voice with violin & cello. Songs, etc
Binkerd, Gordon
Portrait interieur: for mezzo-soprano and violin and cello/ by Gordon Binkerd; poems by Rainer Maria Rilke. — New York; London: Boosey and Hawkes, 1973. — 28p; 4to.
£1.50

(B73-50652)

Binkerd, Gordon
Portrait interieur: for mezzo-soprano and violin and cello/ by Gordon Binkerd; poems by Rainer Maria Rilke. — New York; [London]: Boosey and Hawkes, 1973. — 28p; 8vo.
Miniature score.
£1.25

(B73-51092)

KFNE/VVDW — Mezzo-soprano voice with clarinet. Songs, etc
Amy, Gilbert
D'un desastre obscur': pour voix de mezzo-soprano et clarinette en la/ par Gilbert Amy. — London: Universal, 1973. — 3p; fol.
Unpriced

(B73-51093)

KFQDW — Contralto voice. Songs, etc
Roe, Betty
Noble numbers: five songs for counter-tenor (or contralto) and piano (or harpsichord)/ by Betty Roe; poems by Robert Herrick. — London: Thames, 1972. — 16p; 4to.
Unpriced
Primary classification KHNDW

(B73-50241)

KFT — HIGH VOICE
KFTDW — Songs, etc
Berkeley, Lennox
Counting the beats: song for high voice and piano/ by Lennox Berkeley; poem by Robert Graves. — London: Thames, 1972. — 6p; 4to.
Unpriced

(B73-50228)

Ives, Grayston
The falcon: set for high voice and piano/ by Grayston Ives; words, anon. — Wendover: Roberton, 1972. — 5p; 4to.
Unpriced

(B73-50229)

Naylor, Bernard
Speaking from the snow: suite for high voice and piano/ by Bernard Naylor; poems by C. Day Lewis. — Wendover: Roberton, 1973. — 15p; 4to.
£0.40

(B73-51094)

Raphael, Mark
3 D.H. Lawrence love poems: for high voice and piano/ by Mark Raphael. — London: Thames, 1973. — 16p; 4to.
Contents: Dog-tired - Cherry robbers - Flapper.
Unpriced

(B73-50230)

Reutter, Hermann
Bogenschutzen: Vokalise für eine hohe Singstimme und Klavier/ von Hermann Reutter; Text von F.G. Lorca. — Mainz; London: Schott, 1973. — 11p; 4to.
£1.44

(B73-51095)

Stoker, Richard
Music that brings sweet sleep: song cycle for high voice and piano/ by Richard Stoker; words by Tennyson, George du Maurier, Herrick and Shakespeare. — London: Peters, 1972. — 15p; 4to.
Unpriced

(B73-50231)

KFTE/NURNTDX — With flute, string & keyboard trio. Secular cantatas
Clérambault, Louis Nicolas
[Cantates françoises, liv.1. Orphée]. Orphée: cantata for high voice, flute, violin and continuo/ by Louis-Nicolas Clérambault; edited by David Tunley. — London: Faber Music, 1972. — 4to.
Score (22p.) & 3 parts.
Unpriced

(B73-50232)

KFTE/TQDW — With harp. Songs, etc
Blyton, Carey
Symphony in yellow. Op. 15b: for high voice and harp (or piano)/ by Carey Blyton, words by Oscar Wilde. — London: Boosey and Hawkes, 1973. — 8p; 4to.
£0.40

(B73-51096)

KFV — MIDDLE VOICE
KFVDW — Songs, etc
Parrott, Ian
Flamingoes: song for medium voice and piano/ by Ian Parrott; words by Jane Wilson. — London: Thames, 1973. — 7p; 4to.
Unpriced

(B73-50233)

Reutter, Hermann
Fünf Lieder: für mittlere Stimme und Klavier/ von Hermann Reutter; Gedichte von Marie Luise Kaschnitz. — Mainz; London: Schott, 1973. — 16p; 4to.
£1.20

(B73-50653)

Reutter, Hermann
Vier Lieder: für mittlere Stimme und Klavier/ von Hermann Reutter; Gedichte von Nelly Sachs. — Mainz; London: Schott, 1973. — 11p; 4to.
£1.20

(B73-50654)

Roe, Betty
Nursery rhyme of innocence and experience: song for medium voice and piano/ by Betty Roe; words by Charles Causley. — London: Thames, 1972. — 6p; 8vo.
Unpriced

(B73-50234)

Stoker, Richard
Aspects 1 in 3: song cycle for medium voice and piano/ by Richard Stoker; words by Ralph Waldo Emerson. — London: Peters, 1972. — 8p; 4to.
Three settings of the same words.
Unpriced

(B73-50235)

Warlock, Peter
8 songs: for medium voice and piano/ by Peter Warlock; edited by Fred Tomlinson. — London: Thames, 1972. — 23p; 4to.
Unpriced

(B73-50236)

KFVDW/AYT — Songs, etc. Collections. United States
Contemporary art song album: for medium voice. — New York: Galaxy; London: Galliard, 1972. — 38p; 4to.
Unpriced

(B73-50237)

KFVE/SRDW — With cello. Songs, etc
Silcock, Norman
Two George Herbert songs: for medium voice and cello/ by Norman Silcock. — London: Thames, 1972. — 7p; 8vo.
Contents: The church floor - The windows.
Unpriced

(B73-50238)

KFVE/VRPLTSDW — With flute & guitar. Songs, etc
Roe, Betty
Firstlings: three songs, for medium voice, flute, (clarinet or violin) and guitar/ by Betty Roe; words by Rita Ford. — London: Thames, 1972. — 3p; 8vo.
Unpriced

(B73-50239)

KFX — LOW VOICE
KFXDW — Songs, etc
Reutter, Hermann
Chamber music: four selected poems, for low male voice and piano/ by Hermann Reutter. — Mainz; London: Schott, 1973. — 12p; 4to.
£1.20

(B73-50655)

KG — MALE VOICE
KGHE/NVPNQDX — Tenor voice with woodwind & string sextet. Secular cantatas
Warlock, Peter
The curlew: for tenor solo, flute, English horn, and string quartet/ by Peter Warlock; words by W.B. Yeats. — London: Stainer and Bell, 1973. — 24p; 4to.
A facsimile reprint of the original edition of 1924, with added introductory notes by Fred Tomlinson.
Unpriced

(B73-51097)

KGXE/WSPLRDE — Bass voice with trumpet & organ. Religious cantatas
Hader, Widmar
Hör meinen Protest: Psalm 5 für Bass, Trompete und Orgel/ von Widmar Hader; [text by] Ernesto Cardenal, aus dem spanischen Ubertragen von Stefan Baciu. — Regensburg: Bosse; [London]: [Bärenreiter], 1972. — 15p; 4to.
£1.80

(B73-50240)

KHNDW — Counter-tenor voice. Songs, etc
Roe, Betty
Noble numbers: five songs for counter-tenor (or contralto) and piano (or harpsichord)/ by Betty Roe; poems by Robert Herrick. — London: Thames, 1972. — 16p; 4to.
Unpriced
Also classified at KFQDW

(B73-50241)

KHYE/NYLDE — Speaker with keyboard & percussion. Religious cantatas
Swann, Donald
Requiem for the living: for speaker, mezzo-soprano or baritone solo, mixed chorus, percussion, cimbalom and piano/ by Donald Swann; words by Cecil Day Lewis. — Wendover: Roberton, 1971. — 69p; 8vo.
If the speaker is male, a female singer should be used, and vice versa.
Unpriced

(B73-50242)

LH — DANCES
LJ — Miscellaneous works
Rees, Howard
Honeywell: for three groups of instruments and/or voices/ by Howard Rees. — London: Universal, 1973. — s.sh; obl.fol.
Unpriced
Also classified at FE/LDW

(B73-50656)

LN — ENSEMBLES
LNS — Quartets
Maschera, Florentio
[Libro primo de canzoni da sonare. La Maggia]. Canzona 'La Maggia'/ by Florentio Maschera; edited by Howard Mayer Brown. — London: Oxford University Press, 1973. — 7p; 8vo.
ISBN 0 19 341204 7 : Unpriced
Also classified at TWPMJ

(B73-50657)

LNSQ/XC — Three instruments & piano. Rounds
Foster, Anthony
Dona nobis pacem: a round, arranged for voices in three parts and piano, with optional recorders, violins, and percussion/ by Anthony Foster. — London: Oxford University Press, 1972. — 9p; 4to.
ISBN 0 19 344849 1 : £0.50

(B73-50243)

LNT — Trios
Jacopo da Bologna
Three madrigals: for 3 voices and/or instruments/ by Jacopo da Bologna; edited by Nigel Wilkins. — Lustleigh: Antico, 1973. — 4to.
Score (16p.) & 3 parts. — Contents: 1.Sotto l'imperio - 2.Si com'al canto - 3.Aquil'altera/Creatura gentil'/Uccel di Dio.
Unpriced
Primary classification EZDU

(B73-50104)

Jacopo da Bologna
Three madrigals: for 3 voices and/or instruments/ by Jacopo da Bologna; edited by Nigel Wilkins. — Lustleigh: Antico, 1973. — 4to.
Score (16p.) & 3 parts. — Contents: 1.Sotto l'imperio - 2.Si com'al canto - 3.Aquil'altera/Creatura gentil'/Uccel di Dio.
Unpriced
Primary classification EZDU

(B73-50105)

LNT/X — Trios. Canons
Carter, Elliott
Canon for 3, 'In memoriam Igor Stravinsky': for three equal instrumental voices/ by Elliott Carter. — New York; London: Associated Music, 1972. — 5p; 4to.
Playing scores in C and B flat.
Unpriced

(B73-51098)

LNU — Duets
Chedeville, Esprit Philippe
[Simphonies for two instruments, liv. 1, suite 2, liv. 2, suites. 1, 2]. Simphonies: three easy duets for recorders, flutes, oboes or other melodic instruments/ by Esprit-Philippe Chedeville; edited by Hugo Ruf. — Mainz; London: Schott, 1973. — 20p; 4to.
£1.08

(B73-51099)

Kagel, Mauricio
Zwei-Mann-Orchester/ von Mauricio Kagel. — London: Universal, 1973. — ix,89p; obl. 4to.
Unpriced

(B73-51100)

Runze, Klaus
Zwei Hande- zwölf Tasten/ von Klaus Runze. — Mainz; London: Schott.
Band 2: Spiel mit Noten. — 1973. — 49p; obl. 4to. — Unpriced

(B73-51101)

LP — WORKS FOR UNSPECIFIED INSTRUMENT WITH PIANO
LPG — Suites
Lane, Philip
Five diversions: for melody instrument and piano/ by Philip Lane. — London: Galliard, 1973. — 4to.
Score (20p) & part. — Contents: Soft shoe solitaire - Romanza - Bru up - Sarabandina - Burleske.
Unpriced

(B73-51102)

LPJ — Miscellaneous works
Hedges, Anthony
Count down: duos for melody instrument and piano/ by Anthony Hedges. — London: Fenette Music: Breitkopf and Härtel, 1973. — 4to.
Score (11p.) & 3 parts.
Unpriced

(B73-50244)

M/JR — FILM MUSIC
M/LF — Christmas
Benoy, Arthur William
Prelude for Christmas: for school orchestra/ by A.W. Benoy. — London: Oxford University Press, 1973. — 8to.
Score (17p) & 22 parts - Based on 'I wish you a merry Christmas' and 'Rejoice and be merry'.
ISBN 0 19 361940 7 : Unpriced

(B73-51103)

Benoy, Arthur William
Scherzo for Christmas: for school orchestra/ A.W. Benoy. — London: Oxford University Press, 1973. — 4to.
Score (20p) & 22 parts - Based on 'Shepherds, shake off your drowsy sleep' and 'Unto us is born a son'.
ISBN 0 19 361966 0 : Unpriced

(B73-51104)

MGM — MARCHES
Berlioz, Hector
[Symphonie fantastique. Op.14. Marche au supplice: arr]. March to the scaffold/ by Hector Berlioz; arranged by Anthony Carter. — London: Oxford University Press, 1973. — 33p; 4to.
ISBN 0 19 362158 4 : £1.75

(B73-50658)

MH — DANCES
MH/HM — Ballet
Hérold, Ferdinand
[La Fille mal gardée. Clog dance]. Clog dance/ by Ferdinand Hérold; arranged by John Lanchbery, adapted for amateur orchestra by David Stone. — London: Oxford University Press, 1973. — 4to.
Score (19p) & 20 parts.
ISBN 0 19 364251 4 : Unpriced

(B73-51105)

Hérold, Ferdinand
[La Fille mal gardée. Flute dance]. Flute dance/ by Ferdinand Hérold; arranged by John Lanchbery, adapted for amateur orchestra by David Stone. — London: Oxford University Press, 1973. — 4to.
Score (27p) & 23 parts.
ISBN 0 19 364275 1 : Unpriced

(B73-51106)

MJ — MISCELLANEOUS WORKS
Adams-Jeremiah, Dorothy
Sing, say and play/ by Dorothy Adams-Jeremiah; orchestral accompaniments by Mansel Thomas. — London: Lengnick, 1972. — 4to.
Score (4p.) & 4 parts.
£0.20

(B73-50245)

Beethoven, Ludwig van
[Prometheus. Op.43. *Excerpts*]. Pastorale, Opus 43/ von Ludwig van Beethoven; herausgegeben von Helmut May. — Mainz; London: Schott, 1973. — 23p; 4to.
£1.60

(B73-50246)

Bizet, Georges
[Le Docteur Miracle.. Overture: arr]. Overture/ by Georges Bizet; arranged [for amateur orchestra] by David Stone. — London: Oxford University Press, 1972. — 50p; 4to.
ISBN 0 19 361673 4 : £2.50

(B73-50247)

Durko, Zsolt
Ballad: for youth or amateur orchestra/ by Zsolt Durko. — London: Boosey and Hawkes, 1973. — 23p; 4to.
£1.00

(B73-50660)

Hoag, Charles K
An after-intermission overture: for youth orchestra/ by Charles K. Hoag. — New York; London: Schirmer, 1972. — 4to.
Score (25p.) & 29 parts.
Unpriced

(B73-50248)

Hughes-Jones, Llifon
[Preludes for orchestra, nos.1-2]. Prelude no.1 (on a 15th century
French melody) and Prelude no.2/ by Llifon Hughes-Jones. —
London: Bosworth, 1972. — 4to.
Score (6p.), Piano conductor (3p.), & 10 parts.
£1.60
Also classified at RXMJ

(B73-50661)

Jones, Kelsey
Miramichi ballad: a suite for orchestra/ by Kelsey Jones. —
London: Boosey and Hawkes, 1972. — 4to.
Score (46p.) & 26 parts.
£4.85

(B73-50249)

Taylor, Herbert F
Prelude to a ceremony: for orchestra/ by Herbert F. Taylor. —
London: Bosworth, 1973. — 12p; 4to.
Duration 2 1/4 min.
£0.37

(B73-51107)

Tomlinson, Geoffrey
Contrasts: seven miniatures for school orchestra/ by Geoffrey
Tomlinson. — London: Boosey and Hawkes, 1973. — 4to.
Score (30p.) & 19 parts.
£4.90

(B73-50662)

MK — ARRANGEMENTS
Vivaldi, Antonio
[Il Cimento dell'armonia e dell'invenzione. Op.8, no.3. La Caccia:
arr]. The hunt from 'Autumn' (The four seasons)/ by Antonio
Vivaldi; arranged for orchestra by K.W. Rokos. — London:
Bosworth, 1973. — 12p; 4to.
Duration 2 min.
£0.57

(B73-51108)

MK/AAY — Arrangements. Collections
Benoy, Arthur William
A second book for the young orchestra: ten pieces for school
string orchestra and recorder ensemble with optional flutes,
clarinets, trumpets and piano/ by A.W. Benoy. — London:
Oxford University Press, 1973. — 4to.
Score (36p.) & 11 parts.
ISBN 0 19 361653 x : £1.40

(B73-50663)

Gange, Kenneth
Three classical pieces/ arranged for orchestra by Kenneth Gange.
— London: Bosworth, 1973. — 12p; 4to.
Contents: Minuet and trio, by Beethoven - German dance, by F.A.
Hoffmeister - Two minuets, by Haydn.
£0.50

(B73-51109)

MK/AH — Arrangements. Dances
Praetorius, Michael
[Terpsichore.. Selections: arr]. Dance suite/ by Michael Praetorius;
arranged for orchestra by N.J. Milner-Gulland. — London:
Boosey and Hawkes, 1973. — 4to.
The seventh movement cannot be traced in 'Terpsichore'. — Score (16p.) &
parts.
£5.90

(B73-50250)

MK/AH/AYD — Arrangements. Dances. Collections. England
Playford, John
[English dancing master. Selections: arr]. Three English dances
from Playford's 'English Dancing Master' (1650)/ arranged for
orchestra by David Stone. — London: Boosey and Hawkes, 1973.
— 4to.
Score (24p.) & 25 parts.
£1.80

(B73-51110)

MK/AHR — Arrangements. Minuets
Beethoven, Ludwig van
Two orchestral minuets/ by L. van Beethoven; transcribed and
orchestrated by William Denny and Joseph Kerman. — London:
Oxford University Press, 1973. — 4to.
Score (28p) & 19 parts - The two minuets were never completed but were
preserved in the form of relatively complete drafts in piano score. They are
here transcribed for amateur orchestra.
ISBN 0 19 361430 8 : Unpriced

(B73-51111)

MM — WORKS FOR SYMPHONY ORCHESTRA
MM/HM — Ballet
Glazunov, Alexander
The seasons: ballet in one act and four tableaux/ by Alexander
Glazunow. — Frankfurt: Belaieff; London: Hinrichsen, 1972. —
182p; 8vo.
Miniature score.
£4.50

(B73-50664)

Surinach, Carlos
Acrobats of God: symphonic version of the ballet for orchestra/
by Carlos Surinach. — New York; London: Associated Music,
1972. — 136p; 8vo.
Unpriced

(B73-51112)

MM/X — Canons
Stravinsky, Igor
Canon for concert introduction or encore: a Russian popular
tune/ by Igor Stravinsky. — London: Boosey and Hawkes, 1973.
— 3p; fol.
£0.50

(B73-51113)

MME — Symphonies
Bax, *Sir* Arnold
Symphony no.7/ by Arnold Bax. — London: Chappell, 1972. —
219p; 8vo.
Study score.
Unpriced

(B73-50251)

Berlioz, Hector
New edition of the complete works of Hector Berlioz. — Cassel;
London: Bärenreiter.
Vol.16: Symphonie fantastique; edited by Nicholas Temperley. — 1972. —
xxxv,221p; fol.
Unpriced
Primary classification C/AZ

(B73-50483)

Brian, Havergal
Symphony 2/ by Havergal Brian. — Chelmsford: Musica viva,
1973. — 88p; fol.
Unpriced

(B73-50665)

Brian, Havergal
Symphony 8/ by Havergal Brian. — Chelmsford: Musica Viva,
1973. — 49p; 8vo.
Study score.
Unpriced

(B73-50666)

Brian, Havergal
Symphony 10/ by Havergal Brian. — Chelmsford: Musica Viva,
1973. — 40p; 8vo.
Study score.
Unpriced

(B73-50667)

Brian, Havergal
Symphony 21/ by Havergal Brian. — Chelmsford: Musica Viva,
1973. — 60p; 8vo.
Study score.
Unpriced

(B73-50668)

Gerhard, Roberto
[Symphony no.2, 'Metamorphoses']. Metamorphoses (Symphony
no.2)/ by Roberto Gerhard. — Revised ed.: edited by Alan
Boustead. — Croydon: Belwin-Mills, 1973. — 211p; fol.
Unpriced

(B73-50669)

Haydn, Joseph
Symphony no.51 in B flat major/ by Joseph Haydn; edited by
Gwilym Beechey. — London: Eulenburg, 1973. — viii,36p; 8vo.
Miniature score.
£0.75

(B73-50670)

Haydn, Joseph
Symphony no.54 in G major/ by Joseph Haydn; edited by
Gwilym Beechey. — London: Eulenburg, 1973. — viii,86p; 8vo.
Miniature score.
£1.00

(B73-50671)

Haydn, Joseph
Symphony no.59 in A major/ by Joseph Haydn; edited by
Gwilym Beechey. — London: Eulenburg, 1973. — vi,61p; 8vo.
Miniature score.
£1.00

(B73-51114)

McCabe, John
Symphony no.2/ by John McCabe. — Sevenoaks: Novello, 1973.
— 149p; 4to.
Study score.
£6.00

(B73-51115)

Mozart, Wolfgang Amadeus
[Symphony no.38 in D major. K.504, 'Prague']. Sinfonie in D, (Prager Sinfonie). KV504/ von Mozart; herausgegeben von Laszlo Somfai. — Cassel; London: Bärenreiter, 1971. — 63-125p; fol.
Extracted from the new edition of Mozart's complete works.
£3.50
(B73-50672)

Panufnik, Andrzej
Sinfonia elegaica/ by Andrzej Panufnik. — London: Boosey and Hawkes, 1972. — 60p; 8vo.
Miniature score.
Unpriced
(B73-50252)

Rubbra, Edmund
Symphony no.8, 'Hommage à Teilhard de Chardin'. Op. 132/ by Edmund Rubbra. — South Croydon: Lengnick, 1973. — 103p; 8vo.
£2.00
(B73-50673)

Schubert, Franz
[Symphony no.8 in B minor, 'Unfinished'. D759]. Symphony in B minor, 'Unfinished'/ by Franz Schubert;; edited by Martin Chusid. — London: Chappell, 1972. — 134p; 8vo.
Unpriced
(B73-50253)

Schumann, Robert
[Symphony in G minor]. Sinfonie, G-moll für Orchester/ von Robert Schumann; zum ersten Mal, herausgegeben von Marc Andreae. — Frankfurt: Litolff; London: Peters, 1972. — 100p; 8vo.
Miniature score.
£3.00
(B73-50674)

MMG — Suites
Gál, Hans
Triptych. Op.100: three movements for orchestra/ by Hans Gál. — London: Simrock, 1972. — 74p; 4to.
Duration 27 mins. — Contents: Impromptu - Pavane - Comedy.
Unpriced
(B73-50254)

Tippett, Sir Michael
[Suite in D major]. Suite for the birthday of Prince Charles/ by Michael Tippett. — London: Eulenburg, 1972. — 58p; 8vo.
Miniature score.
£0.80
(B73-50255)

MMH — Dances
Platts, Kenneth
Dance overture. Op. 10: for orchestra/ by Kenneth Platts. — London: Ashdown, 1973. — 34p; fol.
£3.00
(B73-51116)

MMHJQ — Ecossaises
Hamilton, Iain
Ecossaise for orchestra/ by Iain Hamilton. — London: Schott, 1973. — 50p; 8vo.
Miniature score.
£1.50
(B73-50675)

MMJ — Miscellaneous works
Antoniou, Theodor
Op ouverture: for orchestra and three groups of loudspeakers/ by Theodor Antoniou. — Cassel; London: Bärenreiter, 1972. — 39p; 8vo.
Miniature score.
£1.50
(B73-50256)

Bax, Sir Arnold
Tintagel/ by Arnold Bax. — London: Chappell, 1973. — 55p; 8vo.
Study score. — Reduced facsimile of the original ed.
Unpriced
(B73-50676)

Berio, Luciano
Still: for orchestra/ by Luciano Berio. — London: Universal, 1973. — 12p; fol.
Unpriced
(B73-51117)

Bizet, Georges
[Overture]. Ouverture/ par Georges Bizet; publiee pour la premiere fois, partition edité par Antonio d'Almeida. — London: Universal, 1972. — 56p; 4to.
Duration 14 min.
Unpriced
(B73-50677)

Boulez, Pierre
Pli selon pli/ by Pierre Boulez. — London: Universal.
Duration 15 min.
No.5: Tombeau. — 1973. — 82p; fol.
Unpriced
(B73-50678)

Ellis, David
Elegy for orchestra. Op. 30/ by David Ellis. — London: Weinberger, 1970. — 36p; 8vo.
Duration 11 min.
Unpriced
(B73-50679)

Feldman, Morton
The viola in my life (IV)/ by Morton Feldman. — New York; London: Universal, 1973. — 29p; 8vo.
Unpriced
(B73-50680)

Halffter, Cristobal
Fibonaciana: para flauta solista dos percusionistas y cuerda/ per Cristobal Halffter. — London: Universal, 1973. — 57p; 4to.
Unpriced
(B73-50681)

Hoddinott, Alun
The sun, the great luminary of the universe. Op.76/ by Alun Hoddinott. — London: Oxford University Press, 1972. — 32p; 8vo.
ISBN 0 19 364564 5 : £1.50
(B73-50257)

Holst, Gustav
Capriccio for orchestra/ by Gustav Holst; edited by Imogen Holst. — London: Faber Music, 1972. — 22p; 8vo.
Unpriced
(B73-50258)

Meyer, Ernst Hermann
Toccata für Orchester/ von Ernst Hermann Meyer. — Leipzig; [London]: Peters, 1972. — 29p; 4to.
Unpriced
(B73-50259)

Panufnik, Andrzej
Rhapsody for orchestra/ by Andrzej Panufnik. — London: Boosey and Hawkes, 1973. — 54p; 8vo.
Miniature score. — Reduced facsimile of the original edition.
£1.00
(B73-50682)

Penderecki, Krzystof
De natura sonoris no.2: per orchestra/ di Krzystof Penderecki. — Mainz; London: Schott, 1972. — 10p; fol.
Study score.
£2.00
(B73-50260)

Schurmann, Gerard
Attack and celebration: for orchestra/ by Gerard Schurmann. — Sevenoaks: Novello, 1973. — 50p; 4to.
Duration 8 min..
£1.25
(B73-51118)

Scriabin, Alexander
Reverie. Opus 24: for orchestra/ by Alexander Scriabin. — Frankfurt: Belaieff; London: Hinrichsen, 1972. — 16p; 8vo.
Miniature score.
£0.85
(B73-50683)

Sculthorpe, Peter
Sun music 3: for orchestra/ by Peter Sculthorpe. — London: Faber Music, 1973. — 32p; 4to.
Duration 13 mins.
Unpriced
(B73-50261)

Sculthorpe, Peter
Sun music II: for orchestra/ by Peter Sculthorpe. — London: Faber, 1973. — 19p; 4to.
Unpriced
(B73-51119)

Stevens, Bernard
Choriamb for orchestra. Op. 41/ by Bernard Stevens. — Sevenoaks: Novello, 1973. — 73p; 4to.
Duration 12 min.
£2.50
(B73-51120)

Stravinsky, Igor
Four Norwegian moods: for orchestra/ by Igor Stravinsky. — Mainz; London: Schott, 1973. — 52p; 8vo.
Unpriced
(B73-50262)

MP — WORKS FOR SOLO INSTRUMENT (S) & ORCHESTRA
MPQ — Piano & orchestra
Goehr, Alexander
Konzertstück. Op. 26: for piano and small orchestra/ by
Alexander Goehr. — London: Schott, 1973. — 53p; 4to.
£2.00

(B73-50684)

MPQF — Piano & orchestra. Concertos
Vaughan Williams, Ralph
[Concerto for piano]. Piano concerto: for one piano or two pianos
and orchestra/ by Ralph Vaughan William; [with the original solo
part and the version for two pianos made by Joseph Cooper in
collaboration with the composer]. — London: Oxford University
Press, 1972. — 85p; fol.
Duration 25 mins.
ISBN 0 19 369273 2 : £6.00

(B73-50685)

MPSF — Violin & orchestra. Concertos
Banks, Don
Concerto for violin and orchestra/ by Don Banks. — London:
Schott, 1973. — 85p; 8vo.
Miniature score.
£2.50

(B73-51121)

MPSR — Cello & orchestra
Goehr, Alexander
Romanza for cello and orchestra. Op.24/ by Alexander Goehr. —
London: Schott, 1973. — 63p; 8vo.
Miniature score.
£2.50

(B73-51122)

Hoddinott, Alun
Nocturnes and cadenzas. Op.62: for cello and orchestra/ by Alun
Hoddinott. — London: Oxford University Press, 1972. — 64p;
8vo.
Duration 23 mins.
ISBN 0 19 364497 5 : £2.00

(B73-50264)

MPTQF — Harp & Orchestra. Concertos
Mathias, William
[Concerto for harp. Op.50]. Harp concerto. Op.50/ by William
Mathias. — London: Oxford Unpversity Press, 1973. — 142p; 4to.
ISBN 0 19 365588 8 : £3.00

(B73-50686)

MPVRF — Flute & orchestra. Concertos
Arnold, Malcolm
[Concerto for flute, no.2. Op.111]. Flute concerto no 2. Op. 111/
by Malcolm Arnold. — London: Faber Music, 1973. — 40p; fol.
Duration 14 min.
£2.75

(B73-50687)

MPVTF — Oboe & orchestra. Concertos
Rosetti, Franz Anton
[Concerto for oboe in C major]. Konzert für Oboe und
Kammerorchester, C-Dur/ von Francesco Antonio Rosetti; zum
ersten Mal, herausgegeben von Rolf Julius Koch. — Frankfurt;
London: Peters, 1972. — 35p; 4to.
It was felt necessary in the quest of reviving the composition to curtail all
three movements considerably to conform to present-day conditions of
performance - Editor's note.
£3.00

(B73-50688)

MPVVF — Clarinet & orchestra. Concertos
Stamitz, Johann
[Concerto for clarinet in B flat major]. Concerto, B flat major: for
clarinet and orchestra/ by Johann Stamitz; edited by Walter
Lebermann. — London: Bärenreiter, 1972. — iv,32p; 8vo.
Miniature score.
£0.50

(B73-50265)

MPVVK/DW — Clarinet & orchestra. Arrangements. Songs, etc
Wagner, Richard
[Wesendonck Lieder. Träume]. Träume = Dreams: study for
'Tristan and Isolde'/ by Richard Wagner; arranged for B flat
clarinet and orchestra by David Stone. — London: Boosey and
Hawkes, 1972. — 4to.
Score (16p.) & 13 parts.
£0.75

(B73-50266)

MPWTF — Horn & orchestra. Concertos
Hoddinott, Alun
Concerto for horn and orchestra, Opus 65/ by Alun Hoddinott.
— London: Oxford University Press, 1973. — 90p; 8vo.
Duration 14 mins.
ISBN 0 19 364484 3 : £3.50

(B73-50267)

MR — WORKS FOR CHAMBER ORCHESTRA
MRE — Symphonies
Haydn, Joseph
Symphony no.69, in C major, 'Laudon'/ by Joseph Haydn; edited
by Gwilym Beechey. — London: Bärenreiter, 1972. — vi,51p; 8vo.
Miniature score.
Unpriced

(B73-50268)

MRF — Concertos
Handel, George Frideric
Concerto grosso in D major. Op. 6, no.5/ by George Frideric
Handel; edited by Michael Nyman. — London: Eulenburg, 1973.
— viii,33p; 8vo.
Miniature score.
£0.41

(B73-50689)

Handel, George Frideric
Concerto grosso in F major. Op. 6, no.2/ by George Frideric
Handel; edited by Michael Nyman. — London: Eulenburg, 1973.
— viii,28p; 8vo.
Miniature score.
£0.41

(B73-50690)

Handel, George Frideric
Concerto grosso in G major. Op. 6, no.1/ by George Frideric
Handel; edited by Michael Nyman. — London: Eulenburg, 1973.
— viii,28p; 8vo.
Miniature score.
£0.41

(B73-50691)

Handel, George Frideric
Concerto grosso in G minor. Op. 6, no.6/ by George Frideric
Handel; edited by Michael Nyman. — London: Eulenburg, 1973.
— ix,30p; 8vo.
Miniature score.
£0.41

(B73-50692)

MRJ — Miscellaneous works
Arne, Thomas Augustine
[The guardian outwitted. Overture]. Overture: for flutes, oboes,
bassoons, horns, strings and continuo/ by Thomas Augustine
Arne; edited by Gwilym Beechey. — London: Oxford University
Press, 1973. — 4to.
Score (16p.) & 11 parts. — Duration 10 min.
ISBN 0 19 361230 5 : £1.50

(B73-51123)

Greene, Maurice
Overture no.5 in D major/ by Maurice Greene; edited by Richard
Platt. — London: Eulenburg, 1973. — ix,14p; 8vo.
Miniature score.
£0.60

(B73-51124)

Greene, Maurice
Overture no.6 in E flat major/ by Maurice Greene; edited by
Richard Platt. — London: Eulenburg, 1973. — x,17p; 8vo.
Miniature score.
£0.60

(B73-51125)

Haubenstock-Ramati, Roman
Chants et prismes = Gesange und prismen/ par Roman
Haubenstock-Ramati. — Revised 1967. — London: Universal,
1969. — 52p; 8vo.
Duration 8 min - Miniature score.
Unpriced

(B73-51126)

Mozart, Wolfgang Amadeus
Galimathias musicum. KV32: 2 violins, viola, bass, 2 oboes, 2
horns, bassoon and cembalo/ by W.A. Mozart; edited by Alfred
Einstein. — New York; London: Peters, 1971. — 36p; 8vo.
£1.80

(B73-51127)

MRK/AAY — Arrangements. Collections
Binkerd, Gordon
Four chorale-preludes/ transcribed by Gordon Binkerd. — New
York; London: Boosey and Hawkes, 1973. — 4to.
Score (38p.) & 28 parts. — Contents: 1. Es ist das Heil uns kommer her;
composer unknown - 2. Allein zu dir, Herr Jesu Christ; by Johann Pachelbel
- 3. Es ist das Heil uns kommen her; by Dietrich Buxtehude - 4. In dulci
jubilo; by Johann Sebastian Bach.
Set A £6.00; Set B £8.00; Set C £10.00

(B73-50693)

N — CHAMBER MUSIC

N/AZ — Collected works of individual composers

Musica Britannica: a national collection of music. — London: Stainer and Bell.
Vol.37: Sterndale Bennett: piano and chamber music/ edited by Geoffrey Bush. — 1972. — xxiii,165p; fol.
Unpriced
Primary classification C/AYD

(B73-50002)

NU — WIND, STRINGS & KEYBOARD

NUNR — Quintets

Rawsthorne, Alan
Quintet for clarinet, horn, violin, cello and piano/ by Alan Rawsthorne. — London: Oxford University Press, 1972. — 22p; 4to.
ISBN 0 19 358572 3 : £1.50

(B73-50269)

NUNT — Trios

Dussek, Jan Ladislav
Notturno concertante, Op 68: for piano violin and horn (violin) or piano and violin/ by Jan Ladislav Dussek; edited by Christopher D.S. Field. — Cassel, London: Bärenreiter, 1972. — 4to.
Score (44p.) & 3 parts.
£3.30
Also classified at SPJ

(B73-50694)

NUPNQ — Sextets

Takemitsu, Teru
Valeria: per violino, violoncello, chitarra, organo elettrice e due offavani/ 'di Toru Takemitsu. — London: Universal, 1973. — 7p; fol.
Unpriced

(B73-51128)

NURNP — Flute, strings & keyboard. Septets

Jörns, Helge
7 Formen: für Flöte, Gitarre, Cembalo und Zupfoder Streichorchester oder Streichquartett/ von Helge Jörns. — Hamburg; London: Simrock, 1973. — 28ff; 4to.
Unpriced
Also classified at RXMPNURNT

(B73-51129)

NUTNTK/LF — Oboe, strings & keyboard. Trios. Concertos

Bach, Johann Sebastian
[Concerto for oboe, violin, string orchestra in C minor: arr]. Concerto in C minor for oboe, violin, strings and basso continuo/ by Johann Sebastian Bach; reduction for oboe, violin and keyboard by Jürgen Sommer. — Cassel; London: Bärenreiter, 1972. — 4to.
Reconstructed from BWV 1060. — Score (31p.) & 2 parts.
£2.25

(B73-50270)

NV — WIND & STRINGS

NVNQ — Sextets

Hewson, Richard
Miniatures: for wind trio and three violins/ by Richard Hewson. — London: Boosey and Hawkes, 1973. — 4to.
Score (6p) & 6 parts.
£1.25

(B73-50271)

NVNT — Trios

Lehmann, Hans Ulrich
Regions 3: for clarinet, trombone and violoncello/ by Hans Ulrich Lehmann. — Mainz: Ars viva; London: Schott, 1972. — 15p; 4to.
Unpriced

(B73-50272)

NVPNT — Woodwind & strings. Trios

Huber, Klaus
Sabeth: for alto flute (G), cor anglais (F), (viola), and harp/ by Klaus Huber. — Mainz: Ars viva, 1973. — 4to.
Score (27p) & part.
£5.00

(B73-50695)

NVTNS — Oboe & strings. Quartets

Vanhal, Jan
[Quartet for oboe & strings. Op.7, no.5]. Quartet. Opus 7, no.5: for oboe, violin and violoncello/ by Jan Wanhal; edited by D.M. Mulgan. — London: Musica rara, 1972. — 4pt; 4to.
Unpriced

(B73-50273)

Vanhal, Jan
[Quartet for oboe & strings. Op.7, no.6]. Quartet. Opus 7, no.6: for oboe, violin and violoncello/ by Jan Wanhal; edited by D.M. Mulgan. — London: Musica rara, 1972. — 4pt; 4to.
Unpriced

(B73-50274)

Vanhal, Jan
[Quartet for oboe & strings. Op.7, no.4]. Quartet. Opus 7, no.4: for oboe, violin, viola and violoncello/ by Jan Wanhal; edited by D.M. Mulgan. — London: Musica rara, 1972. — 4pt; 4to.
Unpriced

(B73-50275)

NVVQNR — Clarinet in A & strings. Quintets

Meyer, Ernst Hermann
[Quintet for clarinet in A & strings]. Quintett für Klarinette in A, zwei Violinen, Viola und Violoncello/ von Ernst Hermann Meyer. — Leipzig: Peters; [London]: [Hinrichsen], 1971. — 69p; 8vo.
Miniature score.
£1.20

(B73-50276)

NWNQK/AH/AYG(XG101) — Sextets. Arrangements. Dances. Collections. Hungary, 1800-1900

Grabocz, Miklos
Alte ungarische Tanze des 18 Jahrhunderts. — Cassel; London: Bärenreiter.
Score (13p.) & 6 parts.
für Bläserquintett und Cembalo/ von Miklos Grabocz. — 1972. — 4to.
Unpriced

(B73-50696)

NWNT — Trios

Pezel, Johann
[Bicinia variorum instrumentum, no.75]. Bicinia 75 for clarino (trumpet in C), bassoon and continuo/ by Johann Pezel; [edited by] Robert Paul Block. — London: Musica rara, 1972. — 4to.
Score (18p.) & 4 parts.
Unpriced

(B73-50277)

NWPNR — Woodwind & keyboard. Quintets

Danzi, Franz
[Quintet for woodwind & piano quintet in D major. Op.54, no.2]. Quintet in D major. Opus 54, no.2: for piano, flute, oboe, clarinet, and bassoon/ by Franz Danzi; [edited by] Georg Meerwein. — London: Musica rara, 1972. — 4to.
Score (57p.) & 4 parts.
£3.00

(B73-50278)

Danzi, Franz
[Quintet for woodwind & piano quintet in F major. Op.53, no.1]. Quintet in F major. Opus 53, no.1: for piano, flute, oboe, clarinet and bassoon/ by Franz Danzi; [edited by] George Meerwein. — London: Musica rara, 1972. — 4to.
Score (52p.) & 4 parts.
Unpriced

(B73-50279)

NX — STRINGS & KEYBOARD

Purcell, Henry
[Instrumental works. Selections]. Music for strings and keyboard/ by Henry Purcell; edited under the supervision of the Purcell Society by Thurston Dart. — Sevenoaks: Novello, 1969. — 4to.
Scoer (46p) & 4 parts.
£0.80

(B73-51130)

NX/AZ — Strings & keyboard. Collected works of individual composers

Schubert, Franz
[Works, strings and piano]. Complete chamber music for pianoforte and strings/ by Franz Schubert; edited by Ignaz Brull. — New York: Dover; London: Constable, 1973. — 192p; 4to.
An unabridged and unaltered republication of Seriss 7 of Franz Schubert's Werke Kritisch durchgesehene Gessamtausgabe, originally published Leipzig, Breitkopf and Härtel, 1886.
ISBN 0 486 21527 x : £2.25

(B73-51131)

NXNSG — Quartets. Suites

Muffat, Georg
[Florilegium.. Suites]. Suites from the 'Florilegium': for four or five parts (string or wind instruments)/ by Georg Muffat; edited by Waldemar Woehl. — Cassel; London: Bärenreiter, 1972. — 4to.
Score (20p.) & 5 parts. — Contents: Suite no.1 in D major - Suite no.2 in G minor.
£1.95
Also classified at UNSG

(B73-50280)

NXNT — Trios

Grace, Norah
Sketches for three: for violin, cello and piano/ by Norah Grace. — Manchester: Forsyth, 1973. — 4to.
Score (12p.) & 2 parts. — Contents: Andante - Scherzo - Larghetto.
Unpriced

(B73-50281)

Meyer, Ernst Hermann
Trio 1948: für Violine, Violoncello und Klavier/ von Ernst
Hermann Meyer. — Leipzig; [London]: Peters, 1972. — 4to.
Score (28p.) & 2 parts.
Unpriced

(B73-50282)

Rubbra, Edmund
[Trio for violin, cello & piano, no.2. Op. 138]. Piano trio. Op. 138:
for piano, violin and violoncello/ by Edmund Rubbra. — South
Croydon: Lengnick, 1973. — 4to.
Score (27p.) & 2 parts.
£1.00

(B73-51132)

NYD — WIND, STRINGS, KEYBOARD & PERCUSSION
NYDPNM — Woodwind, string, keyboard & percussion. Nonets
Bozay, Attila
Sorozat = Series. Op.19: for chamber ensemble/ by Attila Bozay.
— London: Boosey and Hawkes, 1972. — 36p; 4to.
Duration 12 min.
£1.50

(B73-50283)

NYDR — Flute, strings, keyboard & percussion
Miroglio, Francis
Réfractions/ von Francis Miroglio. — London: Universal, 1973.
— 6ff; obl. 4to.
Unpriced

(B73-51133)

NYDS — Recorders, strings, keyboard & percussion
Hand, Colin
Divertimento for recorders strings piano and percussion/ by Colin
Hand. — London: Schott, 1973. — obl.4to.
Score (54p.) & 10 parts.
£2.50

(B73-50697)

NYE — WIND, STRINGS & PERCUSSION
NYEH/G/AY — Folk dances. Collections
Werdin, Eberhard
Tanze der Volker: ein Spielbuch fur Blas-, Streich-, Zupf- und
Schlaginstrumente mit Improvisations- Möglichkeiten. — Mainz;
London: Schott.
Heft 2. — 1973. — 23p; 8vo. —
£1.00

(B73-50698)

NYENQ — Sextets
Bennett, Richard Rodney
Commedia 1: for six players/ by Richard Rodney Bennett. —
London: Universal, 1973. — 30p; 8vo.
Unpriced

(B73-50699)

**NYESK/AYVS — Recorders, strings & percussion. Arrangements.
Collections. China**
Picken, Laurence
Ancient Chinese tunes: nine pieces arranged for recorders, tuned
percussion, rhythmic percussion, plucked strings, guitar and
optional clarinet in B flat/ by Laurence Picken and Kenneth Pont.
— London: Oxford University Press, 1973. — 38p; 4to.
Score (38p) & 4 parts.
ISBN 0 19 344895 5 : £1.50

(B73-50700)

NYF — WIND, KEYBOARD & PERCUSSION
NYFSHVKK — Recorders, keyboard & percussion. Rumbas
Foster, Anthony
Carol and rumba for recorders, (descant and treble), percussion
and piano/ by Anthony Foster. — London: Oxford University
Press, 1973. — 12p; 4to.
Score (12p.) & 4 parts.
ISBN 0 19 356554 4 : Unpriced

(B73-50701)

NYFXP — Brass, keyboard & percussion
Schnebel, Dieter
Für Stimmen (... missa est)/ von Dieter Schnebel. — Mainz;
London: Schott.
Nr.1,2: Choralvorspiele 1/2, für Orgel, Nebeninstrumente und Tonband. —
1971. — 48p; obl.fol.
Unpriced

(B73-50284)

NYL — KEYBOARD & PERCUSSION
Dainton, Marie Cleeve
Songs for the primaries (with percussion)/ by Marie C. Dainton.
— London: British and Continental, 1972. — 11p; 4to.
£0.30

(B73-50702)

NYLNS — Quartets
Fetler, Paul
Cycles: for percussion (three players) and piano/ by Paul Fetler.
— Mainz; London: Schott, 1973. — 30p; 4to.
£2.40

(B73-51134)

PWNU — KEYBOARD DUETS
PWNUF — Duets. Concertos
Soler, Antonio
[Concertos for 2 keyboard instruments, nos 1-6]. VI conciertos de
dos organos obligados: oder zwei Cembali, zwei Clavichorde, zwei
Klaviere, eine Orgel und ein Cembalo/ von P. Antonio Soler;
herausgegeben von M.S. Kastner. — Mainz; London: Schott.
Band 2. — 1972. — 67p; 4to.
£1.70

(B73-51135)

Soler, Antonio
[Concertos for 2 keyboard instruments, nos.1-6]. VI conciertos de
dos organos obligados: oder zwei und ein Cembalo/ von P.
Antonio Soler; herausgegeben von M.S. Kastner. — Mainz;
London: Schott.
Band 1. — 1972. — 63p; 4to.
£1.70

(B73-51136)

PWP — KEYBOARD SOLOS
PWP/Y — Fugues
Kirnberger, Johann Philipp
[Eight fugues for keyboard]. Acht Fugen für Cembalo oder Orgel/
von Johann Philipp Kirnberger; herausgegeben von Hugo Ruf und
Hans Bemmann. — Mainz; London: Schott, 1973. — 29p; 4to.
£1.80

(B73-51137)

PWPJ — Miscellaneous works
Bach, Johann Sebastian
Inventions and symphonies. [S.772-801]/ by Johann Sebastian
Bach; edited by Georg von Dadelsen. — Cassel; London:
Bärenreiter, 1972. — viii,79p; 4to.
With appendix.
£1.50

(B73-50285)

Bach, Johann Sebastian
[Selections]. Bach/ selected and edited by Henry Duke. —
London: Freeman, 1973. — 28p; 4to.
Unpriced

(B73-50286)

PWPK/CF — Arrangements. Operetta
Sullivan, *Sir* Arthur Seymour
[Operettas. Selections: arr]. Gems of Sullivan/ edited [and
arranged] for piano and organ by Arnold Loxam. — Leeds:
Regina Music.
Vol.1. — 1972. — 24p; 4to.
Unpriced

(B73-50287)

PWPK/CM — Arrangements. Musical plays
Taylor, John
[The water babies. Selections: arr]. The water babies: simplified
children's selection for easy piano/organ/guitar, etc/ music and
lyrics by John Taylor. — London: Chappell, 1973. — 18p; 4to.
£0.80
Also classified at TSPMK/CM

(B73-51138)

Q — PIANO
Q/AC — Tutors
Waterman, Fanny
Piano lessons/ with Fanny Waterman and Marion Harewood. —
London: Faber Music.
The series originally began with the overall title, 'Second year piano lessons'.
Book 2. — 1973. — 72p; 4to.
Unpriced

(B73-51139)

Book 3. — 1973. — 76p; 4to.
Unpriced

(B73-51140)

Waterman, Fanny
Second year piano lessons/ with Fanny Waterman and Marion
Harewood. — London: Faber Music.
Book 1. — 1969. — 76p; 4to.
Unpriced

(B73-51141)

Q/AF — Exercises
Czerny, Carl
[Passagen-Übungen. Op.26.. Selections]. 101 exercises: for piano/
by Carl Czerny; edited by Christopher Gibbons. — London:
Chappell, 1973. — 47p; 4to.
Unpriced

(B73-50288)

Kirkby-Mason, Barbara
Primary grade book for piano/ by Barbara Kirkby-Mason. —
London: Bosworth, 1973. — 15p; 4to.
Unpriced

(B73-50703)

Q/AL — Examinations
Associated Board of the Royal Schools of Music
Pianoforte examinations, 1974. — London: Associated Board of
the Royal Schools of Music.
Grade 1: Lists A and B (primary). — 1974. — 12p; 4to. —
£0.35

(B73-51142)

Grade 2: Lists A and B (elementary). — 1974. — 14p; 4to. —
£0.35

(B73-51143)

Grade 3: Lists A and B (transitional). — 1974. — 12p; 4to. —
Unpriced

(B73-51144)

Grade 4: Lists A and B (lower). — 1974. — 15p; 4to. —
£0.35

(B73-51145)

Grade 5: List A (higher). — 1974. — 10p; 4to. —
£0.35

(B73-51146)

Grade 5: List B (higher). — 1974. — 13p; 4to. —
£0.35

(B73-51147)

Grade 6: List A (intermediate). — 1974. — 15p; 4to. —
£0.35

(B73-51148)

Grade 6: List B (intermediate). — 1974. — 17p; 4to. —
£0.35

(B73-51149)

Grade 7: List A (advanced). — 1974. — 17p; 4to. —
£0.35

(B73-51150)

Grade 7: List B (advanced). — 1974. — 18p; 4to. —
£0.35

(B73-51151)

Guildhall School of Music and Drama
Pianoforte examinations. — South Croydon: Lengnick.
Grade 1. — 1973. — 10p; 4to. —
£0.35

(B73-51152)

Grade 2. — 1973. — 10p; 4to. —
£0.35

(B73-51153)

Grade 3. — 1973. — 12p; 4to. —
£0.35

(B73-51154)

Grade 4. — 1973. — 14p; 4to. —
£0.35

(B73-51155)

Introductory. — 1973. — 7p; 4to. —
£0.35

(B73-51156)

Junior. — 1973. — 10p; 4to. —
£0.35

(B73-51157)

Preliminary. — 1973. — 7p; 4to. —
£0.35

(B73-51158)

Q/EG — Sight reading
London College of Music
Examinations in pianoforte playing and singing: sight reading
tests, sight singing tests as set throughout 1972: grades 1-8 and
diplomas/ London College of Music. — London: Ashdown, 1973.
— 15p; 4to.
£0.30
Also classified at CB/EG

(B73-50289)

QNU — TWO PIANOS, 4 HANDS
QNUK — Arrangements
Bush, Alan
[Variations, nocturne and finale on an old English sea song for
piano and orchestra. Op.60: arr]. Variations, nocturne and finale
on an old English sea song: for piano and orchestra. Op.60/ by
Alab Bush; reduction for two pianos by David Lyon. —
Sevenoaks: Novello, 1973. — 65p; 4to.
£1.75

(B73-50290)

Creston, Paul
[Fantasy for piano & orchestra. Op.32: arr]. Fantasy, Op. 32: for
piano and orchestra/ by Paul Creston: two-piano score. — New
York; London: Schirmer, 1972. — 33p; 4to.
Two copies.
Unpriced

(B73-51159)

QNUK/LF — Arrangements. Concertos
Stevenson, Ronald
[Concerto for piano, no.1, 'Faust triptych': arr]. Piano concerto,
no.1/ by Ronald Stevenson; arranged for two pianos. —
Sevenoaks: Novello, 1973. — 66p; 4to.
*Another version of this work exists for piano solo under the title, 'Prelude,
Fugue and Fantasy'.*
£1.75

(B73-50704)

QNV — ONE PIANO, 4 HANDS
Johnson, Thomas Arnold
Fiesta piano duet/ by Thomas A. Johnson. — London: Bosworth,
1973. — 7p; 4to.
£0.25

(B73-51160)

Clementi, Muzio
[Duettinos for piano. Wotquenne 24-5]. Two duettinos: for piano,
four hands/ by Muzio Clementi; transcribed from the original
autograph by Pietro Spada. — New York; London: Schirmer,
1972. — 35p; 4to.
Unpriced

(B73-51161)

Hamilton, Alasdair
Scherzo for piano duet, 'The keys of Canterbury'/ by Alasdair
Hamilton. — Wendover: Roberton, 1973. — 11p; 4to.
£0.40

(B73-51162)

Johnson, Thomas Arnold
Caprice: piano duet/ by Thomas A. Johnson. — London:
Freeman, 1973. — 5p; 4to.
£0.20

(B73-50705)

Johnson, Thomas Arnold
Seven easy duets for piano/ by Thomas A. Johnson. — London:
Freeman, 1973. — 15p; 4to.
£0.20

(B73-50706)

Longmire, John
Trotting to the fair: pianoforte duet/ by John Longmire. —
London: Bosworth, 1973. — 7p; 4to.
£0.20

(B73-51163)

Parfrey, Raymond
Double bill: piano duet/ by Raymond Parfrey. — Harrow:
Composer to Player Edition, 1969. — 2p; 4to.
Unpriced

(B73-50707)

Parfrey, Raymond
A long trail: piano duet/ by Raymond Parfrey. — Harrow:
Composer to Player Edition, 1969. — 2p; 4to.
Unpriced

(B73-50708)

QNVH — Dances
Parfrey, Raymond
A dance from the mountains: piano duet/ by Raymond Parfrey.
— Harrow: Composer to Player Edition, 1969. — 2p; 4to.
Unpriced

(B73-50709)

QNVHVH — Polkas
Johnson, Thomas Arnold
Polka: piano duet/ by Thomas A. Johnson. — London: Freeman,
1973. — 5p; 4to.
£0.20

(B73-50710)

QNVHVL — Sarabandes
Johnson, Thomas Arnold
Sarabande: piano duet/ by Thomas A. Johnson. — London:
Freeman, 1973. — 5p; 4to.
£0.20

(B73-50711)

QNVHVR — Tangos
Veal, Arthur
Tango: piano duet/ by Arthur Veal. — London: Ashdown, 1973.
— 9p; 4to.
£0.30

(B73-51164)

QNVHW — Waltzes
Johnson, Thomas Arnold
Valse: piano duet/ by Thomas A. Johnson. — London: Freeman,
1973. — 7p; 4to.
£0.20

(B73-50712)

Johnson, Thomas Arnold

Valsette: piano duet/ by Thomas A. Johnson. — London:
Freeman, 1973. — 5p; 4to.
£0.20

(B73-50713)

QNVK/AAY — Arrangements. Collections

Vaczi, Karoly

Piano duet music for beginners/ edited by Karoly Vaczi. —
London: Boosey and Hawkes, 1972. — 39p; 4to.
£0.85

(B73-50714)

Veal, Arthur

The Queen's garland: pieces by Elizabethan composers/ arranged
for piano duet by Arthur Veal. — London: Ashdown, 1973. —
13p; 4to.
Unpriced

(B73-51165)

QNVK/AH/G/AYK — Arrangements. Folk dances. Collections. Spain

Kettering, Eunice Lea

Three Spanish folk dances: for piano, four hands/ arranged by
Eunice Lea Kettering. — New York; London: Schirmer, 1972. —
15p; 4to.
Unpriced

(B73-50291)

QNVQ — ONE PIANO, 6 HANDS

Parfrey, Raymond

Southern sun: piano trio/ by Raymond Parfrey. — Harrow:
Composer to Player Edition, 1969. — 3p; 4to.
Unpriced

(B73-50715)

Enoch, Yvonne

Six 'nonsense' songs: for piano trio, [one, two or three players]/ by
Yvonne Enoch. — London: Bosworth.
Book 1: Nos.1 to 3. — 1972. — 9p; 4to. —
£0.25

(B73-50292)

Book 2: Nos.4 to 6. — 1972. — 9p; 4to. —
£0.25

(B73-50293)

QP — PIANO SOLOS
QP/AF — Exercises

Nikiprowetzky, Tolia

Treize etudes pour piano/ par Tolia Nikiprowetzky. — London:
Boosey and Hawkes, 1973. — 31p; fol.
£1.75

(B73-51166)

QP/AY — Collections

Steinbrenner, Wilfried

The showbooth for bold pianists/ the music chosen by Wilfried
Steinbrenner and Friedrich Wanek. — Mainz; London: Schott,
1972. — 31p; 4to.
Two of the pieces are for four hands.
£1.40

(B73-50716)

QP/AZ — Collected works of individual composers

Liszt, Franz

[Works, piano]. Piano works/ by Franz Liszt. — Cassel; London:
Bärenreiter.
Vol.3: Hungarian rhapsodies 1, nos.1-9/ edited by Zoltan Gardonyi and
Istvan Szelenyi. — 1972. — xviii,115p; 4to.
£2.40

(B73-50717)

Musica Britannica: a national collection of music. — London:
Stainer and Bell.
Vol.37: Sterndale Bennett: piano and chamber music/ edited by Geoffrey
Bush. — 1972. — xxiii,165p; fol.
Unpriced
Primary classification C/AYD

(B73-50002)

Schumann, Robert

[Works, piano]. Piano music of Robert Schumann/ edited by
Clara Schumann. — New York: Dover; London: Constable.
Series 1. — 1972. — 274p; 4to.
ISBN 0 486 21459 1 : £2.25

(B73-50310)

Series 2. — 1972. — 272p; 4to.
ISBN 0 486 21461 3 : £2.25

(B73-50311)

QP/D/AY — Composition. Collections

Grindea, Carola

We make music/ by Carola Grindea and her pupils. — London:
Kahn and Averill, 1972. — 64p; obl. 4to.
ISBN 0 900707 14 3 : £0.75

(B73-50294)

QP/LF/JS/AY — Christmas. Television. Collections

Sing a song for Christmas: a selection from the Southern
Independent Television series. — London: High-Fye, 1973. — 22p;
4to.
£1.25

(B73-51167)

QP/NM — Rhythm

Last, Joan

Time twisters: five contrapuntal pieces for piano, each with a
rhythmic twist/ by Joan Last. — London: Oxford University
Press, 1972. — 8p; 4to.
ISBN 0 19 373146 0 : £0.30

(B73-50295)

QP/T — Variations

Hudes, Eric

Nine variants for piano/ by Eric Hudes. — London: Thames,
1972. — 17p; 4to.
Unpriced

(B73-50718)

Hudes, Eric

Variations for piano/ by Eric Hudes. — London: Thames, 1972.
— 27p; fol.
Unpriced

(B73-50719)

Rawsthorne, Alan

Theme and four studies/ by Alan Rawsthorne. — London: Oxford
University Press, 1973. — 15p; 4to.
ISBN 0 19 373571 7 : Unpriced

(B73-50296)

QPE — Sonatas

Applebaum, David

[Sonata for piano]. Piano sonata/ by David Applebaum. —
London: Chester, 1972. — 16p; fol.
Unpriced

(B73-50297)

Gutche, Gene

[Sonata for piano. Op.32, no.2]. Sonata. Opus 32, no.2: for piano/
by Gene Gutche. — New York: Highgate Press; London:
Galliard, 1973. — 23p; 4to.
Unpriced

(B73-50720)

Mozart, Wolfgang Amadeus

[Sonata for piano in A major. K.331]. Sonata in A. K.331/ by
Mozart; edited by Stanley Sadie, fingering and notes on
performance by Denis Matthews. — London: Associated Board of
the Royal Schools of Music, 1972. — 25p; 4to.
£0.35

(B73-50721)

Mozart, Wolfgang Amadeus

[Sonata for piano in C major. K.309]. Sonata in C/ by Mozart;
edited by Stanley Sadie, fingering by Denis Matthews. — London:
Associated Board of the Royal Schools of Music, 1973. — 25p;
4to.
£0.35

(B73-51168)

Mozart, Wolfgang Amadeus

[Sonata for piano in D major. K.576]. Sonata in D. K.576/ by
Mozart; edited by Stanley Sadie, fingering and notes on
performance by Denis Matthews. — London: Associated Board of
the Royal Schools of Music, 1971. — 21p; 4to.
£0.35

(B73-50722)

Mozart, Wolfgang Amadeus

[Sonata for piano in F major. K.332]. Sonata in F. K.332/ by
Mozart; edited by Stanley Sadie, fingering and notes on
performance by Denis Matthews. — London: Associated Board of
the Royal Schools of Music, 1973. — 26p; 4to.
£0.35

(B73-50723)

Mozart, Wolfgang Amadeus

[Sonata for piano in F major. K.533]. Sonata in F. K.533/ by
Mozart; edited by Stanley Sadie, fingering and notes on
performances by Denis Matthews. — London: Associated Board
of the Royal Schools of Music, 1971. — 27p; 4to.
£0.35

(B73-50724)

QPEM — Sonatinas

Clementi, Muzio
Sonatinas for piano. Opus 36/ by Muzio Clementi; edited by
Christopher Gibbons. — London: Chappell, 1972. — 31p; 4to.
Unpriced

(B73-50298)

Schroeder, Hermann
[Sonatina for piano, no.3, in C minor]. Sonatina no.3 in C minor:
piano solo/ by Hermann Schroeder. — Hamburg; London:
Simrock, 1972. — 11p; 4to.
Unpriced

(B73-50725)

QPG — Suites

Bernstein, Seymour
Birds: a suite of eight impressionistic studies for piano solo/ by
Seymour Bernstein. — New York; London: Schroeder and
Gunther, 1972. — 11p; 4to.
Unpriced

(B73-51169)

Parfrey, Raymond
Suite on three pages: piano solo/ by Raymond Parfrey. —
Harrow: Composer to Player Edition, 1969. — 3p; 4to.
Unpriced

(B73-50726)

QPH — Dances

Barrell, Joyce
Tanzmusik. Op.33: for solo piano/ by Joyce Barrell. — London:
Thames, 1973. — 14p; fol.
Unpriced

(B73-50727)

Hunt, Reginald
Three rhythmic pianoforte pieces/ by Reginald Hunt. — London:
Ashdown, 1973. — 8p; 4to.
Contents: Fandango - Musette - Hornpipe.
£0.30

(B73-51170)

Judd, Margaret
Queen Elizabeth's dances: for piano/ by Margaret Judd. —
London: Bosworth, 1973. — 7p; 4to.
£0.30

(B73-51171)

QPH/H — Dances for dancing

Johnston, Beryl
Twelve Scottish country dances/ by Beryl Johnston; dances
devised by members of the Birmingham Branch Royal Scottish
Country Dance Society. — Birmingham: Royal Scottish Country
Dancing Society (Birmingham Branch), 1973. — 20p; 4to.
Unpriced

(B73-51172)

QPHVHM — Polonaises

Wagner, Richard
Polonaise for piano/ by Richard Wagner; edited by Arthur D.
Walker. — Sevenoaks: Novello, 1973. — 3p; 4to.
£0.27

(B73-50728)

QPJ — Miscellaneous works

Anson, George
Two Chinese sketches: for piano solo/ by George Anson. — New
York; London: Schroeder and Gunther, 1972. — 5p; 4to.
Contents: 1. Love song 2. Street scene.
Unpriced

(B73-50299)

Beethoven, Ludwig van
[Selections]. Beethoven/ selected and edited by Henry Duke. —
London: Freeman, 1973. — 28p; 4to.
Unpriced

(B73-50300)

Burgmüller, Friedrich
[Études faciles et progressives. Op.100]. 25 easy and progressive
studies: for piano/ by Friedrich Burgmüller; edited by Christopher
Gibbons. — London: Chappell, 1973. — 35p; 4to.
Unpriced

(B73-50301)

Chopin, Fréderic
[Selections]. Chopin/ selected and edited by Henry Duke. —
London: Freeman, 1973. — 28p; 4to.
Unpriced

(B73-50302)

Chow Shu-San
Chinese short pieces: for piano/ by Chow Shu-San. — London:
Paterson, 1973. — 16p; 4to.
Unpriced

(B73-50729)

Copland, Aaron
Night thoughts. (Homage to Ives): piano solo/ by Aaron Copland.
— London: Boosey and Hawkes, 1973. — 6p; 4to.
£0.60

(B73-51173)

Debussy, Claude
Estampes: piano solo/ by Claude Debussy; edited by H.
Swarsenski. — London: Peters, 1972. — 26p; 4to.
Unpriced

(B73-50303)

Debussy, Claude
[Prelude for piano. Book1, no.6]. Des pas sur la neige =
Footprints in the snow/ by Claude Debussy; edited by H.
Swarsenski. — London: Peters, 1973. — 3p; 4to.
Unpriced

(B73-51174)

George, Jon
Mediaeval pageant: easy piano pieces/ by Jon George. — London:
Oxford University Press, 1972. — 15p; 4to.
ISBN 0 19 372719 6 : £0.40

(B73-50730)

Goehr, Alexander
Nonomiya. Op 27: for piano/ by Alexander Goehr. — London:
Schott, 1973. — 13p; 4to.
£0.80

(B73-50731)

Kochan, Günter
Fünf Klavierstücke/ von Günter Kochan. — Leipzig; [London]:
Peters, 1972. — 11p; 4to.
Unpriced

(B73-50304)

Liszt, Franz
Liszt: a selection/ edited and annotated by Gordon Green. —
London: Oxford University Press, 1973. — 63p; 4to.
ISBN 0 19 373217 3 : Unpriced

(B73-50732)

Longmire, John
Paradise islands: 3 miniatures for piano/ by John Longmire. —
London: Bosworth, 1973. — 7p; 4to.
£0.20

(B73-51175)

McCabe, John
Gaudí: study no.3, for piano/ by John McCabe. — Sevenoaks:
Novello, 1973. — 25p; 4to.
Duration 15 mins.
£1.00

(B73-50305)

Nieman, Alfred
Five adventures: for piano/ by Alfred Nieman. — London: Boosey
and Hawkes, 1973. — 8p; 4to.
£0.40

(B73-50308)

Parfrey, Raymond
A Highland tale: piano solo/ by Raymond Parfrey. — Harrow:
Composer to Player Edition, 1969. — 2p; 4to.
Unpriced

(B73-50733)

Parfrey, Raymond
Autumn song: piano solo/ by Raymond Parfrey. — Harrow:
Composer to Player Edition, 1969. — 4p; 4to.
Unpriced

(B73-50734)

Parfrey, Raymond
Background of brass: piano solo/ by Raymond Parfrey. —
Harrow: Composer to Player Edition, 1969. — 5p; 4to.
Unpriced

(B73-50735)

Parfrey, Raymond
A flute from afar: piano solo/ by Raymond Parfrey. — Harrow:
Composer to Player Edition, 1969. — 4p; 4to.
Unpriced

(B73-50736)

Parfrey, Raymond
Modes and modulations: piano solo/ by Raymond Parfrey. —
Harrow: Composer to Player Edition, 1969. — 2p; 4to.
Unpriced

(B73-50737)

Parfrey, Raymond
Night spot: piano solo/ by Raymond Parfrey. — Harrow:
Composer to Player Edition, 1969. — 2p; 4to.
Unpriced

(B73-50738)

Parfrey, Raymond
November sunlight: piano solo/ by Raymond Parfrey. — Harrow:
Composer to Player Edition, 1969. — 2p; 4to.
Unpriced

(B73-50739)

Parfrey, Raymond
On a Brittany beach: piano solo/ by Raymond Parfrey. —
Harrow: Composer to Player Edition, 1969. — 2p; 4to.
Unpriced

(B73-50740)

Parfrey, Raymond
Salt caked smokestack: piano solo/ by Raymond Parfrey. —
Harrow: Composer to Player Edition, 1969. — 4p; 4to.
Unpriced

(B73-50741)

Parfrey, Raymond
Serenade in pastels: piano solo/ by Raymond Parfrey. — Harrow:
Composer to Player Edition, 1969. — 2p; 4to.
Unpriced

(B73-50742)

Parfrey, Raymond
Toy bandstand: piano solo/ by Raymond Parfrey. — Harrow:
Composer to Player Edition, 1969. — 2p; 4to.
Unpriced

(B73-50743)

Parfrey, Raymond
Two little chorales: piano solo/ by Raymond Parfrey. — Harrow:
Composer to Player Edition, 1969. — 2p; 4to.
Unpriced

(B73-50744)

Parfrey, Raymond
Youth at the helm: piano solo/ by Raymond Parfrey. — Harrow:
Composer to Player Edition, 1969. — 4p; 4to.
Unpriced

(B73-50745)

Schumann, Robert
[Kinderscenen. Op.15]. Scenes from childhood: for piano/ by
Robert SChumann; edited by Christopher Gibbons. — London:
Chappell, 1973. — 19p; 4to.
Unpriced

(B73-50309)

Scriabin, Alexander
The complete preludes & études for pianoforte solo/ by Alexander
Scriabin; edited by K.N. Igumno and V.I. Mil'shteyn. — New
York; Dover; London: Constable, 1973. — 6,250p; 4to.
Originally published Moscow, Izdatel'stvo Muzyka, 1966-1967.
ISBN 0 486 22919 x : £2.00

(B73-51176)

Sculthorpe, Peter
Night pieces: for piano/ by Peter Sculthorpe. — London: Faber,
1973. — 8p; 4to.
Unpriced

(B73-51177)

Spies, Claudio
Bagatelle: piano solo/ by Claudio Spies. — New York; London:
Boosey and Hawkes, 1973. — 4p; 4to.
£0.75

(B73-50746)

Stoker, Richard
Fireworks: 6 little pieces for piano/ by Richard Stoker. —
London: Ashdown, 1973. — 8p; 4to.
£0.30

(B73-51178)

Taylor, Colin
Whimsies: four miniatures for piano/ by Colin Taylor. — London:
Boosey and Hawkes.
Second set. — 1973. — 14p; 4to. —
£0.60

(B73-50747)

Tcherepnin, Alexander
Twelve preludes for piano. Opus 85/ by Alexander Tcherepnin. —
New ed./ edited by the composer. — Frankfurt: Belaieff;
[London]: [Hinrichsen], 1972. — 20p; 4to.
£1.40

(B73-50312)

Tomlinson, Geoffrey R
Ten miniatures for young pianists/ by Geoffrey R. Tomlinson. —
Manchester: Forsyth, 1972. — 13p; 4to.
Unpriced

(B73-51179)

Westbrook, Francis
Toccata, 'Hommage ⌠a Ravel: piano solo/ by Francis Westbrook.
— Frankfurt; London: Peters, 1973. — 15p; 4to.
Unpriced

(B73-50748)

Wilson, Robert Barclay
Pop-song without words: piano/ by Robert Barclay Wilson. —
London: Cramer, 1973. — 3p; 4to.
Unpriced

(B73-51180)

Wurzburger, Walter
Klavierstück: for solo piano/ by Walter Wurzburger. — London:
Thames, 1973. — 13p; 4to.
Unpriced

(B73-50313)

QPK — Arrangements
Bach, Johann Sebastian
[Selections]. Bach/ transcribed and simplified by Cyril C.
Dalmaine. — London: Warren and Phillips, 1972. — 18p; 4to.
Unpriced

(B73-50314)

Grieg, Edvard
[Selections]. Grieg/ transcribed and simplified by Cyril C.
Dalmaine. — London: Warren and Phillips, 1972. — 22p; 4to.
Unpriced

(B73-50315)

Zipoli, Domenico
[Sonate d'intavolatura for organ. Op. 1. Parte 1. Toccata: arr].
Toccata/ by Zipoli; arranged for piano solo by Ginastera. —
London: Boosey and Hawkes, 1973. — 10p; fol.
£0.75

(B73-51181)

QPK/AGM/JS — Arrangements. Marches. Television
Isaac, Anthony
Warship: theme from the B B C - TV series/ composed and
arranged by Anthony Issac. — London: Valentine, 1973. — 4p;
4to.
£0.20

(B73-50749)

QPK/AH/AYDL — Arrangements. Dances. Collections. Scotland
Gordon, Rob
Rob Gordon's book of Scottish music/ arranged by Ken
Macaulay-Jones. — Glasgow: Kerr, 1970. — 15p; 4to.
Unpriced

(B73-50316)

Hunter, James
Kerr's thistle collection: reels, strathspeys, jigs, hornpipes,
marches/ collected and arranged by James Hunter. — Glasgow:
Kerr, 1972. — 48p; 4to.
Unpriced

(B73-50317)

QPK/AHM/AY — Arrangements. Ballet. Collections
Knight, Judyth
Ballet and its music/ arrangements for piano by Judyth Knight.
— London: Schott, 1973. — 111p; fol.
ISBN 0 901938 03 3 : £3.95

(B73-51182)

QPK/AT/AYDL — Arrangements. Variations. Collections. Scotland
Mackay, Angus
A collection of ancient piobaireachd or highland pipe music/
[collected] by Angus Mackay. — Wakefield: E.P. Publishing,
1972. — [192]p; fol.
Original edition of 1838 republished.
ISBN 0 85409 821 6 : £3.00
Primary classification VY/T/AYDL

(B73-50436)

QPK/CC/AY — Arrangements. Opera. Collections
Moore, Elizabeth
Second book of music for the ballet class/ chosen and arranged by
Elizabeth Moore. — London: Cramer, 1973. — 24p; 4to.
£0.48

(B73-51183)

QPK/DW — Arrangements. Songs, etc
Dexter, Harry
[Scarborough Fair: arr]. Scarborough Fair: rhythmic version for
piano solo/ [arranged] by Harry Dexter. — London: Ashdown,
1972. — 6p; 4to.
£0.20

(B73-50318)

Macleod, A C
[The Skye boat song: arr]. The Skye boat song/ by A.C. Macleod; arranged and edited by Frank E. Brown. — London: Cramer, 1973. — 3p; 4to.
£0.15
(B73-50750)

QPK/DW/G/AYDL — Arrangements. Folk songs. Collections. Scotland
Dorman, Harry
Scottish and French folk tunes/ arranged for piano with guitar chords by Harry Dorman. — London: Warren and Phillips, 1973. — 12p; 4to.
Unpriced
Also classified at QPK/DW/G/AYH
(B73-50319)

QPK/DW/G/AYH — Arrangements. Folk songs. Collections. France
Dorman, Harry
Scottish and French folk tunes/ arranged for piano with guitar chords by Harry Dorman. — London: Warren and Phillips, 1973. — 12p; 4to.
Unpriced
Primary classification QPK/DW/G/AYDL
(B73-50319)

QPK/DW/GJ/JS/AY — Arrangements. Children's songs. Television. Collections
Wickham, E H
Bang on a drum: songs from Play School and Play Away, the B.B.C. Television programmes/ piano arrangements by E.H. Wickham. — London: British Broadcasting Corporation, Keith Prowse Music, 1973. — 48p; 4to.
£0.60
(B73-50320)

QPK/DW/GJ/JT/AY — Arrangements. Children's songs. Radio. Collections
Porteous, Chris
Sing me a story/ edited by Chris Porteous. — London: Church Pastoral Aid Society, 1973. — 34p; 8vo.
The songs in this book have mostly been used on Radio London in 'The Orange and Lemon Club'. — Publisher's note.
ISBN 0 85491 834 5 : £0.35
(B73-50321)

QPK/JR — Arrangements. Films
Bennett, Richard Rodney
Lady Caroline Lamb: piano solo, theme from the film/ by Richard Rodney Bennett. — London: KPM, 1972. — 4p; 4to.
£0.25
(B73-50322)

Leigh, Mitch
[Man of La Mancha: arr]. Man of La Mancha/ by Mitch Leigh; arranged by Denes Agay. — London: KPM, 1973. — 16p; 4to.
£0.85
(B73-50323)

Rota, Nina
The godfather: themes for easy play piano/ [by Nina Rota and others]. — London: Famous Chappell, 1972. — 23p; 4to.
£0.40
(B73-50324)

QRP — HARPSICHORD SOLOS
QRP/AZ — Collected works of individual composers
Handel, George Frideric
[Works, keyboard]. Keyboard works/ by Georg Friedrich Händel. — Cassell; London: Bärenreiter.
Vol.3: Miscellaneous suites and pieces/ edited by Terence Best. — 1970. — viii,85p; fol.
£1.85
(B73-51184)

Valente, Antonio
[Works, harpsichord]. Intavolatura de cimbalo/ by Antonio Valente; edited by Charles Jacobs. — Oxford: Clarendon Press, 1973. — xxxiv,167p; 4to.
This edition includes related music by Valente's contemporaries and vocal models of his transcriptions.
ISBN 0 19 816121 2 : £11.00
(B73-50325)

QRPJ — Miscellaneous works
Middleton, John
Contrasts: for harpsichord/ by John Middleton. — London: Thames, 1973. — 8p; 4to.
Unpriced
(B73-50326)

QSQ — VIRGINALS
QSQ/AY — Collections
Byrd, William
Three anonymous keyboard pieces/ attributed to William Byrd; edited by Oliver Neighbour. — Sevenoaks: Novello, 1973. — 5p; 4to.
£0.30
(B73-50751)

R — ORGAN
R/AC — Tutors
[Kurzer jedoch gründlicher Wegweiser]. Wegweiser: a 17th century German organ tutor/ [edited by] Gwilym Beechey. — Leipzig; [London]: Peters, 1971. — 39p: obl.4to.
Unpriced
(B73-50327)

R/AY — Collections
Marr, Peter
Four medieval pieces: for organ/ edited by Peter Marr. — London: Peters, 1972. — 15p; obl.4to.
Contents: Estampie 1 - Estampie 2 - Flos vernalis - Felix namque.
Unpriced
(B73-50328)

Trevor, Caleb Henry
Organ music for manuals/ edited by C.H. Trevor. — London: Oxford University Press.
Book 3. — 1973. — 32p; 4to. —
ISBN 0 19 375850 4 : £0.75
(B73-50329)
Book 4. — 1973. — 32p; 4to. —
ISBN 0 19 375851 2 : £0.75
(B73-50330)

Trevor, Caleb Henry
Organ music for services of thanksgiving/ edited by C.H. Trevor. — London: Oxford University Press, 1973. — 32p; 4to.
ISBN 0 19 375854 7 : £0.75
(B73-50752)

R/AYD — Collections. England
Phillips, Gordon
English organ music of the eighteenth century/ edited by Gordon Phillips. — London: Peters.
Volume 1. — 1973. — 31p; obl.4to. —
Unpriced
(B73-51185)
Volume 2. — 1973. — 31p; obl 4to. —
Unpriced
(B73-51186)

R/AZ — Collected works of individual composers
Blow, John
[Works, organ]. Thirty voluntaries and verses for the organ/ by John Blow; revised and edited by Watkins Shaw. — Revised edition. — London: Schott, 1972. — x,66p; 4to.
Revised ed. of the 'Complete organ works', published 1958.
£2.30
(B73-50331)

Hummel, Johann Nepomuk
[Works, organ]. Complete organ works [of] J.N. Hummel/ edited by David G. Brock. — London: Hinrichsen, 1972. — 32p: obl.4to.
Unpriced
(B73-50332)

R/T — Variations
Cooper, Paul
Variants for organ/ by Paul Cooper. — London: Chester, 1973. — 11p; 4to.
Unpriced
(B73-51187)

R/W — Rondos
Cole, Bruce
Rondeau for organ/ by Bruce Cole. — London: Boosey and Hawkes, 1973. — 11p; obl.fol.
£0.65
(B73-50753)

R/Y — Fugues
Barrell, Bernard
Prelude and fugue. Op.36: organ/ by Bernard Barrell. — London: Thames, 1972. — 6p; fol.
Unpriced
(B73-50754)

RE — Sonatas
Cooke, Arnold
[Sonata for organ, no.1]. Sonata no.1 for organ/ by Arnold Cooke. — London: Peters, 1973. — 31p; obl.4to.
Unpriced
(B73-50333)

RG — Suites
Crossman, Gerald
Holiday cruise: a musical journey for organ or accordion/ by Gerald Crossman; idea and descriptive material by Miriam Crossman. — London: Bosworth.

1: Southampton, England. — 1973. — 6p; 4to.
£0.20
Also classified at RSPMG

(B73-51188)

2: Vigo, Spain. — 1973. — 6p; 4to.
£0.20
Also classified at RSPMG

(B73-51189)

3: Haifa, Israel. — 1973. — 6p; 4to.
£0.20
Also classified at RSPMG

(B73-51190)

4: Athens, Greece. — 1973. — 6p; 4to.
£0.20
Also classified at RSPMG

(B73-51191)

5: Lisbon, Portugal. — 1973. — 6p; 4to.
£0.20
Also classified at RSPMG

(B73-51192)

RG/KDD — Suites. Weddings
Gange, Kenneth
Wedding music: suite for organ/ by Kenneth Gange. — London: Cramer, 1973. — 8p; 4to.
Contents: Prelude (Bridal march) - Cantilene - Postlude.
Unpriced

(B73-51193)

RGN/KDD — Fanfares. Weddings
Farmer, John A
A wedding fanfare: organ/ by J.A. Farmer. — Lowestoft: Coastal Music Studios, 1972. — 3p; obl.4to.
Unpriced

(B73-50334)

RJ — Miscellaneous works
Arne, Thomas Augustine
[Six favourite concertos.. Selections]. Organ solos/ by Thomas Arne; edited by Gwilym Beechey. — London: Peters, 1972. — 22p; obl.4to.
The concertos contain various movements marked 'organo solo' and these have been assembled here for the present edition.
Unpriced

(B73-50335)

Blow, John
[Works, organ. Selections]. Ten selected organ pieces/ by John Blow; revised and edited by Watkins Shaw. — London: Schott, 1972. — 22p; 4to.
£1.40

(B73-50336)

Brown, Frank Edwin
Two festal contrasts: organ solo/ by Frank E. Brown. — London: Cramer.

No.1: in C. — 1973. — 4p; 4to. —
£0.24

(B73-50755)

No.2: in D. — 1973. — 4p; 4to. —
£0.24

(B73-50756)

Edwards, D W
Ecumenia: a song for unity, for solo organ (with or without solo voice)/ by D.W. Edwards. — Wirral, 67 Lang Lane, West Kirby, Wirral: D.W. Edwards, 1973. — 4p; 8vo.
Unpriced

(B73-50757)

Freedman, Hermann L
Triptych: organ/ by Hermann L. Freedman. — London: Thames, 1972. — 9p; fol.
Unpriced

(B73-50758)

Gilbert, Norman
Pastorale prelude: organ solo/ by Norman Gilbert. — London: Cramer, 1972. — 3p; 4to.
£0.24

(B73-50337)

Gilbert, Norman
Postlude: organ solo/ by Norman Gilbert. — London: Cramer, 1972. — 4p; 4to.
£0.24

(B73-50338)

Hummel, Bertold
Alleluja: für Orgel/ von Bertold Hummel. — Hamburg; London: Simrock, 1972. — 16p; obl.4to.
Unpriced

(B73-50339)

Hunt, Reginald
Fantasy on a ground: for organ/ by Reginald Hunt. — London: Boosey and Hawkes, 1973. — 12p; 4to.
£0.65

(B73-50759)

Jackson, Nicholas
Four images: for organ/ by Nicholas Jackson. — London: Boosey and Hawkes, 1973. — 12p; 4to.
£0.60

(B73-50760)

Kennaway, Lamont
A meditation and impromptu: organ/ by Lamond Kennaway. — Sevenoaks: Paxton, 1973. — 6p; 4to.
£0.35

(B73-51194)

Klebe, Giselher
Surge equilo; et veni auster. Op 60: Paraphrase über ein Thema von Igor Stravinsky, für Orgel/ von Giselher Klebe. — Cassel; London: Bärenreiter, 1972. — 6p; obl.fol.
£1.05

(B73-50761)

Middleton, John
Fantaisie: for organ/ by John Middleton. — London: Thames, 1973. — 10p; 4to.
Unpriced

(B73-50340)

Pachelbel, Johann
[Works, organ. Selections].
[Selections]. Selected organ works/ by Johann Pachelbel. — Cassel; London: Bärenreiter.
5/ edited by Wolfgang Stockmeier. — 1972. — 36p; obl.fol.
£1.20

(B73-50341)

Patterson, Paul
Interludium: for organ/ by Paul Patterson. — London: Weinberger, 1972. — 4p; obl.4to.
Unpriced

(B73-50342)

Patterson, Paul
Visions: for organ/ by Paul Patterson. — London: Weinberger, 1972. — 8p; obl.4to.
Unpriced

(B73-50343)

Preston, Simon
Vox dicentis/ by Simon Preston. — Sevenoaks: Novello, 1973. — 12p; obl.4to.
£0.45

(B73-50344)

Ratcliffe, Desmond
Sixty interludes for service use/ by Desmond Ratcliffe. — Sevenoaks: Novello, 1973. — 38p; 4to.
£1.00

(B73-51195)

Schumann, Robert
[Sketches for pedal-piano. Op.58]. Four sketches/ by Robert Schumann; edited by C.H. Trevor. — London: Oxford University Press, 1973. — 16p; 4to.
ISBN 0 19 375732 x : £0.65

(B73-50762)

Spooner, Ian
Sinfonia: organ/ by Ian Spooner. — London: Boosey and Hawkes, 1973. — 8p; fol.
£0.40

(B73-51196)

Stoker, Richard
A little organ book/ by Richard Stoker. — London: Boosey and Hawkes, 1973. — 8p; fol.
£0.40

(B73-51197)

Stoker, Richard
Three improvisations: organ/ by Richard Stoker. — London: Boosey and Hawkes, 1973. — 6p; fol.
£0.40

(B73-51198)

Stoker, Richard
Three improvisations: organ/ by Richard Stoker. — London: Boosey and Hawkes, 1973. — 6p; fol.
£0.40

(B73-51199)

Thiman, Eric Harding
Five hymn-tune variants: for organ/ by Eric H. Thiman. — Wendover: Roberton, 1971. — 12p; 4to.
Contents: 1. Trumpet tune on 'Moscow' - 2. Meditation on 'Breslau' - 3. Pastorale on 'St. Stephen - 4. Prelude on 'Franconia' - 5. Postlude on 'Regent Street'.
Unpriced

(B73-50345)

Waters, Charles Frederick
Festive processional: organ solo/ by Charles F. Waters. — London: Cramer, 1973. — 4p; 4to.
£0.24

(B73-50763)

Waters, Charles Frederick
Impromptu: organ solo/ by C.F. Waters. — London: Cramer, 1973. — 4p; 4to.
Unpriced

(B73-51200)

Watson, Walter
Affirmation: for organ/ by Walter Watson. — New York; London: Schirmer, 1972. — 11p; 4to.
Unpriced

(B73-50346)

RK — Arrangements
Bach, Johann Sebastian
[Selections: arr]. Bach's greatest hits: for all organ. — London: Chappell, 1973. — 36p; 4to.
£1.00

(B73-51201)

Boyce, William
[Works, orchestra. Selections: arr]. A William Boyce suite/ arranged for organ by F.R.C. Clarke. — Sevenoaks: Paxton, 1973. — 18p; 4to.
£0.45

(B73-51202)

Gibson, Arthur J
Two contrasts/ arranged for organ by Arthur J. Gibson. — London: Ashdown, 1973. — 6p; 4to.
Contents: 1. Slow movement from flute sonata in B minor. S.1030 by J.S. Bach 2. Two trumpet tunes from 'King Arthur' by Henry Purcell.
Unpriced

(B73-50347)

Greig, Edvard
[Selections]. Greatest hits/ by Edvard Grieg; arranged for all organs. — London: Chappell, 1973. — 36p; 4to.
£1.00

(B73-50764)

Tchaikovsky, Peter
[Selections: arr]. Tchaikovsky's greatest hits: for all organ. — London: Chappell, 1973. — 48p; 4to.
Unpriced

(B73-51203)

Vivaldi, Antonio
[Il Cimento dell'armonia e dell'invenzione. Op.8, no.4. Largo: arr]. Largo from the 'Winter' concerto for violin and strings/ by Antonio Vivaldi; arranged for organ by Arthur J. Gibson. — London: Cramer, 1973. — 3p; 4to.
Unpriced

(B73-51204)

RK/AAY — Arrangements. Collections
Rapley, Felton
Marching and waltzing/ compiled for all organs by Felton Rapley. — London: Chappell, 1972. — 35p; 4to.
£0.40

(B73-50348)

RK/AGM — Arrangements. Marches
Clarke, Jeremiah
[The Prince of Denmark's march: arr]. Trumpet voluntary/ by Jeremiah Clarke; arranged for organ solo by Frank E. Brown. — London: Cramer, 1973. — 4p; 4to.
£0.24

(B73-50765)

Lully, Jean Baptiste
[Thésée.. March: arr]. Processional march/ by Lully; arranged for organ by J. Stanley Shirtcliff. — London: Ashdown, 1973. — 4p; 4to.
£0.20

(B73-50349)

Mendelssohn, Felix
[Athalia.. War march of the priests]. War march of the priests/ by Mendelssohn; arranged for the organ by Frank E. Brown. — London: Cramer, 1972. — 8p; 4to.
£0.24

(B73-50350)

RK/AH — Arrangements. Dances
Strauss family
[Works, orchestra. Selections: arr]. The Strauss family: greatest hits for all organ. — London: Chappell, 1973. — 46p; 4to.
£1.00

(B73-50351)

RK/DP/LF/AY — Arrangements. Carols. Christmas. Collections
Rothenberg, Peter
Rund um die Weihnacht: für l-manualige Orgel/ bearbeitet von Peter Rothenberg. — Mainz; London: Schott, 1973. — 32p; 4to.
£1.40

(B73-51205)

RK/DW — Arrangements. Songs, etc
Beethoven, Ludwig van
[Symphony no.9 in D minor. Op.125. Freude, schöner Götterfunken: arr]. Hymn of joy/ by L. van Beethoven; arranged [for organ] by John C. Phillips. — Sevenoaks: Paxton, 1973. — 8p; 4to.
£0.25

(B73-51206)

RK/JR — Arrangements. Films
Bolton, Cecil
Themes from TV and film classics/ arranged for all organ by Cecil Bolton and Jack Moore. — London: Robbins Affiliated Music, 1973. — 40p; 4to.
£0.75
Primary classification RK/JS

RK/JS — Arrangements. Television
Bolton, Cecil
Themes from TV and film classics/ arranged for all organ by Cecil Bolton and Jack Moore. — London: Robbins Affiliated Music, 1973. — 40p; 4to.
£0.75
Also classified at RK/JR

(B73-51207)

RPV — ELECTRIC ORGANS
RPVK/AAY — Arrangements. Collections
Rothenberg, Peter
Dance melodies: for 2 manuals and pedal/ by Peter Rothenberg. — Mainz; London: Schott, 1972. — 20p; 4to.
£1.20

(B73-50352)

RPVK/AHVR — Electronic organ. Arrangements. Tangos
Yradier, Sebastian
[La Paloma: arr]. La Paloma/ by Sebastian Yradier; arranged for Hammond organ by Bobby Fisher. — Scarborough: Fisher & Lane, 1970. — 6p; 4to.
Unpriced

(B73-50353)

RPVK/DW/GJ/AYE — Arrangements. Children's songs. Collections. Germany
Draths, Willi
Die Kinderorgel: leichte Kinderlieder für elektronische Orgel (1 Manuel)/ von Willi Draths. — Mainz; London: Schott, 1973. — 23p; obl. 8vo.
£1.20

(B73-51208)

RSPM — UNACCOMPANIED ACCORDION SOLOS
RSPMG — Suites
Crossman, Gerald
Holiday cruise: a musical journey for organ or accordion/ by Gerald Crossman; idea and descriptive material by Miriam Crossman. — London: Bosworth.
1: Southampton, England. — 1973. — 6p; 4to.
£0.20
Primary classification RG
2: Vigo, Spain. — 1973. — 6p; 4to.
£0.20
Primary classification RG
3: Haifa, Israel. — 1973. — 6p; 4to.
£0.20
Primary classification RG
4: Athens, Greece. — 1973. — 6p; 4to.
£0.20
Primary classification RG
5: Lisbon, Portugal. — 1973. — 6p; 4to.
£0.20
Primary classification RG

RSPMH/G/AYD — Folk dances. Collections. England
Brock, John
A book of Morris dance tunes/ selected and edited by John Brock. — London: English Folk Dance and Song Society, 1973. — 20p; obl. 8vo.
ISBN 0 85418 005 2 : Unpriced

(B73-51209)

RSPMK — Arrangements
Albinoni, Tommaso
[Sonate à tre in G minor. Adagio: arr]. Adagio in G minor on two thematic fragments and a figured bass/ by Tommaso Albinoni; edited by Remo Giazotto, transcribed for piano accordion by G. Romani. — Chesham: Ricordi, 1973. — 4p; 4to.
Duration 10 min..
Unpriced

(B73-51210)

RXM — STRING ORCHESTRA
RXME — Symphonies
Bach, Wilhelm Friedemann
[Symphony in F major. Falck 67]. Sinfonie F-Dur. Falck 67/ von Wilhelm Friedemann Bach; herausgegeben von Walter Lebermann. — Mainz; London: Schott, 1973. — 19p; 4to.
£1.92

(B73-51211)

RXMF — Concertos
Handel, George Frideric
Concerto grosso in A major. Op.6, no.11/ by George Frideric Handel; edited by Michael Nyman. — London: Eulenburg, 1973. — ix,44p; 8vo.
Miniature score.
£0.41

(B73-50766)

Handel, George Frideric
Concerto grosso in A minor. Op. 6, no.4/ by George Frideric Handel; edited by Michael Nyman. — London: Eulenburg, 1973. — viii,26p; 8vo.
Miniature score.
£0.41

(B73-50767)

Handel, George Frideric
Concerto grosso in B flat major. Op. 6, no.7/ by George Frideric Handel; edited by Michael Nyman. — London: Eulenburg, 1973. — viii,18p; 8vo.
Miniature score.
£0.41

(B73-50768)

Handel, George Frideric
Concerto grosso in B minor. Op.6, no.12: by George Frideric Handel/ edited by Michael Nyman. — London: Eulenburg, 1973. — viii,26p; 8vo.
Miniature score.
£0.41

(B73-50769)

Handel, George Frideric
Concerto grosso in C minor. Op: 6, no.8/ by George Frideric Handel; edited by Michael Nyman. — London: Eulenburg, 1973. — ix,23p; 8vo.
Miniature score.
£0.41

(B73-50770)

Handel, George Frideric
Concerto grosso in D minor. Op. 6, no.10/ by George Frideric Handel; edited by Michael Nyman. — London: Eulenburg, 1973. — viii,30p; 8vo.
Miniature score.
£0.41

(B73-50771)

Handel, George Frideric
Concerto grosso in E minor. Op. 6, no.3/ by George Frideric Handel; edited by Michael Nyman. — London: Eulenburg, 1973. — ix,29p; 8vo.
Miniature score.
£0.41

(B73-50772)

Handel, George Frideric
Concerto grosso in F major. Op.6, no.9/ by George Frideric Handel; edited by Michael Nyman. — London: Eulenburg, 1973. — ix,30p; 8vo.
Miniature score.
£0.41

(B73-50773)

RXMJ — Miscellaneous works
Antoniou, Theodor
Kinesis ABCD. Op.31: for two groups of strings/ by Theodor Antoniou. — Cassel; London: Bärenreiter, 1972. — 34p; 8vo.
Miniature score.
£1.50

(B73-50354)

Hughes-Jones, Llifon
[Preludes for orchestra, nos.1-2]. Prelude no.1 (on a 15th century French melody) and Prelude no.2/ by Llifon Hughes-Jones. — London: Bosworth, 1972. — 4to.
Score (6p.), Piano conductor (3p.), & 10 parts.
£1.60
Primary classification MJ

(B73-50661)

Hummel, Bertold
Klangfiguren für Streicher: Studien in modernes Spieltechnik/ von Bertold Hummel. — Mainz; London: Schott, 1972. — 28p; 4to.
£2.00

(B73-50355)

Richter, Franz Xaver
[Sinfonia a quattro for string orchestra in C minor]. Sinfonia a quattro, C-moll: für Streicher/ von Franz Xaver Richter; zum ersten Mal, herausgegeben von Walter Lebermann. — Frankfurt; London: Peters, 1972. — 12p; 4to.
£1.80

(B73-50774)

Smalley, Roger
Strata: for fifteen solo strings/ by Roger Smalley. — London: Faber, 1971. — obl.fol.
The score comprises 38 mostly loose pages, printed on one side of the leaf, and enclosed in a folder, accompanied by a 'form-plan' and a leaflet containing performing instructions.
Unpriced

(B73-50356)

Smith, John Christopher
[The fairies.. Overture]. Overture: for strings and continuo (with optional oboes and optional trumpets)/ by John Christopher Smith. — London: Oxford University Press, 1972. — 14p; 4to.
ISBN 0 19 367637 0 : £1.00

(B73-50357)

Stiles, Frank
Interlude for strings/ by Frank Stiles. — London: Mixolydian Press, 1970. — 7p; 8vo.
Miniature score.
Unpriced

(B73-50775)

Williamson, Malcolm
Epitaphs for Edith Sitwell: for string orchestra/ by Malcolm Williamson. — London: Weinberger, 1973. — 8p; 8vo.
Miniature score.
Unpriced

(B73-50358)

RXMK — Arrangements
Mozart, Wolfgang Amadeus
[Quartet for string instruments in C major. K.157: arr]. Divertimento, C-Dur/ von Wolfgang Amadeus Mozart; für Streichorchester, herausgegeben von Georg Rothke. — Mainz; London: Schott, 1973. — 16p; 4to.
£1.20

(B73-50359)

Wagner, Richard
[Albumblatt for piano in E flat major: arr]. Romance/ by Richard Wagner; transcribed for strings by Maurice Johnstone. — London: Chappell, 1973. — 4to.
Score (8p) & 13 parts.
Unpriced

(B73-51212)

RXMP — SOLO INSTRUMENT (S) & STRING ORCHESTRA
RXMPNURNT — Flute, strings & keyboard trio & string orchestra
Jörns, Helge
7 Formen: für Flöte, Gitarre, Cembalo und Zupfoder Streichorchester oder Streichquartett/ von Helge Jörns. — Hamburg; London: Simrock, 1973. — 28ff; 4to.
Unpriced
Primary classification NURNP

RXMPSF — Violin and string orchestra. Concertos
Panufnik, Andrzej
[Concerto for violin]. Violin concerto/ by Andrzej Panufnik. — London: Boosey and Hawkes, 1973. — 4to.
Score (37p.) & part. — Duration 24 min.
£4.75

(B73-51213)

RXMPVR — Flute & string orchestra
Höller, Karl
[Divertimento for flute & string orchestra. Op. 53a]. Divertimento für Flöte und Streicher. Op. 53a/ von Karl Höller. — Frankfurt; London: Peters, 1972. — 40p; 4to.
£3.50

(B73-50776)

RXMPVRE — Flute & string orchestra. Symphonies

Scarlatti, Alessandro
[Symphony for flute and string ochestra, no,6, in A minor].
Sinfonia Nr,6 a-moll: Flöte, Streicher und Basso continuo/ von
Alessandro Scarlatti; zum ersten Mal herausgegeben von
Rolf-Julius Koch. — Frankfurt; London: Peters, 1972. — 23p;
4to.
Unpriced

(B73-50778)

Scarlatti, Alessandro
[Symphony for flute & string orchestra, no 7, in G minor].
Sinfonia Nr. 7, g-moll: Flöte, Streicher und Basso continuo/ von
Alessandro Scarlatti; zum ersten Mal herausgegeben von
Rolf-Julius Koch. — Frankfurt; London: Peters, 1972. — 16p;
4to.
Unpriced

(B73-50779)

Scarlatti, Alessandro
[Symphony for flute & string orchestra, no.8, in G major].
Sinfonia Nr. 8, G-dur: Flöte, Streicher und Basso continuo/ von
Alessandro Scarlatti; zum ersten Mal herausgegeben von
Rolf-Julius Koch. — Frankfurt; London: Peters, 1972. — 15p;
4to.
Unpriced

(B73-50782)

Scarlatti, Alessandro
[Symphony for flute & string orchestra, no. 9, in G minor].
Sinfonia, Nr.9,g-moll: Flöte, Streicher und Basso continuo/ von
Alessandro Scarlatti; zum ersten Mal herausgegeben von
Rolf-Julius Koch. — Frankfurt; London: Peters, 1972. — 17p;
4to.
Unpriced

(B73-50777)

Scarlatti, Alessandro
[Symphony for flute & string orchestra, No. 10, in A minor].
Sinfonia Nr. 10, a-moll: Flöte. Streicher und Basso continuo/ von
Alessandro Scarlatti; zum ersten Mal herausgegeben von
Rolf-Julius Koch. — Frankfurt; London: Peters, 1972. — 17p;
4to.
Unpriced

(B73-50780)

Scarlatti, Alessandro
[Symphony for flute & string orchestra, no. 11, in C major].
Sinfonia Nr. 11, C-dur: Flöte, Streicher und Basso continuo/ von
Alessandro Scarlatti; zum ersten Mal herausgegeben von
Rolf-Julius Koch. — Frankfurt; London: Peters, 1972. — 18p;
4to.
Bibl.
Unpriced

(B73-50781)

RXMPWS — Trumpet & string orchestra

Scarlatti, Alessandro
[Il Giardino di amore.. Sinfonia]. Sinfonia for trumpet and
strings/ by Alessandro Scarlatti; edited by Michael Talbot. —
London: Musica rara, 1973. — 4to.
Score (16p.) & 8 parts.
Unpriced

(B73-50360)

**RXN/AZ — String ensembles. Collected works of individual
composers**

Schubert, Franz
[Works, string instruments]. Complete chamber music for strings/
by Franz Schubert; edited by Eusebius Mandyczewski and Joseph
Hellmesberger. — New York: Dover; London: Constable, 1973. —
347p; 4to.
An unabridged and unaltered republication of Series 4-6 and pages 93-105 of
Series 21 of Franz Schubert's Werke Kritisch durchgesehene
Gesammtausgabe, originally published Leipzig, Breitkopf and Härtel,
1890-97.
ISBN 0 486 21463 x : £2.25

(B73-51214)

RXNRG — Quintets. Suites

Schein, Johann Hermann
[Banchetto musicale.. Suites]. Three suites for five string or wind
instruments/ by Johann Hermann Schein; edited by Dieter
Krickeberg. — Cassel; London: Bärenreiter, 1972. — 8vo.
Score (24p.) & 5 parts. — Contents: Suites 3,5,7.
£2.70

(B73-50361)

RXNS — Quartets

Bialas, Günter
[Quartet for strings, no.3]. Drittes Streichquartett/ von Günter
Bialas. — Cassel; London: Bärenreiter, 1972. — 18p; 8vo.
Miniature score.
£1.50

(B73-50783)

Boder, Gerd
9 Istanti: für Streichquartett/ von Gerd Boder. — Regensburg:
Bosse; [London]: [Bärenreiter], 1972. — 4pt; 4to.
£2.40

(B73-50784)

Boucourechliev, André
Archipel II: pour quator a cordes: par André Boucourechliev. —
London: Universal, 1973. — obl. fol.
With a separate booklet (8p) containing instructions for performance printed
in German, English and French.
Unpriced

(B73-51215)

Halffter, Cristóbal
[Quartet for strings, no.2, 'Memoires 1970']. II. Streichquartett,
(Memoires 1970)/ von Cristóbal Halffter. — London: Universal,
1973. — 10p; obl fol.
Unpriced

(B73-50785)

Huffer, Konrad
[Quartet for strings]. Streichquartett/ von Konrad Huffer. —
Regensburg: Bosse; [London]: [Bärenreiter], 1972. — 12p; obl.fol.
£3.00

(B73-50362)

Ireland, John
[Quartet for strings, no.1, in D minor. Op. posth]. String quartet,
no.1, in D minor. Op. posth./ by John Ireland; [edited by] Charles
Marks. — London: Boosey and Hawkes, 1973. — 8vo.
Miniature score (35p.) & 4 parts.
Unpriced

(B73-50364)

Ireland, John
[Quartet for strings, no.2, in C minor. Op. posth]. String quartet,
no.2, C minor. Op. posth./ by John Ireland; [edited by] Charles
Marks. — London: Boosey and Hawkes, 1973. — 8vo.
Miniature score (41p.) & 4 parts.
£0.85

(B73-50363)

Makris, Andreas
String quartet in one movement/ by Andreas Makris. — New
York: Galaxy Music; London: Galliard, 1973. — 4to.
Score (38p.) & 4 parts.
Unpriced

(B73-51216)

Pfitzner, Hans
[Quartet for strings in D minor]. String quartet in D minor/ by
Hans Pfitzner; edited by Hans Rectanus. — Cassel, London:
Bärenreiter, 1972. — 4pt; 4to.
£3.60

(B73-50786)

Schmitt, Meinrad
Fantasia piccola: für Streichquartett/ von Meinrad Schmitt. —
Regensburg: Bosse; [London]: [Bärenreiter], 1972. — 4pt; 4to.
£2.10

(B73-50787)

Standford, Patric
Bagatelles. Opus 22: for string quartet/ by Patric Standford. —
Sevenoaks: Novello, 1973. — 4to.
Score (12p.) & 4 parts.
Unpriced

(B73-51217)

Stiles, Frank
[Quartet for strings]. String quartet: by Frank Stiles. — London:
Mixolydian Press, 1970. — 8vo.
Miniature score (42p) & 4 parts.
Unpriced

(B73-50788)

S — VIOLIN

S/AF — Exercises

Heller, Henryk
System of harmonics for violin/ by Henryk Heller; revised and
edited by Adam Heller. — Hamburg; London: Simrock.
Vol.1. — 1971. — 49p; 4to. —
£0.75

(B73-51218)

S/AY — Collections

Doflein, Erich
Neue Musik/ herausgegeben von Erich Doflein. — Neuausgabe
1972. — Mainz; London: Schott.
Heft 9: Neue Violin-Duos. — 1973. — 24p; 4to. —
£1.40
Also classified at SNU/AY

(B73-50365)

SN — VIOLIN ENSEMBLE
SNRPWK/AHR — Four violins & keyboard. Arrangements. Minuets
Handel, George Frideric
[Concerti grossi. Op.3, no.2. Menuet: arr]. Menuet/ by George Frideric Handel; edited for two descant, treble and tenor recorders, or four violins and continuo (with bass recorder/cello), by Freda Dinn. — London: Schott, 1972. — 4to.
Score (4p.) & 5 parts.
Unpriced
Primary classification VSNRPWK/AHR

(B73-50414)

SNTPWE — Two violins & keyboard. Sonatas
Graun, Carl Heinrich
[Sonata for two flutes & basso continuo in E flat major]. Sonata in E flat major for two flutes (violins) and basso continuo/ by Carl Heinrich Graun; first edition, edited by Herbert Köbel, continuo-realization by Ernst Meyerolbersleben. — Cassel; London: Bärenreiter, 1972. — 8vo.
Score (21p.) & 3 parts.
£1.80
Primary classification VRNTPWE

(B73-50404)

SNU/AY — Duets. Collections
Doflein, Erich
Neue Musik/ herausgegeben von Erich Doflein. — Neuausgabe 1972. — Mainz; London: Schott.
Heft 9: Neue Violin-Duos. — 1973. — 24p; 4to. —
£1.40
Primary classification S/AY

(B73-50365)

SNUE — Duets. Sonatas
Szelényi, István
[Sonatina for two violins, no.2]. Sonata no.2 for two violins/ by István Szelényi. — London: Boosey and Hawkes, 1973. — 11p; 4to.
£0.65

(B73-51219)

SP — VIOLIN & PIANO
SPE — Sonatas
Boccherini, Luigi
[Sonata for violin & harpsichord in B flat major]. Sonate, B-Dur, für Violine und Klavier (Cembalo)/ von Luigi Boccherini; herausgegeben von Dieter Vorholz. — Frankfurt; London: Peters, 1972. — 4to.
Score (20p) & part.
£1.50

(B73-50789)

Schubert, Franz
Sonatas for violin and piano. D.384, 385 & 408/ by Franz Schubert; edited by Helmut Wirth. — Cassel, London: Bärenreiter, 1970. — 4to.
Separate edition taken from 'Franz Schubert: neue Ausgabe sämtliche Werke, Series 6, Volume 8. — Score (68p) & part.
£2.10

(B73-50790)

Senallié, Jean Baptiste
[Sonata for violin & basso continuo, liv. 5, no.5 in E minor]. Sonata in E minor for violin and continuo/ by J.B. Senallie; edited by Gwilym Beechey. — London: Oxford University Press, 1973. — 4to.
Score (12p.) & 2 parts.
ISBN 0 19 358796 3 : £0.90

(B73-51220)

Srebotnjak, Alojz
[Sonata for violin & piano, no.2]. Second sonata for violin and piano/ by Alojz Srebotnjak. — New York; London: Schirmer, 1972. — 4to.
Unpriced

(B73-51221)

SPEM — Sonatinas
Srebotnjak, Alojz
[Sonatina for violin & piano, no.1]. Sonatina for violin and piano/ by Alojz Srebotnjak. — New York; London: Schirmer, 1971. — 4to.
Score (16p) & part.
Unpriced

(B73-51222)

SPJ — Miscellaneous works
Dussek, Jan Ladislav
Notturno concertante, Op 68: for piano violin and horn (violin) or piano and violin/ by Jan Ladislav Dussek; edited by Christopher D.S. Field. — Cassel, London: Bärenreiter, 1972. — 4to.
Score (44p) & 3 parts.
£3.30
Primary classification NUNT

(B73-50694)

Rorem, Ned
Day music: for violin and piano/ by Ned Rorem. — New York; London: Boosey and Hawkes, 1973. — 4to.
Score (33p.) & part.
£1.25

(B73-50366)

Schumann, Robert
Adagio and allegro. Op.70: for horn (or violin, or viola, or cello) and piano/ by Robert Schumann. — New York: Schirmer; [London]: [Chappell], 1971. — 4to.
Score (15p) & part.
Unpriced
Primary classification WTPJ

Schumann, Robert
Adagio and allegro. Op.70: for horn (or violin, or viola, or cello) and piano/ by Robert Schumann. — New York: Schirmer; [London]: [Chappell], 1971. — 4to.
Score (15p) & part.
Unpriced
Primary classification WTPJ

Standford, Patric
Peasant songs: for violin and piano/ by Patric Standford. — Sevenoaks: Novello, 1973. — 4to.
Score (13p.) & part.
£0.75

(B73-51223)

SPK/LF — Arrangements. Concertos
Dvorak, Antonin
[Concerto for violin in A minor. Op.53: arr]. Violinkonzert, a moll. Op.53/ von Antonin Dvorak; reduction for violin & piano by Max Rostal. — Mainz; London: Schott, 1973. — 4to.
Score (51p.) & part.
£1.70

(B73-50791)

Hamilton, Iain
[Concerto for violin, no.1: arr]. Concerto no.1: for violin and orchestra/ by Iain Hamilton; reduction for violin and piano. — London: Schott, 1972. — fol.
Not all of the piano part of this reduction can be played by the pianist. The rehearsal pianist will be able to play enough of it to help the soloist.
Duration 27 mins.
£2.50

(B73-50367)

Kelly, Robert
[Concerto for violin. Op.46: arr]. Concerto for violin and orchestra. Opus 46/ by Robert Kelly; reduction for violin and piano. — New York: Highgate Press; London: Galliard, 1973. — 4to.
Score (44p.) & part.
Unpriced

(B73-50792)

Paganini, Nicolo
[Concerto for violin, no.1, in D major. Op.6: arr]. Konzert no.1, D-Dur. Opus 6: für Violine und Orchester/ von Nicolo Paganini; herausgegeben revidiert und mit Fingersatzen versehen von Konstanty Andrzej Kulka und Stefan Herman, Klavierauszug von Friedrich Wanek. — Mainz; London: Schott, 1972. — 4to.
Score (45p.) & part.
£1.40

(B73-50368)

SPLSR — VIOLIN & CELLO
Linde, Hans Peter
Duo concertante für Viola und Violoncello/ von Hans-Peter Linde. — Leipzig; [London]: Peters, 1972. — 12p; 4to.
Two copies.
Unpriced

(B73-50369)

SPM — UNACCOMPANIED VIOLIN
SPM/T — Variations
Rochberg, George
Caprice variations: for unaccompanied violin/ by George Rochberg; edited by Lewis Kaplan. — New York: Galaxy; London: Galliard, 1973. — 52p; 4to.
Unpriced

(B73-50793)

SPMH/G/AYDJJ — Folk dances. Collections. Northumberland
Polwarth, Gwen
Folk songs and dance tunes from the North with fiddle tunes, pipe tunes and street cries/ compiled by Gwen and Mary Polwarth. — Newcastle upon Tyne: Frank Graham, 1970. — 62p; 8vo.
ISBN 0 900409 93 2 : £0.60
Primary classification JE/TSDW/G/AYDJJ

SPMJ — Miscellaneous works
Schurmann, Gerard
Serenade for solo violin/ by Gerard Schurmann; fingering by
Yossi Zironi. — Sevenoaks: Novello, 1973. — 9p; 4to.
Duration 15 mins.
£1.20
(B73-50370)

Wuorinen, Charles
The long and the short: violin solo/ by Charles Wuorinen. —
New York; [London]: Peters, 1972. — 7p; 4to.
Unpriced
(B73-50371)

SQ — VIOLA
SQ/AC — Exercises
Mazas, Jacques Féréol
[75 études mélodiques et progressives pour violon. Op.36, nos.
1-30]. Etudes spéciales. Op.36, nos 1-30: for the viola/ by J.F.
Mazas; transcribed and edited by Leonard Mogill. — New York;
London: Schirmer, 1972. — 46p; 4to.
Unpriced
(B73-50373)

Mazas, Jacques Féréol
[75 études mélodiques et progressives pour violon. Op.36,
nos.31-56]. Etudes brillantes. Op.36, nos 31-56/ by J.F. Mazas;
transcribed and edited by Leonard Mogill. — New York; London:
Schirmer, 1972. — 47p; 4to.
Unpriced
(B73-50372)

Matz, Arnold
Scale and chord studies for viola/ by Arnold Matz. — Leipzig;
[London]: Peters, 1971. — 47p; 4to.
Unpriced
(B73-50374)

Uhl, Alfred
Zwanzig Etuden für Viola/ von Alfred Uhl. — Mainz; London:
Schott, 1973. — 23p; 4to.
£1.30
(B73-51224)

SQP — VIOLA & PIANO
SQP/X — Canons
Anderson, Muriel Bradford
Prelude in canon: viola or horn in F/ by M. Bradford Anderson.
— London: Boosey and Hawkes, 1973. — 4to.
Score (7p)& part.
£0.40
Also classified at WTP/X
(B73-50794)

SQPE — Sonatas
Appleton, Michael J
[Sonata for viola & piano (left hand) in G minor]. Sonata in G
minor for viola and piano (left hand)/ by M.J. Appleton. —
London: Thames, 1973. — fol.
Score (8p.) & part.
Unpriced
(B73-50795)

Bunin, Revol
[Sonata for viola and piano. Op.26]. Sonate für Viola und Klavier.
Opus 26/ von Revol Bunin; Bezeichnung der Violastimme von
Rudolf Barschai. — Leipzig; [London]: Peters, 1972. — 4to.
Score (47p.) & part.
Unpriced
(B73-50375)

Gál, Hans
Sonata for viola and pianoforte. Op. 101/ by Hans Gál. —
London: Simrock, 1973. — 4to.
Score (25p.) & part.
Unpriced
(B73-51225)

Kotzwara, Franz
[Sonata for viola & basso continuo in C major. Op. 2, no.2].
Sonata C-Dur für Viola und Basso continuo/ von Franz
Koczwara; herausgegeben von Ulrich Drüner. — Mainz; London:
Schott, 1973. — 4to.
Score (11p.) & 2 parts.
Unpriced
(B73-50376)

Onslow, George
[Sonata for viola & piano in C minor. Op.16, no.2]. Sonata in C
minor for viola (or violoncello) and piano. Op.16, no.2/ by George
Onslow; edited by Uwe Wegner. — Cassell; London: Bärenreiter,
1972. — 4to.
Score (41p.) & 2 parts. — With a corrigenda slip inserted.
£3.30
(B73-50796)

SQPG — Suites
Gál, Hans
Suite for viola and pianoforte. Op. 102a/ by Hans Gál. —
London: Simrock, 1973. — 4to.
Score (29p) & part.
Unpriced
(B73-51226)

SQPJ — Miscellaneous works
Kiel, Friedrich
[3 Romanzen. Op.69]. Three romances: for viola and pianoforte/
by Friedrich Kiel. — London: Musica rara, 1972. — 15p; 4to.
A facsimile reprint of the original edition published, Berlin: Bote und Boch,
circa 1877.
Unpriced
(B73-50377)

SQPK/AHVL — Arrangements. Sarabandes
Grieg, Edvard
[Holberg suite. Op.40. Sarabande: arr]. Sarabande/ by Edvard
Grieg; arranged for viola and piano by Olaf Piers. — Street:
Cornelius, 1968. — 4to.
Score (2p) & part.
Unpriced
(B73-50797)

SQPK/DW — Arrangements. Songs, etc
Fox, Peter
Two nightsongs/ arranged as an easy solo for viola with piano by
Peter Fox. — Street: Cornelius, 1968. — 4to.
Score (2p) & part. — Contents: 1.Nachts. Op.1, no.5, by Peter Cornelius -
2.Bitte. Op.9, no.3, by Robert Franz.
Unpriced
(B73-50798)

SQPK/LF — Arrangements. Concertos
Martinu, Bohuslav
[Rhapsody concerto for viola: arr]. Rhapsody-concerto for viola
and orchestra/ by Bohuslav Martinu; reduction for viola and
piano by Jürgen Sommer. — Cassel; London: Bärenreiter, 1972.
— 4to.
£1.95
(B73-50378)

Stamitz, Anton
[Concerto for viola in B flat major: arr]. Konzert für Viola,
B-dur/ von Anton Stamitz; erstmals herausgegeben und mit
Kadenzen versehen von Walter Lebermann; Klavierauszug von
Helmut May. — Mainz; London: Schott, 1972. — 4to.
Score (31p.) & part.
£1.70
(B73-50379)

SQPM — UNACCOMPANIED VIOLA
SQPMJ — Miscellaneous works
Stiles, Frank
Four pieces for solo viola/ by Frank Stiles; edited by Winifred
Copperwheat. — London: Mixolydian Press, 1970. — 4p; 4to.
Unpriced
(B73-50799)

Vieuxtemps, Henri
[Capriccio for viola. Op. 55, no.9]. Capriccio für Viola. Op post./
von Henri Vieuxtemps; herausgegeben von Ulrich Druner. —
Mainz; London: Schott, 1973. — 3p; 4to.
£0.80
(B73-51227)

SR — CELLO
SR/AC — Tutors
Doppelbauer, Rupert
Einführung in das Violoncellospiel/ von Rupert Doppelbauer. —
Mainz; London: Schott.
Band 1. — 1973. — 47p; 4to. —
£2.00
(B73-51228)

SR/AF — Exercises
Wheeler, Eunice
Short exercises in position changing for the cello/ by Eunice
Wheeler. — Street: Cornelius.
Bk 1: Position 2 to 5. — 1968. — 4p; 4to. —
Unpriced
(B73-50800)
Bk 2: Positions 6, 7 and thumb. — 1968. — 6p; 4to. —
Unpriced
(B73-50801)

SRN — CELLO ENSEMBLE
SRNTK/AHR — Trios. Arrangements. Minuets
Blow, John
[The self-banished. Minuet: arr]. Minuet/ by John Blow; arranged
for cello trio by Peter Fox. — Street: Cornelius, 1968. — 4to.
Score (2p) & 2 parts. The part of the 1st cello appears on the back page of
the score.
Unpriced
(B73-50802)

SRNU — Duets
Josephs, Wilfred
14 caprices: for cello duet (student and teacher)/ by Wilfred Josephs; edited by Sylvia Bor. — London: Chappell, 1973. — 16p; 4to.
£0.60

(B73-50803)

SRNUK/AAY — Duets. Arrangements. Collections
Koch, Edwin
Leichte Duospiel für Violoncelli/ bearbeitet von Edwin Koch. — Mainz; London: Schott.
Heft 2. — 1973. — 24p; 4to. —
£1.44

(B73-51229)

Koch, Edwin
Leichte Duospiel: fur zwei Violoncelli/ bearbeitet von Edwin Koch. — Mainz; London: Schott.
Heft 1. — 1971. — 24p; 4to. —
£0.90

(B73-51230)

Koch, Edwin
Leichtes Duospiel für zwei Violoncelli/ bearbeitet von Edwin Koch. — Mainz; London: Schott.
Heft 1. — 1971. — 24p; 4to. —
£0.90

(B73-51231)

SRP — CELLO & PIANO
SRPE — Sonatas
Coke, Roger Sacheverell
[Sonata for cello & piano in D minor. Op.24]. First 'cello sonata (in D minor)/ by R. Sacheverell Coke. — London: Chappell, 1972. — 35p; 4to.
Unpriced

(B73-50380)

Gerhard, Roberto
Sonata for cello and piano/ by Roberto Gerhard. — London: Oxford University Press, 1972. — 30p; 4to.
Duration 16 mins.
ISBN 0 19 356738 5 : £1.90

(B73-50381)

Walters, Gareth
Sonata for cello and piano/ by Gareth Walters; cello fingering by George Isaac. — Chesham: Ricordi, 1972. — 4to.
Score (24p.) & part.
Unpriced

(B73-50382)

SRPH — Dances
Downing, Michael
Four little dances: for cello (in first position) and piano/ by Michael Downing. — Street: Cornelius.
Score (2p) & part.
Nos.1 and 2. — 1968. — 4to.
Unpriced

(B73-50804)

Nos.3 and 4. — 1968. — 4to.
Unpriced

(B73-50805)

SRPJ — Miscellaneous works
Berkeley, Lennox
Duo for cello and piano/ by Lennox Berkeley. — London: Chester, 1973. — 4to.
Score (14p.) & part.
Unpriced

(B73-50383)

SRPK — Arrangements
Saint-Saens, Camille
[Carnival des animaux. Le Cygne: arr]. Le Cygne = The swan/ by C. Saint-Saëns; edited for cello (or viola) and piano by Robin de Smet. — Sevenoaks: Paxton, 1972. — 4to.
Score (4p.) & part.
£0.25

(B73-50384)

SRPK/AAY — Arrangements. Collections
Forbes, Watson
Classical and romantic pieces for cello and piano/ arranged by Watson Forbes. — London: Oxford University Press, 1973. — 4to.
Score (24p.) & part.
ISBN 0 19 356471 8 : £0.85

(B73-50806)

SRPK/AHVL — Arrangements. Sarabandes
Grieg, Edvard
[Holberg suite. Op.40. Sarabande: arr]. Sarabande/ by Edvard Grieg; arranged for cello and piano by Olaf Piers. — Street: Cornelius, 1968. — 4to.
Score (2p) & part.
Unpriced

(B73-50807)

SRPK/DW — Arrangements. Songs, etc
Fox, Peter
Two nightsongs/ arranged as an easy solo for cello with piano by Peter Fox. — Street: Cornelius, 1968. — 4to.
Score (2p) & part. — Contents: 1.Nachts. Op.1, no.5, by Peter Cornelius - 2.Bitte. Op.9, no.3, by Robert Franz.
Unpriced

(B73-50808)

SRPK/LF — Arrangements. Concertos
Reicha, Joseph
[Concerto for cello in C major. Op.2, Livre 2: arr]. Concerto, C major: for violoncello and orchestra/ by Joseph Reicha; edited and arranged for cello and piano by B. Hummel and G. Reithmüller. — Hamburg; London: Simrock, 1973. — 4to.
Score (44p.) & part.
Unpriced

(B73-51232)

SRPM — UNACCOMPANIED CELLO
SRPMG — Suites
Brearley, Denis
[Suite for cello, no.2]. Suite no.2 for unaccompanied cello/ by Denis Brearley. — Croydon: Lengnick, 1973. — 4p; 4to.
£0.30

(B73-51233)

Roxburgh, Edwin
Partita for solo violoncello/ by Edwin Roxburgh. — London: United Music, 1973. — 8p; 4to.
Unpriced

(B73-51234)

SRPMJ — Miscellaneous works
Lees, Benjamin
Study no.1 for unaccompanied cello/ by Benjamin Lees. — London: Boosey and Hawkes, 1972. — 8p; 4to.
£0.65

(B73-50385)

Ridout, Alan
Music for three violoncelli/ by Alan Ridout. — London: Schott, 1972. — 4to.
Score (11p.) & 3 parts.
£0.75

(B73-50386)

SSN — DOUBLE BASS ENSEMBLE
SSNS — Quartets
Hartmann, Erich
Quartet for double basses/ by Erich Hartmann. — London: Yorke, 1973. — 4to.
Score (6p) & 4 parts.
Unpriced

(B73-51235)

SSNU — Duets
Bottesini, Giovanni
[Duet for double bass, no.1]. Grand duetto 1: for double bass/ by Giovanni Bottesini; edited by Rodney Slatford. — London: Yorke, 1972. — 32p; 4to.
Unpriced

(B73-50387)

Cole, Bruce
Sonnets: for two double basses/ by Bruce Cole. — Revised ed. — London: Yorke, 1973. — 4p; 4to.
Two copies.
Unpriced

(B73-51236)

Cole, Bruce
Sonnets for two double basses/ by Bruce Cole. — Revised ed. — London: Yorke, 1973. — 4p; 4to.
Two copies.
Unpriced

(B73-51237)

SSP — DOUBLE BASS & PIANO
SSPJ — Miscellaneous works
Iatauro, Michael
Two pieces for string bass and piano/ by Michael Iatauro. — New York; London: Schirmer, 1972. — 4to.
Score (15p.) & part.
Unpriced

(B73-50388)

SSPM — UNACCOMPANIED DOUBLE BASS
Rands, Bernard
Memo 1: for solo contra bass/ by Bernard Rands. — London: Universal, 1973. — 3s,sh; obl.fol.
The 3 single sheets are of oblong folio dimension when opened out.
Unpriced
(B73-50809)

STPM — UNACCOMPANIED VIOL
STR/AC — Treble viol. Tutors
Baines, Francis
A tutor for the treble viol/ by Francis Baines. — Cambridge: Gamut, 1973. — 13p; obl. 4to.
Unpriced
(B73-51238)

STT/AC — Tenor viol. Tutors
Baines, Francis
A tutor for the tenor viol/ by Francis Baines. — Cambridge: Gamut, 1973. — 13p; obl. 4to.
Unpriced
(B73-51239)

STU/AC — Bass viol. Tutors
Baines, Francis
A tutor for the bass viol, (consort bass)/ by Francis Baines. — Cambridge: Gamut, 1973. — 13p; obl 4to.
Unpriced
(B73-51240)

TQP — HARP & PIANO
TQPK — Arrangements
Francaix, Jean
Jeu poetique: en six movements pour harpe et orchestre/ par Jean Francaix, [reduction for harp and piano]. — Mainz; London: Schott, 1973. — 67p; 4to.
£3.00
(B73-50810)

TQPM — UNACCOMPANIED HARP
TQPMJ — Miscellaneous works
Berkeley, Lennox
Nocturne: for harp/ by Lennox Berkeley; edited by David Watkins. — London: Stainer and Bell, 1972. — [4]p; 4to.
£0.50
(B73-50389)

Dodgson, Stephen
Fantasy: for harp/ by Stephen Dodgson; edited by David Watkins. — London: Stainer and Bell, 1972. — 10p; 4to.
£0.66
(B73-50390)

Harries, David
Three stanzas. Op 8: for harp solo/ by David Harries; edited by David Watkins. — London: Stainer & Bell, 1973. — 8p; 4to.
Unpriced
(B73-50811)

Van Delden, Lex
Notturno: for solo harp/ by Lex van Delden. — South Croydon: Lengnick, 1972. — 4p; 4to.
£0.45
(B73-50391)

TS — GUITAR
TS/AC — Tutors
Zanoskar, Hubert
Neue Gitarren-Schule/ von Hubert Zanoskar. — Mainz; London: Schott.
Band 1. — 1969. — 64p; 4to. —
£1.125
(B73-51241)

TS/AF — Exercises
Benham, Patrick
Four short studies: for beginners on the guitar/ by Patrick Benham. — Street: Cornelius, 1969. — 3p; 4to.
Unpriced
(B73-50812)

White, Tony
Seven short and easy studies: for beginners on the Spanish guitar/ by Tony White. — Street: Cornelius, 1967. — 2p; 4to.
Unpriced
(B73-50813)

Zanoskar, Hubert
Übungen und Spielstücke: Beiheft zu Band 1 der neuen Gitarren-Schule/ von Hubert Zanoskar. — Mainz; London: Schott, 1969. — 48p; 4to.
£0.90
(B73-51242)

TSN — GUITAR ENSEMBLE
TSNTK — Trios. Arrangements
Bach, Johann Sebastian
[Invention for keyboard in E major. S.792: arr]. Sinfonia in G/ by Bach; arranged as a guitar trio by Peter Fox. — Street: Cornelius, 1969. — 2p; 4to.
Unpriced
(B73-50814)

Bach, Johann Sebastian
[Das wohltemperirte Clavier. Prelude no.23. S.868: arr]. Prelude no.23. S.868/ by J.S. Bach; arranged for guitar trio by Walter Gramercy. — Street: Cornelius, 1968. — 2p; 4to.
Unpriced
(B73-50815)

TSNU — Duets
Barrell, Joyce
The three inns. — London: Thames.
Contents: The oyster - The shepherd and his dog - The fox.
for two guitars/ by Joyce Barrell. — 1972. — 4p; 4to.
Unpriced
(B73-50392)

TSNUK — Duets. Arrangements
Bach, Johann Sebastian
[Preludes for keyboard. S.935, 939: arr]. Two short preludes/ by Bach; arranged for guitar duet by Peter Fox. — Street: Cornelius, 1969. — 2p; 4to.
Unpriced
(B73-50816)

TSNUK/AAY — Duets. Arrangements. Collections
Spencer, Robert
Elizebethan duets for two guitars/ edited by Robert Spencer; transcribed by Oscar Ohlsen. — London: Stainer and Bell, 1973. — 24p; 4to.
Unpriced
(B73-50817)

Williams, John
Guitar transcriptions from the Cube L.P., 'The height below'/ transcribed by John Williams. — London: Essex Music, 1973. — 44p; 4to.
Unpriced
(B73-51243)

TSNUK/AHVL — Duets. Arrangements. Sarabandes
Bach, Johann Sebastian
[English suite for keyboard, no.5. S.810. Sarabande: arr]. Sarabande/ by Bach; arranged for guitar duet by Walter Gramercy. — Street: Cornelius, 1968. — 2p; 4to.
Unpriced
(B73-50818)

TSPM — UNACCOMPANIED GUITAR
TSPM/T — Variations
Berkeley, Lennox
Theme and variations for guitar/ by Lennox Berkeley; edited and fingered by Angelo Gilardino. — London: Chester, 1973. — 7p; 4to.
Unpriced
(B73-51244)

Smith Brindle, Reginald
Variants on two themes of J.S. Bach: guitar solo B-A-C-H and the fugue subject of the G minor fugue Book 1 of the '48'/ by Reginald Smith Brindle. — London: Peters, 1973. — 11p; 4to.
Duration 15-1/2 min.
Unpriced
(B73-51245)

TSPMG — Suites
Roe, Betty
Summer suite: five easy pieces for guitar/ by Betty Roe. — London: Thames, 1973. — 3p; 4to.
Unpriced
(B73-50819)

Roe, Betty
Summer suite. — London: Thames.
five easy pieces for guitar/ by Betty Roe. — 1973. — 3p; 4to. —
Unpriced
(B73-50393)

TSPMH/G/AYK — Folk dances. Collections. Spain
Mairants, Ivor
Flamenco guitar albums/ compiled by Ivor Mairants. — Croydon: Belwin-Mills.
Album no.3. — 1973. — 31p; 4to. —
Unpriced
(B73-51246)

TSPMHJF — Beguines
Benham, Patrick
    Beguine: for guitar/ by Patrick Benham. — Street: Cornelius,
    1970. — 1p; 4to.
    Unpriced
                                                                                  (B73-50820)

TSPMHVKK — Rumbas
Benham, Patrick
    Elegy and rumba: two short and easy solos for guitar/ by Patrick
    Benham. — Street: Cornelius, 1969. — 2p; 4to.
    Unpriced
                                                                                  (B73-50821)

TSPMJ — Miscellaneous works
Bedford, David
    You asked for it: for acoustic guitar solo/ by David Bedford. —
    London: Universal, 1973. — 7p; 4to.
    Unpriced
                                                                                  (B73-51247)

Brouwer, Leo
    La Espiral eterna: para guitarra/ por Leo Brouwer. — Mainz;
    London: Schott, 1973. — 9p; 4to.
    Duration 7 min.
    £1.08
                                                                                  (B73-51248)

Fetler, Paul
    Four movements: for guitar/ by Paul Fetler. — Mainz; London:
    Schott, 1973. — 11p; 4to.
    £0.90
                                                                                  (B73-50822)

Giuliani, Mauro
    Grande ouverture. Op 61/ von Mauro Giuliani; herausgegeben
    und mit Fingersatz versehen von Anton Stingl. — Mainz; London:
    Schott, 1973. — 15p; 4to.
    £0.80
                                                                                  (B73-50823)

Loyd, Rob
    Rob Loyd folio of graduated guitar solos/ edited by Ike Isaacs. —
    London: Kadence Music, Affiliated Music, 1973. — 24p; 4to.
    £0.75
                                                                                  (B73-51249)

Moscheles, Ignaz
    Grande due concertante: für Gitarre & Klavier/ von Ignaz
    Moschesles und Mauro Giuliani; herausgegeben und bearbeitet von
    Siegfried Behrend. — Hamburg; London: Simrock, 1973. — 4to.
    Score (68p.) & part.
    Unpriced
                                                                                  (B73-51250)

TSPMK — Arrangements
Brahms, Johannes
    [Selections: arr]. Short and easy classics/ by Brahms; arranged for
    Spanish guitar by Peter Fox. — Street: Cornelius.
    Contents: Waltz. Op.39, no.15 - The cottage by the willow tree - Cradle
    song.
    Ser 1. — 1967. — 2p; 4to.
    Unpriced
                                                                                  (B73-50824)

Debussy, Claude
    [Suite bergamasque. Clair de lune: arr]. Clair de lune/ by Claude
    Debussy; arranged as a solo for guitar by Peter Fox, edited by
    Patrick Benham. — Street: Cornelius, 1970. — 4p; 4to.
    Unpriced
                                                                                  (B73-50825)

Henze, Hans Werner
    [El Cimarron. Selections: arr]. Memorias de 'El Cimarron'/ by
    Hans Werner Henze; adapted for guitar by Leo Brouwer. —
    Mainz; London: Schott, 1973. — 19p; 4to.
    £1.60
                                                                                  (B73-50826)

Vaughan Williams, Ralph
    [Sir John in love.. Fantasia on Greensleeves]. Fantasia on
    'Greensleeves'/ by R. Vaughan Williams; arranged for solo guitar
    by Hector Quine. — London: Oxford University Press, 1973. —
    5p; 4to.
    ISBN 0 19 359309 2 : £0.30
                                                                                  (B73-50394)

TSPMK/AHHW/AY — Arrangements. Blues. Collections
Kreidler, Dieter
    Easy rider: leichte Blues-Satz nach alten und neuen Melodien
    bearbeitet für Gitarre/ von Dieter Kreidler. — Mainz; London:
    Schott, 1973. — 16p; 8vo.
    £1.44
                                                                                  (B73-51251)

TSPMK/AHR — Arrangements. Minuets
Bach family
    [Selections: arr]. Three minuets/ by the sons of Bach; arranged for
    guitar by Lennox Hines. — Street: Cornelius, 1968. — 2p; 4to.
    Contents: No.1: by J.C. Bach - No.2 W.F. Bach - No.3: C.P.E. Bach.
    Unpriced
                                                                                  (B73-50827)

TSPMK/AHW — Arrangements. Waltzes
Schubert, Franz
    [Waltzes for piano. D.779, no.12, D.734, no.15 & D.924, no.9:
    arr]. Three waltzes/ by Franz Schubert; arranged for guitar by
    Lennox Hines. — Street: Cornelius, 1968. — 2p; 4to.
    Unpriced
                                                                                  (B73-50828)

Tchaikovsky, Peter
    [Serenade for string orchestra. Op.48. Waltz: arr]. Waltz/ by
    Tchaikowsky; arranged for Spanish guitar by Peter Fox. — Street:
    Cornelius, 1968. — 3p; 4to.
    Unpriced
                                                                                  (B73-50829)

TSPMK/CM — Arrangements. Musical plays
Taylor, John
    [The water babies. Selections: arr]. The water babies: simplified
    children's selection for easy piano/organ/guitar, etc/ music and
    lyrics by John Taylor. — London: Chappell, 1973. — 18p; 4to.
    £0.80
    Primary classification PWPK/CM

TSPMK/DM — Arrangements. Hymns
Bach, Johann Sebastian
    [Herz und Mund und That und Leben. S.147. Wohl mir dass ich
    Jesum habe: arr]. Jesus, joy of man's desiring/ by Johann
    Sebastian Bach; easily arranged for Spanish guitar by Peter Fox.
    — Street: Cornelius, 1967. — 3p; 4to.
    Unpriced
                                                                                  (B73-50830)

TSPMK/DR — Arrangements. Psalms
James, *Brother*
    Brother James's air/ arranged for solo guitar by Hector Quine. —
    London: Oxford University Press, 1973. — 2p; 4to.
    Material from Gordon Jacob's arrangement of this tune for unison voices
    and descant is used here.
    ISBN 0 19 358403 4 : £0.20
                                                                                  (B73-50395)

TSPMK/DW/G/AY — Arrangements. Folk songs. Collections
Cammin, Heinz
    Lied über die Grenze, Folklore fremder Lander/ Bearbeitet von
    Heinz Cammin, Ausgabe für Gitarre solo mit vollstandigem Text.
    — Mainz; London: Schott, 1973. — 16p; 8vo.
    £1.44
                                                                                  (B73-51252)

TSX — SITAR
TSX/AC — Sitar. Tutors
Alford, Clem
    The sitar manual: for the Western musician/ by Clem Alford. —
    London: Keith Prowse, 1973. — 66p; 4to.
    With a chart containing 50 popular ragas.
    £2.75
                                                                                  (B73-50831)

TWPM — UNACCOMPANIED LUTE
TWPMJ — Miscellaneous works
Maschera, Florentio
    [Libro primo de canzoni da sonare. La Maggia]. Canzona 'La
    Maggia'/ by Florentio Maschera; edited by Howard Mayer
    Brown. — London: Oxford University Press, 1973. — 7p; 8vo.
    ISBN 0 19 341204 7 : Unpriced
    Primary classification LNS
                                                                                  (B73-50657)

UM — WIND BAND
Kroeger, Karl
    Divertimento for band/ by Karl Kroeger. — New York; London:
    Boosey and Hawkes, 1972. — 4to.
    Score (40p.) & 69 parts.
    £5.25
                                                                                  (B73-50396)

UMK — Arrangements
Copland, Aaron
    [El Salon Mexico: arr]. El Salon Mexico/ by Aaron Copland;
    transcribed for concert band by Mark H. Hindsley. — New York;
    London: Boosey and Hawkes, 1972. — 4to.
    Score (56p.) & 71 parts.
    £7.50
                                                                                  (B73-50397)

UMM — MILITARY BAND
UMMGM — Marches
Goldman, Edwin Franko
March for all seasons: march/ by Edwin Franko Goldman. — New York; London: Boosey and Hawkes, 1973. — 8vo.
Conductor (4p) & 57 parts.
£1.75

(B73-50398)

Goldman, Edwin Franko
March for peace/ by Edwin Franko Goldman. — New York; London: Boosey and Hawkes, 1973. — 8vo.
Conductor (7p) & 57 parts.
£1.75

(B73-50399)

Goldman, Edwin Franko
Right on march/ by Edwin Franko Goldman. — New York; London: Boosey and Hawkes, 1973. — 8vo.
Conductor (4p) & 57 parts.
£1.75

(B73-50400)

Laudan, Stanley
March of the champions/ by Stanley Laudan; arranged for military band by Terry Creswick. — London: Peter Maurice, 1973. — obl. 8vo.
Conductor & 29 parts. — With several copies of various parts.
Unpriced

(B73-51253)

Neville, Paul
Sword of honour: concert march for band/ by Paul Neville. — London: Boosey and Hawkes, 1973. — 4to.
Score (11p.) & 34 parts. Various parts are in duplicate.
£5.40

(B73-50832)

UMMGM/KH — Regimental marches
Jeanes, E W
The Blues and Royals regimental slow march/ arranged by E.W. Jeanes. — London: Boosey and Hawkes, 1973. — 30pt; obl 8vo.
Various parts are in duplicate.
£1.00

(B73-51254)

UMMJ — Miscellaneous works
Brunelli, Louis Jean
Essay for Cyrano/ by Louis Jean Brunelli. — New York; London: Boosey and Hawkes, 1973. — 4to.
Score (52p) & 73 parts.
£10.00

(B73-50833)

George, Thom Ritter
Western overture/ by Thom Ritter George. — New York; London: Boosey and Hawkes, 1973. — 4to.
Score (31p.) & 72 parts.
£10.00

(B73-50834)

Tull, Fisher
Sketches on a Tudor psalm based on a setting of the second psalm/ by Thomas Tallis: for military band/ by Fisher Tull. — New York; London: Boosey and Hawkes, 1973. — 4to.
Score (59p.) & 73 parts.
£12.50

(B73-51255)

UMMK/AGM/JS — Arrangements. Marches. Television
Trombey, Jack
Eye level: theme from the Thames TV series 'Van der Valk'/ by Jack Trombey; arranged by Norman Richardson. — London: Boosey and Hawkes, 1973. — obl,8vo.
Conductor (4p) & 45 parts.
Unpriced
Primary classification WMK/AGM/JS

UMMK/CM — Arrangements. Musical plays
Bricusse, Leslie
[The good old bad old days. Selections: arr]. The good old bad old days/ by Leslie Bricusse and Anthony Newley; selection arranged by Edrich Siebert. — London: Peter Maurice, 1973. — obl.8vo.
Conductor & 27 parts. With several copies of various parts.
Unpriced

(B73-50401)

UMMK/DW — Arrangements. Songs, etc
Hirsch, Walter
['Deed I do: arr]. 'Deed I do: march/ by Walter Hirsch and Fred Rose; arranged for military band by Terry Creswick. — London: Keith Prowse, 1973. — obl. 8vo.
Conductor & 28 parts. — With several copies of various parts.
Unpriced

(B73-51256)

Siebert, Edrich
Singalong: selection no.1/ arranged for military band by Edrich Siebert. — London: Keith Prowse, 1972. — 8vo.
Conductor & 28 parts. — With several copies of various parts.
Unpriced

(B73-51257)

UMMK/JR — Arrangements. Films
Walton, Sir William
[Richard III. Prelude: arr]. Prelude/ by William Walton; arranged by Norman Richardson. — London: Boosey and Hawkes, 1973. — 4to.
Conductor (9p.) & 31 parts.
£4.50

(B73-50835)

UMMP — SOLO INSTRUMENT (S) & MILITARY BAND
UMMPVUS — Alto saxophone & military band
Grundman, Clare
Concertante for E flat alto saxophone and military band/ by Clare Grundman. — New York; London: Boosey and Hawkes, 1973. — 4to.
Score (44p.) & 73 parts.
£12.00

(B73-51258)

UMMPWTZ — Baritone & military band
Jacob, Gordon
Fantasia: for euphonium (baritone) and band/ by Gordon Jacob. — London: Boosey and Hawkes, 1973. — 4to.
Score (44p.) & 37 parts.
£8.75
Primary classification UMMPWW

(B73-50836)

UMMPWW — Euphonium & military band
Jacob, Gordon
Fantasia: for euphonium (baritone) and band/ by Gordon Jacob. — London: Boosey and Hawkes, 1973. — 4to.
Score (44p.) & 37 parts.
£8.75
Also classified at UMMPWTZ

(B73-50836)

UN — WIND ENSEMBLE
UNQ/W — Sextets, Rondos
Weber, Carl Maria, *Freiherr von*
[Adagio and rondo for wind sextet]. Adagio und Rondo für 2 Klarinetten, 2 Horner und 2 Fagotte/ von Carl Maria von Weber; herausgegeben von Wolfgang Sandner. — Mainz; London: Schott, 1973. — 4to.
Score (20p.) & 6 parts - Probably identical with the work described as 'Harmonie in B' in Jahn, page 429.
£2.88

(B73-51259)

UNR — Quintets
Jones, Kelsey
Quintet for winds: flute, oboe, clarinet in B flat, horn in F, bassoon/ by Kelsey Jones. — London: Peters, 1972. — 4to.
Score (32p.) & 5 parts. — Duration 14 mins.
Unpriced

(B73-50402)

Patterson, Paul
Comedy for five winds: flute, oboe, clarinet in B flat, horn in F and bassoon/ by Paul Patterson. — London: Weinberger, 1973. — 28p; 8vo.
Duration 14 min.
Unpriced

(B73-51260)

UNRG — Quintets. Suites
Standford, Patric
Suite française: for wind quintet/ by Patric Standford. — Sevenoaks: Novello, 1973. — 4to.
Score (13p.) & 5 parts.
£1.10

(B73-51261)

UNSG — Quartets. Suites
Muffat, Georg
[Florilegium.. Suites]. Suites from the 'Florilegium': for four or five parts (string or wind instruments)/ by Georg Muffat; edited by Waldemar Woehl. — Cassel; London: Bärenreiter, 1972. — 4to.
Score (20p.) & 5 parts. — Contents: Suite no.1 in D major - Suite no.2 in G minor.
£1.95
Primary classification NXNSG

(B73-50280)

**UNSK/AH/AYE — Quartets. Arrangements. Dances. Collections.
Germany**
Stone, David
La Renaissance: songs and dances by French and German
composers of the sixteenth and seventeenth centuries/ arranged for
wind quartet by David Stone. — London: Boosey and Hawkes,
1973. — 4to.
Conductor's score (8p) & 5 parts.
Unpriced
Primary classification UNSK/AH/AYH

**UNSK/AH/AYH — Quartets. Arrangements. Dances. Collections.
France**
Stone, David
La Renaissance: songs and dances by French and German
composers of the sixteenth and seventeenth centuries/ arranged for
wind quartet by David Stone. — London: Boosey and Hawkes,
1973. — 4to.
Conductor's score (8p) & 5 parts.
Unpriced
Also classified at UNSK/AH/AYE

(B73-51262)

UNUK — Duets. Arrangements
Mozart, Wolfgang Amadeus
[Duets for two horns. K.487: arr]. 12 easy duets for winds/ by
Wolfgang Amadeus Mozart; transcribed by Henry Charles Smith.
— New York; London: Schirmer.
Volume 1: For flutes, oboes (and saxophones). — 1972. — 14p; 4to.
Unpriced

(B73-50837)

Volume 2: for clarinets trumpets (and F horns). — 1972. — 14p; 4to.
Unpriced

(B73-50838)

VN — WOODWIND ENSEMBLE
VNN — Octets
Poot, Marcel
Mosaïque pour huit instruments a vent bois/ par Marcel Poot. —
London: Universal, 1969. — 24p; 8vo.
Miniature score.
Unpriced

(B73-51263)

Tull, Fisher
Scherzino. Op 27a: for piccolo, three flutes, three B flat clarinets
and B flat bass clarinet/ by Fisher Tull. — New York; London:
Boosey and Hawkes, 1973. — 4to.
Score (23p.) & 8 parts.
£4.00

(B73-50839)

VNPG — Septets. Suites
Hanmer, Ronald
Suite for seven: 2 flutes, oboe, 3 clarinets, bassoon/ by Ronald
Hanmer. — Ampleforth: Emerson, 1973. — 8vo & 4to.
Score (15p.) & 7 parts.
Unpriced

(B73-51264)

VNRG — Quintets. Suites
Buchanan, Gary Robert
Sweets for woodwind quintet/ by Gary Robert Buchanan. — New
York: Galaxy; London: Galliard, 1973. — 4to.
Score (20p) & 5 parts.
Unpriced

(B73-51265)

VNT — Trios
Blezard, William
A pair of pieces: for 2 flutes and clarinet/ by William Blezard. —
London: British and Continental, 1972. — 4pts; 4to.
Contents: 1. Berceuse - 2. Burlesque.
Unpriced

(B73-50840)

Blezard, William
A pair of pieces. — London: British and Continental.
Contents: Berceuse. — 2. Burlesque.
for 2 flutes and clarinet/ by William Blezard. — 1972. — 4pts; 4to.
Unpriced

(B73-50403)

VRN — FLUTE ENSEMBLE
VRNSK — Quartets. Arrangements
Mozart, Wolfgang Amadeus
[Andante for flute clock in F major. K.616: arr]. Andante, F Dur,
KV616: ein Stück für eine Walze in eine kleine Orgel/ von W.A.
Mozart; eingerichtet für 4 Flöten von Stefan Hiby. — Mainz;
London: Schott, 1973. — 4to.
Score (11p.) & 2 parts. The parts for flutes 1, 2 and 3, 4 are printed
severally in score.
£1.20

(B73-50841)

VRNTPWE — Two flutes & keyboard. Sonatas
Graun, Carl Heinrich
[Sonata for two flutes & basso continuo in E flat major]. Sonata in
E flat major for two flutes (violins) and basso continuo/ by Carl
Heinrich Graun; first edition, edited by Herbert Köbel,
continuo-realization by Ernst Meyerolbersleben. — Cassel;
London: Bärenreiter, 1972. — 8vo.
Score (21p.) & 3 parts.
£1.80
Also classified at SNTPWE

(B73-50404)

VRNTQ — Two flutes & piano
Wesley, Samuel
Trio for two flutes & pianoforte/ by Samuel Wesley; edited by
Hugh Cobbe. — London: Oxford University Press, 1973. — 4to.
Score (33p) & 2 parts - Duration 18 min.
ISBN 0 19 359505 2 : £1.60

(B73-51266)

VRNTQHW — Two flutes & piano. Waltzes
Kohler, Ernesto
Valse des fleurs. Op 87: for 2 flutes and piano/ by Ernesto
Kohler; edited by Trevor Wye. — Ampleforth: Emerson, 1973. —
4to.
Score (11p) & 2 parts.
Unpriced

(B73-51267)

VRNUE — Duets. Sonatas
Loeillet, Jean Baptiste, b.1688
[Sonatas for flute duet. Op.5, liv.2, nos,1,4]. Two sonatas for two
flutes/ by J.B. Loeillet; edited by Gwilym Beechey. — London:
Oxford University Press, 1973. — 23p; 4to.
ISBN 0 19 357590 6 : £1.10

(B73-51268)

VRP — FLUTE & PIANO
VRP/AY(XF51) — Collections, 1700-1750
Platt, Richard
Music for flute and basso continuo, 1700-1750: ten pieces/ selected
and edited with a realization of the basso continuo, by Richard
Platt. — London: Oxford University Press, 1972. — 4to.
Score (22p.) & 2 parts.
ISBN 0 19 358270 8 : £0.90

(B73-50405)

VRPJ — Miscellaneous works
Fox, Peter
High stepper!: a short and easy solo for flute and piano/ by Peter
Fox. — Street: Cornelius, 1968. — 4to.
Score (2p) & part.
Unpriced

(B73-50842)

Frankenpohl, Arthur
Introduction and romp: for flute and piano/ by Arthur
Frankenpohl. — New York; London: Schirmer, 1972. — 4to.
Score (15p.) & part.
Unpriced

(B73-50406)

Schulé, Bernard
Petit livre des formes musicales = Spiel mit musikalischen
Formen. Op.83: acht leichter Stücke, für Flöte oder Oboe und
Klavier/ von Bernard Schulé. — Regensburg: Bosse; [London]:
[Bärenreiter], 1972. — 4to.
Score (24p.) & part.
£1.80

(B73-50843)

Wyttenbach, Jurg
Paraphrase: für einen Flötisten und einen Pianisten/ von Jurg
Wyttenbach. — Mainz: Ars viva; London: Schott, 1970. — 28p;
fol.
The three movements are for the following combinations: 1.Flute and piano
- 2.Bass flute and electronic organ - 3.Flute, piano and electronic organ. In
this movement the keyboard instruments are to be played by one person.
£3.00

(B73-50407)

VRPK/AAY — Arrangements. Collections
Moyse, Louis
First solos for the flute player/ transcribed and arranged by Louis
Moyse. — New York; London: Schirmer, 1971. — 4to.
Score (42p.) & part.
Unpriced

(B73-50408)

VRPK/LF — Arrangements. Concertos
Mozart, Wolfgang Amadeus
[Concerto for flute, harp & orchestra in C major. K.299: arr].
Konzert für Flöte, Harfe und Orchester, C-Dur. KV299/ von
Wolfgang Amadeus Mozart; neu durchgesehen von Werner
Richter, Kadenzen zum Konzert, Werner Richter; [reduction for
flute and piano by Emil Prill]. — Frankfurt; London: Peters,
1972. — 4to.
Score (28p) & part.
£3.60

(B73-50844)

VRPLST — FLUTE & VIOL
VRPLSTU — Flute & bass viol
Barrell, Joyce
Dialogues. Op 20: flute and viola da gamba/ by Joyce Barrell. —
London: Thames, 1972. — 15p; fol.
Unpriced

(B73-50845)

VRPLTQ — FLUTE & HARP
VRPLTQE — Sonatas
Alwyn, William
Naiades: fantasy sonata, for flute and harp/ by William Alwyn. —
London: Boosey and Hawkes, 1973. — 4to.
Score (26p.) & part.
Unpriced

(B73-50846)

VRPM — UNACCOMPANIED FLUTE
VRPMK/DE — Arrangements. Religious cantatas
Bach, Johann Sebastian
[Cantatas. Selections: arr]. Flute obbligatos from the cantatas/ by
J.S. Bach; edited by Frans Vester. — London: Universal, 1972. —
53p; 4to.
Unpriced

(B73-50409)

VS — RECORDER
VS/AC — Tutors
Fagan, Margo
Play time: Longman first recorder course/ by Margo Fagan. —
London: Longman.
Stage 1. — 1973. — 25p; obl.8vo. —
ISBN 0 582 18536 x : Unpriced

(B73-50847)

Stage Two. — 1973. — 25p; obl. 8vo. —
ISBN 0 582 18537 8 : £0.25

(B73-51269)

Wastall, Peter
The B and H recorder cards: a programmed method/ designed by
Peter Wastall. — London: Boosey and Hawkes.
20 cards; accompaniments to the cards (35p.).
Set 1. — 1973. — 8vo.
£3.00

(B73-50411)

VSN — RECORDER ENSEMBLE
VSN/AY — Collections
McGrady, Richard J
Four thirteenth century pieces/ arranged for recorders, with
optional percussion and cello, by Richard J. McGrady. —
London: Chester, 1973. — 7p; 4to.
Unpriced

(B73-50412)

VSNPE — Sonatas
Touchin, Colin M
Sonata for recorder group, (2 descants, 2 trebles, 2 tenors, bass).
Op. 2/ by Colin M. Touchin. — Sale: Tomus Publications, 1973.
— 8vo.
Score (20p.) & 4 parts.
Unpriced

(B73-50848)

VSNPG — Septets. Suites
Kear, Warrick
San Casciano: for recorder ensemble, solo sopranino, descants,
trebles, tenors/ by Warrick Kear. — Bury: Tomus, 1973. — 8vo.
Score (14p.) & 4 parts.
Unpriced

(B73-51270)

VSNRK/AH — Arrangements. Dances
Brade, William
[Newe lustige Volten, Couranten zu 5 Stimmen, nos. 11, 16, 17,
25]. First set of quintets for 2 descants, treble, tenor and bass (or
tenor) recorder/ by William Brade; transcribed by Cyril F.
Simkins. — London: Chester, 1973. — 4to.
Score (8p.) & part.
Unpriced

(B73-50413)

VSNRK/Y — Quintets. Fugues
Bach, Wilhelm Friedemann
[Tripelfuge for keyboard in F major. Falck 19: arr]. Tripelfuge/ by
W.F. Bach; arranged for recorder quintet, (sopranino, descant,
treble, tenor, bass) by Dennis A. Bamforth. — Bury: Tomus,
1973. — 8vo.
Score (16p) & 5 parts.
Unpriced

(B73-51271)

VSNRPWK/AHR — Four recorders & keyboard. Arrangements.
Minuets
Handel, George Frideric
[Concerti grossi. Op.3, no.2. Menuet: arr]. Menuet/ by George
Frideric Handel; edited for two descant, treble and tenor
recorders, or four violins and continuo (with bass recorder/cello),
by Freda Dinn. — London: Schott, 1972. — 4to.
Score (4p.) & 5 parts.
Unpriced
Also classified at SNRPWK/AHR

(B73-50414)

VSNRQK/DP/LF/AYB — Four recorders and piano. Arrangements.
Carols. Christmas. Collections. Europe
Benoy, Arthur William
15 European carols/ arranged for recorder ensemble by A.W.
Benoy. — Sevenoaks: Paxton, 1973. — 4to.
Score (17p) & 4 parts.
£1.00

(B73-51272)

VSNSG — Quartets. Suites
Hand, Colin
Fenland suite: for recorder quartet/ by Colin Hand. — London:
Schott, 1973. — 4to.
Score (12p.) & 4 parts.
£0.60

(B73-50849)

VSNSK — Quartets. Arrangements
Vaughan Williams, Ralph
[Three preludes for organ founded on Welsh hymn tunes, no.2].
Prelude on the hymn tune 'Rhosymedre'/ by R. Vaughan
Williams; arranged for SATB recorders by Paul Clark. — London:
Stainer and Bell, 1973. — 4to.
Score (5p) & 4 parts.
Unpriced

(B73-51273)

VSNSK/DU — Quartets. Arrangements. Madrigals
Morley, Thomas
[Madrigalls to foure voyces. Ho! who comes here?]. Ho! who
comes here?: [Madrigal]/ by Thomas Morley; arranged for
recorder quartet, (two trebles, tenor and bass), by Ian Lawrence.
— London: Schott, 1972. — 4to.
£1.00

(B73-50415)

VSNSK/DU/AY — Quartets. Arrangements. Chansons. Collections
Attaingnant, Pierre
[Chansons musicales. Selections: arr]. Eight chansons: for
recorders (Tr T T B or D Tr T B)/ compiled by Pierre
Attaingnant; edited by Laurence Wright. — London: Schott.
Vol.1. — 1973. — 15p; 4to.
£0.75

(B73-51274)

Vol.2. — 1973. — 15p; 4to.
£0.75

(B73-51275)

VSNSK/DW — Arrangements. Songs, etc
Franck, Melchior
Deutsche weltliche Gesäng unnd Täntze/ by Melchior Franck;
edited by Harald Unger. — Cassel; London: Bärenreiter.
Score (14p.) & 5 parts.
1: For descant, treble, tenor and bass recorder. — 1972. — obl.8vo.
£0.90

(B73-50850)

2: For descant recorder, 2 treble recorders and tenor recorder. — 1972. —
obl.8vo.
£0.90

(B73-50851)

[Glogau Songbook. Selections: arr]. Twelve pieces from the
Glogauer Liederbuch/ edited for descant, treble and tenor
recorder by Harald Unger. — Cassel, London: Bärenreiter, 1972.
— 25p; obl.8vo.
£0.75

(B73-50852)

Regnard, Jacques
[Tricinia. Selections: arr]. Deutsche dreistimmige Lieder nach Art
der Neapolitanen oder welschen Villanellen/ by Jacques Regnard;
edited for descant, treble and tenor recorders by Harald Unger. —
Cassel: Bärenreiter, 1972. — 26p; obl.8vo.
£0.75

(B73-50853)

VSNTQHVKK — Two recorders & piano. Rumbas
Gubby, Roy
Air and rumba: descant and treble recorder and piano/ by Roy
Gubby. — London: Boosey and Hawkes, 1973. — 4to.
Score (8p) & 2 parts - The part for descant recorder is printed on the verso
of that for treble recorder and is in duplicate.
Unpriced
(B73-51276)

VSNU — Duets
Genzmer, Harald
[Eleven duets for recorder]. Elf Duette für Sopranblockflöte und
Altblockflöte von Harald Genzmer. — Mainz; London: Schott,
1973. — 12p; 4to.
£1.08
(B73-51277)

VSNUK/DW/AY — Arrangements. Songs. Collections
Unger, Harald
Ten bicinia of the 16th century/ edited for treble and tenor
recorders by Harald Unger. — Cassel; London: Bärenreiter, 1972.
— 21p; obl.8vo.
£0.75
(B73-50854)

VSPLTQ — RECORDER & HARP
VSPLTQTK/DP/LF/AY — Recorder & autoharp. Arrangements.
Christmas carols. Collections
Sadleir, Richard
More carols for recorder, with simple harmonies for auto-harp,
chimes or guitar/ by Richard Sadleir. — London: British and
Continental Music, 1973. — 16p; 8vo.
£0.20
Also classified at VSPLXTPRK/DP/LF/AY
(B73-51278)

VSPLX — RECORDER & PERCUSSION
VSPLXTPRK/DP/LF/AY — Recorder & chime bars. Arrangements.
Christmas carols. Collections
Sadleir, Richard
More carols for recorder, with simple harmonies for auto-harp,
chimes or guitar/ by Richard Sadleir. — London: British and
Continental Music, 1973. — 16p; 8vo.
£0.20
Primary classification VSPLTQTK/DP/LF/AY

VSPM — UNACCOMPANIED RECORDER
VSPM/T — Variations
Linde, Hans Martin
Amorilli mia bella: Hommage a Johann Jacob van Eyck for
recorder solo, descant, treble and bass recorder/ theme by Giulio
Caccini with variations by Johann Jacob van Eyck and Hans
Martin Linde. — Mainz; London: Schott, 1973. — 11p; 4to.
£1.08
(B73-51279)

VSPMK/AAY — Arrangements. Collections
Verrall, Pamela
Singalong tunes for recorder/ arranged by Pamela Verrall. —
London: British and Continental, 1972. — 16p; 4to.
£0.25
(B73-50416)

VSPMK/DW/G/AY — Arrangements. Folk songs. Collections
Sansom, Clive A
Favourites for recorder/ arranged by Clive A. Sansom. —
London: British and Continental.
No.3. — 1972. — 23p; 8vo. —
£0.25
(B73-50417)

VSPMK/DW/G/AYDM — Arrangements. Folk songs. Collections.
Ireland
O Duinn, Micheal
Seinn suas port: ceol don fheadog/ solfa agus cliathnodaireacht,
eagarthoir: Micheal O Duinn. — Dublin (John F. Kennedy Drive,
Naas Rd, Dublin 12): Folens, 1973. — 32p; 8vo.
Unpriced
(B73-51280)

VSQ — SOPRANINO RECORDER
VSQQ/AC — Flageolet. Tutors
Wickham, E H
How to play the flageolet (penny whistle)/ by E.H. Wickham. —
London: Keith Prowse, 1972. — 28p; 8vo.
£0.20
(B73-50418)

VSR — DESCANT RECORDER
VSR/AC — Tutors
Tobin, C
Colour piping/ by C. Tobin. — Bishops Stortford: Helicon Press.
Book 1. — 1973. — 48p; 8vo. —
Unpriced
(B73-51281)

VSR/AF — Exercises
Bergmann, Walter
Descant recorder lessons/ by Walter Bergmann. — London:
Faber, 1973. — 4to.
Score (59p.) & part.
Unpriced
(B73-51282)

VSRPK/AAY — Arrangements. Collections
Camden, John
First solos for the soprano recorder player/ transcribed and
arranged for soprano recorder and piano by John Camden and
Peter Devereux. — New York; [London]: Chappell, 1971. — 4to.
Score (27p.) & part.
Unpriced
(B73-50419)

VSS — TREBLE RECORDER
VSS/AF — Treble recorder. Exercises
Dinn, Freda
Scales and arpeggios: for treble recorder/ by Freda Dinn. —
London: Schott, 1972. — 16p; obl.8vo.
£0.25
(B73-50420)

VSSPE — Sonatas
Barsanti, Francesco
[Sonatas for flute & basso continuo. Op. 1, nos 2, 6]. Two sonatas
for treble recorder and continuo/ by Francesco Barsanti; edited by
Gwilym Beechey. — London: Oxford University Press, 1973. —
4to.
Score (24p.) & 4 parts.
ISBN 0 19 355327 9 : £1.50
(B73-51283)

Genzmer, Harald
[Sonata for treble recorder & piano, no.2]. Zweite Sonata für
Altblockflöte und Klavier/ von Harald Genzmer. — Mainz;
London: Schott, 1973. — 4to.
£1.30
(B73-51284)

Sollima, Eliodoro
Sonata for treble recorder and piano/ by Eliodoro Sollima. —
Mainz; London: Schott, 1973. — 4to.
Score (27p) & part.
£1.40
(B73-50855)

VST — TENOR RECORDER
VSTPJ — Miscellaneous works
Hand, Colin
Plaint: for tenor recorder and harpsichord (or piano)/ by Colin
Hand. — London: Schott, 1973. — 4to.
Score (4p) & part.
£0.50
(B73-50856)

VT — OBOE
VT/AF — Exercises
Hill, Peter
Oboe scales and arpeggios/ compiled by Peter Hill. — Street:
Cornelius, 1969. — 2p; 4to.
Unpriced
(B73-50857)

VTP — OBOE & PIANO
VTPE — Sonatas
Headington, Christopher
Sonatina for oboe and piano/ by Christopher Headington. —
London: Boosey and Hawkes, 1973. — 4to.
Score (20p) & part.
£1.50
(B73-51285)

VTPHP — Jigs
Hand, Colin
Aria and giga: for oboe and piano/ by Colin Hand. — London:
Schott, 1973. — 4to.
Score (5p) & part.
£0.50
(B73-50858)

VTPJ — Miscellaneous works
Paynter, John
Three pieces: for oboe and piano/ by John Paynter. — London:
Oxford University Press, 1972. — 4to.
Score (7p.) & part.
ISBN 0 19 358130 2 : £0.45
(B73-50421)

Roxburgh, Edwin
Images for oboe and piano/ by Edwin Roxburgh. — London:
United Music, 1973. — 10p; 4to.
Two copies of the score.
Unpriced
(B73-51286)

VTPK/AAY — Arrangements. Collections
Craxton, Janet
Second book of oboe solos/ edited and arranged for oboe and piano by Janet Craxton and Alan Richardson. — London: Faber Music, 1972. — 4to.
Score (41p.) & part.
Unpriced

(B73-50422)

Szeszler, Tiber
Oboe music for beginners, with piano accompaniment/ edited by Tiber Szeszler. — London: Boosey and Hawkes, 1972. — 4to.
£0.85

(B73-50859)

Thackray, Roy
Nine short pieces from three centuries/ arranged for oboe and piano by Roy Thackray. — London: Oxford University Press, 1973. — 4to.
Score (17p) & part.
ISBN 0 19 359080 8 : £0.90

(B73-50423)

VTPK/LF — Arrangements. Concertos
Bennett, Richard Rodney
[Concerto for oboe: arr]. Oboe concerto: reduction for oboe and piano. — London: Universal, 1973. — 4to.
Score (27p.) & part. — Duration 16 min.
Unpriced

(B73-51287)

Rosetti, Franz Anton
[Concerto for oboe in C major: arr]. Konzert für Oboe und Kammerorchester, C-Dur/ von Francesco Antonio Rosetti; zum ersten Mal, herausgegeben von Rolf Julius Koch, reduction for 7boe and piano. — Frankfurt; London: Peters, 1972. — 4to.
Score (24p) & part.
£2.20

(B73-50860)

VTPLVV — OBOE & CLARINET
Wurzburger, Walter
Ensemble studies/ by Walter Wurzburger. — London: Thames.
2: Oboe and clarinet. — 1973. — 7p; 4to. —
Unpriced

(B73-50424)

VTPM — UNACCOMPANIED OBOE
VTPMJ — Miscellaneous works
Aston, Peter
Three pieces for oboe solo/ by Peter Aston. — Sevenoaks: Novello, 1973. — 4p; 4to.
£0.30

(B73-50861)

Barrell, Bernard
Divertimento for solo oboe. Op.53/ by Bernard Barrell. — London: Thames, 1973. — 7p; fol.
Unpriced

(B73-50862)

Camilleri, Charles
Talba: for oboe solo/ by Charles Camilleri. — Sevenoaks: Novello, 1973. — 4p; 4to.
£0.50

(B73-50425)

VTQPJ — Oboe d'amore & piano. Miscellaneous works
McCabe, John
Dance-prelude for oboe d'amore (or clarinet) and piano/ by John McCabe. — Sevenoaks: Novello, 1973. — 4to.
Score (8p) & part.
£0.50

(B73-51288)

VUS — ALTO SAXOPHONE
VUSP/T — Variations
Jacob, Gordon
Variations on a Dorian theme: for alto saxophone and piano/ by Gordon Jacob. — Ampleforth: Emerson, 1973. — 4to.
Score (8p) & part.
Unpriced

(B73-50863)

VUSPE — Alto saxophone & piano. Sonatas
Muczynski, Robert
Sonata for alto saxophone and piano. Op.29/ by Robert Muczynski. — New York; London: Schirmer, 1972. — 4to.
Score (15p.) & part.
Unpriced

(B73-50426)

VUSPG — Alto saxophone & piano. Suites
Gál, Hans
Suite for alto saxophone in E flat and pianoforte. Op. 102b/ by Hans Gál. — London: Simrock, 1973. — 4to.
Score (29p) & part.
Unpriced

(B73-51289)

VUSPJ — Miscellaneous works
Grundman, Clare
Concertante for E flat alto saxophone and piano/ by Clare Grundman. — New York; London: Boosey and Hawkes, 1973. — 4to.
Score (16p) & part.
£1.25

(B73-51290)

VV — CLARINET
VV/AF — Exercises
Hill, Peter
Clarinet scales and arpeggios/ compiled by Peter Hill. — Street: Cornelius.
Bk 1: Grades 3 and 4. — 1969. — 2p; 4to. —
Unpriced

(B73-50864)

Hill, Peter
Clarinet scales and arpeggios/ compiled by Peter Hill. — Street: Cornelius.
Bk 2: Grade 5. — 1969. — 2p; 4to. —
Unpriced

(B73-50865)

VVN — CLARINET ENSEMBLE
VVNSK — Quartets. Arrangements
Schumann, Robert
[Kinderscenen. Op.15. Traümerei: arr]. Traümerei/ by Robert Schumann; arranged for clarinet quartet by Peter Hill. — Street: Cornelius, 1969. — 4pt; obl.4to.
Unpriced

(B73-50866)

VVNT — Trios
Verrall, Pamela
Clarinets in concert: clarinet trio/ by Pamela Verrall. — London: British and Continental, 1973. — 12p; 4to.
£0.40

(B73-51291)

VVNTK/AAY — Trios. Arrangements. Collections
Haughton, P J
Ten clarinet trios/ arranged by P.J. Haughton. — London: Oxford University Press, 1973. — 17p; 4to.
ISBN 0 19 357013 0 : £0.50

(B73-50867)

VVNTK/DW/G/AYD — Trios. Arrangements. Folk songs. Collections. England
Pedley, David
Five folk tunes/ arranged for clarinet trio by David Pedley. — London: British and Continental Music, 1973. — 16p; 4to.
£0.30

(B73-50868)

VVNU — Duets
Roper, Keith
Landscapes: for two clarinets/ by Keith Roper. — London: Thames, 1972. — 12p; 4to.
Unpriced

(B73-50869)

VVNU/T — Duets. Variations
Butterworth, Neil
Theme and variations: for two clarinets in B flat/ by Neil Butterworth. — Chesham: Ricordi, 1972. — 6p; 4to.
Unpriced

(B73-50427)

VVP — CLARINET & PIANO
VVPH — Dances
Williamson, Malcolm
Pas de deux: for clarinet (B flat) and piano/ by Malcolm Williamson. — London: Weinberger, 1972. — 4to.
Unpriced

(B73-50428)

VVPJ — Miscellaneous works
Burnett, Michael
Prelude, song and dance: for clarinet and piano/ by Michael Burnett. — Chesham: Ricordi, 1973. — 4to.
Score (10p.) & part.
Unpriced

(B73-50870)

Camilleri, Charles
[Divertimento for clarinet & piano, no.2]. Divertimento no.2: for clarinet and piano/ by Charles Camilleri. — Sevenoaks: Novello, 1973. — 4to.
Score (35p.) & part. — Duration 16 min.
£1.50
(B73-50429)

Fox, Peter
Air and allegro: two short and very easy solos for B flat clarinet/ by Peter Fox. — Street: Cornelius, 1967. — 4to.
Score (2p) & part.
Unpriced
(B73-50871)

Hinton, Alistair
Reflections: two solos for B flat clarinet/ by Alistair Hinton. — Street: Cornelius, 1968. — 4to.
Score (3p) & part. — Contents: 1: Allegretto - 2: March.
Unpriced
(B73-50872)

Hummel, Bertold
5 miniatures: for clarinet and piano/ by Bertold Hummel. — Hamburg; London: Simrock, 1972. — 7p; 4to.
Unpriced
(B73-50873)

Jacob, Gordon
Five pieces for solo clarinet/ by Gordon Jacob. — London: Oxford University Press, 1973. — 7p; 4to.
ISBN 0 19 357368 7 : £0.35
(B73-51292)

Johnson, Thomas Arnold
Scherzo for B flat clarinet and piano/ by Thomas A. Johnson. — London: British and Continental Music, 1973. — 4to.
Score (8p) & part.
Unpriced
(B73-51293)

VVPK — Arrangements
Senaillé, Jean Baptiste
[Sonata for violin & basso continuo in D minor. Sarabanda, Allegro; arr]. Introduction and allegro spiritoso/ by J.B. Senaillé; transcribed and edited for B flat clarinet and piano by Robin de Smet. — London: Fenette Music, Breitkopf and Härtel, 1973. — 4to.
Score (11p.) & part.
Unpriced
(B73-50430)

VVPK/AAY — Arrangements. Collections
Kuszing, Janos
Clarinet music for beginners, with piano accompaniment/ edited by Janos Kuszing. — London: Boosey and Hawkes, 1972. — 4to.
Score (39p.) & part.
£0.85
(B73-50874)

VVPK/DW — Arrangements. Songs, etc
Wagner, Richard
[Wesendonck Lieder. Träume]. Träume = Dreams: study for 'Tristan and Isolde'/ by Richard Wagner; arranged for B flat clarinet and orchestra by David Stone; reduction for clarinet and piano by David Stone. — London: Boosey and Hawkes, 1972. — 4to.
Score (4p.) & part.
£0.50
(B73-50431)

VVPK/LF — Arrangements. Concertos
Rawsthorne, Alan
[Concerto for clarinet & string orchestra: arr]. Concerto for clarinet & string orchestra/ by Alan Rawsthorne; piano reduction by Gerard Schurmann. — London: Oxford University Press, 1973. — 4to.
Score (30p.) & part.
ISBN 0 19 366905 6 : £1.50
(B73-50875)

VVPLVW — CLARINET & BASSOON
VVPLVW/T — Clarinet & bassoon. Variations
Baines, Francis
Comic variations: for clarinet and bassoon/ by Francis Baines. — Ampleforth: June Emerson, 1973. — 4p; fol.
Unpriced
(B73-50432)

VVPLX — CLARINET & PERCUSSION
VVPLX/X — Clarinet & percussion. Canons
Bergsma, William
Illegible canons: for clarinet and percussion/ by William Bergsma. — New York: Galaxy Music; London: Galliard, 1973. — 13p; 4to.
Two copies.
Unpriced
(B73-51294)

VVX — BASSET HORN
VVXPJ — Basset horn & piano. Miscellaneous works
Gilbert, Anthony
Spell respell. Op 14: for electric basset clarinet (or clarinet in A) and piano/ by Anthony Gilbert. — London: Schott, 1973. — 4to.
Two copies of the score.
£0.75
(B73-50876)

VWP — BASSOON & PIANO
VWPHR — Minuets
Hughes, Eric
A low minuet: bassoon or contrabassoon and piano/ by Eric Hughes. — Ampleforth (Spring House, Ampleforth, Yorkshire): June Emerson, 1972. — 4to.
Score (2p.) & part.
Unpriced
(B73-50433)

VWPJ — Miscellaneous works
Noble, Harold
The happy vagabond: bassoon and piano/ by Harold Noble. — London: Peters, 1973. — 4to.
Score (7p.) & part.
£0.48
(B73-50877)

Schenker, Friedrich
Fünf Bagatellen: für Posaune und Klavier/ von Friedrich Schenker. — Leipzig; [London]: Peters, 1972. — 4to.
Score (15p.) & part.
Unpriced
(B73-50434)

Standford, Patric
Four preludes for bassoon and piano/ by Patric Standford. — Sevenoaks: Novello, 1973. — 4to.
Score (12p) & part.
Unpriced
(B73-50435)

VY — BAGPIPES
VY/T/AYDL — Variations. Collections. Scotland
Mackay, Angus
A collection of ancient piobaireachd or highland pipe music/ [collected] by Angus Mackay. — Wakefield: E.P. Publishing, 1972. — [192]p; fol.
Original edition of 1838 republished.
ISBN 0 85409 821 6 : £3.00
Also classified at QPK/AT/AYDL
(B73-50436)

WM — BRASS BAND
WM/AY — Collections
Salvation Army Brass Band Journal (Festival series).. — London: Salvationist Publishing and Supplies.
Contents: A Finnish suite, by Robert Redhead - Youthful recollections; selection, by Phil. B. Catelinet - Theme from 2nd movement of piano concerto, by Grieg; arr. by Ray Steadman-Allen - The pathway: euphonium solo, by Ray Bowes.
Nos 349-352. — 1973. — 60p; obl.8vo.
Unpriced
(B73-50878)

WM/T — Variations
Siebert, Edrich
Dear to my heart: air varié/ by Edrich Siebert. — London: Studio Music, s1972. — 24pt; 8vo.
With several copies of various parts.
Unpriced
(B73-50879)

WMEM — Sinfoniettas
Wilson, Thomas
Sinfonietta for brass band/ by Thomas Wilson. — London: R. Smith, 1973. — 32p; obl 4to.
Unpriced
(B73-50880)

WMG — Suites
Carr, John
The seasons: suite/ by John Carr. — London: R. Smith, 1971. — 38p; obl.4to.
Unpriced
(B73-50881)

Cheesman, Oswald
Suite: for brass band/ by Oswald Cheesman. — London: Chappell, 1972. — 8vo.
Score (16p.) & 27 parts.
Unpriced
(B73-50437)

Gregson, Edward
Partita for brass band/ by Edward Gregson. — London: R. Smith, 1973. — 30p; obl.8vo.
Unpriced
(B73-50882)

Vinter, Gilbert
Entertainments/ by Gilbert Vinter. — London: R. Smith, 1971. — 28p; obl.8vo.
Contents: 1.Caprice - 2.Elegy - 3.March.
Unpriced
(B73-50883)

Yorke, Peter
The shipbuilders: suite for brass band/ by Peter Yorke. — London: Chappell, 1973. — 34p; obl.8vo.
Duration 9 mins.
Unpriced
(B73-50884)

WMHME — Hoe-downs
Siebert, Edrich
Hawaiian hoe-down/ by Edrich Siebert. — London: Studio Music, 1973. — 25pt; 8vo.
With several copies of various parts.
Unpriced
(B73-50885)

WMHVR — Tangos
Barratt, Bob
Tango taquin: for brass band/ by Bob Barratt and Edrich Siebert. — London: Affiliated Music, 1973. — obl. 8vo.
Conductor & 25 parts. — With several copies of various parts.
Unpriced
(B73-51295)

WMHW — Waltzes
Heath, Reginald
Waltz for a beguiling lady/ by Reginald Heath. — London: R. Smith, 1973. — 8vo.
Conductor (2p.) & 24 parts. — With several copies of various parts.
Unpriced
(B73-50886)

Lucas, Leighton
A waltz overture/ by Leighton Lucas. — London: R. Smith, 1972. — 24p; obl.8vo.
Unpriced
(B73-50887)

WMJ — Miscellaneous works
Barratt, Bernard
Parliament Street blues/ by Bernard Barratt. — London: R. Smith, 1973. — 8vo.
Conductor (4p.) & 25 parts. — With several copies of various parts.
Unpriced
(B73-50888)

Gregson, Edward
The Plantagenets: a symphonic study, for brass band/ by Edward Gregson. — London: R. Smith, 1972. — 50p; obl.4to.
Unpriced
(B73-50889)

Hanmer, Ronald
Brass spectacular/ by Ronald Hanmer. — London: Studio Music, 1973. — 8vo.
Conductor (4p.) & 26 parts. With several copies of various parts.
Unpriced
(B73-50890)

Hanmer, Ronald
Episodes for brass/ by Ronald Hanmer. — London: R. Smith, 1972. — 38p; obl.8vo.
Duration 9 mins.
Unpriced
(B73-50891)

Heath, Reginald
Shakespearian rhapsody, 'Prospero and Miranda'/ by Reginald Heath. — London: R. Smith, 1971. — 22p; obl.8vo.
Unpriced
(B73-50892)

Howarth, Elgar
Mosaic for brass band/ by Elgar Howarth. — Sevenoaks: Paxton, 1973. — obl.8vo.
Score (20p) & 25 parts.
£2.50
(B73-51296)

Maurer, Ludwig
[12 kleine Stücke. Selections]. Four fancies: a serenade in E flat for brass band/ by Ludwig Maurer; translated by Bram Gay. — Sevenoaks: Novello, 1973. — 24p; obl. 4to.
Score (24p.) & 25 parts.
£1.25
(B73-50438)

Newsome, Roy
The bass in the balloon: solo for E flat bass/ by Roy Newsome. — London: Studio Music, 1972. — 26pt.; 8vo.
With several copies of various parts.
Unpriced
(B73-51297)

Walters, Gareth
Flourish for brass/ by Gareth Walters. — London: R. Smith, 1972. — 8vo.
Conductor (2p.) & 24 parts. — With several copies of various parts.
Unpriced
(B73-50893)

Watters, Cyril
A Cotswold lullaby/ by Cyril Watters. — London: Studio Music, 1972. — 8vo.
Conductor (3p) & 25 parts. With several copies of various parts.
Unpriced
(B73-50894)

WMK — Arrangements
Franck, Cesar
[Le Chasseur maudit: arr]. The accursed huntsman/ by Cesar Franck; arranged by Edrich Siebert. — London: Studio Music, 1973. — 26pt; 8vo.
With several copies of various parts.
Unpriced
(B73-50895)

WMK/AAY — Arrangements. Collections
Benoy, A W
Pieces for the growing band/ arranged by A.W. Benoy. — London: Hinrichsen, 1972. — 24p; obl.4to.
Contents: 1. Admiral Benbow; traditional English song - 2. Irish battle song; traditional Irish song - 3. Prayer, by Schubert - 4. Hopefulness, by Schubert - 5. Prince Rupert's march; traditional English tune - 6. Old English patter song.
Unpriced
(B73-50896)

WMK/AGM — Arrangements. Marches
Hanmer, Ronald
Vienna marches: a march fantasy based on melodies by Schubert, Mozart, Beethovan, and J. Strauss (father and son)/ arranged by Ronald Hanmer. — London: Studio Music, 1971. — 8vo.
Conductor (7p) & 26 parts.
Unpriced
(B73-50897)

Porter-Brown, Reginald
The medieval men: march/ by Reginald Porter-Brown; arranged by John Gaunt. — London: Studio Music, 1973. — 8vo.
Conductor (3p.) & 26 parts. With several copies of various parts.
Unpriced
(B73-50898)

WMK/AGM/JS — Arrangements. Marches. Television
Trombey, Jack
Eye level: theme from the Thames TV series 'Van der Valk'/ by Jack Trombey; arranged by Norman Richardson. — London: Boosey and Hawkes, 1973. — obl,8vo.
Conductor (4p) & 45 parts.
Unpriced
Also classified at UMMK/AGM/JS
(B73-51298)

WMK/CM — Arrangements. Musical plays
Bricusse, Leslie
[The good old bad old days. Selections: arr]. The good old bad old days/ by Leslie Bricusse and Anthony Newley; selection arranged by Edrich Siebert. — London: Peter Maurice, 1973. — obl.8vo.
Conductor & 25 parts. With several copies of various parts.
Unpriced
(B73-50439)

WMK/DW — Arrangements. Songs, etc
Hirsch, Walter
['Deed I do: arr]. 'Deed I do: march/ by Walter Hirsch and Fred Rose; arranged by Terry Creswick for brass band by Edrich Siebert. — London: Keith Prowse, 1973. — obl. 8vo.
Conductor & 25 parts. — With several copies of various parts.
Unpriced
(B73-51299)

Saint-Saens, Charles
[Samson et Dalila. Mon coeur s'ouvre à ta voix: arr]. Softly awakes my heart/ by C. Saint-Saens; arranged for brass band by John Gaunt. — London: Studio Music, 1972. — 8vo.
Duration 15 min.
Unpriced
(B73-50899)

Siebert, Edrich
Singalong/ arranged for brass band by Edrich Siebert. — London:
KPM Music.
Selection no.1. — 1972. — 8vo.
Conductor (2p.) & 26 parts.
Unpriced

(B73-50440)

WMK/JR — Arrangements. Films
Street, Allan
Great film themes for brass/ arranged for brass and reed band by
Allan Street. — London: Chappell, 1973. — 8vo.
Conductor (8p) & 26 parts.
Unpriced

(B73-50900)

WMP — SOLO INSTRUMENT (S) & BRASS BAND
WMPWR — Cornet & brass band
Gregson, Edward
Prelude and capriccio: for cornet and band/ by Edward Gregson.
— London: R. Smith, 1973. — 8vo.
Short score (16p) & 26 parts - With several copies of various parts -
Duration 8 min.
Unpriced

(B73-51300)

WMPWRNTK — Three cornets & brass band. Arrangements
Docker, Robert
Cornet cascade: a trio for cornets with brass band/ by Robert
Docker; brass band arrangement by Geoffrey Brand. — London:
R. Smith, 1972. — 8vo.
Conductor (8p.) & 29 parts. — Various parts are in duplicate.
Unpriced

(B73-50901)

WMPWRNU — Two cornets & brass band
Carr, John
Two of the tops: a duet for E flat soprano and B flat cornets/ by
John Carr. — London: R. Smith, 1973. — 8vo.
Conductor (2p.) & 26 parts. — With several copies of various parts.
Unpriced

(B73-50902)

WMPWT — Horn & brass band
Hanmer, Ronald
Arioso and caprice: for flugel horn and band/ by Ronald Hanmer.
— London: R. Smith, 1971. — 8vo.
Unpriced

(B73-50903)

WMPWTW/W — Tenor horn & brass band. Rondos
Heath, Reginald
Air and rondo: tenor horn solo/ by Reginald Heath. — London:
R. Smith, 1972. — 8vo.
Conductor (8p.) & 25 parts - With several copies of various parts.
Unpriced

(B73-50905)

WMPWTWK — Tenor horn & brass band. Arrangements
Saint-Saens, Camille
[Le Carnival des animaux. Le Cygne: arr]. The swan/ by C.
Saint-Saens; arranged as E flat tenor horn solo with band
accompaniment by Ronald Hanmer. — London: Studio Music,
1972. — 8vo.
Conductor (3p.) & 25 parts.
Unpriced

(B73-50904)

WMPWU — Trombone & brass band
Newsome, Roy
Tenor trombone rag: trombone solo and brass band/ by Roy
Newsome. — London: Studio Music, 1972. — 8vo.
Conductor (3p.) & 26 parts. With several copies of various parts.
Unpriced

(B73-50906)

WMPWUNT — Three trombones & brass band
Heath, Reginald
Frolic for trombones: a trio for trombones, with brass band/ by
Reginald Heath. — London: R. Smith, 1972. — 8vo.
Conductor (2p.) & 24 parts. — With several copies of various parts.
Unpriced

(B73-50907)

WMPWUU — Bass trombone & brass band
Eaves, Robert
Introduction and burlesque: for bass trombone and band/ by
Robert Eaves. — London: R. Smith, 1971. — 8vo.
Short score (10p.) & 25 parts. — With several copies of various parts.
Unpriced

(B73-50908)

WN — BRASS ENSEMBLE
Gabrieli, Giovanni
Canzone e sonate (1615): for trumpets, optional horns, and
trombones/ by Giovanni Gabrieli; [edited by] Bernard Thomas. —
London: Musica rara.
Score (4p.) & 6 parts.
Canzon 1: for 2 trumpets and 3 trombones (2 trumpets, horn, and
trombones). — 1972. — 4to.
Unpriced

(B73-50441)

Canzon 2: for 3 trumpets and 3 trombones, (3 trumpets, horn and 2
trombones). — 1972. — 4to.
Unpriced

(B73-50442)

Canzon 3: for 2 trumpets and 4 trombones, (2 trumpets, horn and 3
trombones). — 1972. — 4to.
Unpriced

(B73-50443)

Canzon 4: for 4 trumpets and 2 trombones. — 1972. — 4to.
Unpriced

(B73-50444)

Canzon 5: for 4 trumpets and 3 trombones (4 trumpets, and 2 trombones).
— 1972. — 4to.
Unpriced

(B73-50445)

Canzon 6: for 4 trumpets and 3 trombones, (4 trumpets, horn and 2
trombones). — 1972. — 4to.
Unpriced

(B73-50446)

Canzon 7: for 4 trumpets and 3 trombones, (4 trumpets, horn and 2
trombones). — 1972. — 4to.
£2.00

(B73-50447)

Canzon 8: for 3 trumpets and 5 trombones. — 1972. — 4to.
Unpriced

(B73-50448)

Canzon 9: for 3 trumpets and 5 trombones (3 trumpets, horn and 4
trombones). — 1972. — 4to.
£2.50

(B73-50449)

Canzon 10: for 4 trumpets and 4 trombones (4 trumpets, 2 horns and 2
trombones). — 1972. — 4to.
£2.50

(B73-50450)

Canzon 11: for 4 trumpets and 4 trombones. — 1972. — 4to.
£2.50

(B73-50451)

Canzon 12: for 2 trumpets and 6 trombones, (2 trumpets, 2 horns and 4
trombones). — 1972. — 4to.
£2.50

(B73-50452)

Canzon 13: for 4 trumpets and 4 trombones, (4 trumpets, 2 horns and 2
trombones). — 1972. — 4to.
£2.50

(B73-50453)

Canzon 14: for 6 trumpets and 4 trombones. — 1972. — 4to.
£2.50

(B73-50454)

Canzon 15: for 4 trumpets and 6 trombones, (4 trumpets, 2 horns and 4
trombones). — 1972. — 4to.
£3.00

(B73-50455)

Canzon 16: for 6 trumpets and 6 trombones, (6 trumpets, 3 horns and 3
trombones). — 1972. — 4to.
£3.00

(B73-50456)

Canzon 17: for 6 trumpets and 6 trombones. — 1972. — 4to.
£3.00

(B73-50457)

Canzon 18: for 4 trumpets and 10 trombones, (4 trumpets, 2 horns and 8
trombones). — 1972. — 4to.
Unpriced

(B73-50458)

Canzon 19: for trumpets and 12 trombones, (3 trumpets, 3 horns and 9
trombones). — 1972. — 4to.
£3.50

(B73-50459)

Canzon 20: for 5 trumpets and 17 trombones, (5 trumpets, 4 horns and 13
trombones). — 1972. — 4to.
Unpriced

(B73-50460)

WN/AF — Exercises
Pfau, Hans
Bläserspielbuch: 156 leichte Spielsatz, Lieder und Tanze, für
Gruppen und Bläserspielkreise. — Mainz; London: Schott.
Band 1: Aufbauband (Ubungsstücke). — 1972. — 96p; 8vo. —
£3.60

(B73-51301)

WNP — Septets
Newsome, R
Tantalising tubas: brass septet/ by R. Newsome. — London: R.
Smith, 1971. — 8vo.
Score (8p.) & 7 parts.
Unpriced

(B73-50909)

WNPRF — Six brass instruments & organ. Concertos
Baudach, Ulrich
'Te Deum laudamus': Konzert für Orgel, drei Trompeten und drei Posaunen/ von Ulrich Baudach. — Cassel; London: Bärenreiter, 1972. — 36p; 4to.
£2.10

(B73-50461)

WNR — Quintets
Gubby, Roy
The great Panathenaea: for brass quintet/ by Roy Gubby. — London: Boosey and Hawkes, 1973. — 4to.
Score (8p) & 5 parts.
£1.50

(B73-51302)

WNSG — Quartets. Suites
Burnett, Michael
Suite Blaen Myherin: for 2 trumpets, 2 trombones/ by Michael Burnett. — Chesham: Ricordi, 1973. — 4to.
Score (8p.) & 4 parts.
Unpriced

(B73-50910)

Szelenyi, Istvan
[Suite for two trumpets in B and two trombones]. Suite für zwei Trompeten in B und zwei Posaunen/ von Istvan Szelenyi; herausgegeben von Willy Schneider. — Mainz; London: Schott, 1973. — 8vo.
Score (18p.) & 4 parts.
£2.40

(B73-51303)

WNT/T — Trios. Variations
Smith, Derek
Theme and variations: trumpet, horn, trombone/ by Derek Smith. — London: Thames, 1973. — 10p; 8vo.
Unpriced

(B73-50462)

WP — BRASS INSTRUMENT & PIANO
WPJ — Brass instrument & piano. Miscellaneous works
Domroese, Wilhelm
Sechs kleine Stücke: für Blechbläsinstrumente und Klavier/ von Wilhelm Domroese. — Regensburg: Bosse; [London]: [Bärenreiter], 1971. — 4to.
Score (9p.) & part.
£1.50

(B73-50463)

WS — TRUMPET
WS/AF — Exercises
Schneider, Willy
Spielstucke und Etüden: für Trompete oder Flugelhorn oder Kornett/ von Willy Schneider. — Mainz; London: Schott, 1973. — 35p; 8vo.
£1.44

(B73-51304)

WSN — TRUMPET ENSEMBLE
WSNQGN — Sextets. Fanfares
Rubbra, Edmund
Fanfare for Europe on the notes EEC. Op.142: for six trumpets in C/ by Edmund Rubbra. — South Croydon: Lengnick, 1973. — 8vo.
Score (8p.) & 6 parts.
£1.00

(B73-50911)

WSNTPW — Two trumpets & keyboard
Pezel, Johann
[Bicinia variorum instrumentum, nos 63-4, 67-8]. Sonatinas no.63,64,67,68: for two cornetti (trumpets) and basso continuo/ by Johann Pezel; edited by R.P. Block. — London: Musica rara, 1972. — 4to.
Score (16p.) & 3 parts.
Unpriced

(B73-50410)

Pezel, Johann
[Bicinia variorum instrumentum, nos 69-70, 72-3]. Sonatinas no.69,70,72,73: for two clarini (trumpets), and basso continuo/ by Johann Pezel; edited by R.P. Block. — London: Musica rara, 1972. — 4to.
Score (19p.) & 3 parts.
Unpriced

(B73-50464)

WSP — TRUMPET & PIANO
WSPHVR — Tangos
Baker, Mervyn
Trumpet tango: a short and easy solo for trumpet and piano/ by Mervin Baker. — Street: Cornelius, 1968. — 4to.
Score (2p.) & part.
Unpriced

(B73-50912)

WSPJ — Miscellaneous works
Burgon, Geoffrey
Lullaby and aubade: for trumpet and piano/ by Geoffrey Burgon. — London: Stainer and Bell, 1972. — 4to.
Score (3p.) & part.
£0.25

(B73-50465)

WSPK — Arrangements
Scarlatti, Alessandro
[Il Giardino di amore. Sinfonia]. Sinfonia: for trumpet and strings/ by Alessandro Scarlatti; [edited by] Michael Talbot, reduction for trumpet and piano. — London: Musica rara, 1973. — 4to.
Score (8p.) & part.
Unpriced

(B73-50466)

WSPK/AHSW — Arrangements. Paso dobles
Marquina, Pascual
[Spanish gipsy dance: arr]. Spanish gipsy dance: paso doble/ by Pascual Marquina; arranged for trumpet and piano by Edrich Siebert. — London: Schauer and May, 1972. — 4to.
Score (6p.) & part.
Unpriced

(B73-50467)

WTP — HORN & PIANO
WTP/T — Variations
Rossini, Gioacchino Antonio
[Prelude, théme et variations pour cor]. Prelude, theme and variations for horn and piano/ by G. Rossini; edited by R. de Smet. — London: Peters, 1972. — 4to.
Score (20p.) & part for horn in F or E flat.
Unpriced

(B73-50468)

WTP/X — Canons
Anderson, Muriel Bradford
Prelude in canon: viola or horn in F/ by M. Bradford Anderson. — London: Boosey and Hawkes, 1973. — 4to.
Score (7p)& part.
£0.40
Primary classification SQP/X

(B73-50794)

WTPE — Sonatas
Hoddinott, Alun
Sonata for horn and piano. Op.78, no.2/ by Alun Hoddinott. — London: Oxford University Press, 1972. — 4to.
Score (30p.) & part.
ISBN 0 19 357158 7 : £2.00

(B73-50469)

WTPJ — Miscellaneous workd
Hanmer, Ronald
Arioso and caprice: for flugel horn and piano/ by Ronald Hanmer. — London: R. Smith, 1971. — 4to.
Score (11p.) & part.
Unpriced

(B73-50913)

WTPJ — Miscellaneous works
Jacob, Gordon
Ten little studies: for oboe and piano/ by Gordon Jacob. — London: Oxford University Press, 1972. — 4to.
Score (11p.) & part.
ISBN 0 19 357359 8 : £0.60

(B73-50470)

Roper, Keith
Triptych: horn and piano/ by Keith Roper. — London: Thames, 1972. — fol.
Score (19p.) & part.
Unpriced

(B73-50914)

Schumann, Robert
Adagio and allegro. Op.70: for horn (or violin, or viola, or cello) and piano/ by Robert Schumann. — New York: Schirmer; [London]: [Chappell], 1971. — 4to.
Score (15p.) & part.
Unpriced
Also classified at SPJ

(B73-51305)

Schumann, Robert
Adagio and allegro. Op.70: for horn (or violin, or viola, or cello) and piano/ by Robert Schumann. — New York: Schirmer; [London]: [Chappell], 1971. — 4to.
Score (15p.) & part.
Unpriced
Also classified at SPJ

(B73-51306)

WTPK — Arrangements
Mozart, Wolfgang Amadeus
[Quintet for horn & strings in E flat major. K 407: arr]. Horn quintet in E flat/ by Wolfgang Amadeus Mozart; arranged for horn and piano by Mason Jones. — New York; London: Schirmer, 1972. — 4to.
Score (22p) & part.
Unpriced
(B73-51307)

WTPK/AAY — Arrangements. Collections
Johnson, Stuart
An intermediate horn book: for horn in F and piano/ arranged by Stuart Johnson. — London: Oxford University Press, 1973. — 4to.
Score (19p.) & part.
ISBN 0 19 357387 3 : £0.75
(B73-50915)

Langrish, Hugo
Eight easy pieces/ arranged for horn and piano by Hugo Langrish. — London: Oxford University Press, 1973. — 4to.
Score (12p.) & part.
ISBN 0 19 357430 6 : £0.45
(B73-50471)

Onozó, Jones
Horn music for beginners, with piano accompaniment/ edited by Janos Onoze and Matyas Kovacs. — London: Boosey and Hawkes, 1972. — 4to.
Score (40p.) & part.
£0.85
(B73-50916)

WTPK/AH — Arrangements. Dances
Granados, Enrique
[Danzas espanolas, vol.2. Andaluza]. Spanish dance, no.5/ by Enrique Granados; arranged for horn and piano by Ivan C. Phillips. — London: Oxford University Press, 1972. — 4to.
Score (7p.) & part.
ISBN 0 19 356830 6 : £0.35
(B73-50472)

WTPK/DH — Arrangements. Motets, Anthems, Hymns, etc
Mendelssohn, Felix
[Hear my prayer. Op.39, no.1: arr]. O for the wings of a dove/ by Felix Mendelssohn; arr. for horn in F and piano by Dale Blakeney. — Street: Cornelius, 1968. — 4to.
Score (2p.) & part.
Unpriced
(B73-50917)

WTPK/DW — Arrangements. Songs, etc
Fox, Peter
Two nightsongs/ arranged as an easy solo for horn in F with piano by Peter Fox. — Street: Cornelius, 1968. — 4to.
Score (2p) & part. — Contents: 1.Nachts. Op 1, no.5, by Peter Cornelius - 2.Bitte. Op.9, no.3 by Robert Franz.
Unpriced
(B73-50918)

WTPK/LF — Arrangements. Concertos
Láng, István
Concerto bucolico: for horn and orchestra/ by István Láng. — London: Boosey and Hawkes, 1972. — 4to.
Score (20p.) & part. — Reduction for horn & piano.
£1.25
(B73-50473)

WTPM — UNACCOMPANIED HORN
WTPME/AZ — Symphonies. Collected works of individual composers
Brahms, Johannes
[Symphonies]. Complete horn parts of the four symphonies/ by Brahms; compiled by Richard Merewether. — London: Horn Centre, 1972. — 49p; 4to.
£1.50
(B73-50474)

WTW — SAXHORN
WTWP/W — Rondos
Heath, Reginald
Air and rondo: tenor horn solo/ by Reginald Heath. — London: R. Smith, 1972. — 4to & 8vo.
Score (8p.) & part.
Unpriced
(B73-50919)

WUP — TROMBONE & PIANO
WUPHVHM — Polonaises
Baker, Mervyn
Alla polacca: a short and easy solo for trombone and piano/ by Mervyn Baker. — Street: Cornelius, 1968. — 4to.
Score (2p.) & part.
Unpriced
(B73-50920)

WUPK/AHVL — Arrangements. Sarabandes
Grieg, Edvard
[Holberg suite. Op.40. Sarabande: arr]. Sarabande/ by Edvard Grieg; arranged for trombone and piano by Olaf Piers. — Street: Cornelius, 1968. — 4to.
Score (2p) & part.
Unpriced
(B73-50921)

WUPK/DH — Arrangements. Motets, Anthems, Hymns, etc
Mendelssohn, Felix
[Hear my prayer. Op.39, no.1: arr]. O for the wings of a dove/ by Felix Mendelssohn; arr. for trombone and piano by Dale Blakeney. — Street: Cornelius, 1968. — 4to.
Score (2p.) & part.
Unpriced
(B73-50922)

WUPK/LF — Arrangements. Concertos
Ross, Walter
[Concerto for trombone: arr]. Trombone concerto/ by Walter Ross; reduction for trombone and piano. — New York; London: Boosey and Hawkes, 1973. — 46o.
Duration 13 min.
£2.50
(B73-50923)

WUU — BASS TROMBONE
WUUPJ — Miscellaneous works
Eaves, Robert
Introduction and burlesque: for bass trombone and piano/ by Robert Eaves. — London: R. Smith, 1971. — 4to & 8vo.
Score (11p.) & part.
Unpriced
(B73-50924)

WVP — TUBA & PIANO
WVPG — Suites
Jacob, Gordon
[Suite for tuba and piano]. Tuba suite: tuba and piano/ by Gordon Jacob. — London: Boosey and Hawkes, 1973. — 4to.
Score (23p.) & part.
£1.25
(B73-50925)

XM — PERCUSSION BAND
XMJ — Miscellaneous works
Fink, Siegfried
Horeb: scene for percussion according to the first Book of Kings/ by Siegfried Fink. — Hamburg; London: Simrock, 1972. — 12p; 4to.
Unpriced
(B73-50926)

XN — PERCUSSION ENSEMBLE
XNQ — Sextets
Fink, Siegfried
Zulu welcome: South African impression for percussion ensemble, (6 players)/ by Siegfried Fink. — Hamburg; London: Simrock, 1973. — 4to.
Score (11p.) & 3 parts.
Unpriced
(B73-51308)

XNQGM — Sextets. Marches
Fink, Siegfried
Marcha del tambor: Caribbean impression, for percussion ensemble, (6 players)/ by Siegfried Fink. — Hamburg; London: Simrock, 1973. — 4to.
Score (11p.) & 3 parts.
Unpriced
(B73-51309)

Moisy, Heinz von
Brazilian carnival march: for percussion ensemble (6 players)/ by Heinz von Moisy. — Hamburg; London: Simrock, 1972. — 4to.
Score (28p) & 6 parts.
Unpriced
(B73-50927)

XNT — Trios
Konietzny, Heinrich
Triade for xylophon, vibraphone, marimbaphone and three cymbals (3 players)/ by Heinrich Konietzny. — Mainz; London: Schott, 1973. — 18p; 4to.
£1.44
(B73-51310)

XPM — UNACCOMPANIED PERCUSSION
XPM/T — Variations
Brouwer, Leo
Variantes for one percussionist/ by Leo Brouwer. — Mainz; London: Schott, 1973. — 10p; 4to.
£1.10
(B73-50928)

XTQSP — MARIMBA & PIANO
XTQSPJ — Miscellaneous works
  Frackenpohl, Arthur
    Introduction and romp: for marimba or vibraphone and piano/ by
    Arthur Frackenpohl. — New York; London: Schirmer, 1972. —
    4to.
    Score (15p.) & part.
    Unpriced
                                                              (B73-50475)

Z — NON-EUROPEAN MUSIC
ZMQADW/AY — Africa. Nigeria. Songs, etc. Collections
  King, Anthony V
    Songs of Nigeria/ compiled by Anthony V. King. — London:
    University of London Press, 1973. — 47p; 8vo.
    ISBN 0 340 16307 0 : Unpriced
                                                              (B73-50929)

THE BRITISH CATALOGUE OF MUSIC 1

COMPOSER AND TITLE INDEX

3 D.H. Lawrence love poems: for high voice and piano. (Raphael, Mark). *Thames. Unpriced* KFTDW (B73-50230)
3 Romanzen. Op.69. Three romances: for viola and pianoforte. (Kiel, Friedrich). *Musica rara. Unpriced* SQPJ (B73-50377)
5 miniatures. *See* Hummel, Bertold. Five miniatures.
5 miniatures: for clarinet and piano. (Hummel, Bertold). *Simrock. Unpriced* VVPJ (B73-50873)
7 Formen: für Flöte, Gitarre, Cembalo und Zupfoder Streichorchester oder Streichquartett. (Jörns, Helge). *Simrock. Unpriced* NURNP (B73-51129)
8 songs: for medium voice and piano. (Warlock, Peter). *Thames. Unpriced* KFVDW (B73-50236)
9 Istanti. *See* Boder, Gerd. Neun Istanti.
9 Istanti: für Streichquartett. (Boder, Gerd). *Bosse Bärenreiter. £2.40* RXNS (B73-50784)
12 easy duets for winds
Volume 1: For flutes, oboes (and saxophones). (Mozart, Wolfgang Amadeus). *Schirmer. Unpriced* UNUK (B73-50837)
Volume 2: for clarinets trumpets (and F horns). (Mozart, Wolfgang Amadeus). *Schirmer. Unpriced* UNUK (B73-50838)
14 caprices: for cello duet (student and teacher). (Josephs, Wilfred). *Chappell. £0.60* SRNU (B73-50803)
75 études mélodiques et progressives pour violon. Op.36, nos. 1-30. Etudes spéciales. Op.36, nos 1-30: for the viola. (Mazas, Jacques Féréol). *Schirmer. Unpriced* SQ/AC (B73-50373)
75 études mélodiques et progressives pour violon. Op.36, nos.31-56. Etudes brillantes. Op.36, nos 31-56. (Mazas, Jacques Féréol). *Schirmer. Unpriced* SQ/AC (B73-50372)
1898: für Kinderstimmen und Instrumente. (Kagel, Mauricio). *Universal. Unpriced* FDX (B73-51038)
A Highland tale: piano solo. (Parfrey, Raymond). *Composer to Player Edition. Unpriced* QPJ (B73-50733)
Abelard, Peter. Solus ad victimam: SATB. (Leighton, Kenneth). *Oxford University Press. Unpriced* DH/LK (B73-50958) ISBN 0 19 350349 2
Abingdon carols: six carols for SATB. (Kelly, Bryan). *Novello. £0.35* EZDP/LF (B73-50997)
Accursed huntsman. (Franck, Cesar). *Studio Music. Unpriced* WMK (B73-50895)
Ach arme Welt = Alas, poor world: motet for four part chorus of mixed voices a cappella. (Brahms, Johannes). *Schirmer. Unpriced* EZDH (B73-50982)
Ach arme Welt. Op. 110, no.2. Ach arme Welt = Alas, poor world: motet for four part chorus of mixed voices a cappella. (Brahms, Johannes). *Schirmer. Unpriced* EZDH (B73-50982)
Achtzehn acht und neunzig. 1898: für Kinderstimmen und Instrumente. (Kagel, Mauricio). *Universal. Unpriced* FDX (B73-51038)
Acrobats of God: symphonic version of the ballet for orchestra. (Surinach, Carlos). *Associated Music. Unpriced* MM/HM (B73-51112)
Ad flumina Babylonis: for double chorus of mixed voices a cappella. (Najera, Edmund). *Schirmer. Unpriced* EZDR (B73-50102)
Adagio und Rondo für 2 Klarinetten, 2 Horner und 2 Fagotte. (Weber, Carl Maria, *Freiherr von*). *Schott. £2.88* UNQ/W (B73-51259)
Adam and the apple: an occasional carol for various combinations of voices percussion and optional trumpets. (Paget, Michael). *Schirmer. £0.15* FE/XRUDP/LF (B73-50571)
Adam lay ybounden: carol for SATB unaccompanied. (Walker, Robert). *Novello. £0.07* EZDP/LF (B73-51002)
Adams, Jean. A ring of carols: for female or boys' voices and piano. *Paxton. £0.27* FDP/LF (B73-51020)
Adams, Lee. 'Applause' song book: songs from a new musical by Charles Strouse. (Strouse, Charles). *Edwin H. Morris. £1.25* KDW (B73-50210)
Adams-Jeremiah, Dorothy. Sing, say and play. *Lengnick. £0.20* MJ (B73-50245)
Addington service: Holy Communion, Series 3. (Shephard, Richard). *Royal School of Church Music. Unpriced* JDGS (B73-51049)
Addis, Hazel. The scout show book. (Milner, John). *Brown Son and Ferguson. £0.75* JGDW (B73-51079)
Adler, Samuel.
Hinay yom hadin - Behold the day of judgment: four prayers from the High Holyday liturgy, for four-part chorus of mixed voices with soprano and tenor solo (cantor) with optional organ accompaniment
1: Hayom harat olam. *Schirmer. Unpriced* EZDGU (B73-50064)
2: Ayl melech yoshayr. *Schirmer. Unpriced* EZDGU (B73-50065)
4: Avinu malkaynu chanayno. *Schirmer. Unpriced* EZDGU (B73-50066)
Hinay yom hadin = Behold the day of judgment: four prayers from the High Holyday liturgy, for four-part chorus of mixed voices with soprano and tenor solo (cantor) with optional organ accompaniment
3: Uv'shofar gadol. *Schirmer. Unpriced* DGU (B73-50022)
Adoramus te, Christe: SATB unacc. (Lasso, Orlando di). *Oxford University Press. Unpriced* EZDJ (B73-50537) ISBN 0 19 350332 8
Advanced harmony: theory and practice. (Ottman, Robert W). 2nd ed. *Prentice-Hall. £5.00* A/R (B73-03715) ISBN 0 13 012955 0
Adventante Deo = Lift up your heads, gates of my heart: anthem for SATB and organ. (Leighton, Kenneth). *Novello. £0.21* DH (B73-50025)
Affirmation: for organ. (Watson, Walter). *Schirmer. Unpriced* RJ (B73-50346)
After-intermission overture: for youth orchestra. (Hoag, Charles K). *Schirmer. Unpriced* MJ (B73-50248)
Agay, Denes. Man of La Mancha: arr. Man of La Mancha. (Leigh, Mitch). *KPM. £0.85* QPK/JR (B73-50323)
Age of Enlightenment, 1745-1790. *See* New Oxford history of music. Vol.7.
Agnes Cecilia, *Sister*. Suantrái: S S A. *McCullough, Pigott. Unpriced* FDH (B73-51015)
Ahrold, Frank. The courting of the deaf woman: American folk song. *Roberton. £0.10* DW (B73-50515)
Air and rumba: descant and treble recorder and piano. (Gubby, Roy). *Boosey and Hawkes. Unpriced* VSNTQHVKK (B73-51276)
Air composed for Holsworthy Church bells. It came upon the midnight clear. (Wesley, Samuel Sebastian). *Oxford University Press. Unpriced* EZDP/LF (B73-50544) ISBN 0 19 343041 x
Airs francais = Cantate francaise: for soprano and basso continuo. (Handel, George Frideric). First ed. *Bärenreiter. £1.50* KFLDX (B73-50643)
Albertson, Chris. Bessie. *Barrie and Jenkins. £2.95* AKFDW/HHW/E(P) (B73-13017) ISBN 0 214 65409 5
Albinoni, Tommaso. Sonate à tre in G minor. Adagio: arr. Adagio in G minor on two thematic fragments and a figured bass. *Ricordi. Unpriced* RSPMK (B73-51210)
Albumblatt for piano in E flat major: arr. Romance. (Wagner, Richard). *Chappell. Unpriced* RXMK (B73-51212)
Aldeburgh anthology. (Blythe, Ronald). *Snape Maltings Foundation Ltd; 38 Russell Sq., W.C.1: Distributed by Faber Music Ltd. £6.00* A(D) (B73-04215) ISBN 0 571 10003 1
Alford, Clem. The sitar manual: for the Western musician. *Keith Prowse. £2.75* TSX/AC (B73-50831)
Alice's adventures in Wonderland: song book. (Barry, John). *Edwin H. Morris. £1.00* KDW/JR (B73-50214)
All as God wills: for four-part chorus of mixed voices a cappella. (Ford, Virgil T). *Schirmer. Unpriced* EZDH (B73-50074)
All my trials, Lord: West Indian folk song. (Hopkins, Ewart). *Roberton. £0.10* EZDW/LC (B73-50131)
Alla polacca: a short and easy solo for trombone and piano. (Baker, Mervyn). *Cornelius. Unpriced* WUPHVHM (B73-50920)
Alleluia to the Lord of being: for full chorus of mixed voices a cappella. (Fast, Willard S). *Schirmer. Unpriced* EZDH (B73-50072)
Alleluja: für Orgel. (Hummel, Bertold). *Simrock. Unpriced* RJ (B73-50339)
Alleluya psallat: sequence for SATB unaccompanied. (Aston, Peter). *Novello. £0.14* EZDH (B73-50068)
Almeida, Antonio d'. Overture. Ouverture. (Bizet, Georges). *Universal. Unpriced* MMJ (B73-50677)
Almighty Father: chorale for four part chorus of mixed voices a cappella. (Bernstein, Leonard). *Amberson: Schirmer. Unpriced* EZDH (B73-50070)
Alte ungarische Tanze des 18 Jahrhunderts
für Bläserquintett und Cembalo. (Grabocz, Miklos). *Bärenreiter. Unpriced* NWNQK/AH/AYG(XG101) (B73-50696)
Alternative editions. *(Allison and Busby)* Wilmer, Valerie. Jazz people. 2nd ed. *Allison and Busby. £1.00* AMT/E(M) (B73-00882) ISBN 0 85031 085 7
Alwyn, William. Naiades: fantasy sonata, for flute and harp. *Boosey and Hawkes. Unpriced* VRPLTQE (B73-50846)
Amadis des Gaules. (Bach, Johann Christian). *Gregg International. £12.60* CQC (B73-50490) ISBN 0 576 28235 9
Ameln, Konrad.
Biblische Motetten für das Kirchenjahr, Band 1: Spruchmotetten. Spruchmotetten
1: Motets by Wolfgang Carl Briegel, Andreas Raselin and anonymous works. *Bärenreiter. £0.90* EZDJ/AYE (B73-50078)
Biblische Motetten für das Kirchenjahr, Band 1: Spruchmotetten. Spruchmotetten
2: Motets by Johann Christenius and others. *Bärenreiter. £0.90* EZDJ/AYE (B73-50079)
Messiah. Vocal score. Der Messias = The Messiah: oratorio in three parts. (Handel, George Frideric). *Bärenreiter. £2.10* DD (B73-50495)
American Arts Documentation Centre. *See* University of Exeter. *American Arts Documentation Centre.*
Amner, John. Lift up your heads: SSATB. *Oxford University Press. Unpriced* DK (B73-50033) ISBN 0 19 350331 x
Amorilli mia bella: Hommage a Johann Jacob van Eyck for recorder solo, descant, treble and bass recorder. (Linde, Hans Martin). *Schott. £1.08* VSPM/T (B73-51279)
Amy, Gilbert. D'un desastre obscur': pour voix de mezzo-soprano et clarinette en la. *Universal. Unpriced* KFNE/VVDW (B73-51093)
Anatomy of a miracle: Campbell-Orde memorial lecture 1972. (Mayer, *Sir* Robert). *Smythe. £0.45(non-net)* A(W/YD/XLQ76) (B73-28188) ISBN 0 900675 87 x
Ancient Chinese tunes: nine pieces arranged for recorders, tuned percussion, rhythmic percussion, plucked strings, guitar and optional clarinet in B flat. (Picken, Laurence). *Oxford University Press. £1.50* NYESK/AYVS (B73-50700) ISBN 0 19 344895 5
And did those feet in ancient time: for full chorus of mixed voices a cappella. (Chorbajian, John). *Schirmer. Unpriced* EZDH (B73-50071)
And out of his knapsack he drew a fine fiddle: an introduction to the technique of English fiddling. (Timpany, John). *English Folk Dance and Song Society. £0.50* AS/G/E (B73-19500) ISBN 0 85418 088 5
And wilt thou leave me thus?: For SSATBB unaccompanied. (Radford, Anthony). *Thames. Unpriced* EZDW (B73-50561)
Andante for flute clock in F major. K.616: arr. Andante, F Dur, KV616: ein Stück für eine Walze in eine kleine Orgel. (Mozart, Wolfgang Amadeus). *Schott. £1.20* VRNSK (B73-50841)
Anderson, Muriel Bradford. Prelude in canon: viola or horn in F. *Boosey and Hawkes. £0.40* SQP/X (B73-50794)
André Previn. (Greenfield, Edward). *Allan. £2.25* A/EC(P) (B73-21633) ISBN 0 7110 0370 x
Andreae, Marc. Symphony in G minor. Sinfonie, G-moll für Orchester. (Schumann, Robert). *Litolff: Peters. £3.00* MME (B73-50674)
Andrew, Pauline. A children's nativity: a nativity mime with narrative and carols (with ad lib. percussion, recorders, etc.). (Fenton, Lesley). *Keith Prowse Music. £0.40* FDPDE/LF/JN (B73-51027)
Animuccia, Giovanni. Missarum liber primus. 1st ed. reprinted. *Gregg. £12.60* ADG (B73-00361) ISBN 0 576 28220 0
Anne of Green Gables. (Campbell, Norman). *Chappell. £2.00* CM (B73-50937)
Anne of Green Gables. Vocal score. Anne of Green Gables. (Campbell, Norman). *Chappell. £2.00* CM (B73-50937)
Anson, George. Two Chinese sketches: for piano solo. *Schroeder and Gunther. Unpriced* QPJ (B73-50299)
Anthony, James R. French baroque music: from Beaujoyeulx to Rameau. *Batsford. £6.00* A(YH/XDZA153) (B73-32162) ISBN 0 7134 0755 7
Antoniou, Theodor.
Kinesis ABCD. Op.31: for two groups of strings. *Bärenreiter. £1.50* RXMJ (B73-50354)
Op ouverture: for orchestra and three groups of loudspeakers. *Bärenreiter. £1.50* MMJ (B73-50256)
'Applause' song book: songs from a new musical by Charles Strouse. (Strouse, Charles). *Edwin H. Morris. £1.25* KDW (B73-50210)
Apple to the core. (McCabe, Peter). *Sphere. £0.40* AKDW/GB/E(P) (B73-05834) ISBN 0 7221 5899 8
Apple to the core: the unmaking of the Beatles. (McCabe, Peter). *37 Museum St., W.C.1: Martin Brian and O'Keeffe Ltd. £2.00* AKDW/GB(P) (B73-05835) ISBN 0 85616 090 3
Applebaum, David. Sonata for piano. Piano sonata. *Chester. Unpriced* QPE (B73-50297)
Appleford, Patrick. New English Mass, series 3. *Weinberger. £0.25* JDGS (B73-50170)
Appleton, Michael J. Sonata for viola & piano (left hand) in G minor. Sonata in G minor for viola and piano (left hand). *Thames. Unpriced* SQPE (B73-50795)
Arch, Gwyn. This train: folk spiritual, SSA. *British and Continental. Unpriced* FDW/LC (B73-51036)
Archer, Janet. Stories of Britain in song. (Stuart, Forbes). *Longman Young Books. £2.75* KDW/G/AYC (B73-50213) ISBN 0 582 15330 1
Archipel II: pour quator a cordes: par André Boucourechliev. (Boucourechliev, André). *Universal. Unpriced* RXNS (B73-51215)
Aria and giga: for oboe and piano. (Hand, Colin). *Schott. £0.50* VTPHP (B73-50858)
Arioso and caprice: for flugel horn and band. (Hanmer, Ronald). *R. Smith. Unpriced* WMPWT (B73-50903)
Arioso and caprice: for flugel horn and piano. (Hanmer, Ronald). *R. Smith. Unpriced* WTPJ (B73-50913)
Arlen, Harold. The wizard of Oz: song album from the film. *Robbins Music, Francis, Day & Hunter. £0.75* KDW/JR (B73-50639)
Armitage, Grace.
Trees in the valley. Op. 40
1: The plane: unison and piano. (Le Fleming, Christopher). *Boosey and Hawkes. £0.05* FDW (B73-51029)
2: Beeches (copper and green): two part or unison and piano. (La Fleming, Christopher). *Boosey and Hawkes. £0.05* FDW (B73-51028)
3: The holly: SSA and piano. (Le Fleming, Christopher). *Boosey and Hawkes. £0.05* FDW (B73-51030)
4: The willow: unison and piano. (Le Fleming, Christopher). *Boosey and Hawkes. £0.05* FDW (B73-51031)
5: The yew: SA and piano. (Le Fleming, Christopher). *Boosey and Hawkes. £0.05* FDW (B73-51032)
6: The elm: SSA and piano. (Le Fleming, Christopher). *Boosey and Hawkes. £0.05* FDW (B73-51033)
7: Poplars: unison and piano. (Le Fleming, Christopher). *Boosey and Hawkes. £0.05* FDW (B73-51034)
8: The oak: two part or unison and piano. (Le Flemming, Christopher). *Boosey and Hawkes. £0.05* FDW (B73-51035)

Arne, Thomas Augustine.
The guardian outwitted. Overture. Overture: for flutes, oboes, bassoons, horns, strings and continuo. *Oxford University Press. £1.50* MRJ (B73-51123)
ISBN 0 19 361230 5
Six favourite concertos.. Selections. Organ solos. *Peters. Unpriced* RJ (B73-50335)
Arnival des animaux. Le Cygne: arr. The swan. (Saint-Saens, Camille). *Studio Music. Unpriced* WMPWTWK (B73-50904)
Arnold, Denis. The Beethoven companion. *Faber. £2.50* BBJ(N) (B73-17450) ISBN 0 571 10318 9
Arnold, Malcolm. Concerto for flute, no.2. Op.111. Flute concerto no 2. Op. 111. *Faber Music. £2.75* MPVRF (B73-50687)
Arnold, Matthew. Requiescat: canon for two-part high voices (or children's two-part choir). (Stoker, Richard). *Ashdown. £0.10* FTDW/X (B73-50581)
Arnold Bax. (Scott-Sutherland, Colin). *Dent. £3.50* BBH(N) (B73-15413) ISBN 0 460 03861 3
Around the world: songs with chorus and accompaniment for recorders and percussion. (Verrall, Pamela). *British and Continental. £0.40* CN (B73-50938)
Around the world. Vocal score. Around the world: songs with chorus and accompaniment for recorders and percussion. (Verrall, Pamela). *British and Continental. £0.40* CN (B73-50938)
Art of piano playing. (Neuhaus, Heinrich). 2nd ed.. *Barrie and Jenkins. £3.50* AQ/E (B73-14764)
ISBN 0 214 65364 1
Art of record buying: a list of recommended microgroove recordings
1973. *E.M.G. £2.15* A/FD(WT) (B73-15041)
ISBN 0 900982 04 7
As fit as a fiddle: six health education songs for younger children. (Reaks, Brian). *British and Continental. Unpriced* JFDW (B73-50624)
As I went riding by: carol for unison voices with optional descant, and piano. (Graves, Richard). *Novello. £0.07* JFDP/LF (B73-51066)
As the hart panteth after the water brooks: for four-part chorus of mixed voices a cappella. (Betts, Donald). *Associated Music. Unpriced* EZDR (B73-50101)
As time goes by. (Taylor, Derek). *Davis-Poynter. £2.00* A/GB (B73-21631) ISBN 0 7067 0027 9
As we sailed out of London river: male voice chorus (TTBB) and piano. (Sykes, Harold Hinchcliff). *Roberton. £0.10* GDW (B73-50166)
Aspects 1 in 3: song cycle for medium voice and piano. (Stoker, Richard). *Peters. Unpriced* KFVDW (B73-50235)
Aspects of Wagner. (Magee, Bryan). *Panther. £0.35* BWCAC (B73-00360) ISBN 0 586 03774 8
Associated Board of the Royal Schools of Music.
Aural tests issued for the guidance of teachers and candidates
Part 1. Grades 1-5. *Associated Board of the Royal Schools of Music. £0.25* C/EF (B73-50930)
Part 2. Grades 6-7. *Associated Board of the Royal Schools of Music. £0.25* C/EF (B73-50931)
Part 3. Grade 8. *Associated Board of the Royal Schools of Music. £0.25* C/EF (B73-50932)
Pianoforte examinations, 1974
Grade 1: Lists A and B (primary). *Associated Board of the Royal Schools of Music. £0.35* Q/AL (B73-51142)
Grade 2: Lists A and B (elementary). *Associated Board of the Royal Schools of Music. £0.35* Q/AL (B73-51143)
Grade 3: Lists A and B (transitional). *Associated Board of the Royal Schools of Music. Unpriced* Q/AL (B73-51144)
Grade 4: Lists A and B (lower). *Associated Board of the Royal Schools of Music. £0.35* Q/AL (B73-51145)
Grade 5: List A (higher). *Associated Board of the Royal Schools of Music. £0.35* Q/AL (B73-51146)
Grade 5: List B (higher). *Associated Board of the Royal Schools of Music. £0.35* Q/AL (B73-51147)
Grade 6: List A (intermediate). *Associated Board of the Royal Schools of Music. £0.35* Q/AL (B73-51148)
Grade 6: List B (intermediate). *Associated Board of the Royal Schools of Music. £0.35* Q/AL (B73-51149)
Grade 7: List A (advanced). *Associated Board of the Royal Schools of Music. £0.35* Q/AL (B73-51150)
Grade 7: List B (advanced). *Associated Board of the Royal Schools of Music. £0.35* Q/AL (B73-51151)
Associated Television. The piano can be fun. (Junkin, Harry). *Paul. £2.50* AQ/E (B73-05262)
ISBN 0 09 115200 3
Aston, Peter.
Alleluya psallat: sequence for SATB unaccompanied. *Novello. £0.14* EZDH (B73-50068)
Haec dies: dialogues and sonatas on the Resurrection of our Lord, for mixed voices and organ. *Novello. £1.25* DE/LL (B73-50944)
Holy Communion, series 3: for SATB choir, congregation and organ. *Royal School of Church Music. Unpriced* DGS (B73-50951)
Magnificat and Nunc dimittis in F: for SATB and organ. *Oxford University Press. £0.20* DGPP (B73-50948)
ISBN 0 19 351643 8
Three pieces for oboe solo. *Novello. £0.30* VTPMJ (B73-50861)
At the mid hour of night, (from Moore's Irish melodies). (Pasfield, William Reginald). *Ashdown. £0.05* FLDW (B73-50576)
Athalia.. War march of the priests. War march of the priests. (Mendelssohn, Felix). *Cramer. £0.24* RK/AGM (B73-50350)
Atkins, John G. In his hands: a cycle of spiritual and work songs. *British and Continental Music. £0.50* JFE/NYFSDW/LC/AY (B73-50627)
Attack and celebration: for orchestra. (Schurmann, Gerard). *Novello. £1.25* MMJ (B73-51118)
Attaingnant, Pierre.
Chansons musicales. Selections: arr. Eight chansons: for recorders (Tr T T B or D Tr T B)
Vol.1. *Schott. £0.75* VSNSK/DU/AY (B73-51274)
Chansons musicales. Selections: arr. Eight chansons: for recorders (Tr T T B or D Tr T B)
Vol.2. *Schott. £0.75* VSNSK/DU/AY (B73-51275)
A.T.V. *See* Associated Television.
Au fond du temple saint: duet. (Bizet, Georges). *United Music. Unpriced* JNGEDW (B73-51081)
Auerbach, Erich. An eye for music. *Hart-Davis. £15.75* A/E(M/EM) (B73-09575) ISBN 0 246 98552 6
Auld, William. Floroj sen kompar: Britaj popolkantoj. (Hill, Margaret). *British Esperanto Association. Unpriced* JE/TSDW/G/AYC (B73-50176)
Ausonius. The fields of sorrow: for 2 solo sopranos, chorus and orchestra. (Birtwistle, Harrison). *Universal. Unpriced* EMDX (B73-50979)
Austin, W. Chanticleer: SSA. (Hugh-Jones, Elaine). *Oxford University Press. Unpriced* FDP/LF (B73-51024)
ISBN 0 19 342596 3
Autumn song: for unaccompanied chorus (SAT Bar B). (Sculthorpe, Peter). *Faber Music. Unpriced* EZDW (B73-50127)
Autumn song: piano solo. (Parfrey, Raymond). *Composer to Player Edition. Unpriced* QPJ (B73-50734)
Ave Maria, gracia Dei plena: SATB unacc. (Beechey, Gwilym). *Banks. £0.04* EZDP/LF (B73-50991)
Ave Maria: SAAT Bar B. (Parsons, Robert). *Oxford University Press. £0.15* EZDJ (B73-50988)
ISBN 0 19 350335 2
Away in a manger: carol for mixed choir and organ/piano. (Roe, Betty). *Thames. Unpriced* DP/LF (B73-50041)
Away in a manger: carol for mixed choir and organ/piano. (Roe, Betty). *Thames. Unpriced* JDP/LF (B73-50604)
Ayres and dialogues, bk.2. Hymns to the Holy Trinity. Hymns to the Holy Trinity: for solo voice and keyboard continuo. (Lawes, Henry). *Oxford University Press. £0.75* KDH (B73-51082) ISBN 0 19 345493 9
B and H recorder cards: a programmed method
Set 1. (Wastall, Peter). *Boosey and Hawkes. £3.00* VS/AC (B73-50411)
Bach, Johann Christian. Amadis des Gaules. *Gregg International. £12.60* CQC (B73-50490)
ISBN 0 576 28235 9
Bach, Johann Sebastian.
Cantatas. Selections: arr. Flute obbligatos from the cantatas. *Universal. Unpriced* VRPMK/DE (B73-50409)
Concerto for oboe, violin, string orchestra in C minor: arr. Concerto in C minor for oboe, violin, strings and basso continuo. *Bärenreiter. £2.25* NUTNTK/LF (B73-50270)
English suite for keyboard, no.5. S.810. Sarabande: arr. Sarabande. *Cornelius. Unpriced* TSNUK/AHVL (B73-50818)
Herz und Mund und That und Leben. S.147. Wohl mir dass ich Jesum habe: arr. Jesus, joy of man's desiring. *Cornelius. Unpriced* TSPMK/DM (B73-50830)
Invention for keyboard in E major. S.792: arr. Sinfonia in G. *Cornelius. Unpriced* TSNTK (B73-50814)
Inventions and symphonies. S.772-801. *Bärenreiter. £1.50* PWPJ (B73-50285)
Preludes for keyboard. S.935, 939: arr. Two short preludes. *Cornelius. Unpriced* TSNUK (B73-50816)
Selections. Bach. *Freeman. Unpriced* PWPJ (B73-50286)
Selections. Bach. *Warren and Phillips. Unpriced* QPK (B73-50314)
Selections: arr. Bach's greatest hits: for all organ. *Chappell. £1.00* RK (B73-51201)
Das wohltemperirte Clavier. Prelude no.23. S.868: arr. Prelude no.23. S.868. *Cornelius. Unpriced* TSNTK (B73-50815)
Bach, Wilhelm Friedemann.
Symphony in F major. Falck 67. Sinfonie F-Dur. Falck 67. *Schott. £1.92* RXME (B73-51211)
Tripelfuge for keyboard in F major. Falck 19: arr. Tripelfuge. *Tomus. Unpriced* VSNRK/Y (B73-51271)
Bach family. Selections: arr. Three minuets. *Cornelius. Unpriced* TSPMK/AHR (B73-50827)
Bach's greatest hits: for all organ. (Bach, Johann Sebastian). *Chappell. £1.00* RK (B73-51201)
Baciu, Stefan. Hör meinen Protest: Psalm 5 für Bass, Trompete und Orgel. (Hader, Widmar). *Bosse Bärenreiter. £1.80* KGXE/WSPLRDE (B73-50240)
Background of brass: piano solo. (Parfrey, Raymond). *Composer to Player Edition. Unpriced* QPJ (B73-50735)
Bacon, Ernst. In that poor stable: carol for voice(s) and piano or organ. *Novello. £0.10* FDP/LF (B73-51021)
Bagatelle: piano solo. (Spies, Claudio). *Boosey and Hawkes. £0.75* QPJ (B73-50746)
Bagatelles. Opus 22: for string quartet. (Standford, Patric). *Novello. Unpriced* RXNS (B73-51217)
Bailey, Philip. They can make music. *Oxford University Press. £1.75* A(VMX) (B73-16551)
ISBN 0 19 311913 7
Baily, Leslie. Gilbert and Sullivan and their world. *Thames and Hudson. £2.25* BSWACF (B73-27557)
ISBN 0 500 13046 9
Baines, Francis.
Comic variations: for clarinet and bassoon. *June Emerson. Unpriced* VVPLVW/T (B73-50432)
A tutor for the bass viol, (consort bass). *Gamut. Unpriced* STU/AC (B73-51240)
A tutor for the tenor viol. *Gamut. Unpriced* STT/AC (B73-51239)
A tutor for the treble viol. *Gamut. Unpriced* STR/AC (B73-51238)
Baker, Mervyn.
Alla polacca: a short and easy solo for trombone and piano. *Cornelius. Unpriced* WUPHVHM (B73-50920)
Trumpet tango: a short and easy solo for trumpet and piano. *Cornelius. Unpriced* WSPHVR (B73-50912)
Ballad: for youth or amateur orchestra. (Durko, Zsolt). *Boosey and Hawkes. £1.00* MJ (B73-50660)
Ballet and its music. (Knight, Judyth). *Schott. £3.95* QPK/AHM/AY (B73-51182) ISBN 0 901938 03 3
Ballet music: an introduction. (Searle, Humphrey). Second revised ed. *Dover Publications: Constable. £1.50* AMM/HM (B73-32165) ISBN 0 486 22917 3
Bamforth, Dennis A. Tripelfuge for keyboard in F major. Falck 19: arr. Tripelfuge. (Bach, Wilhelm Friedemann). *Tomus. Unpriced* VSNRK/Y (B73-51271)
Banchetto musicale.. Suites. Three suites for five string or wind instruments. (Schein, Johann Hermann). *Bärenreiter. £2.70* RXNRG (B73-50361)
Bang on a drum: songs from Play School and Play Away, the B.B.C. Television programmes. (Wickham, E H). *British Broadcasting Corporation, Keith Prowse Music. £0.60* QPK/DW/GJ/JS/AY (B73-50320)
Banks, Don. Concerto for violin and orchestra. *Schott. £2.50* MPSF (B73-51121)
Bantock: music in the Midlands before the First World War. (Bray, Trevor). *10e Prior Bolton St., N.1: Triad Press. £1.25* BBE(N/XNH8) (B73-24885)
ISBN 0 902070 07 x
Barlow, David. Behold and see: Passiontide introit, for SATB (unaccompanied). *Novello. £0.07* EZDK/LGZ (B73-50087)
Barnard, John, *fl.1641.* First book of selected church musick. 1st ed. reprinted. *Cregg. £72.00* ADGM (B73-16145) ISBN 0 576 28200 6
Barnes, Ken.
Sinatra and the great song stylists. *Allan. £3.00* AKDW/GB/E(M/XN52) (B73-00880)
ISBN 0 7110 0400 5
Twenty years of pop. *K. Mason: Distributed by Barrie and Jenkins. £0.75* ADW/GB(XPK24) (B73-30278)
ISBN 0 85937 024 0
Baroque concerto. (Hutchings, Arthur). 3rd revised ed. *Faber. £4.20* ALF(XFQ31) (B73-17452)
ISBN 0 571 04808 0
Barratt, Bernard. Parliament Street blues. *R. Smith. Unpriced* WMJ (B73-50888)
Barratt, Bob. Tango taquin: for brass band. *Affiliated Music. Unpriced* WMHVR (B73-51295)
Barrell, Bernard.
Divertimento for solo oboe. Op.53. *Thames. Unpriced* VTPMJ (B73-50862)
Prelude and fugue. Op.36: organ. *Thames. Unpriced* R/Y (B73-50754)
Barrell, Joyce.
Dialogues. Op 20: flute and viola da gamba. *Thames. Unpriced* VRPLSTU (B73-50845)
Tanzmusik. Op.33: for solo piano. *Thames. Unpriced* QPH (B73-50727)
The three inns
for two guitars. *Thames. Unpriced* TSNU (B73-50392)
Barry, John. Alice's adventures in Wonderland: song book. *Edwin H. Morris. £1.00* KDW/JR (B73-50214)
Barsanti, Francesco. Sonatas for flute & basso continuo. Op. 1, nos 2, 6. Two sonatas for treble recorder and continuo. *Oxford University Press. £1.50* VSSPE (B73-51283)
ISBN 0 19 355327 9
Barschai, Rudolf. Sonata for viola and piano. Op.26. Sonate für Viola und Klavier. Opus 26. (Bunin, Revol). *Peters. Unpriced* SQPE (B73-50375)
Barthelson, Joyce.
Rock-a my soul: negro spiritual, for 3-part chorus of treble voices with piano accompaniment. *Roberton. £0.13* FLDW/LC (B73-50579)
Somebody's knockin' at your door: spiritual, for 4-part chorus of mixed voices with piano. *Roberton. Unpriced* DW/LC (B73-50519)
Bartók. (Lesznai, Lajos). *26 Albemarle St., W1X 4QY: Dent. £2.50* BBG(N) (B73-24886)
ISBN 0 460 03136 8
Basic principles in pianoforte playing. (Lhevinne, Josef). 1st ed. reprinted. *Dover Publications: Constable. £0.60* AQ/CY (B73-23436) ISBN 0 486 22820 7
Bass in the balloon: solo for E flat bass. (Newsome, Roy). *Studio Music. Unpriced* WMJ (B73-51297)
Bate, Philip. The trumpet and trombone: an outline of their history, development and construction. 2nd ed. *Benn. £3.00* AWS/B (B73-13587) ISBN 0 510 36411 x
Baton: official journal of the Philatelic Music Circle
Vol.1, no.1- ; 1969- . *c/o Hon. Editor, Irene Lawford, 22 Bouverie Gardens, Kenton, Middx HA3 0RG: Philatelic Music Circle. Unpriced* A(ZD/B) (B73-18101)
Baudach, Ulrich.
Furchte dich nicht: SSAB, with Christus spricht: wer mich liebt: SSAB, with Herr, wer festen Herzens ist, dem bewahrst du Frieden: SSA. *Bärenreiter. £0.15* EZDH (B73-50069)
'Te Deum laudamus': Konzert für Orgel, drei Trompeten und drei Posaunen. *Bärenreiter. £2.10* WNPRF (B73-50461)
Baudelaire, Charles. Cinq poèmes de Charles Baudelaire: songs for solo voice and piano. (Debussy, Claude). *Peters. Unpriced* KDW (B73-50631)
Bax, *Sir* Arnold.
Symphony no.7. *Chappell. Unpriced* MME (B73-50251)
Tintagel. *Chappell. Unpriced* MMJ (B73-50676)

Bazire, R V. Ten tunes. (Houghton, Frank). *OMF. Unpriced* DM (B73-50511)
B.B.C. *See* British Broadcasting Corporation.
Be not afraid because the sun goes down: for four-part chorus of mixed voices a cappella. (Fast, Willard S). *Schirmer. Unpriced* EZDW (B73-50114)
Beaumont, Adrian. Dwy gan werin = Two Welsh folk songs. *University of Wales Press. Unpriced* KDW/G/AYDK (B73-51088)
Beaumont, William. Die Zauberflöte. The golden flute: an opera for schools in two acts based on Mozart's 'The magic flute'. (Mozart, Wolfgang Amadeus). *Novello. £1.00* CN (B73-50008)
Beck, Hermann. The symphony. (Rauchhaupt, Ursula von). *Thames and Hudson. £8.50* AMME (B73-26166) ISBN 0 500 01099 4
Bedford, David. You asked for it: for acoustic guitar solo. *Universal. Unpriced* TSPMJ (B73-51247)
Beecham, *Sir* Thomas, *bart.* A mingled chime: leaves from an autobiography. *White Lion Publishers. £2.25* A/EC(P/XA1923) (B73-20240) ISBN 0 85617 163 8
Beechey, Gwilym.
Ave Maria, gracia Dei plena: SATB unacc. *Banks. £0.04* EZDP/LF (B73-50991)
Ayres and dialogues, bk.2. Hymns to the Holy Trinity. Hymns to the Holy Trinity: for solo voice and keyboard continuo. (Lawes, Henry). *Oxford University Press. £0.75* KDH (B73-51082) ISBN 0 19 345493 9
The guardian outwitted. Overture. Overture: for flutes, oboes, bassoons, horns, strings and continuo. (Arne, Thomas Augustine). *Oxford University Press. £1.50* MRJ (B73-51123) ISBN 0 19 361230 5
Kurzer jedoch gründlicher Wegweiser. Wegweiser: a 17th century German organ tutor. *Peters. Unpriced* R/AC (B73-50327)
Six favourite concertos.. Selections. Organ solos. (Arne, Thomas Augustine). *Peters. Unpriced* RJ (B73-50335)
Sonata for violin & basso continuo, liv. 5, no.5 in E minor. Sonata in E minor for violin and continuo. (Senallié, Jean Baptiste). *Oxford University Press. £0.90* SPE (B73-51220) ISBN 0 19 358796 3
Sonatas for flute & basso continuo. Op. 1, nos 2, 6. Two sonatas for treble recorder and continuo. (Barsanti, Francesco). *Oxford University Press. £1.50* VSSPE (B73-51283) ISBN 0 19 355327 9
Sonatas for flute duet. Op.5, liv.2, nos,1,4. Two sonatas for two flutes. (Loeillet, Jean Baptiste, *b.1688*). *Oxford University Press. £1.10* VRNUE (B73-51268) ISBN 0 19 357590 6
Symphony no.51 in B flat major. (Haydn, Joseph). *Eulenburg. £0.75* MME (B73-50670)
Symphony no.54 in G major. (Haydn, Joseph). *Eulenburg. £1.00* MME (B73-50671)
Symphony no.59 in A major. (Haydn, Joseph). *Eulenburg. £1.00* MME (B73-51114)
Symphony no.69, in C major, 'Laudon'. (Haydn, Joseph). *Bärenreiter. Unpriced* MRE (B73-50268)
Beeson, Jack. My heart's in the highlands. Vocal score. My heart's in the highlands: chamber opera in two acts. *Boosey and Hawkes. £10.00* CC (B73-50487)
Beethoven, *Ludwig van.* Prometheus. Op.43. *Excerpts.* Pastorale, Opus 43. *Schott. £1.60* MJ (B73-50246)
Beethoven, Ludwig van.
Selections. Beethoven. *Freeman. Unpriced* QPJ (B73-50300)
Symphony no.9 in D minor. Op.125. Freude, schöner Götterfunken: arr. Hymn of joy. *Paxton. £0.25* RK/DW (B73-51206)
Two orchestral minuets. *Oxford University Press. Unpriced* MK/AHR (B73-51111) ISBN 0 19 361430 8
Beethoven and the age of revolution. (Knight, Frida). *Lawrence and Wishart. £2.50* 780.924 (B73-11184) ISBN 0 85315 266 7
Beethoven and the age of revolution. (Knight, Frida). *Lawrence and Wishart. £2.50* BBJ(N) (B73-11184) ISBN 0 85315 266 7
Beethoven companion. (Arnold, Denis). *Faber. £2.50* BBJ(N) (B73-17450) ISBN 0 571 10318 9
Beggar's opera. Selections. Four songs. (Gay, John). *Oxford University Press. £0.12* EZDW (B73-50555) ISBN 0 19 343673 6
Behold and see: Passiontide introit, for SATB (unaccompanied). (Barlow, David). *Novello. £0.07* EZDK/LGZ (B73-50087)
Behr, Heinz Otto. Neue Kinderlieder: für Kinder - und Familiengottesdienst. *Bosse: Bärenreiter. £0.60* JFEZDM/GJ/AY (B73-50195)
Behrend, Siegfried. Grande due concertante: für Gitarre & Klavier. (Moscheles, Ignaz). *Simrock. Unpriced* TSPMJ (B73-51250)
Belle au bois dormant. *See* Perrault, Charles.
Belloc, Hilaire. Charles Augustus Fortescue: for unison or two-part voices and piano. (Bullard, Alan). *Novello. £0.10* JFDW (B73-50185)
Bemmann, Hans. Eight fugues for keyboard. Acht Fugen für Cembalo oder Orgel. (Kirnberger, Johann Philipp). *Schott. £1.80* PWP/Y (B73-51137)
Benham, Patrick.
Beguine: for guitar. *Cornelius. Unpriced* TSPMHJF (B73-50820)
Elegy and rumba: two short and easy solos for guitar. *Cornelius. Unpriced* TSPMHVKK (B73-50821)
Four short studies: for beginners on the guitar. *Cornelius. Unpriced* TS/AF (B73-50812)
Suite bergamasque. Clair de lune: arr. Clair de lune. (Debussy, Claude). *Cornelius. Unpriced* TSPMK (B73-50825)
Benjamin Britten. (Kendall, Alan, *b.1939*). *Macmillan. £2.95* BBU(N) (B73-31507) ISBN 0 333 15226 3
Bennett, F Roy. Welcome the Christ-child: seven carols for junior voices. *Ashdown. £0.18* JFDP/LF (B73-50619)
Bennett, Richard Rodney.
Commedia 1: for six players. *Universal. Unpriced* NYENQ (B73-50699)
Concerto for oboe: arr. Oboe concerto: reduction for oboe and piano. *Universal. Unpriced* VTPK/LF (B73-51287)
Lady Caroline Lamb: piano solo, theme from the film. *KPM. £0.25* QPK/JR (B73-50322)
Bennett, Sterndale. Musica Britannica: a national collection of music
Vol.37: Sterndale Bennett: piano and chamber music. *Stainer and Bell. Unpriced* C/AYD (B73-50002)
Benoy, A W. Pieces for the growing band. *Hinrichsen. Unpriced* WMK/AAY (B73-50896)
Benoy, Arthur William.
15 European carols. *Paxton. £1.00* VSNRQK/DP/LF/AYB (B73-51272)
A second book for the young orchestra: ten pieces for school string orchestra and recorder ensemble with optional flutes, clarinets, trumpets and piano. *Oxford University Press. £1.40* MK/AAY (B73-50663) ISBN 0 19 361653 x
Prelude for Christmas: for school orchestra. *Oxford University Press. Unpriced* M/LF (B73-51103) ISBN 0 19 361940 7
Scherzo for Christmas: for school orchestra. *Oxford University Press. Unpriced* M/LF (B73-51104) ISBN 0 19 361966 0
Bent, Margaret. Five sequences for the Virgin Mary. *Oxford University Press. Unpriced* EZDJ/AYD (B73-50989) ISBN 0 19 341207 1
Benz, Hamilton. La Serva padrona. Vocal score. La Serva padrona = From maid to mistress. (Pergolesi, Giovanni Battista). *Schirmer. Unpriced* CC (B73-50935)
Bergese, Hans. Der Mond. Vocal score. Der Mond = The moon: a little theatre of the world; English text by Maria Pelikan, vocal score by Hans Bergese. (Orff, Carl). *Schott. £9.60* CC (B73-50934)
Bergmann, Walter. Descant recorder lessons. *Faber. Unpriced* VSR/AF (B73-51282)
Bergsma, William. Illegible canons: for clarinet and percussion. *Galaxy Music: Galliard. Unpriced* VVPLX/X (B73-51294)
Berio, Luciano. Still: for orchestra. *Universal. Unpriced* MMJ (B73-51117)
Berkeley, Lennox.
Counting the beats: song for high voice and piano. *Thames. Unpriced* KFTDW (B73-50228)
Duo for cello and piano. *Chester. Unpriced* SRPJ (B73-50383)
Nocturne: for harp. *Stainer and Bell. £0.50* TQPMJ (B73-50389)
Theme and variations for guitar. *Chester. Unpriced* TSPM/T (B73-51244)
Berlioz, Hector.
New edition of the complete works of Hector Berlioz
Vol.2a: Les Troyens. Acts 1-2; edited by Hugh MacDonald. *Bärenreiter. Unpriced* C/AZ (B73-50479)
Vol.2b: Les Troyens. Acts 3-5; edited by Hugh Macdonald. *Bärenreiter. Unpriced* C/AZ (B73-50480)
Vol.2c: Les Troyens; supplement, edited by Hugh Macdonald. *Bärenreiter. Unpriced* C/AZ (B73-50481)
Vol.5: Huit scenes de Faust; edited by Julian Rushton. *Bärenreiter. Unpriced* C/AZ (B73-50482)
Vol.16: Symphonie fantastique; edited by Nicholas Temperley. *Bärenreiter. Unpriced* C/AZ (B73-50483)
L'Enfance du Christ. L'Adieu des bergers. Vocal score: arr. Thou must leave thy lowly dwelling. The shepherds farewell to the Holy Family. *Novello. £0.10* GDH/LF (B73-51044)
Symphonie fantastique. Op.14. Marche au supplice: arr. March to the scaffold. *Oxford University Press. £1.75* MGM (B73-50658) ISBN 0 19 362158 4
Berlioz style. (Primmer, Brian). *Oxford University Press. £3.75* BBM (B73-05259) ISBN 0 19 713136 0
Bernstein, Leonard.
Mass.. A simple song. A simple song. *Amberson: Schirmer. Unpriced* KDW (B73-50200)
Mass.. Almighty Father. Almighty Father: chorale for four part chorus of mixed voices a cappella. *Amberson: Schirmer. Unpriced* EZDH (B73-50070)
Mass. The word of the Lord. The word of the Lord. *Amberson: Schirmer. Unpriced* KDW (B73-50201)
Bernstein, Seymour. Birds: a suite of eight impressionistic studies for piano solo. *Schroeder and Gunther. Unpriced* QPG (B73-51169)
Bernstein, Walter H. Airs francais = Cantate francaise: for soprano and basso continuo. (Handel, George Frideric). First ed. *Bärenreiter. £1.50* KFLDX (B73-50643)
Berteaut, Simone. Piaf. *Penguin. £0.60* AKF/E(P) (B73-25529) ISBN 0 14 003669 5
Bertha: one act opera. (Rorem, Ned). *Boosey and Hawkes. £2.00* CC (B73-50936)
Bertha. Vocal score. Bertha: one act opera. (Rorem, Ned). *Boosey and Hawkes. £2.00* CC (B73-50936)
Berthold, G. Duetto for two cats with an accompaniment for the pianoforte. *Schott. £0.50* JNFEDW (B73-50628)
Bessie. (Albertson, Chris). *Barrie and Jenkins. £2.95* AKFDW/HHW/E(P) (B73-13017) ISBN 0 214 65409 5
Best, Terence. Works, keyboard. Keyboard works
Vol.3: Miscellaneous suites and pieces. (Handel, George Frideric). *Bärenreiter. £1.85* QRP/AZ (B73-51184)
Betts, Donald. As the hart panteth after the water brooks: for four-part chorus of mixed voices a cappella. *Associated Music. Unpriced* EZDR (B73-50101)
Bevan, Maurice. Two motets: for two high voices and keyboard. (Locke, Matthew). *Thames. Unpriced* JNFTEDJ (B73-50198)
Bevenot, Laurence. New music for Holy Week. *Chapman. £0.40* DFF/LH (B73-50013)
Beyer, Frederick. The man with the blue guitar: for four-part chorus of mixed voices with piano accompaniment. *Schirmer. Unpriced* DW (B73-50043)
Bialas, Günter. Quartet for strings, no.3. Drittes Streichquartett. *Bärenreiter. £1.50* RXNS (B73-50783)
Biber, Carl Heinrich. Tenebrae factae sunt = Darkness was over all: for four-part chorus of mixed voices a cappella. *Schirmer. Unpriced* EZDGKH/LK (B73-50060)
Biblische Motetten für das Kirchenjahr, Band 1: Spruchmotetten. Spruchmotetten
1: Motets by Wolfgang Carl Briegel, Andreas Raselins and anonymous works. (Ameln, Konrad). *Bärenreiter. £0.90* EZDJ/AYE (B73-50078)
Biblische Motetten für das Kirchenjahr, Band 1: Spruchmotetten. Spruchmotetten
2: Motets by Johann Christenius and others. (Ameln, Konrad). *Bärenreiter. £0.90* EZDJ/AYE (B73-50079)
Bicinia variorum instrumentum, no.75. Bicinia 75 for clarino (trumpet in C), bassoon and continuo. (Pezel, Johann). *Musica rara. Unpriced* NWNT (B73-50277)
Bicinia variorum instrumentum, nos 63-4, 67-8. Sonatinas no.63,64,67,68: for two cornetti (trumpets) and basso continuo. (Pezel, Johann). *Musica rara. Unpriced* WSNTPW (B73-50410)
Bicinia variorum instrumentum, nos 69-70, 72-3. Sonatinas no.69,70,72,73: for two clarini (trumpets), and basso continuo. (Pezel, Johann). *Musica rara. Unpriced* WSNTPW (B73-50464)
Binge, Ronald.
The jolly swagman. *Mozart Edition. Unpriced* KDW (B73-50202)
Sailing by: words and music by Ronald Binge. *Mozart Edition. Unpriced* KDW (B73-50203)
The watermill. *Inter-Art. £0.12* FDW (B73-50141)
Binkerd, Gordon.
Four chorale-preludes. *Boosey and Hawkes. Set A £6.00; Set B £8.00; Set C £10.00* MRK/AAY (B73-50693)
Portrait intérieur: for mezzo-soprano and violin and cello. *Boosey and Hawkes. £1.50* KFNE/SPLSRDW (B73-50652)
Portrait interieur: for mezzo-soprano and violin and cello. *Boosey and Hawkes. £1.25* KFNE/SPLSRDW (B73-51092)
Three songs for mezzo soprano and string quartet. *Boosey and Hawkes. £6.25* KFNE/RXNSDW (B73-50651)
Binney, Malcolm. Vocabulary ramblebuggies and educational wordopolis. Vocal score. Vocabulary ramblebuggies and educational wordopolis. (Meryll, Jane). *Belwin-Mills. £0.40* JFDX/GJ (B73-50625)
Bird lives! (Russell, Ross). *27 Goodge St., W1P 1FD: Quartet Books Ltd. £3.75* AVU/HX(P) (B73-22801) ISBN 0 7043 2007 x
Birds: a suite of eight impressionistic studies for piano solo. (Bernstein, Seymour). *Schroeder and Gunther. Unpriced* QPG (B73-51169)
Birds: Czech carol. (Hunter, Ian). *Thames. Unpriced* FEZDP/LF (B73-50153)
Birtwistle, Harrison. The fields of sorrow: for 2 solo sopranos, chorus and orchestra. *Universal. Unpriced* EMDX (B73-50979)
Bishop, Pamela. Songs of the Midlands. (Palmer, Roy). *E.P. Publishing. Unpriced* JE/LDW/G/AYDG (B73-50175) ISBN 0 7158 0377 8
Bizet, Georges.
Le Docteur Miracle.. Overture: arr. Overture. *Oxford University Press. £2.50* MJ (B73-50247) ISBN 0 19 361673 4
Overture. Ouverture. *Universal. Unpriced* MMJ (B73-50677)
Les Pêcheurs de perles. Au fond du temple saint: arr. Au fond du temple saint: duet. *United Music. Unpriced* JNGEDW (B73-51081)
Black, Don. Alice's adventures in Wonderland: song book. (Barry, John). *Edwin H. Morris. £1.00* KDW/JR (B73-50214)
Black music of two worlds. (Roberts, John Storm). *Allen Lane. £3.50* A/HG(X) (B73-16795) ISBN 0 7139 0536 0
Blackwell's music series. *(Blackwell)* Caldwell, John. English keyboard music before the nineteenth century. *Blackwell. £6.00* APW(YD/XA1800) (B73-16149) ISBN 0 631 13770 x
Blake, William.
And did those feet in ancient time: for full chorus of mixed voices a cappella. (Chorbajian, John). *Schirmer. Unpriced* EZDH (B73-50071)
To mercy, pity, peace and love: for four-part chorus of mixed voices a cappella. (Fast, Willard S). *Schirmer. Unpriced* EZDH (B73-50073)
Blakeney, Dale.
Hear my prayer. Op.39, no.1: arr. O for the wings of a dove. (Mendelssohn, Felix). *Cornelius. Unpriced* WTPK/DH (B73-50917)
Hear my prayer. Op.39, no.1: arr. O for the wings of a dove. (Mendelssohn, Felix). *Cornelius. Unpriced* WUPK/DH (B73-50922)
Blanc, James. The story of Ceol Chumann na nOg. (Ceol Chumann na nOg). *Smythe. £0.50(non-net)* A(W/Q/YDN/XA1972) (B73-28189) ISBN 0 900675 80 2
Blaukopf, Kurt. Gustav Mahler. *Allen Lane. £3.50* BME(N) (B73-20237) ISBN 0 7139 0464 x
Blessed are they that dwell in thy house: anthem for a dedication festival, or general use. (Sumsion, Herbert). *Lengnick. £0.18* DK (B73-50038)
Blessed art thou, O God of our fathers: anthem for SATB

and organ. (Milner, Anthony). *Boosey and Hawkes. £0.14* DK (B73-50036)
Blessed be the Lord God of Israel: for two-part chorus of female, male or mixed voices with piano or organ accompaniment. (Swann, Donald). *Roberton. Unpriced* DGNS (B73-50018)
Blezard, William.
A pair of pieces
for 2 flutes and clarinet. *British and Continental. Unpriced* VNT (B73-50403)
A pair of pieces: for 2 flutes and clarinet. *British and Continental. Unpriced* VNT (B73-50840)
Block, Robert Paul.
Bicinia variorum instrumentum, no.75. Bicinia 75 for clarino (trumpet in C), bassoon and continuo. (Pezel, Johann). *Musica rara. Unpriced* NWNT (B73-50277)
Bicinia variorum instrumentum, nos 63-4, 67-8. Sonatinas no.63,64,67,68: for two cornetti (trumpets) and basso continuo. (Pezel, Johann). *Musica rara. Unpriced* WSNTPW (B73-50410)
Bicinia variorum instrumentum, nos 69-70, 72-3. Sonatinas no.69,70,72,73: for two clarini (trumpets), and basso continuo. (Pezel, Johann). *Musica rara. Unpriced* WSNTPW (B73-50464)
Blow, John.
The self-banished. Minuet: arr. Minuet. *Cornelius. Unpriced* SRNTK/AHR (B73-50802)
Works, organ. Thirty voluntaries and verses for the organ. Revised edition. *Schott. £2.30* R/AZ (B73-50331)
Works, organ. Selections. Ten selected organ pieces. *Schott. £1.40* RJ (B73-50336)
Blues and Royals regimental slow march. (Jeanes, E W). *Boosey and Hawkes. £1.00* UMMGM/KH (B73-51254)
Blyth, Alan. Janet Baker. *Allan. £1.75* AKFQ/E(P) (B73-21632) ISBN 0 7110 0424 2
Blythe, Ronald. Aldeburgh anthology. *Snape Maltings Foundation Ltd; 38 Russell Sq., W.C.1: Distributed by Faber Music Ltd. £6.00* A(D) (B73-04215) ISBN 0 571 10003 1
Blyton, Carey. Symphony in yellow. Op. 15b: for high voice and harp (or piano). *Boosey and Hawkes. £0.40* KFTE/TQDW (B73-51096)
Boardman, Harry. Folk songs and ballads of Lancashire. *Oak Publications Music Sales. Unpriced* JEZDW/AYDJD (B73-50613)
Boardman, Lesley. Folk songs and ballads of Lancashire. (Boardman, Harry). *Oak Publications Music Sales. Unpriced* JEZDW/AYDJD (B73-50613)
Boccherini, Luigi. Sonata for violin & harpsichord in B flat major. Sonate, B-Dur, für Violine und Klavier (Cembalo). *Peters. £1.50* SPE (B73-50789)
Boder, Gerd. 9 Istanti: für Streichquartett. *Bosse Bärenreiter. £2.40* RXNS (B73-50784)
Bogenschutzen: Vokalise für eine hohe Singstimme und Klavier. (Reutter, Hermann). *Schott. £1.44* KFTDW (B73-51095)
Bologna, Jacopo da. *See* Jacopo da Bologna.
Bolton, Cecil. Themes from TV and film classics. *Robbins Affiliated Music. £0.75* RK/JS (B73-51207)
Bònis, Ferenc.
Harmonia caelestis: für Sopran, vierstimmigen gemischten Chor und Instrumente
Heft 1: Weihnachtskantaten. (Esterházy, Pál). *Bärenreiter. £1.35* ERXMDH (B73-50525)
Book of Morris dance tunes. (Brock, John). *English Folk Dance and Song Society. Unpriced* RSPMH/G/AYD (B73-51209) ISBN 0 85418 005 2
Boorman, Stanley. Four frottole: for voice and 3 instruments or 4 instruments. *Antico. Unpriced* KE/LNTDW/AYJ (B73-50216)
Bor, Sylvia. 14 caprices: for cello duet (student and teacher). (Josephs, Wilfred). *Chappell. £0.60* SRNU (B73-50803)
Bottesini, Giovanni. Duet for double bass, no.1. Grand duetto 1: for double bass. *Yorke. Unpriced* SSNU (B73-50387)
Boucourechliev, André. Archipel II: pour quator a cordes: par André Boucourechliev. *Universal. Unpriced* RXNS (B73-51215)
Boulanger, Ghislaine. Piaf. (Berteaut, Simone). *Penguin. £0.60* AKF/E(P) (B73-25529) ISBN 0 14 003669 5
Boulez, Pierre. Pli selon pli
No.5: Tombeau. *Universal. Unpriced* MMJ (B73-50678)
Boult, *Sir* Adrian. My own trumpet. *Hamilton. £3.25* A/EC(P) (B73-26819) ISBN 0 241 02445 5
Boustead, Alan. Symphony no.2, 'Metamorphoses'. Metamorphoses (Symphony no.2). (Gerhard, Roberto). Revised ed.: edited by Alan Boustead. *Belwin-Mills. Unpriced* MME (B73-50669)
Bow down thine ear, O Lord: SATB (SS Soli). (Hayes, William). *Oxford University Press. £0.25* DK (B73-50035) ISBN 0 19 350334 4
Bow down thine ear, O Lord: SATB (SS Soli). (Hayes, William). *Oxford University Press. £0.25* DK (B73-50035) ISBN 0 19 350334 4
Boyce, William. Works, orchestra. Selections: arr. A William Boyce suite. *Paxton. £0.45* RK (B73-51202)
Boyd, Malcolm.
Io son pur solo: solo cantata for soprano and basso continuo. (Scarlatti, Alessandro). First edition. *Bärenreiter. £1.20* KFLDX (B73-50222)
Luntan dalla suna Clori: solo cantata for soprano and basso continuo. (Scarlatti, Alessandro). First edition. *Bärenreiter. £1.20* KFLDX (B73-50223)
Palestrina's style: a practical introduction. *Oxford University Press. £0.95* BPC/R (B73-07791) ISBN 0 19 315224 x
Bozay, Attila. Sorozat = Series. Op.19: for chamber ensemble. *Boosey and Hawkes. £1.50* NYDPNM (B73-50283)
Brade, William. Newe lustige Volten, Couranten zu 5 Stimmen, nos. 11, 16, 17, 25. First set of quintets for 2 descant, treble, tenor and bass (or tenor) recorder. *Chester. Unpriced* VSNRK/AH (B73-50413)
Bradley, John. The Christ-child lay on Mary's lap: for SATB unaccompanied. *Novello. £0.07* EZDP/LF (B73-50992)
Brag, Kenneth. Songs of work and freedom. Songs of work and protest. (Fowke, Edith). *Dover: Constable. £1.75* JDW/KJ/AY (B73-51059) ISBN 0 486 22899 1
Brahms, Johannes.
Ach arme Welt. Op. 110, no.2. Ach arme Welt = Alas, poor world: motet for four part chorus of mixed voices a cappella. *Schirmer. Unpriced* EZDH (B73-50982)
German folksongs for four-part chorus, bk,2, no.1. In stiller Nacht. In stiller Nacht = In still of night: for four-part chorus of women's voices a cappella. *Schirmer. Unpriced* FEZDW (B73-51042)
Ich aber bin elend. Op. 110, no.1. Ich aber bin elend = Lord God, I am weary: motet for eight part double chorus of mixed voices a cappella. *Schirmer. Unpriced* EZDH (B73-50983)
Selections: arr. Short and easy classics
Ser 1. *Cornelius. Unpriced* TSPMK (B73-50824)
Symphonies. Complete horn parts of the four symphonies. *Horn Centre. £1.50* WTPME/AZ (B73-50474)
Brahms, Johnnes. Lass dich nur nichts nicht dauren = Let not your heart be troubled: for four-part chorus of mixed voices with organ or piano accompaniment. *Schirmer. Unpriced* DH (B73-50955)
Brahms's three phases: an inaugural lecture-recital delivered before the University of Newcastle upon Tyne on Monday 24 January 1972 and repeated on Wednesday 2 February 1972. (Matthews, Denis). *Newcastle upon Tyne NE1 7RU: University of Newcastle upon Tyne. £0.30* BBTAL (B73-10166) ISBN 0 900565 79 9
Brand, Geoffrey. Cornet cascade: a trio for cornets with brass band. (Docker, Robert). *R. Smith. Unpriced* WMPWRNTK (B73-50901)
Brass spectacular. (Hanmer, Ronald). *Studio Music. Unpriced* WMJ (B73-50890)
Bravo Maurice!: a compilation from the autobiographical writings of Maurice Chevalier. (Chevalier, Maurice). *Allen and Unwin. £3.50* AKG/E(P) (B73-24204) ISBN 0 04 920037 2
Bray, Roger. Liber primus sacrarum cantionum. Laetentur coeli. Laetentur coeli = Be glad ye heavens: SATBB by William Byrd. (Byrd, William). Revised ed. *Oxford University Press. Unpriced* EZDJ (B73-50536) ISBN 0 19 352058 3
Bray, Trevor. Bantock: music in the Midlands before the First World War. *10e Prior Bolton St., N.1: Triad Press. £1.25* BBE(N/XNH8) (B73-24885) ISBN 0 902070 07 x
Brazilian carnival march: for percussion ensemble (6 players). (Moisy, Heinz von). *Simrock. Unpriced* XNQGM (B73-50927)
Break forth into joy: festival anthem, for four-part chorus of mixed voices with organ or piano accompaniment. (Newbury, Kent A). *Schirmer. Unpriced* DK (B73-50037)
Brearley, Denis. Suite for cello, no.2. Suite no.2 for unaccompanied cello. *Lengnick. £0.30* SRPMG (B73-51233)
Breton, Nicholas.
First set of madrigals.. Corydon would kiss her then: arr. Corydon would kiss her then. (East, Michael). *Roberton. £0.10* FEZDU (B73-50154)
First set of madrigals. In the merry month of May: arr. In the merry month of May. (East, Michael). *Roberton. £0.10* FEZDU (B73-50155)
Brett, Bernard. The story of music. (Ingman, Nicholas). *Ward Lock. £2.00* A(X) (B73-00877) ISBN 0 7063 1306 2
Brett, Philip. Mass for five voices, (S A T T B). (Byrd, William). *Stainer and Bell. Unpriced* EZDG (B73-50530)
Brian, Havergal.
Symphony 2. *Musica viva. Unpriced* MME (B73-50665)
Symphony 8. *Musica Viva. Unpriced* MME (B73-50666)
Symphony 10. *Musica Viva. Unpriced* MME (B73-50667)
Symphony 21. *Musica Viva. Unpriced* MME (B73-50668)
Bricusse, Leslie.
'The good old bad old days!': a new musical. *Peter Maurice Music, (KPM Music Group). £0.75* KDW (B73-50204)
The good old bad old days. Selections: arr. The good old bad old days. *Peter Maurice. Unpriced* UMMK/CM (B73-50401)
The good old bad old days. Selections: arr. The good old bad old days. *Peter Maurice. Unpriced* WMK/CM (B73-50439)
Brindle, Reginald Smith. *See Smith Brindle, Reginald.*
British Broadcasting Corporation.
A history of Scottish music. (Elliott, Kenneth). *British Broadcasting Corporation. £0.90* A(YDL/X) (B73-25526) ISBN 0 563 12192 0
Music and the BBC. (Curran, Charles John). *British Broadcasting Corporation. Free* A(W/Q/P) (B73-07798) ISBN 0 563 10209 8
British Federation of Music Festivals. Year book
1973. *106 Gloucester Place, W1H 3DB: British Federation of Music Festivals. £0.60* A(YC/WE/Q) (B73-12433) ISBN 0 901532 04 5
British Institute of Recorded Sound. Music of Claudio Monteverdi: a discography. (Westerlund, Gunnar). *29 Exhibition Rd, S.W.7: British Institute of Recorded Sound. £2.00* BMN/FD(WT) (B73-01061) ISBN 0 900208 05 8
Britten, Benjamin.
Canticle 4. Journey of the Magi: for counter-tenor, tenor, baritone and piano. *Faber Music. Unpriced* JNDDE/LF (B73-50197)
Owen Wingrave. Vocal score. Owen Wingrave. Op 35: an opera in two acts. *Faber. £10.00* CC (B73-50488)
Rejoice in the Lamb. Op.30. Vocal score: arr. Rejoice in the Lamb. Op 30: festival cantata. *Boosey and Hawkes. £1.00* FDE (B73-50564)
Brock, David G. Works, organ. Complete organ works of J.N. Hummel. (Hummel, Johann Nepomuk). *Hinrichsen. Unpriced* R/AZ (B73-50332)
Brock, John. A book of Morris dance tunes. *English Folk Dance and Song Society. Unpriced* RSPMH/G/AYD (B73-51209) ISBN 0 85418 005 2
Brodde, Otto. Geistliche Zwiegesänge
Band 2: Spruch-Bicinien. *Barenreiter. £2.10* DH/AYE (B73-50507)
Brother James's air. (James, *Brother*). *Oxford University Press. £0.20* TSPMK/DR (B73-50395) ISBN 0 19 358403 4
Brouwer, Leo.
El Cimarron. Selections: arr. Memorias de 'El Cimarron'. (Henze, Hans Werner). *Schott. £1.60* TSPMK (B73-50826)
La Espiral eterna: para guitarra. *Schott. £1.08* TSPMJ (B73-51248)
Variantes for one percussionist. *Schott. £1.10* XPM/T (B73-50928)
Brown, Christopher. Four madrigals. Op. 29: for unaccompanied mixed voices. *Oxford University Press. Unpriced* EZDW (B73-50552) ISBN 0 19 343521 7
Brown, David.
Christ rising again: verse anthem for two sopranos, two altos, chorus and organ. (Weelkes, Thomas). *Novello. £0.18* DK (B73-50509)
Magnificat and Nunc dimittis no.5, 'in medio chori'. Evening service no.5, 'in medio chori': for two altos, tenor, two basses, chorus and organ. (Weelkes, Thomas). *Novello. £0.34* DGPP (B73-50949)
Brown, Frank E.
Athalia.. War march of the priests. War march of the priests. (Mendelssohn, Felix). *Cramer. £0.24* RK/AGM (B73-50350)
The Skye boat song: arr. The Skye boat song. (Macleod, A C). *Cramer. £0.15* QPK/DW (B73-50750)
Brown, Frank Edwin.
Come, let us seek the Lord: anthem for general use, SATB. *F. Pitman, Hart. Unpriced* DH (B73-50023)
The Prince of Denmark's march: arr. Trumpet voluntary. (Clarke, Jeremiah). *Cramer. £0.24* RK/AGM (B73-50765)
Two festal contrasts: organ solo
No.1: in C. *Cramer. £0.24* RJ (B73-50755)
No.2: in D. *Cramer. £0.24* RJ (B73-50756)
Brown, Howard Mayer.
Faites de moy toute qu'il vous plaira. (Busnois, Antoine). *Oxford University Press. Unpriced* EZDU (B73-50103) ISBN 0 19 341201 2
Libro primo de canzoni da sonare. La Maggia. Canzona 'La Maggia'. (Maschera, Florentio). *Oxford University Press. Unpriced* LNS (B73-50657) ISBN 0 19 341204 7
Brown, Margaret Hope-. *See* Hope-Brown, Margaret.
Brown, Sebastian. 30 negro spirituals: arranged, for unison (or two-part) singing with piano or guitar accompaniment
Book 1: Two-part versions. Piano edition. *Oxford University Press. Unpriced* FDW/LC/AY (B73-50148) ISBN 0 19 330186 5
Brown Reginald Porter-. *See* Porter-Brown Reginald.
Browne (Sir Thomas) Institute. *See* Sir Thomas Browne Institute.
Brudieu, Joan. Madrigales. Las Canas. Las Canas = The lancers: for four-part chorus of mixed voices a cappella. *Roberton. Unpriced* EZDU (B73-50546)
Brull, Ignaz. Works, strings and piano. Complete chamber music for pianoforte and strings. (Schubert, Franz). *Dover: Constable. £2.25* NX/AZ (B73-51131) ISBN 0 486 21527 x
Brunelli, Louis Jean. Essay for Cyrano. *Boosey and Hawkes. £10.00* UMMJ (B73-50833)
Brunetti, Domenico. Cantemus Domino = Sing unto God: for 3-part chorus of mixed voices with organ. *Roberton. £0.13* DJ (B73-50508)
Buchan, Norman. The Scottish folksinger: 118 modern and traditional folksongs. *Collins. £0.95* JE/TSDW/G/AYDL (B73-50607) ISBN 0 00 411115 x
Buchanan, Gary Robert. Sweets for woodwind quintet. *Galaxy: Galliard. Unpriced* VNRG (B73-51265)
Buchner, Alexander. Musical instruments: an illustrated history. *Octopus Books. £4.25* AL/B(X) (B73-24887) ISBN 0 7064 0015 1
Buchner, Alexander. Musical instruments through the ages. *See* Buchner, Alexander. Musical instruments.
Budden, Julian. The operas of Verdi
1: From 'Oberto' to 'Rigoletto'. *Cassell. £6.00* BVEAC (B73-13585) ISBN 0 304 93756 8
Buddy Lindo: folk songs of Trinidad and Tobago, for unison voices and guitar. (Harvey, John). *Oxford University Press. £0.25* JE/TSDW/G/AYULM (B73-50608) ISBN 0 19 330450 3
Bullard, Alan. Charles Augustus Fortescue: for unison or two-part voices and piano. *Novello. £0.10* JFDW (B73-50185)
Bumpus, John Skelton. A history of English cathedral music

1549-1889. 1st ed. reprinted. *Gregg. £10.80* AD/LE(YD/XDXJ341) (B73-13016) ISBN 0 576 28244 8

Bunin, Revol. Sonata for viola and piano. Op.26. Sonate für Viola und Klavier. Opus 26. *Peters. Unpriced* SQPE (B73-50375)

Bunyan, John.

He that is down needs fear no fall: SSA. (Harris, *Sir* William Henry). *Oxford University Press. Unpriced* FDH (B73-50565) ISBN 0 19 351117 7

Who would true valour see: S.S.A. with piano or organ. (Tomlins, Greta). *Roberton. £0.09* FDM (B73-50137)

Burdett, Brian V. The Christmas carol book: words and music of 24 popular carols chosen and arranged by Brian V. Burdett in collaboration with Shirley M. Sturgeon. *Jarrold. Unpriced* JDP/LF/AY (B73-51052) ISBN 0 85306 437 7

Burgmüller, Friedrich. Etudes faciles et progressives. Op.100. 25 easy and progressive studies: for piano. *Chappell. Unpriced* QPJ (B73-50301)

Burgon, Geoffrey.

The fire of heaven: for unaccompanied triple choir. *Stainer and Bell. Unpriced* EZDE (B73-50529)

Lullaby and aubade: for trumpet and piano. *Stainer and Bell. £0.25* WSPJ (B73-50465)

Burnett, Michael.

Prelude, song and dance: for clarinet and piano. *Ricordi. Unpriced* VVPJ (B73-50870)

Suite Blaen Myherin: for 2 trumpets, 2 trombones. *Ricordi. Unpriced* WNSG (B73-50910)

Bush, Alan. Variations, nocturne and finale on an old English sea song for piano and orchestra. Op.60: arr. Variations, nocturne and finale on an old English sea song: for piano and orchestra. Op.60. *Novello. £1.75* QNUK (B73-50290)

Bush, Geoffrey.

Invitation to the partsong

Volume 1. *Stainer and Bell. Unpriced* EZDW/AYD (B73-51012) ISBN 0 85249 165 4

Musica Britannica: a national collection of music

Vol.37: Sterndale Bennett: piano and chamber music. *Stainer and Bell. Unpriced* C/AYD (B73-50002)

Busnois, Antoine. Faites de moy toute qu'il vous plaira. *Oxford University Press. Unpriced* EZDU (B73-50103) ISBN 0 19 341201 2

But stars remaining: for female voice (unaccompanied) by Nicola Lefanu. (Lefanu, Nicola). *Novello. £0.35* KFEZDW (B73-50641)

Butterworth, Neil. Theme and variations: for two clarinets in B flat. *Ricordi. Unpriced* VVNU/T (B73-50427)

Buxtehude, Dietrich.

Magnificat. Vocal score. Magnificat = My soul doth magnify the Lord: five-part chorus and organ (piano) or five-part string accompaniment (or only 2 violins) and thorough-bass. *Peters: Hinrichsen. £0.45* DGKK (B73-50945)

Das neugebor'ne Kindelein. Vocal score. The little newborn Jesus Child: for chorus of mixed voices (SATB) with organ or instrumental accompaniment. *Lawson-Gould: Roberton. £0.32* DE/LF (B73-50942)

Buzzing, Pauline.

Let's sing and make music: ideas and advice for those who are engaged in Christian education with children and young people. *Denholm House Press. £1.20* A(VF/GR) (B73-04906) ISBN 0 85213 062 7

New child songs: Christian songs for under-eights. *Denholme House Press. £1.50* JFDM/GJ/AY (B73-51065) ISBN 0 85213 074 0

Byrd, William.

Gradualia, Lib 1.. Rorate coeli desuper. Rorate coeli desuper = Drop down, ye heavens: SAATB. *Oxford University Press. Unpriced* EZDGKAD/LEZ (B73-50059) ISBN 0 19 352062 1

Liber primus sacrarum cantionum. Laetentur coeli. Laetentur coeli = Be glad ye heavens: SATBB by William Byrd. Revised ed. *Oxford University Press. Unpriced* EZDJ (B73-50536) ISBN 0 19 352058 3

Liber secundus sacrarum cantionum. Miserere. Miserere mei = Look on me in mercy: SATBB. Revised ed. *Oxford University Press. Unpriced* EZDGKH/LHLN (B73-50532) ISBN 0 19 352053 2

Mass for five voices, (S A T T B). *Stainer and Bell. Unpriced* EZDG (B73-50530)

Three anonymous keyboard pieces. *Novello. £0.30* QSQ/AY (B73-50751)

Byron, George Gordon Noel, *6th Baron Byron.*

Lochnagar. (Gibson, Isabella Mary). *Kerr. Unpriced* KDW (B73-50205)

She walks in beauty: for three-part chorus of mixed voices a cappella. (Lekberg, Sven). *Schirmer. Unpriced* EZDW (B73-50119)

Cairns, David, *b.1926.* Responses: musical essays and reviews. *Secker and Warburg. £3.75* A(D) (B73-13013) ISBN 0 436 08090 7

Caldwell, John. English keyboard music before the nineteenth century. *Blackwell. £6.00* APW(YD/XA1800) (B73-16149) ISBN 0 631 13770 x

Cambridge Ward Method Centre. The Ward method of teaching music. *12 Grange Rd, Cambridge CB3 9DX: Cambridge Ward Method Centre. Unpriced* A(VC) (B73-08419) ISBN 0 9502782 0 3

Camden, John. First solos for the soprano recorder player. *Chappell. Unpriced* VSRPK/AAY (B73-50419)

Camden *(London Borough). Libraries and Arts Department. St Pancras Library.* Delius and America: catalogue of an exhibition of photographs, scores, letters and other material relating to Delius's visits to America and illustrating the American background to 'Koanga' and other works, held May 1-20 at St Pancras Library, London organised by the London Borough of Camden, Libraries and Arts Department. *St Pancras Library, 100 Euston Rd, N.W.1: London Borough of Camden, Libraries and Arts Department. £0.25* BDL(XLD14/WJ) (B73-02642) ISBN 0 9502653 0 6

Cameron, Gordon. Voice of angels, steps of shepherds: carol for SATB and organ. *Novello. £0.07* DP/LF (B73-50965)

Camilleri, Charles.

Divertimento for clarinet & piano, no.2. Divertimento no.2: for clarinet and piano. *Novello. £1.50* VVPJ (B73-50429)

Talba: for oboe solo. *Novello. £0.50* VTPMJ (B73-50425)

Cammin, Heinz. Lied über die Grenze, Folklore fremder Lander. *Schott. £1.44* TSPMK/DW/G/AY (B73-51252)

Campbell, Elaine. Anne of Green Gables. Vocal score. Anne of Green Gables. (Campbell, Norman). *Chappell. £2.00* CM (B73-50937)

Campbell, Norman. Anne of Green Gables. Vocal score. Anne of Green Gables. *Chappell. £2.00* CM (B73-50937)

Campbell-Orde memorial lectures. *(Smythe)* Mayer, *Sir* Robert. The anatomy of a miracle: Campbell-Orde memorial lecture 1972. *Smythe. £0.45(non-net)* A(W/YD/XLQ76) (B73-28188) ISBN 0 900675 87 x

Campion, Thomas. The masque at the Earl of Somerset's marriage. *Scolar Press. £2.75* BCBNACPF (B73-31563) ISBN 0 85967 129 1

Campra, André. Operas. Selections. Operatic airs. *Oxford University Press, for the University of Hull. £3.50* KDW (B73-50629)

Canas = The lancers: for four-part chorus of mixed voices a cappella. (Brudieu, Joan). *Roberton. Unpriced* EZDU (B73-50546)

Canon for 3, 'In memoriam Igor Stravinsky': for three equal instrumental voices. (Carter, Elliott). *Associated Music. Unpriced* LNT/X (B73-51098)

Canon for concert introduction or encore: a Russian popular tune. (Stravinsky, Igor). *Boosey and Hawkes. £0.50* MM/X (B73-51113)

Cantata for Easter, Op.105: for soloists, mixed chorus, organ and percussion. (Gardner, John). *Oxford University Press. Unpriced* ENYLDE/LL (B73-50051) ISBN 0 19 336214 7

Cantate Domino. Sing unto the Lord: for 4-part chorus of mixed voices with optional organ. (Vecchi, Horatio). *Roberton. Unpriced* EZDR (B73-50545)

Cantates françoises, liv.1. Orphée. Orphée: cantata for high voice, flute, violin and continuo. (Clérambault, Louis Nicolas). *Faber Music. Unpriced* KFTE/NURNTDX (B73-50232)

Cantemus Domino = Sing unto God: for 3-part chorus of mixed voices with organ. (Brunetti, Domenico). *Roberton. £0.13* DJ (B73-50508)

Canticle 4. Journey of the Magi: for counter-tenor, tenor, baritone and piano. (Britten, Benjamin). *Faber Music. Unpriced* JNDDE/LF (B73-50197)

Canzona 'La Maggia'. (Maschera, Florentio). *Oxford University Press. Unpriced* LNS (B73-50657) ISBN 0 19 341204 7

Canzone e sonate (1615): for trumpets, optional horns, and trombones

Canzon 1: for 2 trumpets and 3 trombones (2 trumpets, horn, and trombones). (Gabrieli, Giovanni). *Musica rara. Unpriced* WN (B73-50441)

Canzon 2: for 3 trumpets and 3 trombones, (3 trumpets, horn and 2 trombones). (Gabrieli, Giovanni). *Musica rara. Unpriced* WN (B73-50442)

Canzon 3: for 2 trumpets and 4 trombones, (2 trumpets, horn and 3 trombones). (Gabrieli, Giovanni). *Musica rara. Unpriced* WN (B73-50443)

Canzon 4: for 4 trumpets and 2 trombones. (Gabrieli, Giovanni). *Musica rara. Unpriced* WN (B73-50444)

Canzon 5: for 4 trumpets and 3 trombones (4 trumpets, and 2 trombones). (Gabrieli, Giovanni). *Musica rara. Unpriced* WN (B73-50445)

Canzon 6: for 4 trumpets and 3 trombones, (4 trumpets, horn and 2 trombones). (Gabrieli, Giovanni). *Musica rara. Unpriced* WN (B73-50446)

Canzon 7: for 4 trumpets and 3 trombones, (4 trumpets, horn and 2 trombones). (Gabrieli, Giovanni). *Musica rara. £2.00* WN (B73-50447)

Canzon 8: for 3 trumpets and 5 trombones. (Gabrieli, Giovanni). *Musica rara. Unpriced* WN (B73-50448)

Canzon 9: for 3 trumpets and 5 trombones (3 trumpets, horn and 4 trombones). (Gabrieli, Giovanni). *Musica rara. £2.50* WN (B73-50449)

Canzon 10: for 4 trumpets and 4 trombones (4 trumpets, 2 horns and 2 trombones). (Gabrieli, Giovanni). *Musica rara. £2.50* WN (B73-50450)

Canzon 11: for 4 trumpets and 4 trombones. (Gabrieli, Giovanni). *Musica rara. £2.50* WN (B73-50451)

Canzon 12: for 2 trumpets and 6 trombones, (2 trumpets, 2 horns and 4 trombones). (Gabrieli, Giovanni). *Musica rara. £2.50* WN (B73-50452)

Canzon 13: for 4 trumpets and 4 trombones, (4 trumpets, 2 horns and 2 trombones). (Gabrieli, Giovanni). *Musica rara. £2.50* WN (B73-50453)

Canzon 14: for 6 trumpets and 4 trombones. (Gabrieli, Giovanni). *Musica rara. £2.50* WN (B73-50454)

Canzon 15: for 4 trumpets and 6 trombones, (4 trumpets, 2 horns and 4 trombones). (Gabrieli, Giovanni). *Musica rara. £3.00* WN (B73-50455)

Canzon 16: for 6 trumpets and 6 trombones, (6 trumpets, 3 horns and 3 trombones). (Gabrieli, Giovanni). *Musica rara. £3.00* WN (B73-50456)

Canzon 17: for 6 trumpets and 6 trombones. (Gabrieli, Giovanni). *Musica rara. £3.00* WN (B73-50457)

Canzon 18: for 4 trumpets and 10 trombones, (4 trumpets, 2 horns and 8 trombones). (Gabrieli, Giovanni). *Musica rara. Unpriced* WN (B73-50458)

Canzon 19: for trumpets and 12 trombones, (3 trumpets, 3 horns and 9 trombones). (Gabrieli, Giovanni). *Musica rara. £3.50* WN (B73-50459)

Canzon 20: for 5 trumpets and 17 trombones, (5 trumpets, 4 horns and 13 trombones). (Gabrieli, Giovanni). *Musica rara. Unpriced* WN (B73-50460)

Canzonets to three voyces.. Come merry lads, let us away: arr. Come merry lads, let us away. (Youll, Henry). *Roberton. £0.10* FEZDU (B73-50156)

Capell, Richard. Schubert's songs. 3rd ed.. *Pan Books. £0.95* BSFAKDW (B73-29556) ISBN 0 330 23775 6

Capriccio for orchestra. (Holst, Gustav). *Faber Music. Unpriced* MMJ (B73-50258)

Capriccio für Viola. Op post. (Vieuxtemps, Henri). *Schott. £0.80* SQPMJ (B73-51227)

Caprice: piano duet. (Johnson, Thomas Arnold). *Freeman. £0.20* QNV (B73-50705)

Caprice variations: for unaccompanied violin. (Rochberg, George). *Galaxy: Galliard. Unpriced* SPM/T (B73-50793)

Captain Noah and his floating zoo: cantata in popular style. (Flanders, Michael). *Novello. £0.69* DE (B73-50496)

Cardenal, Ernesto. Hör meinen Protest: Psalm 5 für Bass, Trompete und Orgel. (Hader, Widmar). *Bosse Bärenreiter. £1.80* KGXE/WSPLRDE (B73-50240)

Carlo mio. (Cookridge, John Michael). *Janay. £0.06* JFDW (B73-50186)

Carnival des animaux. Le Cygne: arr. Le Cygne = The swan. (Saint-Saens, Camille). *Paxton. £0.25* SRPK (B73-50384)

Carol and rumba for recorders, (descant and treble), percussion and piano. (Foster, Anthony). *Oxford University Press. Unpriced* NYFSHVKK (B73-50701) ISBN 0 19 356554 4

Carol gaily carol: Christmas songs for children with piano accompaniments, with chords for guitar and with parts for descant recorders, glockenspiel, chime bars and percussion. (Harrop, Beatrice). *Black. Unpriced* JFE/NYESDP/LF/AY (B73-51075) ISBN 0 7136 1407 2

Carol of Joseph: for SATB choir. (Rudland, Malcolm). *Thames. Unpriced* EZDP/LF (B73-50099)

Carols for an island Christmas: for SATB, trumpets, string orchestra and piano (with optional boys' voices, woodwind and percussion),. (Ellis, David). *Novello. £0.23* DP/LF (B73-50967)

Carols for an island Christmas. Vocal score. Carols for an island Christmas: for SATB, trumpets, string orchestra and piano (with optional boys' voices, woodwind and percussion),. (Ellis, David). *Novello. £0.23* DP/LF (B73-50967)

Carols for schools: twelve carols for unison voices, recorders or flutes, percussion, guitar and piano. (Rutter, John). *Oxford University Press. £1.60* JFE/NYDPDP/LF/AY (B73-50193) ISBN 0 19 330665 4

Carols of King David: for unison choir, congregation and organ

No.3: Together in unity: Psalm 133. (Williamson, Malcolm). *Weinberger. £0.05* JDR (B73-51056)

Carr, John.

The seasons: suite. *R. Smith. Unpriced* WMG (B73-50881)

Two of the tops: a duet for E flat soprano and B flat cornets. *R. Smith. Unpriced* WMPWRNU (B73-50902)

Carré et Cormon, M. Les Pêcheurs de perles. Au fond du temple saint: arr. Au fond du temple saint: duet. (Bizet, Georges). *United Music. Unpriced* JNGEDW (B73-51081)

Carstairs, Adam. The Czarevitch: songs from the operetta. (Lehár, Franz). *Glocken Verlag. Unpriced* KDW (B73-50206)

Carter, Andrew. Tomorrow shall be my dancing day: English traditional carol. *Banks. £0.05* FDP/LF (B73-51022)

Carter, Anthony. Symphonie fantastique. Op.14. Marche au supplice: arr. March to the scaffold. (Berlioz, Hector). *Oxford University Press. £1.75* MGM (B73-50658) ISBN 0 19 362158 4

Carter, Elliott. Canon for 3, 'In memoriam Igor Stravinsky': for three equal instrumental voices. *Associated Music. Unpriced* LNT/X (B73-51098)

Carter, John. Weep you no more, sad fountains: for four-part chorus of women's voices a cappella. *Schirmer. Unpriced* FEZDW (B73-50157)

Cathedral music.. Bow down thine ear. Bow down thine ear, O Lord: SATB (SS Soli). (Hayes, William). *Oxford University Press. £0.25* DK (B73-50035) ISBN 0 19 350334 4

Cathedral music. *Excerpts.* Bow down thine ear, O Lord: SATB (SS Soli). (Hayes, William). *Oxford University Press. £0.25* DK (B73-50035) ISBN 0 19 350334 4

Catherine and Igor Stravinsky: a family album. (Stravinsky, Thedor). *Boosey and Hawkes. £6.50* BSV(N/XLB39/EM) (B73-13584) ISBN 0 85162 008 6

Causley, Charles. Nursery rhyme of innocence and experience: song for medium voice and piano. (Roe, Betty). *Thames. Unpriced* KFVDW (B73-50234)

Cavalli, Francesco. Musiche sacre. Magnificat. Vocal score. Magnificat for double chorus, cornetti (trumpets), trombones, strings, and keyboard continuo. *Faber Music. Unpriced* DGKK (B73-50946)

Cavenaugh, Irene. A prayer: for treble voices and organ. (Lloyd, Richard). *Lengnick. £0.06* FLDH (B73-50160)

Ceol Chumann na nOg. The story of Ceol Chumann na nOg. *Smythe. £0.50(non-net)* A(W/Q/YDN/XA1972) (B73-28189) ISBN 0 900675 80 2

Chaikovskiĭ, Peter Il'ich. *See* Tchaikovsky, Peter.

Chamber music: four selected poems, for low male voice and piano. (Reutter, Hermann). *Schott. £1.20* KFXDW (B73-50655)

Champion, Thomas. *See* Campion, Thomas.

Chansons musicales. Selections: arr. Eight chansons: for recorders (Tr T T B or D Tr T B)
Vol.1. (Attaingnant, Pierre). *Schott. £0.75* VSNSK/DU/AY (B73-51274)

Chansons musicales. Selections: arr. Eight chansons: for recorders (Tr T T B or D Tr T B)
Vol.2. (Attaingnant, Pierre). *Schott. £0.75* VSNSK/DU/AY (B73-51275)

Chanticleer: SSA. (Hugh-Jones, Elaine). *Oxford University Press. Unpriced* FDP/LF (B73-51024) ISBN 0 19 342596 3

Chants et prismes = Gesange und prismen. (Haubenstock-Ramati, Roman). Revised 1967. *Universal. Unpriced* MRJ (B73-51126)

Chapman, Edward.
Thou spirit of love divine: SATB accompanied. *Roberton. Unpriced* DH (B73-50024)
Thou spirit of love divine: unison song. *Roberton. £0.09* JDH (B73-50171)

Chapman, Frederick Bennett. Flute technique. 4th ed. *Oxford University Press. £0.90* AVR/CY (B73-26821) ISBN 0 19 318609 8

Chappell, Warren. The sleeping beauty. *Kaye and Ward. £1.25* AM/HMBN (B73-24333) ISBN 0 7182 0949 4

CHAPPELL'S book of Christmas carols. *Chappell. £0.75* JDP/LF/AY (B73-51053)

Charles Augustus Fortescue: for unison or two-part voices and piano. (Bullard, Alan). *Novello. £0.10* JFDW (B73-50185)

Chase, Richard. Old songs and singing games. *Dover: Constable. Unpriced* JFEZDW/GS/AYT (B73-51078) ISBN 0 486 22879 7

Chasseur maudit: arr. The accursed huntsman. (Franck, Cesar). *Studio Music. Unpriced* WMK (B73-50895)

Chatterley, Albert. Sticks and stones: a classroom music project for young children and audience. *Novello. £0.64* JFE/LPDX/GR (B73-50626)

Chedeville, Esprit Philippe. Simphonies for two instruments, liv. 1, suite 2, liv. 2, suites. 1, 2. Simphonies: three easy duets for recorders, flutes, oboes or other melodic instruments. *Schott. £1.08* LNU (B73-51099)

Cheesman, Oswald. Suite: for brass band. *Chappell. Unpriced* WMG (B73-50437)

Chesterton, Gilbert Keith. The Christ-child lay on Mary's lap: for SATB unaccompanied. (Bradley, John). *Novello. £0.07* EZDP/LF (B73-50992)

Chevalier, Maurice. Bravo Maurice!: a compilation from the autobiographical writings of Maurice Chevalier. *Allen and Unwin. £3.50* AKG/E(P) (B73-24204) ISBN 0 04 920037 2

Children of the world unite. (Cook, Roger). *Cookaway Music: Distributed by Music Sales. £0.20* JFDW/ (B73-50189)

Children's favourites. *Southern Music: Music Sales. £0.40* KFDW/AY (B73-50220)

Children's nativity: a nativity mime with narrative and carols (with ad lib. percussion, recorders, etc.). (Fenton, Lesley). *Keith Prowse Music. £0.40* FDPDE/LF/JN (B73-51027)

Chinese short pieces: for piano. (Chow Shu-San). *Paterson. Unpriced* QPJ (B73-50729)

Choirmaster in action. (Reynolds, Gordon). *Novello. £0.50* AD/E (B73-15415) ISBN 0 85360 057 0

Chopin, Fréderic. Selections. Chopin. *Freeman. Unpriced* QPJ (B73-50302)

Chorbajian, John.
And did those feet in ancient time: for full chorus of mixed voices a cappella. *Schirmer. Unpriced* EZDH (B73-50071)
For lo the winter is past: for full chorus of mixed voices a cappella. *Schirmer. Unpriced* EZDW (B73-50111)
There is a silence: for full chorus of mixed voices a cappella. *Schirmer. Unpriced* EZDW (B73-50112)

Choriamb for orchestra. Op. 41. (Stevens, Bernard). *Novello. £2.50* MMJ (B73-51120)

Chorstudien: for mixed choir. (Regner, Hermann). *Schott. Unpriced* EZ/AF (B73-50056)

Chow Shu-San. Chinese short pieces: for piano. *Paterson. Unpriced* QPJ (B73-50729)

Christ-child lay on Mary's lap: for SATB unaccompanied. (Bradley, John). *Novello. £0.07* EZDP/LF (B73-50992)

Christ rising again: verse anthem for two sopranos, two altos, chorus and organ. (Weelkes, Thomas). *Novello. £0.18* DK (B73-50509)

Christmas carol book: words and music of 24 popular carols chosen and arranged by Brian V. Burdett in collaboration with Shirley M. Sturgeon. (Burdett, Brian V). *Jarrold. Unpriced* JDP/LF/AY (B73-51052) ISBN 0 85306 437 7

Christmas fable. (Douglas, James). *Roberton. £0.07* EZDP/LF (B73-50097)

Christmas hymn. Opus 109a: SATB (or S. only) and organ. (Gardner, John). *Oxford University Press. Unpriced* DH/LF (B73-50957) ISBN 0 19 343016 9

CHRISTMAS magic: your own favourite songs and carols. *Chappell. Unpriced* JDW/LF/AY (B73-51060)

Christ's carol: SATB unaccompanied. (Vale, Charles). *Roberton. £0.07* EZDP/LF (B73-51001)

Christus resurgens: SATB unacc. (Johnson, Robert Sherlaw). *Oxford University Press. £0.20* EZDH/LL (B73-50985) ISBN 0 19 343036 3

Church bells of Herefordshire: their inscriptions and founders
Vol.4: Putley-Yazor. (Sharpe, Frederick). *'Derwen', Launton, Oxon.: F. Sharpe. £1.75* AXSR(YDHR) (B73-00362) ISBN 0 9500835 8 5

Chusid, Martin. Symphony no.8 in B minor, 'Unfinished'. D759. Symphony in B minor, 'Unfinished'. (Schubert, Franz). *Chappell. Unpriced* MME (B73-50253)

Cimarron. Selections: arr. Memorias de 'El Cimarron'. (Henze, Hans Werner). *Schott. £1.60* TSPMK (B73-50826)

Cimento dell'armonia e dell'invenzione. Op.8, no.4. Largo: arr. Largo from the 'Winter' concerto for violin and strings. (Vivaldi, Antonio). *Cramer. Unpriced* RK (B73-51204)

Cinq poèmes de Charles Baudelaire: songs for solo voice and piano. (Debussy, Claude). *Peters. Unpriced* KDW (B73-50631)

Clair de lune. (Debussy, Claude). *Cornelius. Unpriced* TSPMK (B73-50825)

Clarinets in concert: clarinet trio. (Verrall, Pamela). *British and Continental. £0.40* VVNT (B73-51291)

Clark, David Lindsey. Music for guitar and lute. (Exeter City Library). *Castle St., Exeter, Devon EX4 3PQ: Exeter City Library. £0.10* ATS(TC) (B73-27122) ISBN 0 904128 00 8

Clark, Paul. Three preludes for organ founded on Welsh hymn tunes, no.2. Prelude on the hymn tune 'Rhosymedre'. (Vaughan Williams, Ralph). *Stainer and Bell. Unpriced* VSNSK (B73-51273)

Clark, Richard C. Israelsbrünnlein. Zion spricht: arr. Zion spricht = Zion speaks. (Schein, Johann Hermann). *Roberton. Unpriced* EZDH (B73-50535)

Clarke, F R C. Works, orchestra. Selections: arr. A William Boyce suite. (Boyce, William). *Paxton. £0.45* RK (B73-51202)

Clarke, Jeremiah. The Prince of Denmark's march: arr. Trumpet voluntary. *Cramer. £0.24* RK/AGM (B73-50765)

Classical and romantic pieces for cello and piano. (Forbes, Watson). *Oxford University Press. £0.85* SRPK/AAY (B73-50806) ISBN 0 19 356471 8

Classical polyphony. (Rubio, Samuel). *Blackwell. £3.45* A/RM (B73-04219) ISBN 0 631 11740 7

Classical songs for children. The Penguin book of accompanied songs. (Harewood, Marion). *Penguin Books. £0.75* JFDW/AY (B73-50190) ISBN 0 14 070839 1

Classical style: Haydn, Mozart, Beethoven. (Rosen, Charles). *Faber. £2.00* A(X) (B73-04668) ISBN 0 571 10234 4

Clementi, Muzio.
Duettinos for piano. Wotquenne 24-5. Two duettinos: for piano, four hands. *Schirmer. Unpriced* QNV (B73-51161)
Sonatinas for piano. Opus 36. *Chappell. Unpriced* QPEM (B73-50298)

Clérambault, Louis Nicolas. Cantates françoises, liv.1. Orphée. Orphée: cantata for high voice, flute, violin and continuo. *Faber Music. Unpriced* KFTE/NURNTDX (B73-50232)

Clockwork music: an illustrated history of mechanical musical instruments from the musical box to the pianola, from automaton lady virginal players to orchestrion. (Ord-Hume, Arthur Wolfgang Julius Gerald). *Allen and Unwin. £5.95* A/FH/B (B73-14765) ISBN 0 04 789004 5

Clog dance. (Hérold, Ferdinand). *Oxford University Press. Unpriced* MH/HM (B73-51105) ISBN 0 19 364251 4

Cobb, Donald. Heaven conserve thy course in quietness: for women's chorus and viola, or piano. *Galaxy Music: Galliard. Unpriced* FE/SQDH (B73-51039)

Cobbe, Hugh. Trio for two flutes & pianoforte. (Wesley, Samuel). *Oxford University Press. £1.60* VRNTQ (B73-51266) ISBN 0 19 359505 2

Coke, Roger Sacheverell. Sonata for cello & piano in D minor. Op.24. First 'cello sonata (in D minor). *Chappell. Unpriced* SRPE (B73-50380)

Coker, Wilson. Music & meaning: a theoretical introduction to musical aesthetics. *Free Press: Collier-Macmillan. £4.50* A/CC (B73-05832) ISBN 0 02 906350 7

Colasse, Pascal. Enée et Lavinie. 1st ed. reprinted. *Gregg. £12.00* BCLSAC (B73-16143) ISBN 0 576 28236 7

Cole, Bruce.
Rondeau for organ. *Boosey and Hawkes. £0.65* R/W (B73-50753)
Sonnets: for two double basses. Revised ed. *Yorke. Unpriced* SSNU (B73-51236)
Sonnets for two double basses. Revised ed. *Yorke. Unpriced* SSNU (B73-51237)

Coleman, Ray. The 'Melody Maker' file
1974. *161 Fleet St., EC4P 4AA: IPC Specialist and Professional Press Ltd. £1.00* AKDW/GB/E(M) (B73-31505) ISBN 0 617 00093 x

Collaer, Paul. Music of the Americas: an illustrated music ethnology of the Eskimo and American Indian peoples. *Curzon Press. £6.50* BZP (B73-02064) ISBN 0 7007 0004 8

Collection of ancient piobaireachd or highland pipe music. (Mackay, Angus). *E.P. Publishing. £3.00* VY/T/AYDL (B73-50436) ISBN 0 85409 821 6

Colman, John. Madrigals and motets of four centuries: a choral songbook of 18 European classics, for mixed voices. (Richter, Clifford). *Associated Music. Unpriced* CB/AY (B73-50933)

Colour piping
Book 1. (Tobin, C). *Helicon Press. Unpriced* VSR/AC (B73-51281)

Colquhoun, Neil. New Zealand folksongs: song of a young country. *Bailey and Swinfen. £1.35* JE/TSDW/G/AYXR (B73-50609) ISBN 0 561 00189 8

Coltman, Derek. Edgard Varèse. (Ouellette, Fernand). *Calder and Boyars. £3.95* BVB(N) (B73-07096) ISBN 0 7145 0208 1

Colum, Padraic. O men from the fields: SATB unacc. (Deale, Edgar Martin). *Oxford University Press. Unpriced* EZDP/LF (B73-50993) ISBN 0 19 343038 x

Come all ye children: carol for unison voices and piano (organ). (Roe, Betty). *Thames. Unpriced* JFDP/LF (B73-50184)

Come day, go day, God send Sunday: the songs and life story, told in his own words, of John Maguire, traditional singer and farmer from Co. Fermanagh. (Maguire, John). *Routledge and Kegan Paul. £2.95* AKGDW/G/E(P) (B73-24205) ISBN 0 7100 7634 7

Come Holy Ghost, eternal God: set for SATBB and organ. (Naylor, Bernard). *Roberton. £0.10* DH/LN (B73-50960)

Come, let us seek the Lord: anthem for general use, SATB. (Brown, Frank Edwin). *F. Pitman, Hart. Unpriced* DH (B73-50023)

Come, let us sing you a song in canon: cantata. (Tippett, *Sir* Michael). *Schott. £0.50* DX/X (B73-50047)

Come merry lads, let us away. (Youll, Henry). *Roberton. £0.10* FEZDU (B73-50156)

Come, sound his praise abroad: for four-part chorus of mixed voices a cappella. (Ford, Virgil T). *Schirmer. Unpriced* EZDH (B73-50075)

Comedy for five winds: flute, oboe, clarinet in B flat, horn in F and bassoon. (Patterson, Paul). *Weinberger. Unpriced* UNR (B73-51260)

Comic variations: for clarinet and bassoon. (Baines, Francis). *June Emerson. Unpriced* VVPLVW/T (B73-50432)

Commedia 1: for six players. (Bennett, Richard Rodney). *Universal. Unpriced* NYENQ (B73-50699)

Compendia: computer-generated aids to literary and linguistic research. *(W.S. Maney and Son)* Preston, Michael J. A complete concordance to the songs of the early Tudor court. *Hudson Rd, Leeds LS9 7DL: W.S. Maney and Son. £6.50* ADWBP (B73-20977) ISBN 0 901286 03 6

Complete concordance to the songs of the early Tudor court. (Preston, Michael J). *Hudson Rd, Leeds LS9 7DL: W.S. Maney and Son. £6.50* ADWBP (B73-20977) ISBN 0 901286 03 6

Complete preludes & études for pianoforte solo. (Scriabin, Alexander). *Constable. £2.00* QPJ (B73-51176) ISBN 0 486 22919 x

Compose music. (Palmer, King). 2nd ed. *Teach Yourself Books. £0.65* A/D (B73-07097) ISBN 0 340 05552 9

Concertante for E flat alto saxophone and piano. (Grundman, Clare). *Boosey and Hawkes. £1.25* VUSPJ (B73-51290)

Concerti ecclesiastici. Op.4. *Excerpts.* Non vos relinquam orphanos = I will not leave you fatherless: SSA or T.T. Bar. (Donati, Ignazio). *Oxford University Press. Unpriced* FDJ (B73-50135) ISBN 0 19 350336 0

Concerti ecclesiastici. Op.4. Nun vos relinquam orphanos. Non vos relinquam orphanos = I will not leave you fatherless: SSA or T.T. Bar. (Donati, Ignazio). *Oxford University Press. Unpriced* FDJ (B73-51035) ISBN 0 19 350336 0

Concerto bucolico: for horn and orchestra. (Láng, István). *Boosey and Hawkes. £1.25* WTPK/LF (B73-50473)

Concise Oxford dictionary of music. (Scholes, Percy Alfred). 2nd ed. reprinted with corrections. *Oxford University Press. £1.50* A(C) (B73-30855) ISBN 0 19 311302 3

Concise Oxford dictionary of opera. (Rosenthal, Harold). 1st ed. reprinted with corrections. *Oxford University Press. £2.00* AC(C) (B73-30857) ISBN 0 19 311305 8

Conducting a choir: a guide for amateurs. (Holst, Imogen). *Oxford University Press. £1.30* AD/E (B73-16147) ISBN 0 19 313407 1

Conductor, The. Sounding Brass; and, The Conductor
Vol.1-, no.1- ; Apr. 1972-. *Novello. £0.15* AWM(B) (B73-26820)

Connolly, James. The James Connolly songbook. *9 St Nicholas Church Place, Cove St., Cork: Cork Workers Club. £0.15* BCMLADW(ZC) (B73-25527) ISBN 0 904086 00 3

Contemporary art song album: for medium voice. *Galaxy: Galliard. Unpriced* KFVDW/AYT (B73-50237)

Contrasts: for harpsichord. (Middleton, John). *Thames. Unpriced* QRPJ (B73-50326)

Contrasts: seven miniatures for school orchestra. (Tomlinson, Geoffrey). *Boosey and Hawkes. £4.90* MJ (B73-50662)

Conversations with Klemperer. (Heyworth, Peter). *Gollancz. £3.00* A/EC(P) (B73-16148) ISBN 0 575 01652 3

Cook, Roger. Children of the world unite. *Cookaway Music: Distributed by Music Sales. £0.20* JFDW/ (B73-50189)

Cooke, Arnold. Sonata for organ, no.1. Sonata no.1 for organ. *Peters. Unpriced* RE (B73-50333)

Cookridge, John Michael.
Carlo mio. *Janay. £0.06* JFDW (B73-50186)
Don't look down. *Bayley and Ferguson. £0.10* JFDW (B73-50621)
Gonna alter m'ways. *Janay. £0.06* JDW (B73-50173)
Gypsy Marie. *Bayley and Ferguson. £0.10* JFDW (B73-50622)
I'll ask the Lord. *Janay. £0.06* JFDW (B73-50187)
The other man's shoes: a modern spiritual. *Janay. £0.06* JFDM (B73-50181)
The seasons of love. *Janay. £0.06* JDW (B73-50174)
Unless love prevails: a modern spiritual for SA with pianoforte accompaniment. *McCullough, Pigott. £0.10* FDM (B73-51018)

Coombes, Douglas.
Psalm 96: S.S. accompanied. *Keith Prowse. Unpriced* FLDR (B73-50163)
Songs for singing together: fifty songs from around the world, taken from the B B C's music programme for schools 'Singing together'. *British Broadcasting*

Corporation. £1.25 JFDW/G/JT/AY (B73-51072)
Cooper, Frank. Robert Schumann: the man and his music. (Walker, Alan, *b.1930*). *Barrie and Jenkins. £7.50* BSG (B73-04217) ISBN 0 214 66805 3
Cooper, Joseph. Concerto for piano. Piano concerto: for one piano or two pianos and orchestra. (Vaughan Williams, Ralph). *Oxford University Press. £6.00* MPQF (B73-50685) ISBN 0 19 369273 2
Cooper, Paul. Variants for organ. *Chester. Unpriced* R/T (B73-51187)
Copland, Aaron.
Night thoughts. (Homage to Ives): piano solo. *Boosey and Hawkes. £0.60* QPJ (B73-51173)
El Salon Mexico: arr. El Salon Mexico. *Boosey and Hawkes. £7.50* UMK (B73-50397)
Copley, ian. The trumpet carol: for mixed voices and trumpets. *Thames. Unpriced* EWSNTDP/LF (B73-50526)
Copley, Ian. The waifs' carol: for unison voices (optional second part) and piano. *Thames. Unpriced* JDP/LF (B73-50603)
Copper, Bob. Songs and Southern breezes: country folk and country ways. *Heinemann. £3.50* ADW/G(YDCV) (B73-27558) ISBN 0 434 14456 8
Copperwheat, Winifred. Four pieces for solo viola. (Stiles, Frank). *Mixolydian Press. Unpriced* SQPMJ (B73-50799)
Corell, Roger. Autumn song: for unaccompanied chorus (SAT Bar B). (Sculthorpe, Peter). *Faber Music. Unpriced* EZDW (B73-50127)
Cork Workers Club. The James Connolly songbook. (Connolly, James). *9 St Nicholas Church Place, Cove St., Cork: Cork Workers Club. £0.15* BCMLADW(ZC) (B73-25527) ISBN 0 904086 00 3
Cormier, Robert de. *See* De Cormier, Robert.
Cornet cascade: a trio for cornets with brass band. (Docker, Robert). *R. Smith. Unpriced* WMPWRNTK (B73-50901)
Corpus Christi carol: for unison voices with optional divisions, and piano or organ. (Drayton, Paul). *Novello. £0.10* FDP/LF (B73-51023)
Corydon would kiss her then. (East, Michael). *Roberton. £0.10* FEZDU (B73-50154)
Cotswold lullaby. (Watters, Cyril). *Studio Music. Unpriced* WMJ (B73-50894)
Count down: duos for melody instrument and piano. (Hedges, Anthony). *Fenette Music: Breitkopf and Härtel. Unpriced* LPJ (B73-50244)
Counting the beats: song for high voice and piano. (Berkeley, Lennox). *Thames. Unpriced* KFTDW (B73-50228)
Courting of the deaf woman: American folk song. (Ahrold, Frank). *Roberton. £0.10* DW (B73-50515)
Coventry carol: unison song. (Greaves, Terence). *Chappell. Unpriced* JFDP/LF (B73-50183)
Coverdale, Miles. Coverdale's carol. Opus 75: for SATB unaccompanied. (Joubert, John). *Novello. £0.07* EZDP/LF (B73-50542)
Coverdale's carol. Opus 75: for SATB unaccompanied. (Joubert, John). *Novello. £0.07* EZDP/LF (B73-50542)
Coward, *Sir* Noel. Works, songs. The Noel Coward collection: songs
Volume 1. *Chappell. £0.60* KDW/AZ (B73-50630)
Coyle, Margaret. Sing for joy: twenty seven songs for infants. *Mayhew-McGrimmon. £0.50* JFDM/GJ (B73-50617) ISBN 0 85597 019 7
Cradle: SSATB unacc. (Neander, Valentin). *Banks. £0.04* EZDP/LF (B73-50999)
Craft of music: an inaugural lecture delivered in the University of Exeter on 2 November 1972. (Doe, Paul Maurice). *University of Exeter. £0.30* A (B73-06588) ISBN 0 900771 69 0
Cram, James D.
Sacred harp. Three hymns: arranged for four-part chorus of mixed voices with tenor solo a cappella
1: Paradise. *Chappell. Unpriced* EZDM (B73-50091)
Sacred harp. Three hymns: arranged for four-part chorus of mixed voices with tenor solo a cappella
2: The morning trumpet. *Chappell. Unpriced* EZDM (B73-50092)
Sacred harp. Three hymns: arranged for four-part chorus of mixed voices with tenor solo a cappella
3: Sweet rivers. *Chappell. Unpriced* EZDM (B73-50093)
Crashaw, Richard. Invitation to music: anthem for SATB and organ. (Naylor, Bernard). *Roberton. £0.13* DH (B73-50026)
Crawley, Christopher. The Sir Gawayn carols: SATB. *Oxford University Press. Unpriced* DP/LF (B73-50966) ISBN 0 19 343042 8
Craxton, Harold. The snowdrop: unison song. *Cramer. Unpriced* JFDW (B73-50623)
Craxton, Janet. Second book of oboe solos. *Faber Music. Unpriced* VTPK/AAY (B73-50422)
Creston, Paul. Fantasy for piano & orchestra. Op.32: arr. Fantasy, Op. 32: for piano and orchestra. *Schirmer. Unpriced* QNUK (B73-51159)
Creswick, Terry.
'Deed I do: arr. 'Deed I do: march. (Hirsch, Walter). *Keith Prowse. Unpriced* UMMK/DW (B73-51256)
'Deed I do: arr. 'Deed I do: march. (Hirsch, Walter). *Keith Prowse. Unpriced* WMK/DW (B73-51299)
March of the champions. (Laudan, Stanley). *Peter Maurice. Unpriced* UMMGM (B73-51253)
Crivelli, Giovanni Battista. Il Primo libro delli motetti concertati.. Ut flos, ut rosa. Ut flos, ut rosa. = Like flowers, like roses bloom the crowns: S.S. or T.T. *Oxford University Press. Unpriced* FLDJ (B73-50162) ISBN 0 19 350337 9
Crofts, John. Ayres and dialogues, bk.2. Hymns to the Holy Trinity. Hymns to the Holy Trinity: for solo voice and keyboard continuo. (Lawes, Henry). *Oxford University Press. £0.75* KDH (B73-51082) ISBN 0 19 345493 9
Crosse, Gordon. Memories of morning. Night: a monodrama for mezzosoprano and orchestra. *Oxford University Press. £3.00* KFNE/MDX (B73-50650) ISBN 0 19 362487 7
Crossman, Gerald.
Holiday cruise: a musical journey for organ or accordion
1: Southampton, England. *Bosworth. £0.20* RG (B73-51188)
2: Vigo, Spain. *Bosworth. £0.20* RG (B73-51189)
3: Haifa, Israel. *Bosworth. £0.20* RG (B73-51190)
4: Athens, Greece. *Bosworth. £0.20* RG (B73-51191)
5: Lisbon, Portugal. *Bosworth. £0.20* RG (B73-51192)
Crossman, Miriam.
Holiday cruise: a musical journey for organ or accordion
1: Southampton, England. (Crossman, Gerald). *Bosworth. £0.20* RG (B73-51188)
2: Vigo, Spain. (Crossman, Gerald). *Bosworth. £0.20* RG (B73-51189)
3: Haifa, Israel. (Crossman, Gerald). *Bosworth. £0.20* RG (B73-51190)
4: Athens, Greece. (Crossman, Gerald). *Bosworth. £0.20* RG (B73-51191)
5: Lisbon, Portugal. (Crossman, Gerald). *Bosworth. £0.20* RG (B73-51192)
Crotch, William. Methinks I hear the full celestial choir: for 5-part chorus of mixed voices unaccompanied. *Roberton. £0.13* EZDH (B73-50533)
Cruel wars: 100 soldiers' songs from Agincourt to Ulster. (Dallas, Karl). *Wolfe. £1.60* JE/TSDW/KG/AYC (B73-50612) ISBN 0 7234 0493 3
Cruft, Adrian. Jubilate Deo (St Peter ad Vincula): canticle or anthem for SATB chorus and brass ensemble. Op.51. *Boosey and Hawkes. £1.15* EWNPDGNT (B73-50055)
Curlew: for tenor solo, flute, English horn, and string quartet. (Warlock, Peter). *Stainer and Bell. Unpriced* KGHE/NVPNQDX (B73-51097)
Curran, Charles John. Music and the BBC. *British Broadcasting Corporation. Free* A(W/Q/P) (B73-07798) ISBN 0 563 10209 8
Curtis, Alan. Sweelinck's keyboard music: a study of English elements in seventeenth-century Dutch composition. 2nd ed. *Leiden University Press for the Sir Thomas Browne Institute, Leiden: Distributed by Oxford University Press. £7.75* BSXAPW (B73-09001) ISBN 0 19 647470 1
Cuyler, Louise. The Emperor Maximilian I and music. *Oxford University Press. £10.75* A(YE/XCS79) (B73-24453) ISBN 0 19 315223 1
Cwpwrdd Nansi. (Richards, Nansi). *Gwasg Gomer. £0.75* ATQ/E(P) (B73-19501)
Cycle of cats: three songs for soprano and alto voices with piano. (Price, Beryl). *Oxford University Press. £0.60* FDW (B73-50146) ISBN 0 19 337853 1
Cycles: for percussion (three players) and piano. (Fetler, Paul). *Schott. £2.40* NYLNS (B73-51134)
Cygne = The swan. (Saint-Saens, Camille). *Paxton. £0.25* SRPK (B73-50384)
Cyporyn, Dennis. The bluegrass songbook: eighty-eight original folk and old-time mountain tunes. *Collier: Collier-Macmillan. £1.25* JE/TSDW/GCG/AY (B73-50610) ISBN 0 02 060380 0
Czajanek, Victor. Weihnacht wie bist so schon = Christmas so wondrous fair: carol from Upper Austria, for four-part chorus of mixed voices a cappella. *Schirmer. Unpriced* EZDP/LF (B73-50096)
Czarevitch: songs from the operetta. (Lehár, Franz). *Glocken Verlag. Unpriced* KDW (B73-50206)
Czerny, Carl. Passagen-Übungen. Op.26.. Selections. 101 exercises: for piano. *Chappell. Unpriced* Q/AF (B73-50288)
Dadelsen, Georg von. Inventions and symphonies. S.772-801. (Bach, Johann Sebastian). *Bärenreiter. £1.50* PWPJ (B73-50285)
Dainton, Marie Cleeve. Songs for the primaries (with percussion). *British and Continental. £0.30* NYL (B73-50702)
Dale, Mervyn. Eight nonsense songs. *Ashdown. £0.40* KDW (B73-51086)
Dallapiccola, Luigi. Liriche greche: per soprano e diverso gruppi strumentali. *Eulenberg. £2.80* KFLE/MDW (B73-50224)
Dallas, Karl. The cruel wars: 100 soldiers' songs from Agincourt to Ulster. *Wolfe. £1.60* JE/TSDW/KG/AYC (B73-50612) ISBN 0 7234 0493 3
Dalmaine, Cyril Carr.
Selections. Bach. (Bach, Johann Sebastian). *Warren and Phillips. Unpriced* QPK (B73-50314)
Selections. Grieg. (Grieg, Edvard). *Warren and Phillips. Unpriced* QPK (B73-50315)
D'Almeida, Antonio. *See* Almeida, Antonio d'.
Dance from the mountains: piano duet. (Parfrey, Raymond). *Composer to Player Edition. Unpriced* QNVH (B73-50709)
Dance melodies: for 2 manuals and pedal. (Rothenberg, Peter). *Schott. £1.20* RPVK/AAY (B73-50352)
Dance overture. Op. 10: for orchestra. (Platts, Kenneth). *Ashdown. £3.00* MMH (B73-51116)
Dance-prelude for oboe d'amore (or clarinet) and piano. (McCabe, John). *Novello. £0.50* VTQPJ (B73-51288)
Dankworth, Avril.
Make music fun. *Dryad Press. £0.45* AX/BC (B73-10168)

Voices and instruments. *Hart-Davis. £1.50* A/DZ(VF) (B73-27555) ISBN 0 247 12513 x
Danzas espanolas, vol.2. Andaluza. Spanish dance, no.5. (Granados, Enrique). *Oxford University Press. £0.35* WTPK/AH (B73-50472) ISBN 0 19 356830 6
Danzi, Franz.
Quintet for woodwind & piano quintet in D major. Op.54, no.2. Quintet in D major. Opus 54, no.2: for piano, flute, oboe, clarinet, and bassoon. *Musica rara. £3.00* NWPNR (B73-50278)
Quintet for woodwind & piano quintet in F major. Op.53, no.1. Quintet in F major. Opus 53, no.1: for piano, flute, oboe, clarinet and bassoon. *Musica rara. Unpriced* NWPNR (B73-50279)
Dare, Marie. A widow bird sate mourning: SATB unaccompanied. *Roberton. £0.07* EZDW (B73-50113)
Darling Nelly Gray: arr. Nelly Gray: plantation song. (Hanby, B R). *Schott. £0.30* GEZDW (B73-50583)
Dart, Thurston.
Instrumental works. Selections. Music for strings and keyboard. (Purcell, Henry). *Novello. £0.80* NX (B73-51130)
Invitation to madrigals
6: for SSATB and SSAT Ba B; transcribed and edited by David Scott. *Stainer and Bell. Unpriced* EZDU/AY (B73-50551) ISBN 0 903000 02 4
Darvas, Gábor. Mass, 'L'homme armé'. Missa 'L'homme armé': for mixed choir (S.Ms.A.T., Bar, B) a cappella. (Okeghem, Jean). *Boosey and Hawkes. £1.00* EZDG (B73-50058)
Darvas, Gabor. Missa 'L'Homme armé': for mixed choir (SATB) a cappella. (Dufay, Guillaume). *Boosey and Hawkes. £1.00* EZDG (B73-50981)
Daubney, Brian. Ko-Ai and the dragon: a story to music. *Belwin-Mills Music. £160* CQN (B73-50494)
David, Hans Theodore. J.S. Bach's 'Musical Offering': history, interpretation and analysis. *Dover Publications: Constable. £1.25* BBCAN (B73-05261) ISBN 0 486 22768 5
Davies, David. En route. (Harry, Lynn). *K.P.M. Unpriced* GDW (B73-50164)
Davies, Laurence, *b.1926*. Franck. *Dent. £1.90* BFT(N) (B73-12434) ISBN 0 460 03134 1
Davies, Laurence Hector. Hear my prayer, O Lord. (Purcell, Henry). *Roberton. £0.07* FDK (B73-50136)
Davison, Peter. Songs of the British music hall. *Oak Publications: Music Sales. Unpriced* KE/TSDW/JV/AY (B73-50219) ISBN 0 8256 0099 5
Day Lewis, Cecil.
Five Irish songs: for mixed chorus a cappella
5: Jig; words by Cecil Day-Lewis. (Maw, Nicholas). *Boosey and Hawkes. £0.20* EZDW (B73-50560)
Speaking from the snow: suite for high voice and piano. (Naylor, Bernard). *Roberton. £0.40* KFTDW (B73-51094)
Day music: for violin and piano. (Rorem, Ned). *Boosey and Hawkes. £1.25* SPJ (B73-50366)
De Cormier, Robert.
Wayfaring stranger: for 2/3 part chorus of female or children's voices unaccompanied. *Roberton. £0.07* FEZDM (B73-50573)
Wayfaring stranger: for 4-part chorus of mixed voices unaccompanied. *Roberton. £0.10* EZDM (B73-50541)
De la Mare, Walter. As we sailed out of London river: male voice chorus (TTBB) and piano. (Sykes, Harold Hinchcliff). *Roberton. £0.10* GDW (B73-50166)
De Mondonville, Joseph. *See* Mondonville, Joseph de.
De natura sonoris no.2: per orchestra. (Penderecki, Krzystof). *Schott. £2.00* MMJ (B73-50260)
De Smet, Robert. Prelude, théme et variations pour cor. Prelude, theme and variations for horn and piano. (Rossini, Gioacchino Antonio). *Peters. Unpriced* WTP/T (B73-50468)
De Smet, Robin.
Carnival des animaux. Le Cygne: arr. Le Cygne = The swan. (Saint-Saens, Camille). *Paxton. £0.25* SRPK (B73-50384)
Sonata for violin & basso continuo in D minor. Sarabanda, Allegro; arr. Introduction and allegro spiritoso. (Senaillé, Jean Baptiste). *Fenette Music, Breitkopf and Härtel. Unpriced* VVPK (B73-50430)
De Szkhavos, Andrew Horvath.
De Victoria, Tomas Luis *See* Victoria, Tomas Luis de.
Deale, Edgar Martin. O men from the fields: SATB unacc. *Oxford University Press. Unpriced* EZDP/LF (B73-50993) ISBN 0 19 343038 x
Dear to my heart: air varié. (Siebert, Edrich). *Studio Music. Unpriced* WM/T (B73-50879)
Dearmer, Percy. Who would true valour see: S.S.A. with piano or organ. (Tomlins, Greta). *Roberton. £0.09* FDM (B73-50137)
Dearnley, Christopher.
Communion service, series 3: unison (and optional SATB). *Oxford University Press. Unpriced* JDGS (B73-50600) ISBN 0 19 351645 4
Magnificat and Nunc dimittis: SATBB. (Wise, Michael). *Oxford University Press. £0.15* DGPP (B73-50950) ISBN 0 19 351635 7
Debussy, Claude.
Cinq poèmes de Charles Baudelaire: songs for solo voice and piano. *Peters. Unpriced* KDW (B73-50631)
Estampes: piano solo. *Peters. Unpriced* QPJ (B73-50303)
Prelude for piano. Book1, no.6. Des pas sur la neige = Footprints in the snow. *Peters. Unpriced* QPJ (B73-51174)
Suite bergamasque. Clair de lune: arr. Clair de lune. *Cornelius. Unpriced* TSPMK (B73-50825)
Trois ballads de François Villon: songs for solo voice and piano. *Peters. Unpriced* KDW (B73-50632)
Trois chansons de France, and Trois poèmes de Tristan l'Hermite: songs for solo voice and piano. *Peters. Unpriced* KDW (B73-50633)
Trois poèmes de Stéphane Mallarmé: songs for solo voice and piano. *Peters. Unpriced* KDW (B73-50634)

Debussy. (Nichols, Roger). *Oxford University Press. £1.20* BDJ (B73-24201) ISBN 0 19 315426 9

Decca Group records, musicassettes and stereo 8 cartridges, main catalogue
1973: up to and including September 1972. *Decca Record Co. £5.00* A/FD(WM) (B73-07316) ISBN 0 901364 04 5

Deck the hall: carol for mixed voices. (Roe, Betty). *Thames. Unpriced* EZDP/LF (B73-50543)

'Deed I do: arr. 'Deed I do: march. (Hirsch, Walter). *Keith Prowse. Unpriced* UMMK/DW (B73-51256)

'Deed I do: arr. 'Deed I do: march. (Hirsch, Walter). *Keith Prowse. Unpriced* WMK/DW (B73-51299)

Delden, Lex van. *See* Van Delden, Lex.

Delius, Frederick.
Songs. Selections. Ten songs. *Galliard. Unpriced* KDW (B73-50635)
A village Romeo and Juliet. Vocal score. A village Romeo and Juliet. *Boosey and Hawkes. £7.50* CC (B73-50005)

Delius and America: catalogue of an exhibition of photographs, scores, letters and other material relating to Delius's visits to America and illustrating the American background to 'Koanga' and other works, held May 1-20 at St Pancras Library, London organised by the London Borough of Camden, Libraries and Arts Department. (Camden *(London Borough). Libraries and Arts Department. St Pancras Library). St Pancras Library, 100 Euston Rd, N.W.1: London Borough of Camden, Libraries and Arts Department. £0.25* BDL(XLD14/WJ) (B73-02642) ISBN 0 9502653 0 6

Delius Society. Newsletter. Delius and America: catalogue of an exhibition of photographs, scores, letters and other material relating to Delius's visits to America and illustrating the American background to 'Koanga' and other works, held May 1-20 at St Pancras Library, London organised by the London Borough of Camden, Libraries and Arts Department. (Camden *(London Borough). Libraries and Arts Department. St Pancras Library). St Pancras Library, 100 Euston Rd, N.W.1 London Borough of Camden, Libraries and Arts Department. £0.25* BDL(XLD14/WJ) (B73-02642) ISBN 0 9502653 0 6

Deng, Francis Mading. The Dinka and their songs. *Clarendon Press. £6.50* BZNDADW/G (B73-27559) ISBN 0 19 815138 1

Dennison, Peter. Musica Britannica: a national collection of music
Vol.34: Pelham Humfrey: Complete church music I; transcribed and edited by Peter Dennison. *Stainer and Bell. Unpriced* C/AYD (B73-50478)

Denny, William. Two orchestral minuets. (Beethoven, Ludwig van). *Oxford University Press. Unpriced* MK/AHR (B73-51111) ISBN 0 19 361430 8

Department of Education and Science. *See* Great Britain. *Department of Education and Science.*

Des pas sur la neige = Footprints in the snow. (Debussy, Claude). *Peters. Unpriced* QPJ (B73-51174)

Des Prés, Josquin. *See* Josquin des Prés.

Desch, Rudolf.
Darling Nelly Gray: arr. Nelly Gray: plantation song. (Hanby, B R). *Schott. £0.30* GEZDW (B73-50583)
Von allerlei Hunden: eine frohliche Kantate, für Kinderchor, Klavier, Glockenspiel, Zupfbass, und Schlagwerk, (grosse und kleine Trommel, Holztrommel, Tamburin, Becken, Triangel). *Schott. £1.40* FE/NYLDX (B73-50570)

Devereux, Peter. First solos for the soprano recorder player. (Camden, John). *Chappell. Unpriced* VSRPK/AAY (B73-50419)

Dexter, Harry.
Scarborough Fair: arr. Scarborough Fair: rhythmic version for piano solo. *Ashdown. £0.20* QPK/DW (B73-50318)
The constant lover: early 18th century songs. *Ashdown. Unpriced* GEZDW (B73-50168)

Di pera mora = Cruel they beauty: 16th century Spanish dance song, for 4-part chorus of mixed voices unaccompanied. (Merril, Marlin). *Roberton. Unpriced* EZDU (B73-50549)

Dialogues. Op 20: flute and viola da gamba. (Barrell, Joyce). *Thames. Unpriced* VRPLSTU (B73-50845)

Dickinson, Alan Edgar Frederic. The music of Berlioz. *Faber. £8.00* BBM (B73-00878) ISBN 0 571 09618 2

Dickson, Andrew. The nativity: SATB unacc. *Banks. £0.05* EZDP/LF (B73-50994)

Dickson, Andrew Wilson- *See* Wilson-Dickson, Andrew.

Dickson, Martin. Heard ye the mighty roar?: Song. (Wilson, Robert Barclay). *Cramer. Unpriced* KDW (B73-50212)

Dictionary of twentieth-century composers, 1911-1971. (Thompson, Kenneth). *Faber. £12.00* A/D(M/XML61/C) (B73-09574) ISBN 0 571 09002 8

Die mit Tränen säen: motet for two five-part choirs and basso continuo. (Schütz, Heinrich). *Bärenreiter. £1.50* EWUNPPWDH (B73-50527)

Dinham, Kenneth J. L'Enfance du Christ. L'Adieu des bergers. Vocal score: arr. Thou must leave thy lowly dwelling. The shepherds farewell to the Holy Family. (Berlioz, Hector). *Novello. £0.10* GDH/LF (B73-51044)

Dinka and their songs. (Deng, Francis Mading). *Clarendon Press. £6.50* BZNDADW/G (B73-27559) ISBN 0 19 815138 1

Dinn, Freda.
Concerti grossi. Op.3, no.2. Menuet: arr. Menuet. (Handel, George Frideric). *Schott. Unpriced* VSNRPWK/AHR (B73-50414)
Scales and arpeggios: for treble recorder. *Schott. £0.25* VSS/AF (B73-50420)

Divertimento for solo oboe. Op.53. (Barrell, Bernard). *Thames. Unpriced* VTPMJ (B73-50862)

Dixit Dominus and Magnificat. K.193. (Mozart, Wolfgang Amadeus). *Schirmer. Unpriced* DGKB (B73-50498)

Docker, Robert. Cornet cascade: a trio for cornets with brass band. *R. Smith. Unpriced* WMPWRNTK (B73-50901)

Docteur Miracle.. Overture: arr. Overture. (Bizet, Georges). *Oxford University Press. £2.50* MJ (B73-50247) ISBN 0 19 361673 4

Dodgson, Stephen. Fantasy: for harp. *Stainer and Bell. £0.66* TQPMJ (B73-50390)

Doe, Paul. Sanctus and Magnificat: anonymous 14th century. *University of Exeter Press. Unpriced* DGE (B73-50497)

Doe, Paul Maurice. The craft of music: an inaugural lecture delivered in the University of Exeter on 2 November 1972. *University of Exeter. £0.30* A (B73-06588) ISBN 0 900771 69 0

Doflein, Erich. Neue Musik
Heft 9: Neue Violin-Duos. Neuausgabe 1972. *Schott. £1.40* S/AY (B73-50365)

Dolge, Alfred. Pianos and their makers: a comprehensive history of the development of the piano from the monochord to the concert grand player piano. *Dover Publications: Constable. £2.50* AQ/B(XA1910) (B73-15416) ISBN 0 486 22856 8

Domroese, Wilhelm. Sechs kleine Stücke: für Blechbläsinstrumente und Klavier. *Bosse: Bärenreiter. £1.50* WPJ (B73-50463)

Dona nobis pacem: a round, arranged for voices in three parts and piano, with optional recorders, violins, and percussion. (Foster, Anthony). *Oxford University Press. £0.50* LNSQ/XC (B73-50243) ISBN 0 19 344849 1

Donati, Ignazio.
Concerti ecclesiastici. Op.4. *Excerpts.* Non vos relinquam orphanos = I will not leave you fatherless: SSA or T.T. Bar. *Oxford University Press. Unpriced* FDJ (B73-50135) ISBN 0 19 350336 0
Concerti ecclesiastici. Op.4. Nun vos relinquam orphanos. Non vos relinquam orphanos = I will not leave you fatherless: SSA or T.T. Bar. *Oxford University Press. Unpriced* FDJ (B73-51035) ISBN 0 19 350336 0

Donington, Robert. A performer's guide to Baroque music. *Faber. £7.00* A/E(XDYQ176) (B73-27556) ISBN 0 571 09797 9

Don't look down. (Cookridge, John Michael). *Bayley and Ferguson. £0.10* JFDW (B73-50621)

Doppelbauer, Rupert. Einführung in das Violoncellospiel Band 1. *Schott. £2.00* SR/AC (B73-51228)

Dorman, Harry. Scottish and French folk tunes. *Warren and Phillips. Unpriced* QPK/DW/G/AYDL (B73-50319)

Double bill: piano duet. (Parfrey, Raymond). *Composer to Player Edition. Unpriced* QNV (B73-50707)

Douglas, Alan. Electronic music production. *Pitman. £2.50* APV/B (B73-02643) ISBN 0 273 31523 4

Douglas, James. A Christmas fable. *Roberton. £0.07* EZDP/LF (B73-50097)

Douglas, Sheila. Scottish folk directory
1973. *12 Mansfield Rd, Scone, Perth: Sheila Douglas. £0.20* A/G/E(YDL/Q) (B73-14762) ISBN 0 903919 00 1

Dowland, John.
Weep you no more, sad fountains: for four-part chorus of women's voices a cappella. (Carter, John). *Schirmer. Unpriced* FEZDW (B73-50157)
Works, psalms. Complete psalms for SATB. *Stainer and Bell. Unpriced* EZDR/AZ (B73-51005) ISBN 0 85249 168 9

Downing, Michael.
Four little dances: for cello (in first position) and piano Nos.1 and 2. *Cornelius. Unpriced* SRPH (B73-50804)
Nos.3 and 4. *Cornelius. Unpriced* SRPH (B73-50805)

Draths, Willi. Die Kinderorgel: leichte Kinderlieder für elektronische Orgel (1 Manuel). *Schott. £1.20* RPVK/DW/GJ/AYE (B73-51208)

Draussen am Rain = Uti var hage: Schwedisches Volkslied, für gemischten Chor a cappella. (Steinfeld, Karl-Heinz). *Bosworth. £0.10* EZDW (B73-50562)

Drayton, Paul. Corpus Christi carol: for unison voices with optional divisions, and piano or organ. *Novello. £0.10* FDP/LF (B73-51023)

Drinkrow, John. The vintage operetta book. *Osprey Publishing. £1.95* ACFBN (B73-03717) ISBN 0 85045 102 7

Drop slow tears: for mixed chorus and piano with optional instrumental accompaniment. (Kechley, Gerald). *Galaxy Music: Galliard. Unpriced* DH (B73-50954)

Droste, Doreen. The song of wandering Aengus: SATB a cappella by Doreen Droste. *Galaxy: Galliard. Unpriced* EZDW (B73-50553)

Drums in my ears. (Green, Benny). *10 Earlham St., WC2H 9LP: Davis-Poynter. £2.50* AMT(D/XPQ17) (B73-10167) ISBN 0 7067 0066 x

Druner, Ulrich.
Capriccio for viola. Op. 55, no.9. Capriccio für Viola. Op post. (Vieuxtemps, Henri). *Schott. £0.80* SQPMJ (B73-51227)
Sonata for viola & basso continuo in C major. Op. 2, no.2. Sonata C-Dur für Viola und Basso continuo. (Kotzwara, Franz). *Schott. Unpriced* SQPE (B73-50376)

Du Maurier, George. Music that brings sweet sleep: song cycle for high voice and piano. (Stoker, Richard). *Peters. Unpriced* KFTDW (B73-50231)

Duetto for two cats with an accompaniment for the pianoforte. (Berthold, G). *Schott. £0.50* JNFEDW (B73-50628)

Dufay, Guillaume. Missa 'L'Homme armé': for mixed choir (SATB) a cappella. *Boosey and Hawkes. £1.00* EZDG (B73-50981)

Dufty, William. Lady sings the blues. (Holiday, Billie). *24 Highbury Cres., N5 1RX: Barrie and Jenkins. £2.95* AKFDW/HHW/E(P) (B73-12435) ISBN 0 214 66872 x

Duke, Henry.
Selections. Bach. (Bach, Johann Sebastian). *Freeman. Unpriced* PWPJ (B73-50286)
Selections. Beethoven. (Beethoven, Ludwig van). *Freeman. Unpriced* QPJ (B73-50300)
Selections. Chopin. (Chopin, Fréderic). *Freeman. Unpriced* QPJ (B73-50302)

D'un desastre obscur': pour voix de mezzo-soprano et clarinette en la. (Amy, Gilbert). *Universal. Unpriced* KFNE/VVDW (B73-51093)

Duncan, Ronald. Classical songs for children. The Penguin book of accompanied songs. (Harewood, Marion). *Penguin Books. £0.75* JFDW/AY (B73-50190) ISBN 0 14 070839 1

Dunn, James P.
Faultte d'argent = Life without money: for five-part chorus of mixed voices a cappella. (Josquin Des Prés). *Schirmer. Unpriced* EZDU (B73-50106)
Madrigali a quattro voci.. Non vidi mai. Non vidi mai = After a rainy evening: for four-part chorus of mixed voices a cappella. (Marenzio, Luca). *Schirmer. Unpriced* EZDU (B73-50107)
Il quinto libro de madrigale a sei voci. Leggiadre ninfe. Leggiadre ninfe = You graceful nymphs: for six-part chorus of mixed voices a cappella. (Marenzio, Luca). *Schirmer. Unpriced* EZDU (B73-50548)
Il secondo libro de madrigali a sei voce.. In un bel bosco. In un bel bosco = In a fair greenwood: for six-part chorus of mixed voices a cappella. (Marenzio, Luca). *Schirmer. Unpriced* EZDU (B73-50109)
Il terzo libro de madrigali a cinque voci.. Togli, dolce ben mio. Togli, dolce ben mio = Take thou, my sweetheart, these lovely flow'rs: for five-part chorus of mixed voices a cappella. (Marenzio, Luca). *Chappell. Unpriced* EZDU (B73-50110)

Durham University. *See* University of Durham.

Durko, Zsolt. Ballad: for youth or amateur orchestra. *Boosey and Hawkes. £1.00* MJ (B73-50660)

Dürr, Walther.
Io son pur solo: solo cantata for soprano and basso continuo. (Scarlatti, Alessandro). First edition. *Bärenreiter. £1.20* KFLDX (B73-50222)
Luntan dalla suna Clori: solo cantata for soprano and basso continuo. (Scarlatti, Alessandro). First edition. *Bärenreiter. £1.20* KFLDX (B73-50223)

Dussek, Jan Ladislav. Notturno concertante, Op 68: for piano violin and horn (violin) or piano and violin. *Bärenreiter. £3.30* NUNT (B73-50694)

Dvorak, Antonin. Concerto for violin in A minor. Op.53: arr. Violinkonzert, a moll. Op.53. *Schott. £1.70* SPK/LF (B73-50791)

Dwy gan werin = Two Welsh folk songs. (Beaumont, Adrian). *University of Wales Press. Unpriced* KDW/G/AYDK (B73-51088)

Eames, Vera McNess-. *See* McNess-Eames, Vera.

Early English organ music from the Middle Ages to 1837. (Routh, Francis). *Barrie and Jenkins. £6.75* AR(XCQ438) (B73-04220) ISBN 0 214 66804 5

East, Michael.
First set of madrigals.. Corydon would kiss her then: arr. Corydon would kiss her then. *Roberton. £0.10* FEZDU (B73-50154)
First set of madrigals. In the merry month of May: arr. In the merry month of May. *Roberton. £0.10* FEZDU (B73-50155)

Easter: a marriage anthem, SATB and organ. (Scott, Anthony). *Boosey and Hawkes. £0.20* DH/LL (B73-50031)

Eastern monarchs: SATB unacc. (Smith, Peter Melville). *Banks. Unpriced* EZDP/LFP (B73-51004)

Easy rider: leichte Blues-Satz nach alten und neuen Melodien bearbeitet für Gitarre. (Kreidler, Dieter). *Schott. £1.44* TSPMK/AHHW/AY (B73-51251)

Eaves, Robert.
Introduction and burlesque: for bass trombone and band. *R. Smith. Unpriced* WMPWUU (B73-50908)
Introduction and burlesque: for bass trombone and piano. *R. Smith. Unpriced* WUUPJ (B73-50924)

Eberhardt, Carl. Praxis der Chorprobe: Arbeitsheft für die Choreinstudierung. *Peters. £2.50* EZ/AF (B73-50528)

Ecco quel fiero istante = Lo, now the hour of parting. K.436. (Mozart, Wolfgang Amadeus). *Schirmer. Unpriced* FDW (B73-50143)

Econd book for the young orchestra: ten pieces for school string orchestra and recorder ensemble with optional flutes, clarinets, trumpets and piano. (Benoy, Arthur William). *Oxford University Press. £1.40* MK/AAY (B73-50663) ISBN 0 19 361653 x

Ecossaise for orchestra. (Hamilton, Iain). *Schott. £1.50* MMHJQ (B73-50675)

Ecumenia: a song for unity, for solo organ (with or without solo voice). (Edwards, D W). *D.W. Edwards. Unpriced* RJ (B73-50757)

Edgard Varèse. (Ouellette, Fernand). *Calder and Boyars. £3.95* BVB(N) (B73-07096) ISBN 0 7145 0208 1

Edinburgh scene. *(Ramsay Head Press)* Music in Edinburgh: consumers' guide to places of music. *19 Coates Cres., Edinburgh EH3 7AF: Ramsay Head Press. £0.25* A(YDLH) (B73-08420) ISBN 0 902859 10 2

Edwards, D W. Ecumenia: a song for unity, for solo organ (with or without solo voice). *D.W. Edwards. Unpriced* RJ (B73-50757)

Ehmann, Heinrich. Psalmen Davids, 1619. Die mit Tränen säen. Die mit Tränen säen: motet for two five-part choirs and basso continuo. (Schütz, Heinrich). *Bärenreiter. £1.50* EWUNPPWDH (B73-50527)
Ehmann, Wilhelm. Psalmen Davids, 1619. Die mit Tränen säen. Die mit Tränen säen: motet for two five-part choirs and basso continuo. (Schütz, Heinrich). *Bärenreiter. £1.50* EWUNPPWDH (B73-50527)
Ehret, Walter.
Gloria et honore: arr. Glory and honor: for four-part chorus of mixed voices a cappella. (Giorgi, Giovanni). *Schirmer. Unpriced* EZDJ (B73-50986)
Madrigali a cinque voci. Pastorella gratiosella. Shepherd maiden, fair and graceful: for 5-part chorus of mixed voices unaccompanied. (Vecchi, Horatio). *Roberton. Unpriced* EZDU (B73-50550)
Mass. K.262.. Sanctus. Vocal score. Sanctus = Holy holy holy. (Mozart, Wolfgang Amadeus). *Schirmer. Unpriced* DGE (B73-50015)
Das neugebor'ne Kindelein. Vocal score. The little newborn Jesus Child: for chorus of mixed voices (SATB) with organ or instrumental accompaniment. (Buxtehude, Dietrich). *Lawson-Gould: Roberton. £0.32* DE/LF (B73-50942)
Eight nonsense songs. (Dale, Mervyn). *Ashdown. £0.40* KDW (B73-51086)
Einführung in das Violoncellospiel
Band 1. (Doppelbauer, Rupert). *Schott. £2.00* SR/AC (B73-51228)
Einstein, Alfred. Galimathias musicum. KV32: 2 violins, viola, bass, 2 oboes, 2 horns, bassoon and cembalo. (Mozart, Wolfgang Amadeus). *Peters. £1.80* MRJ (B73-51127)
Elder, J D. Buddy Lindo: folk songs of Trinidad and Tobago, for unison voices and guitar. (Harvey, John). *Oxford University Press. £0.25* JE/TSDW/G/AYULM (B73-50608) ISBN 0 19 330450 3
Eldridge, Guy. When I survey the wondrous cross: Passiontide anthem founded on the folk tune 'O waly waly', for SATB and organ. *Novello. £0.10* DH/LGZ (B73-50030)
Electronic music: a listener's guide. (Schwartz, Elliot). *Secker and Warburg. £5.00* APV (B73-16150) ISBN 0 436 44410 0
Electronic music production. (Douglas, Alan). *Pitman. £2.50* APV/B (B73-02643) ISBN 0 273 31523 4
Electronics in music. (Judd, Frederick Charles). *Spearman. £3.15* APV/B (B73-05263) ISBN 0 85435 301 1
Elegy and rumba: two short and easy solos for guitar. (Benham, Patrick). *Cornelius. Unpriced* TSPMHVKK (B73-50821)
Elegy for orchestra. Op. 30. (Ellis, David). *Weinberger. Unpriced* MMJ (B73-50679)
Elegy: soprano, flute horn, cello. (Walker, Eldon). *Thames. Unpriced* KFLE/NVNTDW (B73-50645)
Elgar as I knew him. (Reed, William Henry). 2nd ed.. *Gollancz. £2.60* BEP(N/XMB33) (B73-16141) ISBN 0 575 01641 8
Elgar, his life and works. (Maine, Basil). *Chivers. £2.85(to members of the Library Association)* BEP(N) (B73-14761) ISBN 0 85594 835 3
Eliot, Thomas Stearns.
Canticle 4. Journey of the Magi: for counter-tenor, tenor, baritone and piano. (Britten, Benjamin). *Faber Music. Unpriced* JNDDE/LF (B73-50197)
A cycle of cats: three songs for soprano and alto voices with piano. (Price, Beryl). *Oxford University Press. £0.60* FDW (B73-50146) ISBN 0 19 337853 1
Elite editions. *(N. Simrock)* Fink, Siegfried. Tablature 72. *N. Simrock; 67 Belsize La., NW3 5AX: Distributed by R. Schauer. £0.45* AX(QU) (B73-16796) ISBN 0 9502847 0 x
Elizebethan duets for two guitars. (Spencer, Robert). *Stainer and Bell. Unpriced* TSNUK/AAY (B73-50817)
Ellenberg, David. Les Pêcheurs de perles. Au fond du temple saint: arr. Au fond du temple saint: duet. (Bizet, Georges). *United Music. Unpriced* JNGEDW (B73-51081)
Ellenberg, Diana. Les Pêcheurs de perles. Au fond du temple saint: arr. Au fond du temple saint: duet. (Bizet, Georges). *United Music. Unpriced* JNGEDW (B73-51081)
Ellerton, J. Our day of praise is done: SATB. (Harris, *Sir* William Henry). *Oxford University Press. Unpriced* DH (B73-50504) ISBN 0 19 351118 5
Elliott, Kenneth. A history of Scottish music. *British Broadcasting Corporation. £0.90* A(YDL/X) (B73-25526) ISBN 0 563 12192 0
Ellis, David.
Carols for an island Christmas. Vocal score. Carols for an island Christmas: for SATB, trumpets, string orchestra and piano (with optional boys' voices, woodwind and percussion),. *Novello. £0.23* DP/LF (B73-50967)
Elegy for orchestra. Op. 30. *Weinberger. Unpriced* MMJ (B73-50679)
Elsworth, Cecilie. The family motoring book. *Tom Stacey. £1.00* JE/TSDW/AY (B73-50605) ISBN 0 85468 025 x
Elton, Antony. The Minister of Justice: opera. *Antony Elton. Unpriced* CQC (B73-50939)
Emerson, Ralph Waldo. Aspects 1 in 3: song cycle for medium voice and piano. (Stoker, Richard). *Peters. Unpriced* KFVDW (B73-50235)
Emperor Maximilian I and music. (Cuyler, Louise). *Oxford University Press. £10.75* A(YE/XCS79) (B73-24453) ISBN 0 19 315223 1
En route. (Harry, Lynn). *K.P.M. Unpriced* GDW (B73-50164)
Enée et Lavinie. (Colasse, Pascal). 1st ed. reprinted. *Gregg. £12.00* BCLSAC (B73-16143) ISBN 0 576 28236 7
Engelbert Humperdinck: the authorised biography. (Short, Don). *New English Library. £0.40* AKDW/GB/E(P) (B73-02065) ISBN 0 450 01453 3
England, Paul. L'Enfance du Christ. L'Adieu des bergers. Vocal score: arr. Thou must leave thy lowly dwelling. The shepherds farewell to the Holy Family. (Berlioz, Hector). *Novello. £0.10* GDH/LF (B73-51044)
English church music: a collection of essays
1973. *Addington Palace, Croydon, CR9 5AD: Royal School of Church Music. £0.90* AD/LD(YD/D) (B73-18105) ISBN 0 85402 052 7
English dancing master. Selections: arr. Three English dances from Playford's 'English Dancing Master' (1650). (Playford, John). *Boosey and Hawkes. £1.80* MK/AH/AYD (B73-51110)
English Folk Dance and Song Society.
And out of his knapsack he drew a fine fiddle: an introduction to the technique of English fiddling. (Timpany, John). *English Folk Dance and Song Society. £0.50* AS/G/E (B73-19500) ISBN 0 85418 088 5
Folk directory
1973. *English Folk Dance and Song Society. £1.25 (£0.75 to members of the English Folk Dance and Song Society)* A/G(BC) (B73-07790) ISBN 0 85418 087 7
I'll sing you two o: words of more familiar folk songs for campfire, ceilidh and club. (Wales, Tony). *English Folk Dance and Song Society. £0.40* ADW/G(YC) (B73-22269) ISBN 0 85418 089 3
English folk song - some conclusions. (Sharp, Cecil James). 4th revised ed. *E.P. Publishing. £1.75* ADW/G(YD) (B73-02067) ISBN 0 85409 929 8
English folk-song and dance. (Kidson, Frank). *E.P. Publishing. £2.10* ADW/G(YD) (B73-00881) ISBN 0 85409 917 4
English keyboard music before the nineteenth century. (Caldwell, John). *Blackwell. £6.00* APW(YD/XA1800) (B73-16149) ISBN 0 631 13770 x
English suite for keyboard, no.5. S.810. Sarabande: arr. Sarabande. (Bach, Johann Sebastian). *Cornelius. Unpriced* TSNUK/AHVL (B73-50818)
English theatre music in the eighteenth century. (Fiske, Roger). *Oxford University Press. £12.50* AC(YD/XEZQ102) (B73-13015) ISBN 0 19 316402 7
Enoch, Yvonne.
Six 'nonsense' songs: for piano trio, one, two or three players Book 1: Nos.1 to 3. *Bosworth. £0.25* QNVQ (B73-50292)
Book 2: Nos.4 to 6. *Bosworth. £0.25* QNVQ (B73-50293)
Ensemble studies
2: Oboe and clarinet. (Wurzburger, Walter). *Thames. Unpriced* VTPLVV (B73-50424)
Entertainments. (Vinter, Gilbert). *R. Smith. Unpriced* WMG (B73-50883)
Episode de la vie d'un artiste. *See* Symphonie fantastique.
Episodes for brass. (Hanmer, Ronald). *R. Smith. Unpriced* WMJ (B73-50891)
Epitaphs for Edith Sitwell: for string orchestra. (Williamson, Malcolm). *Weinberger. Unpriced* RXMJ (B73-50358)
Ernest George White Society. Think afresh about the voice: a reappraisal of the teaching of Ernest George White. (Hewlett, Arthur Donald). 2nd ed. *Hillcrest, Ringwood, Deal, Kent: Ernest George White Society. £0.75* AB/E(VC/P) (B73-19499) ISBN 0 9501610 1 2
Ernst, Trudy. Alleluia to the Lord of being: for full chorus of mixed voices a cappella. (Fast, Willard S). *Schirmer. Unpriced* EZDH (B73-50072)
Erstlinge musicalischer Andachten.. Jauchzet Gott, alle Lande. Jauchzet Gott, alle Lande = Make a joyful noise unto God: sacred concerto for soprano, two violins and basso continuo. (Weiland, Julius Johann). *Bärenreiter. £1.50* KFLE/SNTPWDE (B73-50225)
Espiral eterna: para guitarra. (Brouwer, Leo). *Schott. £1.08* TSPMJ (B73-51248)
Essay for Cyrano. (Brunelli, Louis Jean). *Boosey and Hawkes. £10.00* UMMJ (B73-50833)
Estampes: piano solo. (Debussy, Claude). *Peters. Unpriced* QPJ (B73-50303)
Esterházy, Pál.
Harmonia caelestis: für Sopran, vierstimmigen gemischten Chor und Instrumente
Heft 1: Weihnachtskantaten. *Bärenreiter. £1.35* ERXMDH (B73-50525)
'Etudes brillantes. Op.36, nos 31-56. (Mazas, Jacques Féréol). *Schirmer. Unpriced* SQ/AC (B73-50372)
'Etudes faciles et progressives. Op.100. 25 easy and progressive studies: for piano. (Burgmüller, Friedrich). *Chappell. Unpriced* QPJ (B73-50301)
'Etudes spéciales. Op.36, nos 1-30: for the viola. (Mazas, Jacques Féréol). *Schirmer. Unpriced* SQ/AC (B73-50373)
Evans, E L. The young child's carol. *British and Continental. Unpriced* EZDP (B73-50095)
Evans, Roger. Roger Evans book of folk songs and how to play them: all guitar chords, melody, lyrics & easy to understand guitar accompaniments. *Robbins, Francis, Day & Hunter. £0.60* KE/TSDW/G/AY (B73-50217)
Even such is time: cantata for tenor solo, chorus and orchestra (or organ). (Vale, Charles). *Thames. Unpriced* DE (B73-50011)
Even such is time. Vocal score. Even such is time: cantata for tenor solo, chorus and orchestra (or organ). (Vale, Charles). *Thames. Unpriced* DE (B73-50011)
Evening: for voice and piano. (Niles, John Jacob). *Schirmer. Unpriced* KDW (B73-50208)
Ewen, David. The new encyclopedia of the opera. *Vision Press. £7.20* AC(C) (B73-32163) ISBN 0 85478 033 5
Exeter City Library. Music for guitar and lute. *Castle St., Exeter, Devon EX4 3PQ: Exeter City Library. £0.10* ATS(TC) (B73-27122) ISBN 0 904128 00 8
Exeter University. *See* University of Exeter.
Experience of opera. (Lang, Paul Henry). *Faber. £4.00* AC(XFYB201) (B73-06590) ISBN 0 571 10146 1
Exultabunt sancti: arr. Thou art mighty: for four-part chorus of mixed voices. (Haydn, Michael). *Schirmer. Unpriced* EZDJ (B73-50987)
Exultet mundus gaudio: introduction and sequence of nine carols for the Christian year, for SSAATTBB chorus, SATB soli and two-part chorus of trebles. (Naylor, Bernard). *Roberton. £0.50* EZDP (B73-50094)
Eyck, Johann Jacob van. Amorilli mia bella: Hommage a Johann Jacob van Eyck for recorder solo, descant, treble and bass recorder. (Linde, Hans Martin). *Schott. £1.08* VSPM/T (B73-51279)
Eyck, Johann Jacob van. *See* Eyck, Johann Jacob van.
Eye for music. (Auerbach, Erich). *Hart-Davis. £15.75* A/E(M/EM) (B73-09575) ISBN 0 246 98552 6
Eye level: theme from the Thames TV series 'Van der Valk'. (Trombey, Jack). *Boosey and Hawkes. Unpriced* WMK/AGM/JS (B73-51298)
Faber, Frederick William. Faith of our fathers: anthem for a Dedication service. (Westbrook, Francis). *Roberton. £0.10* DH (B73-50027)
Fagan, Eleanora. *See* Holiday, Billie.
Fagan, Margo.
Play time: Longman first recorder course
Stage 1. *Longman. Unpriced* VS/AC (B73-50847) ISBN 0 582 18536 x
Stage Two. *Longman. £0.25* VS/AC (B73-51269) ISBN 0 582 18537 8
Fair Organ Preservation Society. Organs, rides and engines on parade
Vol.2. *3 Bentley Rd, Denton, Manchester M34 AH2: F.O.P.S. £0.50* A/FM (B73-04221) ISBN 0 9502701 0 5
Fairies.. Overture. Overture: for strings and continuo (with optional oboes and optional trumpets). (Smith, John Christopher). *Oxford University Press. £1.00* RXMJ (B73-50357) ISBN 0 19 367637 0
Fairy tailor: unison song. (Noble, Harold). *Bosworth. £0.10* JFDW (B73-51070)
Faites de moy toute qu'il vous plaira. (Busnois, Antoine). *Oxford University Press. Unpriced* EZDU (B73-50103) ISBN 0 19 341201 2
Faith of our fathers: anthem for a Dedication service. (Westbrook, Francis). *Roberton. £0.10* DH (B73-50027)
Falcon: set for high voice and piano. (Ives, Grayston). *Roberton. Unpriced* KFTDW (B73-50229)
Falconer, E J. Christ's carol: SATB unaccompanied. (Vale, Charles). *Roberton. £0.07* EZDP/LF (B73-51001)
Family motoring book. (Elsworth, Cecilie). *Tom Stacey. £1.00* JE/TSDW/AY (B73-50605) ISBN 0 85468 025 x
Fancies: a cycle of choral settings with small orchestra. (Rutter, John). *Oxford University Press. Unpriced* DW (B73-50045) ISBN 0 19 338071 4
Fancies. Riddle song. Riddle song: SATB. (Rutter, John). *Oxford University Press. Unpriced* DW (B73-50517) ISBN 0 19 343031 2
Fancies. Vocal score. Fancies: a cycle of choral settings with small orchestra. (Rutter, John). *Oxford University Press. Unpriced* DW (B73-50045) ISBN 0 19 338071 4
Fanfare for Europe on the notes EEC. Op.142: for six trumpets in C. (Rubbra, Edmund). *Lengnick. £1.00* WSNQGN (B73-50911)
Fantaisie: for organ. (Middleton, John). *Thames. Unpriced* RJ (B73-50340)
Fantasia: for euphonium (baritone) and band. (Jacob, Gordon). *Boosey and Hawkes. £8.75* UMMPWW (B73-50836)
Fantasia on 'Greensleeves'. (Vaughan Williams, Ralph). *Oxford University Press. £0.30* TSPMK (B73-50394) ISBN 0 19 359309 2
Fantasia piccola: für Streichquartett. (Schmitt, Meinrad). *Bosse: Bärenreiter. £2.10* RXNS (B73-50787)
Fantasia (quasi variazione) on the 'Old 104th' psalm tune: for solo piano, mixed chorus and orchestra. (Vaughan Williams, Ralph). *Oxford University Press. £1.75* EMDR (B73-50050) ISBN 0 19 338922 3
Fantasy: for harp. (Dodgson, Stephen). *Stainer and Bell. £0.66* TQPMJ (B73-50390)
Fantasy on a ground: for organ. (Hunt, Reginald). *Boosey and Hawkes. £0.65* RJ (B73-50759)
Fantasy, Op. 32: for piano and orchestra. (Creston, Paul). *Schirmer. Unpriced* QNUK (B73-51159)
Far away across the mountain: for four-part chorus of mixed voices a cappella. (Lekberg, Sven). *Schirmer. Unpriced* EZDW (B73-50118)
Farmer, John A. A wedding fanfare: organ. *Coastal Music Studios. Unpriced* RGN/KDD (B73-50334)
Farrant, John, *b.1575.* Te Deum and Jubilate: SATB. Revised ed. *Oxford University Press. £0.30* DGNP (B73-50499) ISBN 0 19 352106 7
Farson, Daniel. Marie Lloyd & music hall. *28 Maiden La., WC2E 7JP: Tom Stacey Ltd. £3.00* AKFDW/JV/E(P) (B73-03721) ISBN 0 85468 082 9
Fast, Willard S.
Alleluia to the Lord of being: for full chorus of mixed voices a cappella. *Schirmer. Unpriced* EZDH (B73-50072)
Be not afraid because the sun goes down: for four-part chorus of mixed voices a cappella. *Schirmer. Unpriced* EZDW (B73-50114)
Go, lovely rose: for full chorus of mixed voices a cappella. *Schirmer. Unpriced* EZDW (B73-50115)

To mercy, pity, peace and love: for four-part chorus of mixed voices a cappella. *Schirmer. Unpriced* EZDH (B73-50073)
When I was one-and-twenty: for four-part chorus of mixed voices a cappella. *Schirmer. Unpriced* EZDW (B73-50116)
Faucet: for four-part chorus of men's voices with piano accompaniment. (Miller, Lewis M). *Schirmer. Unpriced* GDW (B73-50165)
Faultte d'argent = Life without money: for five-part chorus of mixed voices a cappella. (Josquin Des Prés). *Schirmer. Unpriced* EZDU (B73-50106)
Favorite French folk songs: sixty-five traditional songs of France and Canada. (Mills, Alan). *Oak Publications: Music Sales. £0.95* JE/TSDW/G/AYSXH (B73-50178)
Favorite Spanish folksongs: traditional songs from Spain and Latin America. (Paz, Elena). *Oak Publications: Music Sales. £0.95* JE/TSDW/G/AYU (B73-50179)
Favourites for recorder
No.3. (Sansom, Clive A). *British and Continental. £0.25* VSPMK/DW/G/AY (B73-50417)
Fawcett, John. Lord dismiss us with thy blessing: a choral benediction, for four-part chorus of mixed voices a cappella. (Ford, Virgil T). *Schirmer. Unpriced* EZDM (B73-50088)
Federico, G A. La Serva padrona. Vocal score. La Serva padrona = From maid to mistress. (Pergolesi, Giovanni Battista). *Schirmer. Unpriced* CC (B73-50935)
Feld, Jindrich. Inventionen: für gemischten Chor. *Bärenreiter. £1.35* EZDW (B73-50554)
Feldman, Morton.
I met Heine on the Rue Furstenberg. *Universal. Unpriced* KE/NYDNQDX (B73-50640)
Rothko chapel. *Universal. Unpriced* ENYJDW (B73-50524)
The viola in my life (IV). *Universal. Unpriced* MMJ (B73-50680)
Fellowes, Edmund Horace. Te Deum and Jubilate: SATB. (Farrant, John, *b.1575*). Revised ed. *Oxford University Press. £0.30* DGNP (B73-50499) ISBN 0 19 352106 7
Fenland suite: for recorder quartet. (Hand, Colin). *Schott. £0.60* VSNSG (B73-50849)
Fenton, Lesley. A children's nativity: a nativity mime with narrative and carols (with ad lib. percussion, recorders, etc.). *Keith Prowse Music. £0.40* FDPDE/LF/JN (B73-51027)
Ferguson, Samuel. Five Irish songs: for mixed chorus a cappella
2: Dear dark head; words by Samuel Ferguson. (Maw, Nicholas). *Boosey and Hawkes. £0.09* EZDW (B73-50557)
Ferguson, *Sir* Samuel.
Three folk songs: for unaccompanied mixed choir
No.2: The lark in the clear air: Irish folk song; words by Sir Samuel Ferguson. (Ives, Grayston). *Roberton. £0.10* EZDW/G/AY (B73-50130)
Three folk songs
for unaccompanied mixed choir
No.3: The tailor and the mouse: English folk song. (Ives, Grayston). *Roberton. £0.13* EZDW/G/AY (B73-50128)
Three folk songs: for unaccompanied mixed choir
No.3: The tailor and the mouse: English folk song. (Ives, Grayston). *Roberton. £0.13* EZDW/G/AY (B73-50563)
Festival Matins.. Blessed be the Lord God of Israel. Blessed be the Lord God of Israel: for two-part chorus of female, male or mixed voices with piano or organ accompaniment. (Swann, Donald). *Roberton. Unpriced* DGNS (B73-50018)
Festival Matins.. O come let us sing unto the Lord. O come let us sing unto the Lord: for two-part chorus of female, male or mixed voices with piano accompaniment. (Swann, Donald). *Roberton. Unpriced* DGNPV (B73-50016)
Festive processional: organ solo. (Waters, Charles Frederick). *Cramer. £0.24* RJ (B73-50763)
Fetler, Paul.
Cycles: for percussion (three players) and piano. *Schott. £2.40* NYLNS (B73-51134)
Four movements: for guitar. *Schott. £0.90* TSPMJ (B73-50822)
Fibonaciana: para flauta solista dos percusionistas y cuerda. (Halffter, Cristobal). *Universal. Unpriced* MMJ (B73-50681)
Fiddle-dee: SSAA unaccompanied. (Kodály, Zoltán). *Boosey and Hawkes. £0.05* FEZDW (B73-51041)
Field, Christopher D.S. Notturno concertante, Op 68: for piano violin and horn (violin) or piano and violin. (Dussek, Jan Ladislav). *Bärenreiter. £3.30* NUNT (B73-50694)
Fielding, Henry. The Grub-Street opera. *Oliver and Boyd. £2.00* ACLMBM (B73-31566) ISBN 0 05 002755 7
Fields of sorrow: for 2 solo sopranos, chorus and orchestra. (Birtwistle, Harrison). *Universal. Unpriced* EMDX (B73-50979)
Fiesta piano duet. (Johnson, Thomas Arnold). *Bosworth. £0.25* QNV (B73-51160)
Fifty famous composers. (Hughes, Gervase). Revised and enlarged ed. *Pan Books. £0.60* A/D(YB/M) (B73-00359) ISBN 0 330 13064 1
Fifty years of Robert Mayer concerts, 1923-1972. (Reid, Charles, *b.1900*). *Smythe. £0.55(non-net)* A(W/Q/P) (B73-28190) ISBN 0 900675 78 0
Filardino, Angelo. Theme and variations for guitar. (Berkeley, Lennox). *Chester. Unpriced* TSPM/T (B73-51244)
Fille mal gardée. Clog dance. Clog dance. (Hérold, Ferdinand). *Oxford University Press. Unpriced* MH/HM (B73-51105) ISBN 0 19 364251 4
Fille mal gardée. Flute dance. Flute dance. (Hérold, Ferdinand). *Oxford University Press. Unpriced* MH/HM (B73-51106) ISBN 0 19 364275 1
Fink, Siegfried.
Horeb: scene for percussion according to the first Book of Kings. *Simrock. Unpriced* XMJ (B73-50926)
Marcha del tambor: Caribbean impression, for percussion ensemble, (6 players). *Simrock. Unpriced* XNQGM (B73-51309)
Tablature 72. *N. Simrock; 67 Belsize La., NW3 5AX Distributed by R. Schauer. £0.45* AX(QU) (B73-16796) ISBN 0 9502847 0 x
Zulu welcome: South African impression for percussion ensemble, (6 players). *Simrock. Unpriced* XNQ (B73-51308)
Fire of heaven: for unaccompanied triple choir. (Burgon, Geoffrey). *Stainer and Bell. Unpriced* EZDE (B73-50529)
Fireworks: 6 little pieces for piano. (Stoker, Richard). *Ashdown. £0.30* QPJ (B73-51178)
First book of selected church musick. (Barnard, John, *fl.1641*). 1st ed. reprinted. *Cregg. £72.00* ADGM (B73-16145) ISBN 0 576 28200 6
First Christmas. (Green, Philip). *Belwin-Mills. £0.20* KDP/LF (B73-51085)
First set of madrigals.. Corydon would kiss her then: arr. Corydon would kiss her then. (East, Michael). *Roberton. £0.10* FEZDU (B73-50154)
First set of madrigals. In the merry month of May: arr. In the merry month of May. (East, Michael). *Roberton. £0.10* FEZDU (B73-50155)
Firstlings: three songs, for medium voice, flute, (clarinet or violin) and guitar. (Roe, Betty). *Thames. Unpriced* KFVE/VRPLTSDW (B73-50239)
Fischer, Hans Conrad. Ludwig van Beethoven: a study in text and pictures. *Macmillan. £4.00* BBJ(N) (B73-03211) ISBN 0 333 12114 7
Fisher, Bobby. La Paloma: arr. La Paloma. (Yradier, Sebastian). *Fisher & Lane. Unpriced* RPVK/AHVR (B73-50353)
Fiske, Roger. English theatre music in the eighteenth century. *Oxford University Press. £12.50* AC(YD/XEZQ102) (B73-13015) ISBN 0 19 316402 7
Fitton, Mary. Bravo Maurice!: a compilation from the autobiographical writings of Maurice Chevalier. (Chevalier, Maurice). *Allen and Unwin. £3.50* AKG/E(P) (B73-24204) ISBN 0 04 920037 2
Five adventures: for piano. (Nieman, Alfred). *Boosey and Hawkes. £0.40* QPJ (B73-50308)
Five centuries of keyboard music: an historical survey of music for harpsichord and piano. (Gillespie, John). *Dover Publications: Constable. £2.50* APW(X) (B73-13586) ISBN 0 486 22855 x
Five diversions: for melody instrument and piano. (Lane, Philip). *Galliard. Unpriced* LPG (B73-51102)
Five hymn-tune variants: for organ. (Thiman, Eric Harding). *Roberton. Unpriced* RJ (B73-50345)
Five Indian poems: for mixed choir and small orchestra. (Hughes, Robert). *Chappell. Unpriced* DW (B73-50516)
Five Irish songs: for mixed chorus a cappella
1: I shall not die for thee; words by Douglas Hyde. (Maw, Nicholas). *Boosey and Hawkes. £0.09* EZDW (B73-50556)
2: Dear dark head; words by Samuel Ferguson. (Maw, Nicholas). *Boosey and Hawkes. £0.09* EZDW (B73-50557)
3: Popular song; words anon. (Maw, Nicholas). *Boosey and Hawkes. £0.09* EZDW (B73-50558)
4: Ringleted youth of my love; words by Douglas Hyde. (Maw, Nicholas). *Boosey and Hawkes. £0.14* EZDW (B73-50559)
5: Jig; words by Cecil Day-Lewis. (Maw, Nicholas). *Boosey and Hawkes. £0.20* EZDW (B73-50560)
Five sequences for the Virgin Mary. (Bent, Margaret). *Oxford University Press. Unpriced* EZDJ/AYD (B73-50989) ISBN 0 19 341207 1
Flamenco guitar albums
Album no.3. (Mairants, Ivor). *Belwin-Mills. Unpriced* TSPMH/G/AYK (B73-51246)
Flamingoes: song for medium voice and piano. (Parrott, Ian). *Thames. Unpriced* KFVDW (B73-50233)
Flanders, Dennis. A Westminster childhood. (Raynor, John, *b.1909*). *Cassell. £3.25* BRGY(N/XA1921) (B73-24203) ISBN 0 304 29183 8
Flanders, Michael. Captain Noah and his floating zoo. Vocal score. Captain Noah and his floating zoo: cantata in popular style. *Novello. £0.69* DE (B73-50496)
Fleming, Christopher le. *See* Le Fleming, Christopher.
Fletcher, Phineas. Drop slow tears: for mixed chorus and piano with optional instrumental accompaniment. (Kechley, Gerald). *Galaxy Music: Galliard. Unpriced* DH (B73-50954)
Florilegium.. Suites. Suites from the 'Florilegium': for four or five parts (string or wind instruments). (Muffat, Georg). *Bärenreiter. £1.95* NXNSG (B73-50280)
Floroj sen kompar: Britaj popolkantoj. (Hill, Margaret). *British Esperanto Association. Unpriced* JE/TSDW/G/AYC (B73-50176)
Flourish for brass. (Walters, Gareth). *R. Smith. Unpriced* WMJ (B73-50893)
Flute dance. (Hérold, Ferdinand). *Oxford University Press. Unpriced* MH/HM (B73-51106) ISBN 0 19 364275 1
Flute from afar: piano solo. (Parfrey, Raymond). *Composer to Player Edition. Unpriced* QPJ (B73-50736)
Flute obbligatos from the cantatas. (Bach, Johann Sebastian). *Universal. Unpriced* VRPMK/DE (B73-50409)
Flute technique. (Chapman, Frederick Bennett). 4th ed. *Oxford University Press. £0.90* AVR/CY (B73-26821) ISBN 0 19 318609 8
Fog: for voices and instruments. (Paynter, John). *Universal. Unpriced* FE/LDW (B73-50569)
Folk directory
1973. *English Folk Dance and Song Society. £1.25 (£0.75 to members of the English Folk Dance and Song Society)* A/G(BC) (B73-07790) ISBN 0 85418 087 7
Folk harps. (Jaffrennou, Gildas). *Book Division, Station Rd, Kings Langley, Herts.: Model and Allied Publications. £2.50* ATQ/BC (B73-30280) ISBN 0 85242 313 6
Folk song to-day
Vol.2. (Wales, Tony). *E F D S. £0.20* JEZDW/G/AY (B73-50614)
Vol.4. (Wales, Tony). *E F D S. £0.20* JEZDW/G/AY (B73-50615)
Folk song today
Vol.5. (Wales, Tony). *E F D S. £0.20* JEZDW/G/AY (B73-50616)
Folk songs and dance tunes from the North with fiddle tunes, pipe tunes and street cries. (Polwarth, Gwen). *Frank Graham. £0.60* JE/TSDW/G/AYDJJ (B73-51062) ISBN 0 900409 93 2
Folk songs of France: 25 traditional French songs with guitar chords, in both French and English. (Scott, Barbara). *Oak Publications: Music Sales. £0.95* JE/TSDW/G/AYH (B73-50177)
For lo the winter is past: for full chorus of mixed voices a cappella. (Chorbajian, John). *Schirmer. Unpriced* EZDW (B73-50111)
Forbes, Watson. Classical and romantic pieces for cello and piano. *Oxford University Press. £0.85* SRPK/AAY (B73-50806) ISBN 0 19 356471 8
Ford, Rita. Firstlings: three songs, for medium voice, flute, (clarinet or violin) and guitar. (Roe, Betty). *Thames. Unpriced* KFVE/VRPLTSDW (B73-50239)
Ford, Virgil T.
All as God wills: for four-part chorus of mixed voices a cappella. *Schirmer. Unpriced* EZDH (B73-50074)
Come, sound his praise abroad: for four-part chorus of mixed voices a cappella. *Schirmer. Unpriced* EZDH (B73-50075)
Lord dismiss us with thy blessing: a choral benediction, for four-part chorus of mixed voices a cappella. *Schirmer. Unpriced* EZDM (B73-50088)
Form and transformation in music and poetry of the English Renaissance. (Johnson, Paula). *Yale University Press. £3.50* A(YD/XDY81/ZB) (B73-03716) ISBN 0 300 01544 5
Forristal, Desmond. Superstar or son of God? *Pranstown House, Booterstown Ave., Booterstown, Dublin: Veritas Publications: Talbot Press. £0.15* BWKRACM/LH (B73-25528) ISBN 0 901810 60 6
Fortner, Wolfgang. Versuch eines Agon um ...?: for 7 vocalists and orchestra. *Schott. £3.84* JNAYME/MDX (B73-51080)
Fortune, Nigel. The Beethoven companion. (Arnold, Denis). *Faber. £2.50* BBJ(N) (B73-17450) ISBN 0 571 10318 9
Foster, Anthony.
Carol and rumba for recorders, (descant and treble), percussion and piano. *Oxford University Press. Unpriced* NYFSHVKK (B73-50701) ISBN 0 19 356554 4
Dona nobis pacem: a round, arranged for voices in three parts and piano, with optional recorders, violins, and percussion. *Oxford University Press. £0.50* LNSQ/XC (B73-50243) ISBN 0 19 344849 1
Fountainwell drama texts. *(Oliver and Boyd)* Fielding, Henry. The Grub-Street opera. *Oliver and Boyd. £2.00* ACLMBM (B73-31566) ISBN 0 05 002755 7
Four chorale-preludes. (Binkerd, Gordon). *Boosey and Hawkes. Set A £6.00; Set B £8.00; Set C £10.00* MRK/AAY (B73-50693)
Four fancies: a serenade in E flat for brass band. (Maurer, Ludwig). *Novello. £1.25* WMJ (B73-50438)
Four frottole: for voice and 3 instruments or 4 instruments. (Boorman, Stanley). *Antico. Unpriced* KE/LNTDW/AYJ (B73-50216)
Four images: for organ. (Jackson, Nicholas). *Boosey and Hawkes. £0.60* RJ (B73-50760)
Four little dances: for cello (in first position) and piano
Nos.1 and 2. (Downing, Michael). *Cornelius. Unpriced* SRPH (B73-50804)
Nos.3 and 4. (Downing, Michael). *Cornelius. Unpriced* SRPH (B73-50805)
Four madrigals. Op. 29: for unaccompanied mixed voices. (Brown, Christopher). *Oxford University Press. Unpriced* EZDW (B73-50552) ISBN 0 19 343521 7
Four medieval pieces: for organ. (Marr, Peter). *Peters. Unpriced* R/AY (B73-50328)
Four movements: for guitar. (Fetler, Paul). *Schott. £0.90* TSPMJ (B73-50822)
Four Norwegian moods: for orchestra. (Stravinsky, Igor). *Schott. Unpriced* MMJ (B73-50262)
Four short studies: for beginners on the guitar. (Benham, Patrick). *Cornelius. Unpriced* TS/AF (B73-50812)
Four sketches. (Schumann, Robert). *Oxford University Press. £0.65* RJ (B73-50762) ISBN 0 19 375732 x
Four winds: unison, with optional second part. (Parry, William Howard). *Lengnick. £0.06* JFDW (B73-50188)
Fowke, Edith. Songs of work and freedom. Songs of work and protest. *Dover: Constable. £1.75* JDW/KJ/AY (B73-51059) ISBN 0 486 22899 1
Fox, Peter.
Air and allegro: two short and very easy solos for B flat clarinet. *Cornelius. Unpriced* VVPJ (B73-50871)
Herz und Mund und That und Leben. S.147. Wohl mir dass ich Jesum habe: arr. Jesus, joy of man's desiring. (Bach, Johann Sebastian). *Cornelius. Unpriced* TSPMK/DM (B73-50830)

High stepper!: a short and easy solo for flute and piano. *Cornelius. Unpriced* VRPJ (B73-50842)
Invention for keyboard in E major. S.792: arr. Sinfonia in G. (Bach, Johann Sebastian). *Cornelius. Unpriced* TSNTK (B73-50814)
Preludes for keyboard. S.935, 939: arr. Two short preludes. (Bach, Johann Sebastian). *Cornelius. Unpriced* TSNUK (B73-50816)
Selections: arr. Short and easy classics
Ser 1. (Brahms, Johannes). *Cornelius. Unpriced* TSPMK (B73-50824)
The self-banished. Minuet: arr. Minuet. (Blow, John). *Cornelius. Unpriced* SRNTK/AHR (B73-50802)
Serenade for string orchestra. Op.48. Waltz: arr. Waltz. (Tchaikovsky, Peter). *Cornelius. Unpriced* TSPMK/AHW (B73-50829)
Suite bergamasque. Clair de lune: arr. Clair de lune. (Debussy, Claude). *Cornelius. Unpriced* TSPMK (B73-50825)
Two nightsongs. *Cornelius. Unpriced* SQPK/DW (B73-50798)
Two nightsongs. *Cornelius. Unpriced* SRPK/DW (B73-50808)
Two nightsongs. *Cornelius. Unpriced* WTPK/DW (B73-50918)
Two nightsongs. (Fox, Peter). *Cornelius. Unpriced* SQPK/DW (B73-50798)
Two nightsongs. (Fox, Peter). *Cornelius. Unpriced* SRPK/DW (B73-50808)
Two nightsongs. (Fox, Peter). *Cornelius. Unpriced* WTPK/DW (B73-50918)
Frackenpohl, Arthur. Introduction and romp: for marimba or vibraphone and piano. *Schirmer. Unpriced* XTQSPJ (B73-50475)
Francaix, Jean. Jeu poetique: en six movements pour harpe et orchestre. *Schott. £3.00* TQPK (B73-50810)
Franck, Cesar. Le Chasseur maudit: arr. The accursed huntsman. *Studio Music. Unpriced* WMK (B73-50895)
Franck, Melchior.
Deutsche weltliche Gesäng unnd Täntze
1: For descant, treble, tenor and bass recorder. *Bärenreiter. £0.90* VSNSK/DW (B73-50850)
2: For descant recorder, 2 treble recorders and tenor recorder. *Bärenreiter. £0.90* VSNSK/DW (B73-50851)
Frank, Helen. Mozart: genius of harmony. (Lingg, Ann M). *Kennikat Press. £7.40* BMS(N) (B73-14126) ISBN 0 8046 1743 0
Frankenpohl, Arthur. Introduction and romp: for flute and piano. *Schirmer. Unpriced* VRPJ (B73-50406)
Freedman, Hermann L. Triptych: organ. *Thames. Unpriced* RJ (B73-50758)
Freeland, Anita. Exultet mundus gaudio: introduction and sequence of nine carols for the Christian year, for SSAATTBB chorus, SATB soli and two-part chorus of trebles. (Naylor, Bernard). *Roberton. £0.50* EZDP (B73-50094)
French baroque music: from Beaujoyeulx to Rameau. (Anthony, James R). *Batsford. £6.00* A(YH/XDZA153) (B73-32162) ISBN 0 7134 0755 7
French horn: some notes on the evolution of the instrument and of its technique. (Morley-Pegge, Reginald). 2nd ed. *E. Benn. £3.95* AWT/B (B73-15417) ISBN 0 510 36601 5
Freundlich, Irwin. Guide to the pianist's repertoire. (Hinson, Maurice). *Indiana University Press. £6.60* AQ(WT) (B73-17042) ISBN 0 253 32700 8
Frolic for trombones: a trio for trombones, with brass band. (Heath, Reginald). *R. Smith. Unpriced* WMPWUNT (B73-50907)
Fruhlingsfeier. Op.48, no.3. Spring repose: for four-part chorus of mixed voices a cappella. (Mendelssohn, Felix). *Schirmer. Unpriced* EZDW (B73-50123)
Frye, Ellen. The marble threshing floor: a collection of Greek folksongs. *Texas University Press for the American Folklore Society. Unpriced* JDW/G/AYPE (B73-51058) ISBN 0 292 75005 6
Fugue on 'Hey diddle diddle': for SATB unaccompanied. (Ophenbeidt). *Thames. Unpriced* EZDW (B73-50125)
Fuller, John.
Herod, do your worst. Sleep little baby. Sleep little baby: Christmas song for unison voices and piano. (Kelly, Bryan). *Novello. £0.07* JDP/LF (B73-51050)
Herod, do your worst. Sleep little baby: arr. Sleep little baby: Christmas song. (Kelly, Bryan). *Novello. £0.07* DP/LF (B73-50969)
Fulton, Norman. Two Christmas songs. Opus 37. *Oxford University Press. £0.50* KDP/LF (B73-51084) ISBN 0 19 345341 x
Fum fum fum!: Traditional Spanish carol. (Parker, Alice). *Schirmer. Unpriced* FDP/LF (B73-50139)
Fünf Bagatellen: für Posaune und Klavier. (Schenker, Friedrich). *Peters. Unpriced* VWPJ (B73-50434)
Fünf Lieder: für mittlere Stimme und Klavier. (Reutter, Hermann). *Schott. £1.20* KFVDW (B73-50653)
Fünf Madrigale: für gemischten Chor. (Reda, Siegfried). *Bärenreiter. £0.40* EZDH (B73-50067)
Für Stimmen (... missa est)!
Nr. 3: Madrisha II; fur 3 Chorgruppen. (Schnebel, Dieter). *Schott. £4.80* EZDW (B73-51011)
Für Stimmen (... missa est)
Nr.1,2: Choralvorspiele 1/2, für Orgel, Nebeninstrumente und Tonband. (Schnebel, Dieter). *Schott. Unpriced* NYFXP (B73-50284)
Furchte dich nicht: SSAB, with Christus spricht: wer mich liebt: SSAB, with Herr, wer festen Herzens ist, dem bewahrst du Frieden: SSA. (Baudach, Ulrich). *Bärenreiter. £0.15* EZDH (B73-50069)
Fussan, Werner. Swing and sing: Tanzsuite für gemischten Chor (auch Kammerchor) und Rhythmusgruppe. *Schott. Unpriced* DW/AY (B73-50518)
Gabrieli, Giovanni.
Canzone e sonate (1615): for trumpets, optional horns, and trombones
Canzon 1: for 2 trumpets and 3 trombones (2 trumpets, horn, and trombones). *Musica rara. Unpriced* WN (B73-50441)
Canzon 2: for 3 trumpets and 3 trombones, (3 trumpets, horn and 2 trombones). *Musica rara. Unpriced* WN (B73-50442)
Canzon 3: for 2 trumpets and 4 trombones, (2 trumpets, horn and 3 trombones). *Musica rara. Unpriced* WN (B73-50443)
Canzon 4: for 4 trumpets and 2 trombones. *Musica rara. Unpriced* WN (B73-50444)
Canzon 5: for 4 trumpets and 3 trombones (4 trumpets, and 2 trombones). *Musica rara. Unpriced* WN (B73-50445)
Canzon 6: for 4 trumpets and 3 trombones, (4 trumpets, horn and 2 trombones). *Musica rara. Unpriced* WN (B73-50446)
Canzon 7: for 4 trumpets and 3 trombones, (4 trumpets, horn and 2 trombones). *Musica rara. £2.00* WN (B73-50447)
Canzon 8: for 3 trumpets and 5 trombones. *Musica rara. Unpriced* WN (B73-50448)
Canzon 9: for 3 trumpets and 5 trombones (3 trumpets, horn and 4 trombones). *Musica rara. £2.50* WN (B73-50449)
Canzon 10: for 4 trumpets and 4 trombones (4 trumpets, 2 horns and 2 trombones). *Musica rara. £2.50* WN (B73-50450)
Canzon 11: for 4 trumpets and 4 trombones. *Musica rara. £2.50* WN (B73-50451)
Canzon 12: for 2 trumpets and 6 trombones, (2 trumpets, 2 horns and 4 trombones). *Musica rara. £2.50* WN (B73-50452)
Canzon 13: for 4 trumpets and 4 trombones, (4 trumpets, 2 horns and 2 trombones). *Musica rara. £2.50* WN (B73-50453)
Canzon 14: for 6 trumpets and 4 trombones. *Musica rara. £2.50* WN (B73-50454)
Canzon 15: for 4 trumpets and 6 trombones, (4 trumpets, 2 horns and 4 trombones). *Musica rara. £3.00* WN (B73-50455)
Canzon 16: for 6 trumpets and 6 trombones, (6 trumpets, 3 horns and 3 trombones). *Musica rara. £3.00* WN (B73-50456)
Canzon 17: for 6 trumpets and 6 trombones. *Musica rara. £3.00* WN (B73-50457)
Canzon 18: for 4 trumpets and 10 trombones, (4 trumpets, 2 horns and 8 trombones). *Musica rara. Unpriced* WN (B73-50458)
Canzon 19: for trumpets and 12 trombones, (3 trumpets, 3 horns and 9 trombones). *Musica rara. £3.50* WN (B73-50459)
Canzon 20: for 5 trumpets and 17 trombones, (5 trumpets, 4 horns and 13 trombones). *Musica rara. Unpriced* WN (B73-50460)
Sacrae symphoniae, bk.1. Plaudite. Vocal score. Plaudite: for triple chorus of mixed voices. *Schirmer. Unpriced* DJ (B73-50961)
Gál, Hans.
Sonata for viola and pianoforte. Op. 101. *Simrock. Unpriced* SQPE (B73-51225)
Suite for alto saxophone in E flat and pianoforte. Op. 102b. *Simrock. Unpriced* VUSPG (B73-51289)
Suite for viola and pianoforte. Op. 102a. *Simrock. Unpriced* SQPG (B73-51226)
Triptych. Op.100: three movements for orchestra. *Simrock. Unpriced* MMG (B73-50254)
Gale, Norman. The snowdrop: unison song. (Craxton, Harold). *Cramer. Unpriced* JFDW (B73-50623)
Gange, Kenneth.
Three classical pieces. *Bosworth. £0.50* MK/AAY (B73-51109)
Wedding music: suite for organ. *Cramer. Unpriced* RG/KDD (B73-51193)
Garden, Edward. Tchaikovsky. *Dent. £1.95* BTD(N) (B73-11185) ISBN 0 460 03105 8
Gardner, John.
Cantata for Easter, Op.105: for soloists, mixed chorus, organ and percussion. *Oxford University Press. Unpriced* ENYLDE/LL (B73-50051) ISBN 0 19 336214 7
A Christmas hymn. Opus 109a: SATB (or S. only) and organ. *Oxford University Press. Unpriced* DH/LF (B73-50957) ISBN 0 19 343016 9
A Shakespeare sequence. Op.66.. Who is Sylvia? Who is Sylvia?: SSAA. *Oxford University Press. Unpriced* FDW (B73-50142) ISBN 0 19 342594 7
Solstice carol. Op. 115. *Chappell. Unpriced* DP (B73-50964)
Gardner, Ward. Lullay, lullay, thou lytil child: SATB unacc. *Banks. £0.03* EZDP/LF (B73-50995)
Gardonyi, Zoltan. Works, piano. Piano works
Vol.3: Hungarian rhapsodies 1, nos.1-9. (Liszt, Franz). *Bärenreiter. £2.40* QP/AZ (B73-50717)
Garran, Robert Randolph. Schubert and Schumann songs and translations. *Melbourne University Press: Distributed by Angus and Robertson. £4.15* BSGADW (B73-13019) ISBN 0 522 83999 1
Gascoyne, David. Six poems from 'Miserere'. (Naylor, Bernard). *Roberton. £0.30* EZDW (B73-50124)
Gaudí: study no.3, for piano. (McCabe, John). *Novello. £1.00* QPJ (B73-50305)
Gaudium et spes: Beunza: para 32 voces y cinta por Cristobal Halffter. (Halffter, Cristobal). *Universal. Unpriced* EZDE (B73-50980)
Gaunt, John.
The medieval men: march. (Porter-Brown, Reginald). *Studio Music. Unpriced* WMK/AGM (B73-50898)
Samson et Dalila. Mon coeur s'ouvre à ta voix: arr. Softly awakes my heart. (Saint-Saens, Charles). *Studio Music. Unpriced* WMK/DW (B73-50899)
Gay, Bram. 12 kleine Stücke. Selections. Four fancies: a serenade in E flat for brass band. (Maurer, Ludwig). *Novello. £1.25* WMJ (B73-50438)
Gay, John. Beggar's opera. Selections. Four songs. *Oxford University Press. £0.12* EZDW (B73-50555) ISBN 0 19 343673 6
Geistliche Zwiegesänge
Band 2: Spruch-Bicinien. (Brodde, Otto). *Barenreiter. £2.10* DH/AYE (B73-50507)
Geistliches Lied. Op.30. Lass dich nur nichts nicht dauren. Lass dich nur nichts nicht dauren = Let not your heart be troubled: for four-part chorus of mixed voices with organ or piano accompaniment. (Brahms, Johnnes). *Schirmer. Unpriced* DH (B73-50955)
Gems of Sullivan
Vol.1. (Sullivan, *Sir* Arthur Seymour). *Regina Music. Unpriced* PWPK/CF (B73-50287)
Gentle are its songs. (Wright, Kenneth Anthony). *P.O. Box 775, W9 1LN: Sir Gerald Nabarro (Publications) Ltd. £3.50* AD(YDKRL/WB/XPG26) (B73-16140) ISBN 0 903699 00 1
Gentle genius: the story of Felix Mendelssohn. (Marek, George Richard). *Hale. £4.50* BMJ(N) (B73-16142) ISBN 0 7091 3900 4
Genzmer, Harald.
Eleven duets for recorder. Elf Duette für Sopranblockflöte und Altblockflöte von Harald Genzmer. *Schott. £1.08* VSNU (B73-51277)
Sonata for treble recorder & piano, no.2. Zweite Sonata für Altblockflöte und Klavier. *Schott. £1.30* VSSPE (B73-51284)
George, Jon. Mediaeval pageant: easy piano pieces. *Oxford University Press. £0.40* QPJ (B73-50730) ISBN 0 19 372719 6
George, Thom Ritter. Western overture. *Boosey and Hawkes. £10.00* UMMJ (B73-50834)
George Frideric Handel - the Newman Flower Collection in the Henry Watson Music Library: a catalogue. (Henry Watson Music Library). *Central Library, Manchester M2 5PD: Manchester Public Libraries. £3.50* BHC(WJ) (B73-00557) ISBN 0 901315 18 4
George Ridley, Gateshead poet and vocalist. (Ridley, George). *Graham. £0.40* AKDW/G/E(YDJHT/P) (B73-19498) ISBN 0 902833 81 2
Gerhard, Roberto.
Sonata for cello and piano. *Oxford University Press. £1.90* SRPE (B73-50381) ISBN 0 19 356738 5
Symphony no.2, 'Metamorphoses'. Metamorphoses (Symphony no.2). Revised ed.: edited by Alan Boustead. *Belwin-Mills. Unpriced* MME (B73-50669)
German folksongs for four-part chorus, bk,2, no.1. In stiller Nacht. In stiller Nacht = In still of night: for four-part chorus of women's voices a cappella. (Brahms, Johannes). *Schirmer. Unpriced* FEZDW (B73-51042)
Gershwin, George. Songs. Selections. The Gershwin years: songs. *Chappell. £1.50* KDW (B73-51087)
Gershwin years: songs. (Gershwin, George). *Chappell. £1.50* KDW (B73-51087)
Geviksman, Vitali. Japanische Elegien: Vokal-instrumental-Zyklus in sieben Teilen nach Worten altjapanischer Dichter, fur Soprano und Kammerensemble. *Peters. £3.50* KFLE/NYLNQDW (B73-50646)
Giannaris, George. Mikis Theodorakis: music and social change. *Allen and Unwin. £3.95* BTF(N) (B73-20238) ISBN 0 04 920038 0
Giardino di amore.. Sinfonia. Sinfonia for trumpet and strings. (Scarlatti, Alessandro). *Musica rara. Unpriced* RXMPWS (B73-50360)
Giardino di amore. Sinfonia. Sinfonia: for trumpet and strings. (Scarlatti, Alessandro). *Musica rara. Unpriced* WSPK (B73-50466)
Giazotto, Remo. Sonate à tre in G minor. Adagio: arr. Adagio in G minor on two thematic fragments and a figured bass. (Albinoni, Tommaso). *Ricordi. Unpriced* RSPMK (B73-51210)
Gibbons, Christopher.
Etudes faciles et progressives. Op.100. 25 easy and progressive studies: for piano. (Burgmüller, Friedrich). *Chappell. Unpriced* QPJ (B73-50301)
Kinderscenen. Op.15. Scenes from childhood: for piano. (Schumann, Robert). *Chappell. Unpriced* QPJ (B73-50309)
Passagen-Ubungen. Op.26.. Selections. 101 exercises: for piano. (Czerny, Carl). *Chappell. Unpriced* Q/AF (B73-50288)
Sonatinas for piano. Opus 36. (Clementi, Muzio). *Chappell. Unpriced* QPEM (B73-50298)
Gibbons, Irene Rosalind. Music of the Americas: an illustrated music ethnology of the Eskimo and American Indian peoples. (Collaer, Paul). *Curzon Press. £6.50* BZP (B73-02064) ISBN 0 7007 0004 8
Gibbs, Alan. St. Margaret's Communion, Series 3: for congregation and choir in unison (optional SATB) with organ or piano. *Royal School of Church Music. Unpriced* JDGS (B73-51047)
Gibson, Arthur J.
Il Cimento dell'armonia e dell'invenzione. Op.8, no.4. Largo: arr. Largo from the 'Winter' concerto for violin and strings. (Vivaldi, Antonio). *Cramer. Unpriced* RK (B73-51204)
Two contrasts. *Ashdown. Unpriced* RK (B73-50347)
Gibson, Isabella Mary. Lochnagar. *Kerr. Unpriced* KDW (B73-50205)

Gilbert, Anthony. Spell respell. Op 14: for electric basset clarinet (or clarinet in A) and piano. *Schott. £0.75* VVXPJ (B73-50876)
Gilbert, Norman.
Pastorale prelude: organ solo. *Cramer. £0.24* RJ (B73-50337)
Postlude: organ solo. *Cramer. £0.24* RJ (B73-50338)
Gilbert, Raymond. Let all men everywhere rejoice: anthem for SATB and organ (or brass, percussion and organ). (Wills, Arthur). *Novello. £0.14* DH (B73-50028)
Gilbert and Sullivan and their world. (Baily, Leslie). *Thames and Hudson. £2.25* BSWACF (B73-27557) ISBN 0 500 13046 9
Gillespie, John. Five centuries of keyboard music: an historical survey of music for harpsichord and piano. *Dover Publications: Constable. £2.50* APW(X) (B73-13586) ISBN 0 486 22855 x
Ginastera, Alberto. Sonate d'intavolatura for organ. Op. 1. Parte 1. Toccata: arr. Toccata. (Zipoli, Domenico). *Boosey and Hawkes. £0.75* QPK (B73-51181)
Giorgi, Giovanni. Gloria et honore: arr. Glory and honor: for four-part chorus of mixed voices a cappella. *Schirmer. Unpriced* EZDJ (B73-50986)
Giuliani, Mauro. Grande ouverture. Op 61. *Schott. £0.80* TSPMJ (B73-50823)
Give ear to my words: general anthem, for four-part chorus of mixed voices a cappella. (Newbury, Kent A). *Schirmer. Unpriced* EZDK (B73-50082)
Glazer, Joe. Songs of work and freedom. Songs of work and protest. (Fowke, Edith). *Dover: Constable. £1.75* JDW/KJ/AY (B73-51059) ISBN 0 486 22899 1
Glazunov, Alexander. The seasons: ballet in one act and four tableaux. *Belaieff: Hinrichsen. £4.50* MM/HM (B73-50664)
Glazunow, Alexander. *See* Glazunov, Alexander.
Glennon, James. Understanding music. *Hale. £6.00* A (B73-04214) ISBN 0 7091 3539 4
Glogau Songbook. Selections: arr. Twelve pieces from the Glogauer Liederbuch. *Bärenreiter. £0.75* VSNTK/DW (B73-50852)
Gloria: a Christmas fanfare or introit, for four-part chorus of mixed voices with piano or organ accompaniment. (Newbury, Kent A). *Schirmer. Unpriced* DH/LF (B73-50029)
Gloria et honore: arr. Glory and honor: for four-part chorus of mixed voices a cappella. (Giorgi, Giovanni). *Schirmer. Unpriced* EZDJ (B73-50986)
Gloria in excelsis Deo: for four-part chorus of mixed voices a cappella. (Sprague, Richard L). *Schirmer. Unpriced* EZDH/LF (B73-50077)
Glory and honor: for four-part chorus of mixed voices a cappella. (Giorgi, Giovanni). *Schirmer. Unpriced* EZDJ (B73-50986)
Glory of the violin. The violin. (Wechsberg, Joseph). *Calder and Boyars. £5.00* AS/B(X) (B73-29559) ISBN 0 7145 1020 3
Go, lovely rose: for full chorus of mixed voices a cappella. (Fast, Willard S). *Schirmer. Unpriced* EZDW (B73-50115)
Godfather: themes for easy play piano. (Rota, Nina). *Famous Chappell. £0.40* QPK/JR (B73-50324)
God's strange ways: SATB a cappella. (Rose, Gregory). *Boosey and Hawkes. £0.14* EZDH (B73-50984)
Godspell: film souvenir song book. (Schwartz, Stephen). *Valando Music. £1.00* KDW/JR (B73-50638)
Goehr, Alexander.
Konzertstück. Op. 26: for piano and small orchestra. *Schott. £2.00* MPQ (B73-50684)
Nonomiya. Op 27: for piano. *Schott. £0.80* QPJ (B73-50731)
Romanza for cello and orchestra. Op.24. *Schott. £2.50* MPSR (B73-51122)
Triptych. Op.25
No.1: Naboth's vineyard. *Schott. £3.00* CQC (B73-50940)
Golden flute: an opera for schools in two acts based on Mozart's 'The magic flute'. (Mozart, Wolfgang Amadeus). *Novello. £1.00* CN (B73-50008)
Goldfish bowl. (Lutyens, Elisabeth). *Cassell. £4.00* BLU(N) (B73-04669) ISBN 0 304 93663 4
Goldman, Edwin Franko.
March for all seasons: march. *Boosey and Hawkes. £1.75* UMMGM (B73-50398)
March for peace. *Boosey and Hawkes. £1.75* UMMGM (B73-50399)
Right on march. *Boosey and Hawkes. £1.75* UMMGM (B73-50400)
Gonna alter m'ways. (Cookridge, John Michael). *Janay. £0.06* JDW (B73-50173)
Good old bad old days. (Bricusse, Leslie). *Peter Maurice. Unpriced* UMMK/CM (B73-50401)
Good old bad old days. (Bricusse, Leslie). *Peter Maurice. Unpriced* WMK/CM (B73-50439)
'Good old bad old days!': a new musical. (Bricusse, Leslie). *Peter Maurice Music, (KPM Music Group). £0.75* KDW (B73-50204)
Goodwin, Inge. Gustav Mahler. (Blaukopf, Kurt). *Allen Lane. £3.50* BME(N) (B73-20237) ISBN 0 7139 0464 x
Gordon, Rob. Rob Gordon's book of Scottish music. *Kerr. Unpriced* QPK/AH/AYDL (B73-50316)
Gorwyd Iesu Grist = Christus natus est: two part carol by Gordon Weston; traditional words, Welsh version by Ivor Owen. (Weston, Gordon). *University of Wales Press. £0.15* FDP/LF (B73-51026)
Gounod. (Harding, James). *Allen and Unwin. £4.75* BGRN(N) (B73-20976) ISBN 0 04 780021 6
Grabocz, Miklos. Alte ungarische Tanze des 18 Jahrhunderts
für Bläserquintett und Cembalo. *Bärenreiter. Unpriced* NWNQK/AH/AYG(XG101) (B73-50696)
Grace, Norah. Sketches for three: for violin, cello and piano. *Forsyth. Unpriced* NXNT (B73-50281)
Gradualia, Lib 1.. Rorate coeli desuper. Rorate coeli desuper = Drop down, ye heavens: SAATB. (Byrd, William). *Oxford University Press. Unpriced* EZDGKAD/LEZ (B73-50059) ISBN 0 19 352062 1
Graf, Herbert. The opera and its future in America. *Kennikat Press. £9.75* AC(XA1940) (B73-24202) ISBN 0 8046 1744 9
Grain of wheat: 12 songs of grouping and growing. (Oswin, Mary). *Mayhew-McCrimmon. £0.47* JDM (B73-50601)
Gramercy, Walter.
English suite for keyboard, no.5. S.810. Sarabande: arr. Sarabande. (Bach, Johann Sebastian). *Cornelius. Unpriced* TSNUK/AHVL (B73-50818)
Das wohltemperirte Clavier. Prelude no.23. S.868: arr. Prelude no.23. S.868. (Bach, Johann Sebastian). *Cornelius. Unpriced* TSNTK (B73-50815)
'Gramophone' jubilee book. (Wimbush, Roger). *177 Kenton Rd, Harrow, Middx: General Gramophone Publications Ltd. £2.50* A/FD(XNC51/D) (B73-13020) ISBN 0 902470 04 3
Gramski, Marek. Lwowskie piosenki
Cześć 3: Pod znakiem Marsa. (Uhma, Stefan). *240 King's St., W6 9JT: Kola Lwowian. £0.50* ADW/G(YMUL) (B73-24206) ISBN 0 9503005 0 0
Granados, Enrique. Danzas espanolas, vol.2. Andaluza. Spanish dance, no.5. *Oxford University Press. £0.35* WTPK/AH (B73-50472) ISBN 0 19 356830 6
Grande due concertante: für Gitarre & Klavier. (Moscheles, Ignaz). *Simrock. Unpriced* TSPMJ (B73-51250)
Grande ouverture. Op 61. (Giuliani, Mauro). *Schott. £0.80* TSPMJ (B73-50823)
Graun, Carl Heinrich. Sonata for two flutes & basso continuo in E flat major. Sonata in E flat major for two flutes (violins) and basso continuo. *Bärenreiter. £1.80* VRNTPWE (B73-50404)
Graves, Richard.
As I went riding by: carol for unison voices with optional descant, and piano. *Novello. £0.07* JFDP/LF (B73-51066)
The fairies.. Overture. Overture: for strings and continuo (with optional oboes and optional trumpets). (Smith, John Christopher). *Oxford University Press. £1.00* RXMJ (B73-50357) ISBN 0 19 367637 0
In pastures green: unison, 2nd part ad lib. *Bosworth. £0.07* JDR (B73-51055)
Graves, Robert. Counting the beats: song for high voice and piano. (Berkeley, Lennox). *Thames. Unpriced* KFTDW (B73-50228)
Great Britain. *Department of Education and Science. Schools Council. See* Schools Council.
Great Britain. *Schools Council. See* Schools Council.
Great film themes for brass. (Street, Allan). *Chappell. Unpriced* WMK/JR (B73-50900)
Great Panathenaea: for brass quintet. (Gubby, Roy). *Boosey and Hawkes. £1.50* WNR (B73-51302)
Great songs of the fifties. *Wise, Music Sales. £1.50* KDW/GB/AY(XPKIO) (B73-51089)
Greatest hits. (Greig, Edvard). *Chappell. £1.00* RK (B73-50764)
Greaves, Terence. Coventry carol: unison song. *Chappell. Unpriced* JFDP/LF (B73-50183)
Green, Archie. Only a miner: studies in recorded coal-mining songs. *University of Illinois Press. £5.65* ADW/GNGC(YT) (B73-06593) ISBN 0 252 00181 8
Green, Benny. Drums in my ears. *10 Earlham St., WC2H 9LP: Davis-Poynter. £2.50* AMT(D/XPQ17) (B73-10167) ISBN 0 7067 0066 x
Green, Gordon. Liszt: a selection. (Liszt, Franz). *Oxford University Press. Unpriced* QPJ (B73-50732) ISBN 0 19 373217 3
Green, Philip.
The first Christmas. *Belwin-Mills. £0.20* KDP/LF (B73-51085)
Hail Mary. *Belwin-Mills. £0.20* KDJ (B73-51083)
Let me bring love. Suffer little children. Suffer little children. *Belwin-Mills. £0.20* FDH (B73-51017)
Green groves: more English folk songs. (Hamer, Fred). *EFDS. £0.75* KE/TSDW/G/AYD (B73-50218)
Greenaway, Roger. Children of the world unite. (Cook, Roger). *Cookaway Music: Distributed by Music Sales. £0.20* JFDW/ (B73-50189)
Greene, Maurice.
Overture no.5 in D major. *Eulenburg. £0.60* MRJ (B73-51124)
Overture no.6 in E flat major. *Eulenburg. £0.60* MRJ (B73-51125)
Greenfield, Edward.
André Previn. *Allan. £2.25* A/EC(P) (B73-21633) ISBN 0 7110 0370 x
The stereo record guide
Vol.8: Composer index Me-Z. *Squires Gate, Station Approach, Blackpool, Lancs. FY82 SP: Long Playing Record Library Ltd. £1.95* A/FF(WT) (B73-08019) ISBN 0 901143 06 5
Greening, Anthony.
Gradualia, Lib 1.. Rorate coeli desuper. Rorate coeli desuper = Drop down, ye heavens: SAATB. (Byrd, William). *Oxford University Press. Unpriced* EZDGKAD/LEZ (B73-50059) ISBN 0 19 352062 1
Lift up your heads: SSATB. (Amner, John). *Oxford University Press. Unpriced* DK (B73-50033) ISBN 0 19 350331 x
The Lord's Prayer: SATB unacc. (Stone, Robert). *Oxford University Press. £0.05* EZDTF (B73-51006) ISBN 0 19 350345 x
Magnificat and Nunc dimittis: SATBB. (Wise, Michael). *Oxford University Press. £0.15* DGPP (B73-50950) ISBN 0 19 351635 7
Te Deum and Jubilate: SATB. (Farrant, John, *b.1575*). Revised ed. *Oxford University Press. £0.30* DGNP (B73-50499) ISBN 0 19 352106 7
Gregory, Robin. The trombone: the instrument and its music. *Faber. £6.50* AWU (B73-06594) ISBN 0 571 08816 3
Gregson, Edward.
Partita for brass band. *R. Smith. Unpriced* WMG (B73-50882)
The Plantagenets: a symphonic study, for brass band. *R. Smith. Unpriced* WMJ (B73-50889)
Prelude and capriccio: for cornet and band. *R. Smith. Unpriced* WMPWR (B73-51300)
Greig, Edvard. Selections. Greatest hits. *Chappell. £1.00* RK (B73-50764)
Grieb, Herbert. O God of every race and creed: for four-part chorus of mixed voices with organ or piano accompaniment. *Schirmer. Unpriced* DM (B73-50040)
Grieg, Edvard.
Holberg suite. Op.40. Sarabande: arr. Sarabande. *Cornelius. Unpriced* SQPK/AHVL (B73-50797)
Holberg suite. Op.40. Sarabande: arr. Sarabande. *Cornelius. Unpriced* SRPK/AHVL (B73-50807)
Holberg suite. Op.40. Sarabande: arr. Sarabande. *Cornelius. Unpriced* WUPK/AHVL (B73-50921)
Selections. Grieg. *Warren and Phillips. Unpriced* QPK (B73-50315)
Griffin, Jack. The mountain of the Lord: anthem for SATB and organ. *Roberton. £0.10* DK (B73-50034)
Grindea, Carola. We make music. *Kahn and Averill. £0.75* QP/D/AY (B73-50294) ISBN 0 900707 14 3
Grout, Donald Jay. A history of western music. Revised ed. *Dent. £5.95* A(YB/X) (B73-18798) ISBN 0 460 03517 7
Grub-Street opera. (Fielding, Henry). *Oliver and Boyd. £2.00* ACLMBM (B73-31566) ISBN 0 05 002755 7
Gruber, Franz. Stille Nacht, heilige Nacht: arr. Silent night. *Thames. Unpriced* FEZDP/LF (B73-50152)
Grundman, Clare.
Concertante for E flat alto saxophone and military band. *Boosey and Hawkes. £12.00* UMMPVUS (B73-51258)
Concertante for E flat alto saxophone and piano. *Boosey and Hawkes. £1.25* VUSPJ (B73-51290)
Guardian outwitted. Overture. Overture: for flutes, oboes, bassoons, horns, strings and continuo. (Arne, Thomas Augustine). *Oxford University Press. £1.50* MRJ (B73-51123) ISBN 0 19 361230 5
Gubby, Roy.
Air and rumba: descant and treble recorder and piano. *Boosey and Hawkes. Unpriced* VSNTQHVKK (B73-51276)
The great Panathenaea: for brass quintet. *Boosey and Hawkes. £1.50* WNR (B73-51302)
Guide to the pianist's repertoire. (Hinson, Maurice). *Indiana University Press. £6.60* AQ(WT) (B73-17042) ISBN 0 253 32700 8
Guildhall School of Music and Drama.
Pianoforte examinations
Grade 1. *Lengnick. £0.35* Q/AL (B73-51152)
Grade 2. *Lengnick. £0.35* Q/AL (B73-51153)
Grade 3. *Lengnick. £0.35* Q/AL (B73-51154)
Grade 4. *Lengnick. £0.35* Q/AL (B73-51155)
Introductory. *Lengnick. £0.35* Q/AL (B73-51156)
Junior. *Lengnick. £0.35* Q/AL (B73-51157)
Preliminary. *Lengnick. £0.35* Q/AL (B73-51158)
Guitar transcriptions from the Cube L.P., 'The height below'. (Williams, John). *Essex Music. Unpriced* TSNUK/AAY (B73-51243)
Gulland, N J Milner-. *See* Milner-Gulland, N J.
Gurgel, Horst. Hänsel und Gretel. Vocal score. Hänsel und Gretel: Märchenspiel in drei Bildern. (Humperdinck, Engelbert). *Peters: Hinrichsen. Unpriced* CC (B73-50006)
Gustav Mahler. (Blaukopf, Kurt). *Allen Lane. £3.50* BME(N) (B73-20237) ISBN 0 7139 0464 x
Gutche, Gene. Sonata for piano. Op.32, no.2. Sonata. Opus 32, no.2: for piano. *Highgate Press: Galliard. Unpriced* QPE (B73-50720)
Gypsy Marie. (Cookridge, John Michael). *Bayley and Ferguson. £0.10* JFDW (B73-50622)
Hader, Widmar. Hör meinen Protest: Psalm 5 für Bass, Trompete und Orgel. *Bosse: Bärenreiter. £1.80* KGXE/WSPLRDE (B73-50240)
Haec dies: dialogues and sonatas on the Resurrection of our Lord, for mixed voices and organ. (Aston, Peter). *Novello. £1.25* DE/LL (B73-50944)
Hagopian, Viola L. Italian Ars Nova music: a bibliographic guide to modern editions and related literature. 2nd ed., revised and expanded. *University of California Press. £4.50* A(YJ/XCL91/T) (B73-20592) ISBN 0 520 02223 8
Hail Mary. (Green, Philip). *Belwin-Mills. £0.20* KDJ (B73-51083)
Hainsworth, Brian. Songs by Sinatra, 1939-1970. *Little Timbers, Wyncroft Grove, Bramhope, Leeds LS16 9DG: B. Hainsworth. £1.00* AKG/FD(P/WT) (B73-12708) ISBN 0 9502861 0 9
Hales, Bernell W. Lullaby. (Keel, Frederick). *Galaxy: Galliard. Unpriced* DW (B73-50976)
Halffter, Cristobal.
Fibonaciana: para flauta solista dos percusionistas y cuerda. *Universal. Unpriced* MMJ (B73-50681)
Gaudium et spes: Beunza: para 32 voces y cinta por Cristobal Halffter. *Universal. Unpriced* EZDE (B73-50980)
Halffter, Cristóbal.
Noche pasiva del sentido, (San Juan de la Cruz).

Universal. Unpriced KFLE/NYLNUDE (B73-50647)
Quartet for strings, no.2, 'Memoires 1970'. II. Streichquartett, (Memoires 1970). *Universal. Unpriced* RXNS (B73-50785)
Hall, Ian. Westminster Te Deum: for SATB and organ. *Weinberger. £0.25* DGNQ (B73-50017)
Hall, Joseph. Immortal babe: carol for accompanied two-part chorus. (Moore, Philip). *Thames. Unpriced* FDP/LF (B73-50566)
Hall, Peter. The Scottish folksinger: 118 modern and traditional folksongs. (Buchan, Norman). *Collins. £0.95* JE/TSDW/G/AYDL (B73-50607) ISBN 0 00 411115 x
Hamer, Fred. Green groves: more English folk songs. *EFDS. £0.75* KE/TSDW/G/AYD (B73-50218)
Hamilton, Alasdair. Scherzo for piano duet, 'The keys of Canterbury'. *Roberton. £0.40* QNV (B73-51162)
Hamilton, Iain.
Concerto for violin, no.1: arr. Concerto no.1: for violin and orchestra. *Schott. £2.50* SPK/LF (B73-50367)
Ecossaise for orchestra. *Schott. £1.50* MMHJQ (B73-50675)
Hammar, Russell A. Methinks I hear the full celestial choir: for 5-part chorus of mixed voices unaccompanied. (Crotch, William). *Roberton. £0.13* EZDH (B73-50533)
Hanby, B R. Darling Nelly Gray: arr. Nelly Gray: plantation song. *Schott. £0.30* GEZDW (B73-50583)
Hand, Colin.
Aria and giga: for oboe and piano. *Schott. £0.50* VTPHP (B73-50858)
Divertimento for recorders strings piano and percussion. *Schott. £2.50* NYDS (B73-50697)
Fenland suite: for recorder quartet. *Schott. £0.60* VSNSG (B73-50849)
Plaint: for tenor recorder and harpsichord (or piano). *Schott. £0.50* VSTPJ (B73-50856)
Handel, George Frideric.
Airs francais = Cantate francaise: for soprano and basso continuo. First ed. *Bärenreiter. £1.50* KFLDX (B73-50643)
Concerti grossi. Op.3, no.2. Menuet: arr. Menuet. *Schott. Unpriced* VSNRPWK/AHR (B73-50414)
Concerto grosso in A major. Op.6, no.11. *Eulenburg. £0.41* RXMF (B73-50766)
Concerto grosso in A minor. Op. 6, no.4. *Eulenburg. £0.41* RXMF (B73-50767)
Concerto grosso in B flat major. Op. 6, no.7. *Eulenburg. £0.41* RXMF (B73-50768)
Concerto grosso in B minor. Op.6, no.12: by George Frideric Handel. *Eulenburg. £0.41* RXMF (B73-50769)
Concerto grosso in C minor. Op: 6, no.8. *Eulenburg. £0.41* RXMF (B73-50770)
Concerto grosso in D major. Op. 6, no.5. *Eulenburg. £0.41* MRF (B73-50689)
Concerto grosso in D minor. Op. 6, no.10. *Eulenburg. £0.41* RXMF (B73-50771)
Concerto grosso in E minor. Op. 6, no.3. *Eulenburg. £0.41* RXMF (B73-50772)
Concerto grosso in F major. Op. 6, no.2. *Eulenburg. £0.41* MRF (B73-50690)
Concerto grosso in F major. Op.6, no.9. *Eulenburg. £0.41* RXMF (B73-50773)
Concerto grosso in G major. Op. 6, no.1. *Eulenburg. £0.41* MRF (B73-50691)
Concerto grosso in G minor. Op. 6, no.6. *Eulenburg. £0.41* MRF (B73-50692)
Messiah. Vocal score. Der Messias = The Messiah: oratorio in three parts. *Bärenreiter. £2.10* DD (B73-50495)
Works, keyboard. Keyboard works
Vol.3: Miscellaneous suites and pieces. *Bärenreiter. £1.85* QRP/AZ (B73-51184)
Handl, Jacob.
Resonet in laudibus = Joseph dearest, Joseph mine: for four-part chorus of mixed voices. *Roberton. Unpriced* EZDP/LF (B73-50098)
Tomus primus operis musici.. Pueri concinite. Pueri concinite: for four equal voices SSSA or SSAA a cappella. *Roberton. Unpriced* EZDJ/LF (B73-50080)
Tonus primus operis musici. Regem natum. Regem natum = Our king is born: for 4-part chorus of mixed voices unaccompanied. *Roberton. Unpriced* EZDJ/LF (B73-50538)
Hanmer, Roger. Le Carnival des animaux. Le Cygne: arr. The swan. (Saint-Saens, Camille). *Studio Music. Unpriced* WMPWTWK (B73-50904)
Hanmer, Ronald.
Arioso and caprice: for flugel horn and band. *R. Smith. Unpriced* WMPWT (B73-50903)
Arioso and caprice: for flugel horn and piano. *R. Smith. Unpriced* WTPJ (B73-50913)
Brass spectacular. *Studio Music. Unpriced* WMJ (B73-50890)
Episodes for brass. *R. Smith. Unpriced* WMJ (B73-50891)

Suite for seven: 2 flutes, oboe, 3 clarinets, bassoon. *Emerson. Unpriced* VNPG (B73-51264)
Vienna marches: a march fantasy based on melodies by Schubert, Mozart, Beethovan, and J. Strauss (father and son). *Studio Music. Unpriced* WMK/AGM (B73-50897)

Hänsel und Gretel: Märchenspiel in drei Bildern. (Humperdinck, Engelbert). *Peters: Hinrichsen. Unpriced* CC (B73-50006)
Hänsel und Gretel. Vocal score. Hänsel und Gretel: Märchenspiel in drei Bildern. (Humperdinck, Engelbert). *Peters: Hinrichsen. Unpriced* CC (B73-50006)
Hanson, Byron. Dixit Dominus and Magnificat. Vocal score. Dixit Dominus and Magnificat. K.193. (Mozart, Wolfgang Amadeus). *Schirmer. Unpriced* DGKB (B73-50498)
Happy vagabond: bassoon and piano. (Noble, Harold). *Peters. £0.48* VWPJ (B73-50877)
Harburg, E.Y. The wizard of Oz: song album from the film. (Arlen, Harold). *Robbins Music, Francis, Day & Hunter. £0.75* KDW/JR (B73-50639)
Harding, James. Gounod. *Allen and Unwin. £4.75* BGRN(N) (B73-20976) ISBN 0 04 780021 6

Hare, Ian. Thou, O God, art praised in Sion: SATB anthem for harvest festival or general use. *Oxford University Press. Unpriced* DK/LP (B73-50510) ISBN 0 19 350340 9
Harebell: unison song. (Noble, Harold). *Studio Music. Unpriced* JFDW (B73-51071)
Harewood, Marion. Classical songs for children. The Penguin book of accompanied songs. *Penguin Books. £0.75* JFDW/AY (B73-50190) ISBN 0 14 070839 1
Harewood, Marion.
Harich-Schneider, Eta. A history of Japanese music. *Oxford University Press. £21.00* BZHP(X) (B73-10162) ISBN 0 19 316203 2

Harker, David. George Ridley, Gateshead poet and vocalist. (Ridley, George). *Graham. £0.40* AKDW/G/E(YDJHT/P) (B73-19498) ISBN 0 902833 81 2

Harmonia caelestis: für Sopran, vierstimmigen gemischten Chor und Instrumente
Heft 1: Weħnachtskantaten. (Esterházy, Pál). *Bärenreiter. £1.35* ERXMDH (B73-50525)
Harpsichord and clavichord: an introductory study. (Russell, Raymond). 2nd ed. *Faber. £7.50* AQR/B(XA1900) (B73-17453) ISBN 0 571 04795 5
Harries, David. Three stanzas. Op 8: for harp solo. *Stainer & Bell. Unpriced* TQPMJ (B73-50811)
Harris, Jerry Weseley. Missae totius anni: Missa O magnum mysterium. Santus: arr. Sanctus = Holy holy holy. (Victoria, Tomás Luis de). *Schirmer. Unpriced* FEZDGE (B73-50149)
Harris, Rolf. Write your own pop song with Rolf Harris. *Wolfe: Keith Prowse Music Publishing Co. Ltd. £2.00* ADW/GB/D (B73-26165) ISBN 0 7234 0509 3
Harris, *Sir* William Henry.
He that is down needs fear no fall: SSA. *Oxford University Press. Unpriced* FDH (B73-50565) ISBN 0 19 351117 7
Our day of praise is done: SATB. *Oxford University Press. Unpriced* DH (B73-50504) ISBN 0 19 351118 5
Harrison, Sidney. The young person's guide to playing the piano. 2nd ed. *Faber. £1.50* AQ/E (B73-20241) ISBN 0 571 04787 4
Harron, Donald. Anne of Green Gables. Vocal score. Anne of Green Gables. (Campbell, Norman). *Chappell. £2.00* CM (B73-50937)
Harrop, Beatrice.
Carol gaily carol: Christmas songs for children with piano accompaniments, with chords for guitar and with parts for descant recorders, glockenspiel, chime bars and percussion. *Black. Unpriced* JFE/NYESDP/LF/AY (B73-51075) ISBN 0 7136 1407 2
Someone's singing, Lord: hymns and songs for children with piano accompaniments, with chords for guitar, and with parts for descant recorders, glockenspiel, chime bars and percussion. *Black. Unpriced* JFDM/AY (B73-50182) ISBN 0 7136 1355 6
Harry, Lynn. En route. *K.P.M. Unpriced* GDW (B73-50164)
Hartmann, Erich. Quartet for double basses. *Yorke. Unpriced* SSNS (B73-51235)
Hartzell, Eugene. The symphony. (Rauchhaupt, Ursula von). *Thames and Hudson. £8.50* AMME (B73-26166) ISBN 0 500 01099 4
Harvey, John. Buddy Lindo: folk songs of Trinidad and Tobago, for unison voices and guitar. *Oxford University Press. £0.25* JE/TSDW/G/AYULM (B73-50608) ISBN 0 19 330450 3
Hassler, Hans Leo. Kirchengesäng: Psalmen und geistliche Lieder.. Selections. Kirchengesänge, Psalmen und geistliche Lieder: Choralsätz für gemischten Chor. *Bärenreiter. £1.35* EZDM (B73-50089)
Haubenstock-Ramati, Roman. Chants et prismes = Gesange und prismen. Revised 1967. *Universal. Unpriced* MRJ (B73-51126)
Haughton, P J. Ten clarinet trios. *Oxford University Press. £0.50* VVNTK/AAY (B73-50867) ISBN 0 19 357013 0
Have good courage: SSA unaccompanied. (Kodaly, Zoltán). *Boosey and Hawkes. £0.14* FEZDW (B73-50574)
Hawaiian hoe-down. (Siebert, Edrich). *Studio Music. Unpriced* WMHME (B73-50885)
Haydn, Joseph.
Mass no.3 in D minor, 'Nelson Mass'. Messe D-moll, (Nelson-Messe): für vierstimmigen Chor, Soli, Orchester und Orgel. *Peters: Hinrichsen. Unpriced* EMDG (B73-50049)
Mass no.16 in B flat major, 'Theresa mass'.. Sanctus. Vocal score. Sanctus. *Schirmer. Unpriced* DGE (B73-50014)
Mass. no.16 in B flat major, 'Theresa mass'.. Sanctus. Vocal score: arr. Sanctus. *Schirmer. Unpriced* FDGE (B73-50133)
Symphony no.51 in B flat major. *Eulenburg. £0.75* MME (B73-50670)
Symphony no.54 in G major. *Eulenburg. £1.00* MME (B73-50671)
Symphony no.59 in A major. *Eulenburg. £1.00* MME (B73-51114)
Symphony no.69, in C major, 'Laudon'. *Bärenreiter. Unpriced* MRE (B73-50268)
Haydn, Michael. Exultabunt sancti: arr. Thou art mighty: for four-part chorus of mixed voices. *Schirmer. Unpriced* EZDJ (B73-50987)
Hayes, Morris D. Israelsbrünnlein. Zion spricht: arr. Zion spricht = Zion speaks. (Schein, Johann Hermann). *Roberton. Unpriced* EZDH (B73-50535)
Hayes, William.
Cathedral music.. Bow down thine ear. Bow down thine ear, O Lord: SATB (SS Soli). *Oxford University Press. £0.25* DK (B73-50035) ISBN 0 19 350334 4
Cathedral music. *Excerpts.* Bow down thine ear, O Lord: SATB (SS Soli). *Oxford University Press. £0.25* DK (B73-50035) ISBN 0 19 350334 4
He that is down needs fear no fall: SSA. (Harris, *Sir* William Henry). *Oxford University Press. Unpriced* FDH (B73-50565) ISBN 0 19 351117 7
Headington, Christopher. Sonatina for oboe and piano. *Boosey and Hawkes. £1.50* VTPE (B73-51285)
Hear my prayer, O Lord. (Purcell, Henry). *Roberton. £0.07* FDK (B73-50136)
Hear my prayer. Op.39, no.1: arr. O for the wings of a dove. (Mendelssohn, Felix). *Cornelius. Unpriced* WTPK/DH (B73-50917)
Hear my prayer. Op.39, no.1: arr. O for the wings of a dove. (Mendelssohn, Felix). *Cornelius. Unpriced* WUPK/DH (B73-50922)
Heard ye the mighty roar?: Song. (Wilson, Robert Barclay). *Cramer. Unpriced* KDW (B73-50212)
Heath, Fenno.
In that great gettin' up morning: spiritual. *Schirmer. Unpriced* GEZDW/LC (B73-50169)
Love-song: for four-part chorus of mixed voices a cappella. *Schirmer. Unpriced* EZDW (B73-50117)
Heath, Reginald.
Air and rondo: tenor horn solo. *R. Smith. Unpriced* WMPWTW/W (B73-50905)
Air and rondo: tenor horn solo. *R. Smith. Unpriced* WTWP/W (B73-50919)
Frolic for trombones: a trio for trombones, with brass band. *R. Smith. Unpriced* WMPWUNT (B73-50907)
Shakespearian rhapsody, 'Prospero and Miranda'. *R. Smith. Unpriced* WMJ (B73-50892)
Waltz for a beguiling lady. *R. Smith. Unpriced* WMHW (B73-50886)
Heaven conserve thy course in quietness: for women's chorus and viola, or piano. (Cobb, Donald). *Galaxy Music: Galliard. Unpriced* FE/SQDH (B73-51039)
Hedges, Anthony.
Count down: duos for melody instrument and piano. *Fenette Music: Breitkopf and Härtel. Unpriced* LPJ (B73-50244)
A manger carol: for soli and SATB unaccompanied. *Novello. £0.07* EZDP/LF (B73-50996)
Hedges, Hazel. Psalm of praise: for full chorus of mixed voices with organ or piano accompaniment. *Schirmer. Unpriced* DGNT (B73-50019)
Heller, Henryk. System of harmonics for violin
Vol.1. *Simrock. £0.75* S/AF (B73-51218)
Hellmesberger, Joseph. Works, string instruments. Complete chamber music for strings. (Schubert, Franz). *Dover: Constable. £2.25* RXN/AZ (B73-51214) ISBN 0 486 21463 x
Henneberg, Claus. Owen Wingrave. Vocal score. Owen Wingrave. Op 35: an opera in two acts. (Britten, Benjamin). *Faber. £10.00* CC (B73-50488)
Henriksen, Josef. Jack be nimble: a collection of rounds for choral societies, choirs and schools. *St. Gregory. £0.45* FEZ/XC/AY (B73-50572)
Henry Watson Music Library. George Frideric Handel - the Newman Flower Collection in the Henry Watson Music Library: a catalogue. *Central Library, Manchester M2 5PD: Manchester Public Libraries. £3.50* BHC(WJ) (B73-00557) ISBN 0 901315 18 4
Henze, Hans Werner. El Cimarron. Selections: arr. Memorias de 'El Cimarron'. *Schott. £1.60* TSPMK (B73-50826)
Herbert, George.
Easter: a marriage anthem, SATB and organ. (Scott, Anthony). *Boosey and Hawkes. £0.20* DH/LL (B73-50031)
Let all the world in every corner sing: for four-part chorus of women's voices a cappella. (Lekberg, Sven). *Schirmer. Unpriced* FEZDH (B73-50150)
Two George Herbert songs: for medium voice and cello. (Silcock, Norman). *Thames. Unpriced* KFVE/SRDW (B73-50238)
Herman, Stefan. Concerto for violin, no.1, in D major. Op.6: arr. Konzert no.1, D-Dur. Opus 6: für Violine und Orchester. (Paganini, Nicolo). *Schott. £1.40* SPK/LF (B73-50368)
Hermire, Tristan P. Trois chansons de France, and Trois poèmes de Tristan l'Hermite: songs for solo voice and piano. (Debussy, Claude). *Peters. Unpriced* KDW (B73-50633)
Herod, do your worst. Sleep little baby. Sleep little baby: Christmas song for unison voices and piano. (Kelly, Bryan). *Novello. £0.07* JDP/LF (B73-51050)
Herod, do your worst. Sleep little baby: arr. Sleep little baby: Christmas song. (Kelly, Bryan). *Novello. £0.07* DP/LF (B73-50969)
Hérold, Ferdinand.
La Fille mal gardée. Clog dance. Clog dance. *Oxford University Press. Unpriced* MH/HM (B73-51105) ISBN 0 19 364251 4
La Fille mal gardée. Flute dance. Flute dance. *Oxford University Press. Unpriced* MH/HM (B73-51106) ISBN 0 19 364275 1

Herrick, Robert.
Herrick's carol: for women's voices and piano. (Nicholson, Ralph). *Weinberger. £0.08* FDP/LF (B73-50138)
Music that brings sweet sleep: song cycle for high voice and piano. (Stoker, Richard). *Peters. Unpriced* KFTDW (B73-50231)
Noble numbers: five songs for counter-tenor (or contralto) and piano (or harpsichord). (Roe, Betty). *Thames. Unpriced* KHNDW (B73-50241)
Herrick's carol: for women's voices and piano. (Nicholson, Ralph). *Weinberger. £0.08* FDP/LF (B73-50138)
Herrmann, William.
Mass no.16 in B flat major, 'Theresa mass'.. Sanctus. Vocal score. Sanctus. (Haydn, Joseph). *Schirmer. Unpriced* DGE (B73-50014)
Mass. no.16 in B flat major, 'Theresa mass'.. Sanctus. Vocal score: arr. Sanctus. (Haydn, Joseph). *Schirmer. Unpriced* FDGE (B73-50133)
Hetherington, John, *b.1907.* Melba: a biography. *Faber. £1.40* AKFL/E(P) (B73-11782) ISBN 0 571 10286 7
Hewlett, Arthur Donald. Think afresh about the voice: a reappraisal of the teaching of Ernest George White. 2nd ed. *Hillcrest, Ringwood, Deal, Kent: Ernest George White Society. £0.75* AB/E(VC/P) (B73-19499) ISBN 0 9501610 1 2
Hewson, Richard. Miniatures: for wind trio and three violins. *Boosey and Hawkes. £1.25* NVNQ (B73-50271)
Heyworth, Peter. Conversations with Klemperer. *Gollancz. £3.00* A/EC(P) (B73-16148) ISBN 0 575 01652 3
Hiby, Stefan. Andante for flute clock in F major. K.616: arr. Andante, F Dur, KV616: ein Stück für eine Walze in eine kleine Orgel. (Mozart, Wolfgang Amadeus). *Schott. £1.20* VRNSK (B73-50841)
Hickman, Reginald Elwick Beatty. Music trades international year book
1973. *157 Hagden La., Watford, Herts. WD1 8LW: Trade Papers (London) Ltd. £1.55* A(YC/BC) (B73-14513) ISBN 0 903462 01 x
High school band: SSATB (S. solo) unacc. (Paynter, John). *Oxford University Press. Unpriced* EZDW (B73-51009) ISBN 0 19 343039 8
High stepper!: a short and easy solo for flute and piano. (Fox, Peter). *Cornelius. Unpriced* VRPJ (B73-50842)
Hill, Margaret. Floroj sen kompar: Britaj popolkantoj. *British Esperanto Association. Unpriced* JE/TSDW/G/AYC (B73-50176)
Hill, Peter.
Clarinet scales and arpeggios
Bk 1: Grades 3 and 4. *Cornelius. Unpriced* VV/AF (B73-50864)
Bk 2: Grade 5. *Cornelius. Unpriced* VV/AF (B73-50865)
Kinderscenen. Op.15. Traümerei: arr. Traümerei. (Schumann, Robert). *Cornelius. Unpriced* VVNSK (B73-50866)
Oboe scales and arpeggios. *Cornelius. Unpriced* VT/AF (B73-50857)
Hinay yom hadin - Behold the day of judgment: four prayers from the High Holyday liturgy, for four-part chorus of mixed voices with soprano and tenor solo (cantor) with optional organ accompaniment
1: Hayom harat olam. (Adler, Samuel). *Schirmer. Unpriced* EZDGU (B73-50064)
2: Ayl melech yoshayr. (Adler, Samuel). *Schirmer. Unpriced* EZDGU (B73-50065)
4: Avinu malkaynu chanayno. (Adler, Samuel). *Schirmer. Unpriced* EZDGU (B73-50066)
Hinay yom hadin = Behold the day of judgment: four prayers from the High Holyday liturgy, for four-part chorus of mixed voices with soprano and tenor solo (cantor) with optional organ accompaniment
3: Uv'shofar gadol. (Adler, Samuel). *Schirmer. Unpriced* DGU (B73-50022)
Hindsley, Mark H. El Salon Mexico: arr. El Salon Mexico. (Copland, Aaron). *Boosey and Hawkes. £7.50* UMK (B73-50397)
Hines, Lennox.
Selections: arr. Three minuets. (Bach family). *Cornelius. Unpriced* TSPMK/AHR (B73-50827)
Waltzes for piano. D.779, no.12, D.734, no.15 & D.924, no.9: arr. Three waltzes. (Schubert, Franz). *Cornelius. Unpriced* TSPMK/AHW (B73-50828)
Hinson, Maurice. Guide to the pianist's repertoire. *Indiana University Press. £6.60* AQ(WT) (B73-17042) ISBN 0 253 32700 8
Hinton, Alistair. Reflections: two solos for B flat clarinet. *Cornelius. Unpriced* VVPJ (B73-50872)
Hirsch, Abby. The photography of rock. *Cobb House, Nuffield, Henley-on-Thames, Oxon. RG9 5RU: Aidan Ellis Publishing Ltd. £1.95* AKDW/HK(M//M) (B73-22267) ISBN 0 85628 006 2
Hirsch, Walter.
'Deed I do: arr. 'Deed I do: march. *Keith Prowse. Unpriced* UMMK/DW (B73-51256)
'Deed I do: arr. 'Deed I do: march. *Keith Prowse. Unpriced* WMK/DW (B73-51299)
Historical monographs relating to St George's Chapel, Windsor Castle. *(Oxley and Son (Windsor) Ltd for the Dean and Canons of St George's Chapel in Windsor Castle)* Windsor Castle. *St George's Chapel.* The musical manuscripts of St George's Chapel, Windsor Castle: a descriptive catalogue. *2 Victoria St., Windsor, Berks.: Oxley and Son (Windsor) Ltd for the Dean and Canons of St George's Chapel in Windsor Castle. £1.25* AD/LD(YDEUW/TE) (B73-09262) ISBN 0 902187 16 3
History of English cathedral music 1549-1889. (Bumpus, John Skelton). 1st ed. reprinted. *Gregg. £10.80* AD/LE(YD/XDXJ341) (B73-13016) ISBN 0 576 28244 8
History of Japanese music. (Harich-Schneider, Eta). *Oxford University Press. £21.00* BZHP(X) (B73-10162) ISBN 0 19 316203 2
History of Scottish music. (Elliott, Kenneth). *British Broadcasting Corporation. £0.90* A(YDL/X) (B73-25526) ISBN 0 563 12192 0
History of western music. (Grout, Donald Jay). Revised ed. *Dent. £5.95* A(YB/X) (B73-18798) ISBN 0 460 03517 7
History of Western music
1: Music from the Middle Ages to the Renaissance. (Sternfeld, Frederick William). *Weidenfeld and Nicolson. £7.00* A(X) (B73-32161) ISBN 0 297 99594 4
History of western music
5: Music in the modern age. (Sternfeld, F W). *Weidenfeld and Nicolson. £6.50* A(X) (B73-18797) ISBN 0 297 99561 8
Ho! who comes here?: Madrigal. (Morley, Thomas). *Schott. £1.00* VSNSK/DU (B73-50415)
Hoag, Charles K.
An after-intermission overture: for youth orchestra. *Schirmer. Unpriced* MJ (B73-50248)
O be joyful: for six-part chorus of mixed voices, SSA-TBB a cappella. *Schirmer. Unpriced* EZDGNT (B73-50063)
Hoddinott, Alun.
Concerto for horn and orchestra, Opus 65. *Oxford University Press. £3.50* MPWTF (B73-50267) ISBN 0 19 364484 3
Nocturnes and cadenzas. Op.62: for cello and orchestra. *Oxford University Press. £2.00* MPSR (B73-50264) ISBN 0 19 364497 5
Sonata for horn and piano. Op.78, no.2. *Oxford University Press. £2.00* WTPE (B73-50469) ISBN 0 19 357158 7
The sun, the great luminary of the universe. Op.76. *Oxford University Press. £1.50* MMJ (B73-50257) ISBN 0 19 364564 5
Holberg suite. Op.40. Sarabande: arr. Sarabande. (Grieg, Edvard). *Cornelius. Unpriced* SQPK/AHVL (B73-50797)
Holberg suite. Op.40. Sarabande: arr. Sarabande. (Grieg, Edvard). *Cornelius. Unpriced* SRPK/AHVL (B73-50807)
Holberg suite. Op.40. Sarabande: arr. Sarabande. (Grieg, Edvard). *Cornelius. Unpriced* WUPK/AHVL (B73-50921)
Holiday, Billie. Lady sings the blues. *24 Highbury Cres., N5 1RX: Barrie and Jenkins. £2.95* AKFDW/HHW/E(P) (B73-12435) ISBN 0 214 66872 x
Holiday cruise: a musical journey for organ or accordion
1: Southampton, England. (Crossman, Gerald). *Bosworth. £0.20* RG (B73-51188)
2: Vigo, Spain. (Crossman, Gerald). *Bosworth. £0.20* RG (B73-51189)
3: Haifa, Israel. (Crossman, Gerald). *Bosworth. £0.20* RG (B73-51190)
4: Athens, Greece. (Crossman, Gerald). *Bosworth. £0.20* RG (B73-51191)
5: Lisbon, Portugal. (Crossman, Gerald). *Bosworth. £0.20* RG (B73-51192)
Höller, Karl. Divertimento for flute & string orchestra. Op. 53a. Divertimento für Flöte und Streicher. Op. 53a. *Peters. £3.50* RXMPVR (B73-50776)
Holman, Derek. Magnificat & Nunc dimittis in A: for treble voices and organ. *Lengnick. £0.18* FLDGPP (B73-50159)
Holst, Gustav. Capriccio for orchestra. *Faber Music. Unpriced* MMJ (B73-50258)
Holst, Imogen.
Capriccio for orchestra. (Holst, Gustav). *Faber Music. Unpriced* MMJ (B73-50258)
Conducting a choir: a guide for amateurs. *Oxford University Press. £1.30* AD/E (B73-16147) ISBN 0 19 313407 1
Home from the range: for full chorus of mixed voices a cappella. (Wilson, Richard). *Schirmer. Unpriced* EZDX (B73-50132)
Honeywell: for three groups of instruments and/or voices. (Rees, Howard). *Universal. Unpriced* LJ (B73-50656)
Honri, Peter. Peter Honri presents - working the halls: the Honris in one hundred years of British music hall ... *D.C. Heath. £2.80* 792.70280922 (B73-29564) ISBN 0 347 00013 4
Hood, Thomas. There is a silence: for full chorus of mixed voices a cappella. (Chorbajian, John). *Schirmer. Unpriced* EZDW (B73-50112)
Hope-Brown, Margaret. Music with everything. *F. Warne. £3.00* A/D(VG) (B73-30643) ISBN 0 7232 1722 x
Hopkins, Bill, *b.1943.* Stockhausen: life and work. (Wörner, Karl Heinrich). *Faber. £6.00* BSO(N) (B73-03714) ISBN 0 571 08997 6
Hopkins, Ewart. All my trials, Lord: West Indian folk song. *Roberton. £0.10* EZDW/LC (B73-50131)
Hopkins, Gerard Manley. May Magnificat: three choruses for mixed voices by John Paynter. (Paynter, John). *Oxford University Press. £0.35* EZDW (B73-50126) ISBN 0 19 343692 2
Hopkins, John. Fantasia (quasi variazione) on the 'Old 104th' psalm tune: for solo piano, mixed chorus and orchestra. (Vaughan Williams, Ralph). *Oxford University Press. £1.75* EMDR (B73-50050) ISBN 0 19 338922 3
Hör meinen Protest: Psalm 5 für Bass, Trompete und Orgel. (Hader, Widmar). *Bosse: Bärenreiter. £1.80* KGXE/WSPLRDE (B73-50240)
Horder, Mervyn, *Baron.* The orange carol book. *Schott. £0.50* DP/LF/AY (B73-50972) ISBN 0 901938 10 6
Horeb: scene for percussion according to the first Book of Kings. (Fink, Siegfried). *Simrock. Unpriced* XMJ (B73-50926)
Horn, David. The literature of American music: a fully annotated catalogue of the books and song collections in Exeter University Library. (University of Exeter. *Library*). *Northcote House, The Queen's Drive, Exeter, Devon: University of Exeter (American Arts Documentation Centre): University of Exeter Library. £1.00* A(YT/T) (B73-13195) ISBN 0 902746 02 2
Horn music for beginners, with piano accompaniment. (Onozó, Jones). *Boosey and Hawkes. £0.85* WTPK/AAY (B73-50916)
Horovitz, Joseph. Lady Macbeth: a scena for mezzo-soprano and piano. *Novello. £0.65* KFNDX (B73-50227)
Horton, John.
The music group
Book 4. *Schott. Unpriced* CB/AY (B73-50004)
Book 5. *Schott. £1.30* CB/AY (B73-50485)
Book 6. *Schott. £1.30* CB/AY (B73-50486)
Houghton, Frank. Ten tunes. *OMF. Unpriced* DM (B73-50511)
Houghton, Stanley. Ten tunes. (Houghton, Frank). *OMF. Unpriced* DM (B73-50511)
Houseman, Alfred Edward. When I was one-and-twenty: for four-part chorus of mixed voices a cappella. (Fast, Willard S). *Schirmer. Unpriced* EZDW (B73-50116)
Houston Symphony Orchestra, 1913-1971. (Roussel, Hubert). *University of Texas Press. £3.40* AMM/E(QB/XMN59) (B73-10709) ISBN 0 292 73000 4
How can my love: chanson for SATB. (Le Jeune, Claude). *J.A. Parkinson. Unpriced* EZDU (B73-50547)
How lovely is thy dwelling place: for four-part chorus of mixed voices a cappella. (Newbury, Kent A). *Schirmer. Unpriced* EZDK (B73-50083)
How to play the flageolet (penny whistle). (Wickham, E H). *Keith Prowse. £0.20* VSQQ/AC (B73-50418)
Howarth, Elgar. Mosaic for brass band. *Paxton. £2.50* WMJ (B73-51296)
Huber, Klaus. Sabeth: for alto flute (G), cor anglais (F), (viola), and harp. *Ars viva. £5.00* NVPNT (B73-50695)
Huch, Ricarda. Neun Lieder: für eine Manner oder Frauenstimme (mittel bis hoch) und Klavier. (Reutter, Hermann). *Schott. £1.50* KDW (B73-50636)
Hudes, Eric.
Nine variants for piano. *Thames. Unpriced* QP/T (B73-50718)
Variations for piano. *Thames. Unpriced* QP/T (B73-50719)
Huffer, Konrad. Quartet for strings. Streichquartett. *Bosse Bärenreiter. £3.00* RXNS (B73-50362)
Hugh-Jones, Elaine. Chanticleer: SSA. *Oxford University Press. Unpriced* FDP/LF (B73-51024) ISBN 0 19 342596 3
Hughes, Edward. It's who you're with that counts: SATB. *British and Continental. Unpriced* DP/LF (B73-50968)
Hughes, Eric.
A low minuet: bassoon or contrabassoon and piano. *Spring House, Ampleforth, Yorkshire: June Emerson. Unpriced* VWPHR (B73-50433)
Music of Claudio Monteverdi: a discography. (Westerlund, Gunnar). *29 Exhibition Rd, S.W.7: British Institute of Recorded Sound. £2.00* BMN/FD(WT) (B73-01061) ISBN 0 900208 05 8
Hughes, Gervase. Fifty famous composers. Revised and enlarged ed. *Pan Books. £0.60* A/D(YB/M) (B73-00359) ISBN 0 330 13064 1
Hughes, Gervase. Pan book of great composers. *See* Hughes, Gervase. Fifty famous composers.
Hughes, Robert. Five Indian poems: for mixed choir and small orchestra. *Chappell. Unpriced* DW (B73-50516)
Hughes-Jones, Llifon. Preludes for orchestra, nos.1-2. Prelude no.1 (on a 15th century French melody) and Prelude no.2. *Bosworth. £1.60* MJ (B73-50661)
Hume, Arthur Wolfgang Julius Ord-. *See* Ord-Hume, Arthur Wolfgang Julius.
Hummel, Bertold.
5 miniatures: for clarinet and piano. *Simrock. Unpriced* VVPJ (B73-50873)
Alleluja: für Orgel. *Simrock. Unpriced* RJ (B73-50339)
Concerto for cello in C major. Op.2, Livre 2: arr. Concerto, C major: for violoncello and orchestra. (Reicha, Joseph). *Simrock. Unpriced* SRPK/LF (B73-51232)
Klangfiguren für Streicher: Studien in modernes Spieltechnik. *Schott. £2.00* RXMJ (B73-50355)
Hummel, Johann Nepomuk. Works, organ. Complete organ works of J.N. Hummel. *Hinrichsen. Unpriced* R/AZ (B73-50332)
Humperdinck, Engelbert. Hänsel und Gretel. Vocal score. Hänsel und Gretel: Märchenspiel in drei Bildern. *Peters Hinrichsen. Unpriced* CC (B73-50006)
Humphreys, Garry Paul. Singers: a directory of freelance amateur singers in London and the Home Counties
'73: 2nd ed. *14 Barlby Rd, W10 6AR: Autolycus Publications. £0.35* ADW/G(YD) (B73-20239) ISBN 0 903413 10 8
Hunt, Donald. Magnificat for treble solo, choir and organ, and, Nunc dimittis for bass solo, choir and organ. *Boosey and Hawkes. £0.25* DGPP (B73-50502)
Hunt, Reginald.
Fantasy on a ground: for organ. *Boosey and Hawkes. £0.65* RJ (B73-50759)
O good ale: unison song with piano accompaniment (and ad lib. parts for violins, descant recorders, guitars, tambourine, glockenspiel, cymbals and drums). *Ashdown. £0.10* JFDW (B73-51068)
Three rhythmic pianoforte pieces. *Ashdown. £0.30* QPH

(B73-51170)
Hunt from 'Autumn' (The four seasons). (Vivaldi, Antonio). *Bosworth. £0.57* MK (B73-51108)
Hunter, Ian. The birds: Czech carol. *Thames. Unpriced* FEZDP/LF (B73-50153)
Hunter, Ian T. Stille Nacht, heilige Nacht: arr. Silent night. (Gruber, Franz). *Thames. Unpriced* FEZDP/LF (B73-50152)
Hunter, James. Kerr's thistle collection: reels, strathspeys, jigs, hornpipes, marches. *Kerr. Unpriced* QPK/AH/AYDL (B73-50317)
Hurd, Michael. Swingin' Samson: a cantata in popular style for unison voices (with divisions) and piano with guitar chord-symbols. *Novello. £0.35* FDE (B73-51013)
Hutchings, Arthur.
The baroque concerto. 3rd revised ed. *Faber. £4.20* ALF(XFQ31) (B73-17452) ISBN 0 571 04808 0
Schubert. Revised ed. *Dent. £2.00* BSF(N) (B73-04216) ISBN 0 460 03139 2
Hyde, Douglas.
Five Irish songs: for mixed chorus a cappella
1: I shall not die for thee; words by Douglas Hyde. (Maw, Nicholas). *Boosey and Hawkes. £0.09* EZDW (B73-50556)
4: Ringleted youth of my love; words by Douglas Hyde. (Maw, Nicholas). *Boosey and Hawkes. £0.14* EZDW (B73-50559)
Hymn of joy. (Beethoven, Ludwig van). *Paxton. £0.25* RK/DW (B73-51206)
Hymn to the Virgin. Opus 20: Christmas anthem for two part female, or boys, voices, trumpet (optional) and organ. (Spearing, Robert). *Novello. £0.07* FDP/LF (B73-51025)
Hymns to the Holy Trinity: for solo voice and keyboard continuo. (Lawes, Henry). *Oxford University Press. £0.75* KDH (B73-51082) ISBN 0 19 345493 9
I have a dream: for mixed chorus and piano with soprano solo. (Reed, Phyllis Luidens). *Galaxy Music: Galliard. Unpriced* DH (B73-50956)
I long for thy salvation: general anthem, for four-part chorus of mixed voices a cappella. (Newbury, Kent A). *Schirmer. Unpriced* EZDK (B73-50084)
I met Heine on the Rue Furstenberg. (Feldman, Morton). *Universal. Unpriced* KE/NYDNQDX (B73-50640)
I will lift up mine eyes. Psalm 121: anthem for chorus, echo chorus and organ. (Williamson, Malcolm). *Weinberger. £0.05* FDR (B73-50567)
Iatauro, Michael. Two pieces for string bass and piano. *Schirmer. Unpriced* SSPJ (B73-50388)
Ich aber bin elend = Lord God, I am weary: motet for eight part double chorus of mixed voices a cappella. (Brahms, Johannes). *Schirmer. Unpriced* EZDH (B73-50983)
Ich aber bin elend. Op. 110, no.1. Ich aber bin elend = Lord God, I am weary: motet for eight part double chorus of mixed voices a cappella. (Brahms, Johannes). *Schirmer. Unpriced* EZDH (B73-50983)
Igumnov, K N. The complete preludes & études for pianoforte solo. (Scriabin, Alexander). *Constable. £2.00* QPJ (B73-51176) ISBN 0 486 22919 x
I'll ask the Lord. (Cookridge, John Michael). *Janay. £0.06* JFDW (B73-50187)
I'll sing you two o: words of more familiar folk songs for campfire, ceilidh and club. (Wales, Tony). *English Folk Dance and Song Society. £0.40* ADW/G(YC) (B73-22269) ISBN 0 85418 089 3
Illegible canons: for clarinet and percussion. (Bergsma, William). *Galaxy Music: Galliard. Unpriced* VVPLX/X (B73-51294)
Images for oboe and piano. (Roxburgh, Edwin). *United Music. Unpriced* VTPJ (B73-51286)
Immortal babe: carol for accompanied two-part chorus. (Moore, Philip). *Thames. Unpriced* FDP/LF (B73-50566)
Impressionism in music. (Palmer, Christopher). *Hutchinson. £3.00* A(XHK111) (B73-20236) ISBN 0 09 115140 6
In festo natalis Domini: for 4-part chorus of mixed voices unaccompanied. (Victoria, Tomas Luis de). *Roberton. Unpriced* EZDJ/LF (B73-50539)
In his hands: a cycle of spiritual and work songs. (Atkins, John G). *British and Continental Music. £0.50* JFE/NYFSDW/LC/AY (B73-50627)
In pastures green: unison, 2nd part ad lib. (Graves, Richard). *Bosworth. £0.07* JDR (B73-51055)
In stiller Nacht = In still of night: for four-part chorus of women's voices a cappella. (Brahms, Johannes). *Schirmer. Unpriced* FEZDW (B73-51042)
In that great gettin' up morning: spiritual. (Heath, Fenno). *Schirmer. Unpriced* GEZDW/LC (B73-50169)
In that poor stable: carol for voice(s) and piano or organ. (Bacon, Ernst). *Novello. £0.10* FDP/LF (B73-51021)
In the bleak mid winter: carol for SATB unaccompanied. (Walker, Robert). *Novello. £0.07* EZDP/LF (B73-51003)
In the merry month of May. (East, Michael). *Roberton. £0.10* FEZDU (B73-50155)
In tune: over 60 hymns and songs, for churches schools and groups. (Maynard, John). *Vanguard. Unpriced* JDM/AY (B73-50172)
In un bel bosco = In a fair greenwood: for six-part chorus of mixed voices a cappella. (Marenzio, Luca). *Schirmer. Unpriced* EZDU (B73-50109)
Incorporated Society of Musicians. Handbook and register of members
1972-73. *48 Gloucester Place, W1H 3HJ: Incorporated Society of Musicians. £2.50* A(YC/Q/MM) (B73-04667) ISBN 0 902900 04 8
Ingman, Nicholas. The story of music. *Ward Lock. £2.00* A(X) (B73-00877) ISBN 0 7063 1306 2
Instruments of the orchestra. *(E. Benn)* Morley-Pegge, Reginald. The French horn: some notes on the evolution of the instrument and of its technique. 2nd ed. *E. Benn. £3.95* AWT/B (B73-15417) ISBN 0 510 36601 5
Intavolatura de cimbalo. (Valente, Antonio). *Clarendon Press. £11.00* QRP/AZ (B73-50325) ISBN 0 19 816121 2
Interlude for strings. (Stiles, Frank). *Mixolydian Press. Unpriced* RXMJ (B73-50775)
Interludium: for organ. (Patterson, Paul). *Weinberger. Unpriced* RJ (B73-50342)
Intermediate horn book: for horn in F and piano. (Johnson, Stuart). *Oxford University Press. £0.75* WTPK/AAY (B73-50915) ISBN 0 19 357387 3
Introduction and burlesque: for bass trombone and band. (Eaves, Robert). *R. Smith. Unpriced* WMPWUU (B73-50908)
Introduction and burlesque: for bass trombone and piano. (Eaves, Robert). *R. Smith. Unpriced* WUUPJ (B73-50924)
Introduction and romp: for flute and piano. (Frankenpohl, Arthur). *Schirmer. Unpriced* VRPJ (B73-50406)
Introduction and romp: for marimba or vibraphone and piano. (Frackenpohl, Arthur). *Schirmer. Unpriced* XTQSPJ (B73-50475)
Invitation to madrigals
6: for SSATB and SSAT Ba B; transcribed and edited by David Scott. (Dart, Thurston). *Stainer and Bell. Unpriced* EZDU/AY (B73-50551) ISBN 0 903000 02 4
Invitation to madrigals: for S S A T B & S S A T B a B
Volume 7. (Scott, David). *Stainer and Bell. Unpriced* EZDU/AY (B73-51007) ISBN 0 85249 167 0
Invitation to music: anthem for SATB and organ. (Naylor, Bernard). *Roberton. £0.13* DH (B73-50026)
Invitation to the partsong
Volume 1. (Bush, Geoffrey). *Stainer and Bell. Unpriced* EZDW/AYD (B73-51012) ISBN 0 85249 165 4
Io son pur solo: solo cantata for soprano and basso continuo. (Scarlatti, Alessandro). First edition. *Bärenreiter. £1.20* KFLDX (B73-50222)
Iphigénie en Tauride. (Piccini, Niccolò). *Gregg International. £12.00* CQC (B73-50492) ISBN 0 576 28239 1
Ireland, John.
Quartet for strings, no.1, in D minor. Op. posth. String quartet, no.1, in D minor. Op. posth. *Boosey and Hawkes. Unpriced* RXNS (B73-50364)
Quartet for strings, no.2, in C minor. Op. posth. String quartet, no.2, C minor. Op. posth. *Boosey and Hawkes. £0.85* RXNS (B73-50363)
Is it nothing to you?: for four-part chorus of mixed voices with organ or piano accompaniment. (Pedrette, Edward). *Schirmer. Unpriced* DK/LH (B73-50039)
Isaac, Anthony. Warship: theme from the B B C - TV series. *Valentine. £0.20* QPK/AGM/JS (B73-50749)
Isaac, George. Sonata for cello and piano. (Walters, Gareth). *Ricordi. Unpriced* SRPE (B73-50382)
Isherwood, Robert M. Music in the service of the king: France in the seventeenth century. *Cornell University Press. £7.90* A(YH/XCQ316) (B73-17451) ISBN 0 8014 0734 6
Israelsbrünnlein. Zion spricht: arr. Zion spricht = Zion speaks. (Schein, Johann Hermann). *Roberton. Unpriced* EZDH (B73-50535)
It came upon the midnight clear. (Wesley, Samuel Sebastian). *Oxford University Press. Unpriced* EZDP/LF (B73-50544) ISBN 0 19 343041 x
Italian Ars Nova music: a bibliographic guide to modern editions and related literature. (Hagopian, Viola L). 2nd ed., revised and expanded. *University of California Press. £4.50* A(YJ/XCL91/T) (B73-20592) ISBN 0 520 02223 8
It's all in the book: 20 hymns and songs for young people. (Maynard, John). *Vanguard Music. Unpriced* JFDM/GJ/AY (B73-50618)
It's snowing: S.A.T.B. (Rose, Gregory). *Boosey and Hawkes. £0.15* EZDW (B73-51010)
It's who you're with that counts: SATB. (Hughes, Edward). *British and Continental. Unpriced* DP/LF (B73-50968)
Ives, Grayston.
The falcon: set for high voice and piano. *Roberton. Unpriced* KFTDW (B73-50229)
Three folk songs: for unaccompanied mixed choir
No.1: Buy broom besoms: North country street song. *Roberton. £0.10* EZDW/G/AY (B73-50129)
No.2: The lark in the clear air: Irish folk song; words by Sir Samuel Ferguson. *Roberton. £0.10* EZDW/G/AY (B73-50130)
No.3: The tailor and the mouse: English folk song. *Roberton. £0.13* EZDW/G/AY (B73-50563)
J, M. *See* Jacobson, Maurice.
Jack be nimble: a collection of rounds for choral societies, choirs and schools. (Henriksen, Josef). *St. Gregory. £0.45* FEZ/XC/AY (B73-50572)
Jackson, Francis.
Anthems for choirs
Volume 1. *Oxford University Press. £0.12* DH/AY (B73-50506) ISBN 0 19 353215 8
Communion service, series 3, in the key of E. Op. 41: (treble, alto, tenor, bass). *Oxford University Press. £0.20* DGS (B73-50952) ISBN 0 19 395240 8
Jackson, Nicholas. Four images: for organ. *Boosey and Hawkes. £0.60* RJ (B73-50760)
Jacob, Gordon.
Brother James's air. (James, *Brother*). *Oxford University Press. £0.20* TSPMK/DR (B73-50395) ISBN 0 19 358403 4
Fantasia: for euphonium (baritone) and band. *Boosey and Hawkes. £8.75* UMMPWW (B73-50836)
Five pieces for solo clarinet. *Oxford University Press. £0.35* VVPJ (B73-51292) ISBN 0 19 357368 7
Suite for tuba and piano. Tuba suite: tuba and piano. *Boosey and Hawkes. £1.25* WVPG (B73-50925)
Ten little studies: for oboe and piano. *Oxford University Press. £0.60* WTPJ (B73-50470) ISBN 0 19 357359 8
Variations on a Dorian theme: for alto saxophone and piano. *Emerson. Unpriced* VUSP/T (B73-50863)
Jacobs, Arthur. A new dictionary of music. 3rd ed. *Penguin. £0.50* A(C) (B73-31504) ISBN 0 14 051012 5
Jacobs, Robert Louis. Wagner writes from Paris: stories, essays and articles by the young composer. (Wagner, Richard). *Allen and Unwin. £3.85* A(D) (B73-19496) ISBN 0 04 780022 4
Jacobson, Maurice.
Resonet in laudibus = Joseph dearest, Joseph mine: for four-part chorus of mixed voices. (Handl, Jacob). *Roberton. Unpriced* EZDP/LF (B73-50098)
Tomus primus operis musici.. Pueri concinite. Pueri concinite: for four equal voices SSSA or SSAA a cappella. (Handl, Jacob). *Roberton. Unpriced* EZDJ/LF (B73-50080)
Jacopo da Bologna.
Three madrigals: for 3 voices and/or instruments. *Antico. Unpriced* EZDU (B73-50104)
Three madrigals: for 3 voices and/or instruments. *Antico. Unpriced* EZDU (B73-50105)
Jaffrennou, Gildas. Folk harps. *Book Division, Station Rd, Kings Langley, Herts.: Model and Allied Publications. £2.50* ATQ/BC (B73-30280) ISBN 0 85242 313 6
James, *Brother*. Brother James's air. *Oxford University Press. £0.20* TSPMK/DR (B73-50395) ISBN 0 19 358403 4
James Connolly songbook. (Connolly, James). *9 St Nicholas Church Place, Cove St., Cork: Cork Workers Club. £0.15* BCMLADW(ZC) (B73-25527) ISBN 0 904086 00 3
Janet Baker. (Blyth, Alan). *Allan. £1.75* AKFQ/E(P) (B73-21632) ISBN 0 7110 0424 2
Japanische Elegien: Vokal-instrumental-Zyklus in sieben Teilen nach Worten altjapanischer Dichter, fur Soprano und Kammerensemble. (Geviksman, Vitali). *Peters. £3.50* KFLE/NYLNQDW (B73-50646)
Jauchzet Gott, alle Lande = Make a joyful noise unto God: sacred concerto for soprano, two violins and basso continuo. (Weiland, Julius Johann). *Bärenreiter. £1.50* KFLE/SNTPWDE (B73-50225)
Jazz masters of the thirties. (Stewart, Rex). *Macmillan: Collier-Macmillan. £1.90* AMT/E(M/XN21) (B73-08421) ISBN 0 02 614690 8
Jazz people. (Wilmer, Valerie). 2nd ed. *Allison and Busby. £1.00* AMT/E(M) (B73-00882) ISBN 0 85031 085 7
Jean-Baptiste Lully. (Scott, Ralph Henry Forster). *Owen. £3.00* BLT(N) (B73-14125) ISBN 0 7206 0432 x
Jeanes, E W. The Blues and Royals regimental slow march. *Boosey and Hawkes. £1.00* UMMGM/KH (B73-51254)
Jefferson, Alan. The life of Richard Strauss. *David and Charles. £3.95* BSU(N) (B73-31509) ISBN 0 7153 6199 6
Jenbach, Bela. The Czarevitch: songs from the operetta. (Lehár, Franz). *Glocken Verlag. Unpriced* KDW (B73-50206)
Jeremiah, Dorothy Adams-. *See* Adams-Jeremiah, Dorothy.
Jergenson, Dale. Sacrae symphoniae, bk.1. Plaudite. Vocal score. Plaudite: for triple chorus of mixed voices. (Gabrieli, Giovanni). *Schirmer. Unpriced* DJ (B73-50961)
Jesu, send us peace: SATB. (Wilson-Dickson, Andrew). *Banks. Unpriced* DH (B73-50505)
Jesus, joy of man's desiring. (Bach, Johann Sebastian). *Cornelius. Unpriced* TSPMK/DM (B73-50830)
Jeu poetique: en six movements pour harpe et orchestre. (Francaix, Jean). *Schott. £3.00* TQPK (B73-50810)
John of the Cross, *Saint*. Noche pasiva del sentido, (San Juan de la Cruz). (Halffter, Cristóbal). *Universal. Unpriced* KFLE/NYLNUDE (B73-50647)
Johnny Cash - winners got scars too. (Wren, Christopher, *b.1936*). *W.H. Allen. £2.00* AKDW/GCW/(P) (B73-09000) ISBN 0 491 00794 9
Johnson, Edward. Stokowski: essays in analysis of his art. *Triad Press. £1.95* A/EC(P/D) (B73-14763) ISBN 0 902070 06 1
Johnson, Paula. Form and transformation in music and poetry of the English Renaissance. *Yale University Press. £3.50* A(YD/XDY81/ZB) (B73-03716) ISBN 0 300 01544 5
Johnson, Robert Sherlaw.
Christus resurgens: SATB unacc. *Oxford University Press. £0.20* EZDH/LL (B73-50985) ISBN 0 19 343036 3
The praises of heaven and earth: for solo soprano piano, and electronic tape. *Oxford University Press. £1.20* KFLDH (B73-50221) ISBN 0 19 345480 7
Johnson, Stuart. An intermediate horn book: for horn in F and piano. *Oxford University Press. £0.75* WTPK/AAY (B73-50915) ISBN 0 19 357387 3
Johnson, Thomas Arnold.
Caprice: piano duet. *Freeman. £0.20* QNV (B73-50705)
Fiesta piano duet. *Bosworth. £0.25* QNV (B73-51160)
Polka: piano duet. *Freeman. £0.20* QNVHVH (B73-50710)
Sarabande: piano duet. *Freeman. £0.20* QNVHVL (B73-50711)
Scherzo for B flat clarinet and piano. *British and Continental Music. Unpriced* VVPJ (B73-51293)

Seven easy duets for piano. *Freeman. £0.20* QNV (B73-50706)
Valse: piano duet. *Freeman. £0.20* QNVHW (B73-50712)
Valsette: piano duet. *Freeman. £0.20* QNVHW (B73-50713)
Johnson preserv'd: opera in 3 acts. (Watt, Jill). *Hinrichsen. Unpriced* BSNKAC (B73-09577)
Johnston, Beryl. Twelve Scottish country dances. *Royal Scottish Country Dancing Society (Birmingham Branch). Unpriced* QPH/H (B73-51172)
Johnstone, Maurice. Albumblatt for piano in E flat major: arr. Romance. (Wagner, Richard). *Chappell. Unpriced* RXMK (B73-51212)
Jolly swagman. (Binge, Ronald). *Mozart Edition. Unpriced* KDW (B73-50202)
Jones, Daniel. Sea: for chorus and piano. *Eisteddfod genedlaethol frenhinol Cymru. Unpriced* DW (B73-50044)
Jones, E Olwen. Chwe can werin gymreig = Six Welsh folk songs. *Schott. £1.00* JFE/XMDW/G/AYDK (B73-51077)
Jones, Elaine Hugh-. *See* Hugh-Jones, Elaine.
Jones, Kelsey.
Miramichi ballad: a suite for orchestra. *Boosey and Hawkes. £4.85* MJ (B73-50249)
Quintet for winds: flute, oboe, clarinet in B flat, horn in F, bassoon. *Peters. Unpriced* UNR (B73-50402)
Jones, Ken Macaulay-. *See* Macaulay-Jones, Ken.
Jones, Llifon Hughes-. *See* Hughes-Jones, Llifon.
Jones, Mason. Quintet for horn & strings in E flat major. K 407: arr. Horn quintet in E flat. (Mozart, Wolfgang Amadeus). *Schirmer. Unpriced* WTPK (B73-51307)
Jörns, Helge. 7 Formen: für Flöte, Gitarre, Cembalo und Zupfoder Streichorchester oder Streichquartett. *Simrock. Unpriced* NURNP (B73-51129)
Josephs, Wilfred. 14 caprices: for cello duet (student and teacher). *Chappell. £0.60* SRNU (B73-50803)
Josquin Des Prés. Faultte d'argent = Life without money: for five-part chorus of mixed voices a cappella. *Schirmer. Unpriced* EZDU (B73-50106)
Joubert, John. Coverdale's carol. Opus 75: for SATB unaccompanied. *Novello. £0.07* EZDP/LF (B73-50542)
Joyce, James. Chamber music: four selected poems, for low male voice and piano. (Reutter, Hermann). *Schott. £1.20* KFXDW (B73-50655)
J.S. Bach's 'Musical Offering': history, interpretation and analysis. (David, Hans Theodore). *Dover Publications: Constable. £1.25* BBCAN (B73-05261) ISBN 0 486 22768 5
Jubilate Deo (St Peter ad Vincula): canticle or anthem for SATB chorus and brass ensemble. Op.51. (Cruft, Adrian). *Boosey and Hawkes. £1.15* EWNPDGNT (B73-50055)
Jubilate jazz: for SATB with instrumental accompaniment. (Sansom, Clive A). *Paterson. Unpriced* ELDGNT (B73-50048)
Judd, Frederick Charles. Electronics in music. *Spearman. £3.15* APV/B (B73-05263) ISBN 0 85435 301 1
Judd, Margaret. Queen Elizabeth's dances: for piano. *Bosworth. £0.30* QPH (B73-51171)
Junkin, Harry. The piano can be fun. *Paul. £2.50* AQ/E (B73-05262) ISBN 0 09 115200 3
Kagel, Mauricio.
Achtzehn acht und neunzig. 1898: für Kinderstimmen und Instrumente. *Universal. Unpriced* FDX (B73-51038)
Staatstheater: szenische Komposition, 1967-70. *Universal. Unpriced* C/J (B73-50484)
Tremens: szenische Montage eines Tests, für zwei Darsteller, elektrische Instrumente, Schlagzeug, Tonbänder und Projektionen. *Universal. Unpriced* CQM (B73-50493)
Zwei-Mann-Orchester. *Universal. Unpriced* LNU (B73-51100)
Karkoschka, Erhard. Notation in new music: a critical guide to interpretation and realisation. *c/o A. Kalmus, 38 Eldon Way, Paddock Wood, Tonbridge, Kent: Universal Edition. £8.00* A(QU/XN53) (B73-06589) ISBN 0 900938 28 5
Karpeles, Maud. English folk song - some conclusions. (Sharp, Cecil James). 4th revised ed. *E.P. Publishing. £1.75* ADW/G(YD) (B73-02067) ISBN 0 85409 929 8
Kaschnitz, Marie Luise. Fünf Lieder: für mittlere Stimme und Klavier. (Reutter, Hermann). *Schott. £1.20* KFVDW (B73-50653)
Kastner, Macario Santiago.
Concertos for 2 keyboard instruments, nos 1-6. VI conciertos de dos organos obligados: oder zwei Cembali, zwei Clavichorde, zwei Klaviere, eine Orgel und ein Cembalo
Band 2. (Soler, Antonio). *Schott. £1.70* PWNUF (B73-51135)
Concertos for 2 keyboard instruments, nos.1-6. VI conciertos de dos organos obligados: oder zwei und ein Cembalo
Band 1. (Soler, Antonio). *Schott. £1.70* PWNUF (B73-51136)
Kear, Warrick. San Casciano: for recorder ensemble, solo sopranino, descants, trebles, tenors. *Tomus. Unpriced* VSNPG (B73-51270)
Kechley, Gerald. Drop slow tears: for mixed chorus and piano with optional instrumental accompaniment. *Galaxy Music: Galliard. Unpriced* DH (B73-50954)
Keel, Frederick. Lullaby. *Galaxy: Galliard. Unpriced* DW (B73-50976)
Keller, Gottfried. A village Romeo and Juliet. Vocal score. A village Romeo and Juliet. (Delius, Frederick). *Boosey and Hawkes. £7.50* CC (B73-50005)
Kelly, Bryan.
Abingdon carols: six carols for SATB. *Novello. £0.35* EZDP/LF (B73-50997)
Communion service, series 3: SATB. *Oxford University Press. £0.20* DGS (B73-50953) ISBN 0 19 395238 6
Herod, do your worst. Sleep little baby. Sleep little baby: Christmas song for unison voices and piano. *Novello. £0.07* JDP/LF (B73-51050)
Herod, do your worst. Sleep little baby: arr. Sleep little baby: Christmas song. *Novello. £0.07* DP/LF (B73-50969)
Kelly, Michael, *b.1762.* Solo recital: the reminiscences of Michael Kelly. Abridged ed.. *Folio Society. £2.90 to members of the Society only* AKGH/E(P) (B73-03213) ISBN 0 85067 055 1
Kelly, Robert. Concerto for violin. Op.46: arr. Concerto for violin and orchestra. Opus 46. *Highgate Press: Galliard. Unpriced* SPK/LF (B73-50792)
Kendall, Alan, *b.1939.* Benjamin Britten. *Macmillan. £2.95* BBU(N) (B73-31507) ISBN 0 333 15226 3
Kennaway, Lamont. A meditation and impromptu: organ. *Paxton. £0.35* RJ (B73-51194)
Kenward, Jean. Sing for Christmas: 6 songs for unison voices (optional 2nd part). (Roe, Betty). *Thames. Unpriced* JFDP/LF (B73-50620)
Keohler, Thomas. The trees stand silent: for five-part chorus of mixed voices SSATB a cappella. (Lekberg, Sven). *Schirmer. Unpriced* EZDW (B73-50120)
Kerman, Joseph. Two orchestral minuets. (Beethoven, Ludwig van). *Oxford University Press. Unpriced* MK/AHR (B73-51111) ISBN 0 19 361430 8
Kerr's thistle collection: reels, strathspeys, jigs, hornpipes, marches. (Hunter, James). *Kerr. Unpriced* QPK/AH/AYDL (B73-50317)
Kettering, Eunice Lea. Three Spanish folk dances: for piano, four hands. *Schirmer. Unpriced* QNVK/AH/G/AYK (B73-50291)
Kidson, Frank. English folk-song and dance. *E.P. Publishing. £2.10* ADW/G(YD) (B73-00881) ISBN 0 85409 917 4
Kiel, Friedrich. 3 Romanzen. Op.69. Three romances: for viola and pianoforte. *Musica rara. Unpriced* SQPJ (B73-50377)
Kinderorgel: leichte Kinderlieder für elektronische Orgel (1 Manuel). (Draths, Willi). *Schott. £1.20* RPVK/DW/GJ/AYE (B73-51208)
Kinderscenen. Op.15. Scenes from childhood: for piano. (Schumann, Robert). *Chappell. Unpriced* QPJ (B73-50309)
Kinderscenen. Op.15. Traümerei: arr. Traümerei. (Schumann, Robert). *Cornelius. Unpriced* VVNSK (B73-50866)
Kinesis ABCD. Op.31: for two groups of strings. (Antoniou, Theodor). *Bärenreiter. £1.50* RXMJ (B73-50354)
King, Anthony V. Songs of Nigeria. *University of London Press. Unpriced* ZMQADW/AY (B73-50929) ISBN 0 340 16307 0
King, Arthur. Vocabulary ramblebuggies and educational wordopolis. Vocal score. Vocabulary ramblebuggies and educational wordopolis. (Meryll, Jane). *Belwin-Mills. £0.40* JFDX/GJ (B73-50625)
King, Audrey. My little garden plot: unison children's voices. *Bosworth. £0.10* JFDW (B73-51069)
King, Martin Luther. I have a dream: for mixed chorus and piano with soprano solo. (Reed, Phyllis Luidens). *Galaxy Music: Galliard. Unpriced* DH (B73-50956)
Kinwelmersh, Francis. Come Holy Ghost, eternal God: set for SATBB and organ. (Naylor, Bernard). *Roberton. £0.10* DH/LN (B73-50960)
Kirchengesäng: Psalmen und geistliche Lieder.. Selections. Kirchengesänge, Psalmen und geistliche Lieder: Choralsätz für gemischten Chor. (Hassler, Hans Leo). *Bärenreiter. £1.35* EZDM (B73-50089)
Kirchengesänge, Psalmen und geistliche Lieder: Choralsätz für gemischten Chor. (Hassler, Hans Leo). *Bärenreiter. £1.35* EZDM (B73-50089)
Kirkby-Mason, Barbara. Primary grade book for piano. *Bosworth. Unpriced* Q/AF (B73-50703)
Kirnberger, Johann Philipp. Eight fugues for keyboard. Acht Fugen für Cembalo oder Orgel. *Schott. £1.80* PWP/Y (B73-51137)
Kiss me goodnight, Sergeant Major: the songs and ballads of World War II. (Page, Martin, *b.1938*). *Hart-Davis, MacGibbon. £1.60* ADW/KG(XPE7) (B73-29557) ISBN 0 246 10748 0
Klangfiguren für Streicher: Studien in modernes Spieltechnik. (Hummel, Bertold). *Schott. £2.00* RXMJ (B73-50355)
Klavierstück: for solo piano. (Wurzburger, Walter). *Thames. Unpriced* QPJ (B73-50313)
Klebe, Giselher. Surge equilo; et veni auster. Op 60: Paraphrase uber ein Thema von Igor Stravinsky, für Orgel. *Bärenreiter. £1.05* RJ (B73-50761)
Klein, Maynard.
Ach arme Welt. Op. 110, no.2. Ach arme Welt = Alas, poor world: motet for four part chorus of mixed voices a cappella. (Brahms, Johannes). *Schirmer. Unpriced* EZDH (B73-50982)
Dixit Dominus and Magnificat. Vocal score. Dixit Dominus and Magnificat. K.193. (Mozart, Wolfgang Amadeus). *Schirmer. Unpriced* DGKB (B73-50498)
Ecco quel fiero istante = Lo, now the hour of parting. K.436. (Mozart, Wolfgang Amadeus). *Schirmer. Unpriced* FDW (B73-50143)
German folksongs for four-part chorus, bk,2, no.1. In stiller Nacht. In stiller Nacht = In still of night: for four-part chorus of women's voices a cappella. (Brahms, Johannes). *Schirmer. Unpriced* FEZDW (B73-51042)
Ich aber bin elend. Op. 110, no.1. Ich aber bin elend = Lord God, I am weary: motet for eight part double chorus of mixed voices a cappella. (Brahms, Johannes). *Schirmer. Unpriced* EZDH (B73-50983)
Lass dich nur nichts nicht dauren = Let not your heart be troubled: for four-part chorus of mixed voices with organ or piano accompaniment. (Brahms, Johnnes). *Schirmer. Unpriced* DH (B73-50955)
Luci care, luci bello = Eyes of beauty, eyes flashing bright. K.346: nocturne. (Mozart, Wolfgang Amadeus). *Schirmer. Unpriced* FDW (B73-50144)
Mi lagnero tacendo = Silent, I long for thy love. K.437: nocturne. (Mozart, Wolfgang Amadeus). *Chappell. Unpriced* FDW (B73-50145)
Weihnacht wie bist so schon = Christmas so wondrous fair: carol from Upper Austria, for four-part chorus of mixed voices a cappella. (Czajanek, Victor). *Schirmer. Unpriced* EZDP/LF (B73-50096)
Klemperer, Otto, *b.1885.* Conversations with Klemperer. (Heyworth, Peter). *Gollancz. £3.00* A/EC(P) (B73-16148) ISBN 0 575 01652 3
Kluge, Barbara. The trumpet carol: for mixed voices and trumpets. (Copley, ian). *Thames. Unpriced* EWSNTDP/LF (B73-50526)
Knight, Frida.
Beethoven and the age of revolution. *Lawrence and Wishart. £2.50* BBJ(N) (B73-11184) ISBN 0 85315 266 7
Beethoven and the age of revolution. *Lawrence and Wishart. £2.50* 780.924 (B73-11184) ISBN 0 85315 266 7
Knight, Judyth. Ballet and its music. *Schott. £3.95* QPK/AHM/AY (B73-51182) ISBN 0 901938 03 3
Ko-Ai and the dragon: a story to music. (Daubney, Brian). *Belwin-Mills Music. £160* CQN (B73-50494)
Köbel, Herbert. Sonata for two flutes & basso continuo in E flat major. Sonata in E flat major for two flutes (violins) and basso continuo. (Graun, Carl Heinrich). *Bärenreiter. £1.80* VRNTPWE (B73-50404)
Koch, Edwin.
Leichte Duospiel für Violoncelli
Heft 2. *Schott. £1.44* SRNUK/AAY (B73-51229)
Leichte Duospiel: fur zwei Violoncelli
Heft 1. *Schott. £0.90* SRNUK/AAY (B73-51230)
Leichtes Duospiel für zwei Violoncelli
Heft 1. *Schott. £0.90* SRNUK/AAY (B73-51231)
Koch, Kenneth. Bertha. Vocal score. Bertha: one act opera. (Rorem, Ned). *Boosey and Hawkes. £2.00* CC (B73-50936)
Koch, Rolf Julius.
Concerto for oboe in C major. Konzert für Oboe und Kammerorchester, C-Dur. (Rosetti, Franz Anton). *Peters. £3.00* MPVTF (B73-50688)
Concerto for oboe in C major: arr. Konzert für Oboe und Kammerorchester, C-Dur. (Rosetti, Franz Anton). *Peters. £2.20* VTPK/LF (B73-50860)
Koch, Rolf-Julius.
Symphony for flute and string ochestra, no,6, in A minor. Sinfonia Nr,6 a-moll: Flöte, Streicher und Basso continuo. (Scarlatti, Alessandro). *Peters. Unpriced* RXMPVRE (B73-50778)
Symphony for flute & string orchestra, no 7, in G minor. Sinfonia Nr. 7, g-moll: Flöte, Streicher und Basso continuo. (Scarlatti, Alessandro). *Peters. Unpriced* RXMPVRE (B73-50779)
Symphony for flute & string orchestra, no. 9, in G minor. Sinfonia, Nr.9,g-moll: Flöte, Streicher und Basso continuo. (Scarlatti, Alessandro). *Peters. Unpriced* RXMPVRE (B73-50777)
Symphony for flute & string orchestra, No. 10, in A minor. Sinfonia Nr. 10, a-moll: Flöte. Streicher und Basso continuo. (Scarlatti, Alessandro). *Peters. Unpriced* RXMPVRE (B73-50780)
Symphony for flute & string orchestra, no. 11, in C major. Sinfonia Nr. 11, C-dur: Flöte, Streicher und Basso continuo. (Scarlatti, Alessandro). *Peters. Unpriced* RXMPVRE (B73-50781)
Symphony for flute & string orchestra, no.8, in G major. Sinfonia Nr. 8, G-dur: Flöte, Streicher und Basso continuo. (Scarlatti, Alessandro). *Peters. Unpriced* RXMPVRE (B73-50782)
Kochan, Günter. Fünf Klavierstücke. *Peters. Unpriced* QPJ (B73-50304)
Kock, Erich. Ludwig van Beethoven: a study in text and pictures. (Fischer, Hans Conrad). *Macmillan. £4.00* BBJ(N) (B73-03211) ISBN 0 333 12114 7
Koczwara, Franz. *See* Kotzwara, Franz.
Kodály, Zoltán. 333 reading exercises. Revised English ed. *Boosey and Hawkes. £0.40* C/EG (B73-50003)
Kodály, Zoltán. Choral method. *(Boosey and Hawkes)*
Kodály, Zoltán. 333 reading exercises. Revised English ed. *Boosey and Hawkes. £0.40* C/EG (B73-50003)
Kodály, Zoltán. Pentatonic music
Vol.4: 140 Churash melodies. *Boosey and Hawkes. £0.30* JFEZDW/PP/AY (B73-50196)
Kodály, Zoltán.
Fiddle-dee: SSAA unaccompanied. *Boosey and Hawkes. £0.05* FEZDW (B73-51041)
Kodaly, Zoltán. Have good courage: SSA unaccompanied. *Boosey and Hawkes. £0.14* FEZDW (B73-50574)
Kodály, Zoltán. Pentatonic music
Vol.4: 140 Churash melodies. *Boosey and Hawkes. £0.30* JFEZDW/PP/AY (B73-50196)
Koenig, Ruth. Notation in new music: a critical guide to interpretation and realisation. (Karkoschka, Erhard). *c/o A. Kalmus, 38 Eldon Way, Paddock Wood, Tonbridge, Kent: Universal Edition. £8.00* A(QU/XN53) (B73-06589) ISBN 0 900938 28 5
Kohler, Ernesto. Valse des fleurs. Op 87: for 2 flutes and piano. *Emerson. Unpriced* VRNTQHW (B73-51267)

Konietzny, Heinrich. Triade for xylophon, vibraphone, marimbaphone and three cymbals (3 players). *Schott. £1.44* XNT (B73-51310)

Konzertstück. Op. 26: for piano and small orchestra. (Goehr, Alexander). *Schott. £2.00* MPQ (B73-50684)

Kotzwara, Franz. Sonata for viola & basso continuo in C major. Op. 2, no.2. Sonata C-Dur für Viola und Basso continuo. *Schott. Unpriced* SQPE (B73-50376)

Kovacs, Matyas. Horn music for beginners, with piano accompaniment. (Onozó, Jones). *Boosey and Hawkes. £0.85* WTPK/AAY (B73-50916)

Kreidler, Dieter. Easy rider: leichte Blues-Satz nach alten und neuen Melodien bearbeitet für Gitarre. *Schott. £1.44* TSPMK/AHHW/AY (B73-51251)

Krickeberg, Dieter. Banchetto musicale.. Suites. Three suites for five string or wind instruments. (Schein, Johann Hermann). *Bärenreiter. £2.70* RXNRG (B73-50361)

Kroeger, Karl. Divertimento for band. *Boosey and Hawkes. £5.25* UMJ (B73-50396)

Kulka, Konstanty Andrzej. Concerto for violin, no.1, in D major. Op.6: arr. Konzert no.1, D-Dur. Opus 6: für Violine und Orchester. (Paganini, Nicolo). *Schott. £1.40* SPK/LF (B73-50368)

Kümmerling, Harald.
Biblische Motetten für das Kirchenjahr, Band 1: Spruchmotetten. Spruchmotetten
1: Motets by Wolfgang Carl Briegel, Andreas Raselin and anonymous works. (Ameln, Konrad). *Bärenreiter. £0.90* EZDJ/AYE (B73-50078)
Biblische Motetten für das Kirchenjahr, Band 1: Spruchmotetten. Spruchmotetten
2: Motets by Johann Christenius and others. (Ameln, Konrad). *Bärenreiter. £0.90* EZDJ/AYE (B73-50079)

Kurzer jedoch gründlicher Wegweiser. Wegweiser: a 17th century German organ tutor. *Peters. Unpriced* R/AC (B73-50327)

Kuszing, Janos. Clarinet music for beginners, with piano accompaniment. *Boosey and Hawkes. £0.85* VVPK/AAY (B73-50874)

La Serva padrona = From maid to mistress. (Pergolesi, Giovanni Battista). *Schirmer. Unpriced* CC (B73-50935)

Laboravi clamans: motet for SSATB and organ. (Rameau, Jean Philippe). *Peters. Unpriced* DJ (B73-50032)

Lady Caroline Lamb: piano solo, theme from the film. (Bennett, Richard Rodney). *KPM. £0.25* QPK/JR (B73-50322)

Lady Macbeth: a scena for mezzo-soprano and piano. (Horovitz, Joseph). *Novello. £0.65* KFNDX (B73-50227)

Lady sings the blues. (Holiday, Billie). *24 Highbury Cres., N5 1RX: Barrie and Jenkins. £2.95* AKFDW/HHW/E(P) (B73-12435) ISBN 0 214 66872 x

Laetentur coeli = Be glad ye heavens: SATBB by William Byrd. (Byrd, William). Revised ed. *Oxford University Press. Unpriced* EZDJ (B73-50536) ISBN 0 19 352058 3

Laloux, Fernand. Two national songs: SATB unaccompanied
1: The robin's last will. *Boosey and Hawkes. Unpriced* EZDW (B73-51008)

Lanchbery, John.
La Fille mal gardée. Clog dance. Clog dance. (Hérold, Ferdinand). *Oxford University Press. Unpriced* MH/HM (B73-51105) ISBN 0 19 364251 4

La Fille mal gardée. Flute dance. Flute dance. (Hérold, Ferdinand). *Oxford University Press. Unpriced* MH/HM (B73-51106) ISBN 0 19 364275 1

Landscapes: for two clarinets. (Roper, Keith). *Thames. Unpriced* VVNU (B73-50869)

Lane, Philip. Five diversions: for melody instrument and piano. *Galliard. Unpriced* LPG (B73-51102)

Láng, István. Concerto bucolico: for horn and orchestra. *Boosey and Hawkes. £1.25* WTPK/LF (B73-50473)

Lang, Paul Henry. The experience of opera. *Faber. £4.00* AC(XFYB201) (B73-06590) ISBN 0 571 10146 1

Langrish, Hugo. Eight easy pieces. *Oxford University Press. £0.45* WTPK/AAY (B73-50471) ISBN 0 19 357430 6

Langstaff, John. Soldier, soldier, won't you marry me? *World's Work. £1.20* ADW/G(YD) (B73-20978) ISBN 0 437 54105 3

Lascelles, Maria Donata, *Countess of Harewood.*
Piano lessons
Book 2. (Waterman, Fanny). *Faber Music. Unpriced* Q/AC (B73-51139)
Book 3. (Waterman, Fanny). *Faber Music. Unpriced* Q/AC (B73-51140)
Second year piano lessons
Book 1. (Waterman, Fanny). *Faber Music. Unpriced* Q/AC (B73-51141)

Lass dich nur nichts nicht dauren = Let not your heart be troubled: for four-part chorus of mixed voices with organ or piano accompaniment. (Brahms, Johnes). *Schirmer. Unpriced* DH (B73-50955)

Lasso, Orlando di. Adoramus te, Christe: SATB unacc. *Oxford University Press. Unpriced* EZDJ (B73-50537) ISBN 0 19 350332 8

Last, Joan. Time twisters: five contrapuntal pieces for piano, each with a rhythmic twist. *Oxford University Press. £0.30* QP/NM (B73-50295) ISBN 0 19 373146 0

Last rose of summer, (from Moore's Irish melodies). (Pasfield, William Reginald). *Ashdown. £0.05* FLDW (B73-50577)

Laudan, Stanley. March of the champions. *Peter Maurice. Unpriced* UMMGM (B73-51253)

Law of the Lord. Op.61, no.2: an introit, SATB unacc. (Mathias, William). *Oxford University Press. £0.05* EZDK (B73-50990) ISBN 0 19 350341 7

Lawes, Henry. Ayres and dialogues, bk.2. Hymns to the Holy Trinity. Hymns to the Holy Trinity: for solo voice and keyboard continuo. *Oxford University Press. £0.75* KDH (B73-51082) ISBN 0 19 345493 9

Lawrence, Berta. Four winds: unison, with optional second part. (Parry, William Howard). *Lengnick. £0.06* JFDW (B73-50188)

Lawrence, David Herbert. 3 D.H. Lawrence love poems: for high voice and piano. (Raphael, Mark). *Thames. Unpriced* KFTDW (B73-50230)

Lawrence, Ian. Madrigalls to foure voyces. Ho! who comes here? Ho! who comes here?: Madrigal. (Morley, Thomas). *Schott. £1.00* VSNSK/DU (B73-50415)

Lawrence, Roy. Sing life, sing love: songs. (Lewis, Pete). *Holmes McDougall. Unpriced* JFDM/AY (B73-51064) ISBN 0 7157 1005 2

Layton, Robert. The stereo record guide
Vol.8: Composer index Me-Z. *Squires Gate, Station Approach, Blackpool, Lancs. FY82 SP: Long Playing Record Library Ltd. £1.95* A/FF(WT) (B73-08019) ISBN 0 901143 06 5

Le Fleming, Christopher.
Trees in the valley. Op. 40
1: The plane: unison and piano. *Boosey and Hawkes. £0.05* FDW (B73-51029)
2: Beeches (copper and green): two part or unison and piano. *Boosey and Hawkes. £0.05* FDW (B73-51028)
3: The holly: SSA and piano. *Boosey and Hawkes. £0.05* FDW (B73-51030)
4: The willow: unison and piano. *Boosey and Hawkes. £0.05* FDW (B73-51031)
5: The yew: SA and piano. *Boosey and Hawkes. £0.05* FDW (B73-51032)
6: The elm: SSA and piano. *Boosey and Hawkes. £0.05* FDW (B73-51033)
7: Poplars: unison and piano. *Boosey and Hawkes. £0.05* FDW (B73-51034)
8: The oak: two part or unison and piano. *Boosey and Hawkes. £0.05* FDW (B73-51035)

Le Jeune, Claude. Meslanges liv 2. S'ebahit-on si je vous aime. How can my love: chanson for SATB. *J.A. Parkinson. Unpriced* EZDU (B73-50547)

Leader of faithful souls. (Taberer, Alfred A). *Bankhead Press. £0.01* DM (B73-50512)

Lear, Edward.
Eight nonsense songs. (Dale, Mervyn). *Ashdown. £0.40* KDW (B73-51086)
How pleasant to know Mr. Lear: for narrator and orchestra. (Roxburgh, Edwin). *United Music. Unpriced* HYE/M (B73-51046)

Lebermann, Walter.
Concerto for clarinet in B flat major. Concerto, B flat major: for clarinet and orchestra. (Stamitz, Johann). *Bärenreiter. £0.50* MPVVF (B73-50265)
Concerto for viola in B flat major: arr. Konzert für Viola, B-dur. (Stamitz, Anton). *Schott. £1.70* SQPK/LF (B73-50379)
Sinfonia a quattro for string orchestra in C minor. Sinfonia a quattro, C-moll: für Streicher. (Richter, Franz Xaver). *Peters. £1.80* RXMJ (B73-50774)
Symphony in F major. Falck 67. Sinfonie F-Dur. Falck 67. (Bach, Wilhelm Friedemann). *Schott. £1.92* RXME (B73-51211)

Lees, Benjamin. Study no.1 for unaccompanied cello. *Boosey and Hawkes. £0.65* SRPMJ (B73-50385)

Lefanu, Nicola.
But stars remaining: for female voice (unaccompanied) by Nicola Lefanu. *Novello. £0.35* KFEZDW (B73-50641)
Il Cantico dei cantici II = The song of songs. Ch. 2: dramatic scena for female voice (unaccompanied). *Novello. £0.35* KFEZDW (B73-50642)

Leggiadre ninfe = You graceful nymphs
for six-part chorus of mixed voices a cappella. (Marenzio, Luca). *Schirmer. Unpriced* EZDU (B73-50108)

Leggiadre ninfe = You graceful nymphs: for six-part chorus of mixed voices a cappella. (Marenzio, Luca). *Schirmer. Unpriced* EZDU (B73-50548)

Lehár, Franz. The Czarevitch: songs from the operetta. *Glocken Verlag. Unpriced* KDW (B73-50206)

Lehmann, Hans Ulrich. Regions 3: for clarinet, trombone and violoncello. *Ars viva: Schott. Unpriced* NVNT (B73-50272)

Leibovitch, K A. The art of piano playing. (Neuhaus, Heinrich). 2nd ed.. *Barrie and Jenkins. £3.50* AQ/E (B73-14764) ISBN 0 214 65364 1

Leichte Duospiel für Violoncelli
Heft 2. (Koch, Edwin). *Schott. £1.44* SRNUK/AAY (B73-51229)

Leichte Duospiel: fur zwei Violoncelli
Heft 1. (Koch, Edwin). *Schott. £0.90* SRNUK/AAY (B73-51230)

Leichtes Duospiel für zwei Violoncelli
Heft 1. (Koch, Edwin). *Schott. £0.90* SRNUK/AAY (B73-51231)

Leigh, Mitch. Man of La Mancha: arr. Man of La Mancha. *KPM. £0.85* QPK/JR (B73-50323)

Leigh, Spencer. Paul Simon - now and then. *C52 The Temple, 24 Dale St., Liverpool L2 5RL: Raven Books. £0.60* AKDW/GB/E(P) (B73-28187) ISBN 0 85977 008 7

Leighton, Kenneth.
Adventante Deo = Lift up your heads, gates of my heart: anthem for SATB and organ. *Novello. £0.21* DH (B73-50025)
The second service = Magnificat and Nunc dimittis. Op.62: SATB. *Oxford University Press. £0.30* DGPP (B73-50021) ISBN 0 19 395236 x
Solus ad victimam: SATB. *Oxford University Press. Unpriced* DH/LK (B73-50958) ISBN 0 19 350349 2

Leitch, Donovan. The pied piper: songs from the film. *Donovan Music. £0.30* KDW/JR (B73-50215)

Lekberg, Sven.
Far away across the mountain: for four-part chorus of mixed voices a cappella. *Schirmer. Unpriced* EZDW (B73-50118)
Let all the world in every corner sing: for four-part chorus of women's voices a cappella. *Schirmer. Unpriced* FEZDH (B73-50150)
O Lord, thou hast searched me. *Schirmer. Unpriced* KDK (B73-50199)
She walks in beauty: for three-part chorus of mixed voices a cappella. *Schirmer. Unpriced* EZDW (B73-50119)
The trees stand silent: for five-part chorus of mixed voices SSATB a cappella. *Schirmer. Unpriced* EZDW (B73-50120)
We are the music-makers: for four-part chorus of mixed voices with descant a cappella. *Schirmer. Unpriced* EZDW (B73-50121)
Weep you no more, sad fountains: for four-part chorus of mixed voices a cappella. *Schirmer. Unpriced* EZDW (B73-50122)

Lennon, John. Lennon remembers: the 'Rolling Stone' interviews with John Lennon and Yoko Ono. (Wenner, Jann). *Talmy. £2.25* AKG/E(P) (B73-07792) ISBN 0 900735 10 4

Lennon, Yoko. *See* Ono, Yoko.

Lennon remembers: the 'Rolling Stone' interviews with John Lennon and Yoko Ono. (Wenner, Jann). *Talmy. £2.25* AKG/E(P) (B73-07792) ISBN 0 900735 10 4

Leppard, Raymond. Musiche sacre. Magnificat. Vocal score. Magnificat for double chorus, cornetti (trumpets), trombones, strings, and keyboard continuo. (Cavalli, Francesco). *Faber Music. Unpriced* DGKK (B73-50946)

Lesznai, Lajos. Bartók. *26 Albemarle St., W1X 4QY: Dent. £2.50* BBG(N) (B73-24886) ISBN 0 460 03136 8

Let all men everywhere rejoice: anthem for SATB and organ (or brass, percussion and organ). (Wills, Arthur). *Novello. £0.14* DH (B73-50028)

Let all the world in every corner sing: for four-part chorus of women's voices a cappella. (Lekberg, Sven). *Schirmer. Unpriced* FEZDH (B73-50150)

Let me bring love. Suffer little children. Suffer little children. (Green, Philip). *Belwin-Mills. £0.20* FDH (B73-51017)

Let the word of Christ dwell in you richly: general anthem, for four-part chorus of mixed voices a cappella. (Newbury, Kent A). *Schirmer. Unpriced* EZDK (B73-50085)

Lethbridge, Lionel. Opera song book
2: Eight operatic choruses for unison, two-part, or SAB voices and piano. *Oxford University Press. £0.50* DW/AY (B73-50046) ISBN 0 19 330521 6

Let's sing and make music: ideas and advice for those who are engaged in Christian education with children and young people. (Buzzing, Pauline). *Denholm House Press. £1.20* A(VF/GR) (B73-04906) ISBN 0 85213 062 7

Levey, Michael. The life & death of Mozart. *30 Gray's Inn Rd, WC1X 8JL: Cardinal. £0.90* BMS(N) (B73-22798) ISBN 0 351 17178 9

Lewis, Cecil Day- *See* Day-Lewis, Cecil.

Lewis, Cecil Day.
But stars remaining: for female voice (unaccompanied) by Nicola Lefanu. (Lefanu, Nicola). *Novello. £0.35* KFEZDW (B73-50641)
Requiem for the living: for speaker, mezzo-soprano or baritone solo, mixed chorus, percussion, cimbalom and piano. (Swann, Donald). *Roberton. Unpriced* KHYE/NYLDE (B73-50242)

Lewis, Cecil Day. *See* Day Lewis, Cecil.

Lewis, Pete. Sing life, sing love: songs. *Holmes McDougall. Unpriced* JFDM/AY (B73-51064) ISBN 0 7157 1005 2

Lhevinne, Josef. Basic principles in pianoforte playing. 1st ed. reprinted. *Dover Publications: Constable. £0.60* AQ/CY (B73-23436) ISBN 0 486 22820 7

Liber primus sacrarum cantionum. Laetentur coeli. Laetentur coeli = Be glad ye heavens: SATBB by William Byrd. (Byrd, William). Revised ed. *Oxford University Press. Unpriced* EZDJ (B73-50536) ISBN 0 19 352058 3

Liber secundus sacrarum cantionum. Miserere. Miserere mei = Look on me in mercy: SATBB. (Byrd, William). Revised ed. *Oxford University Press. Unpriced* EZDGKH/LHLN (B73-50532) ISBN 0 19 352053 2

Libro primo de canzoni da sonare. La Maggia. Canzona 'La Maggia'. (Maschera, Florentio). *Oxford University Press. Unpriced* LNS (B73-50657) ISBN 0 19 341204 7

Lied über die Grenze, Folklore fremder Lander. (Cammin, Heinz). *Schott. £1.44* TSPMK/DW/G/AY (B73-51252)

Life & death of Mozart. (Levey, Michael). *30 Gray's Inn Rd, WC1X 8JL: Cardinal. £0.90* BMS(N) (B73-22798) ISBN 0 351 17178 9

Life and music of John Field, 1782-1837, creator of the nocturne. (Piggott, Patrick). *Faber. £10.00* BFK(N) (B73-31512) ISBN 0 571 10145 3

Life of Richard Strauss. (Jefferson, Alan). *David and Charles. £3.95* BSU(N) (B73-31509) ISBN 0 7153 6199 6

Life of song: the story of Kenny MacRae. (MacRae, Donald). *38 Lilybank Gardens, Glasgow G12 8SA: D. MacRae. £0.40* AKG/E(P) (B73-05260) ISBN 0 9502730 0 7

Lift up your head, O ye gates. Op. 44, no.2. (Mathias, William). *Oxford University Press. Unpriced* DK (B73-50962) ISBN 0 19 350344 1

Lift up your heads: SSATB. (Amner, John). *Oxford*

University Press. Unpriced DK (B73-50033)
ISBN 0 19 350331 x

Linde, Hans Martin. Amorilli mia bella: Hommage a Johann Jacob van Eyck for recorder solo, descant, treble and bass recorder. *Schott. £1.08* VSPM/T (B73-51279)

Linde, Hans Peter. Duo concertante für Viola und Violoncello. *Peters. Unpriced* SPLSR (B73-50369)

Lingg, Ann M. Mozart: genius of harmony. *Kennikat Press. £7.40* BMS(N) (B73-14126) ISBN 0 8046 1743 0

Liriche greche: per soprano e diverso gruppi strumentali. (Dallapiccola, Luigi). *Eulenberg. £2.80* KFLE/MDW (B73-50224)

Listen Easy
No.1- ; Oct. 1972-. *43 Queen St., Hitchin, Herts.: B.C. Enterprises. £0.20* A/GB(B) (B73-08998)

Listening: three-part song for female voices and piano. (Thiman, Eric Harding). *Roberton. £0.10* FDW (B73-50147)

Liszt, Franz.
Liszt: a selection. *Oxford University Press. Unpriced* QPJ (B73-50732) ISBN 0 19 373217 3
Works, piano. Piano works
Vol.3: Hungarian rhapsodies 1, nos.1-9. *Bärenreiter. £2.40* QP/AZ (B73-50717)

Liszt: a selection. (Liszt, Franz). *Oxford University Press. Unpriced* QPJ (B73-50732) ISBN 0 19 373217 3

Literature of American music: a fully annotated catalogue of the books and song collections in Exeter University Library. (University of Exeter. *Library*). *Northcote House, The Queen's Drive, Exeter, Devon: University of Exeter (American Arts Documentation Centre): University of Exeter Library. £1.00* A(YT/T) (B73-13195) ISBN 0 902746 02 2

Little newborn Jesus Child: for chorus of mixed voices (SATB) with organ or instrumental accompaniment. (Buxtehude, Dietrich). *Lawson-Gould: Roberton. £0.32* DE/LF (B73-50942)

Little organ book. (Stoker, Richard). *Boosey and Hawkes. £0.40* RJ (B73-51197)

Lloyd, Richard. A prayer: for treble voices and organ. *Lengnick. £0.06* FLDH (B73-50160)

Lobel, Anita. Soldier, soldier, won't you marry me? (Langstaff, John). *World's Work. £1.20* ADW/G(YD) (B73-20978) ISBN 0 437 54105 3

Lochnagar. (Gibson, Isabella Mary). *Kerr. Unpriced* KDW (B73-50205)

Locke, Matthew. Two motets: for two high voices and keyboard. *Thames. Unpriced* JNFTEDJ (B73-50198)

Lockspeiser, Edward. Music and painting: a study in comparative ideas from Turner to Schoenberg. *Cassell. £4.25* A(ZF) (B73-14124) ISBN 0 304 29149 8

Lockton, Edward. The fairy tailor: unison song. (Noble, Harold). *Bosworth. £0.10* JFDW (B73-51070)

Loeillet, Jean Baptiste, *b.1688.* Sonatas for flute duet. Op.5, liv.2, nos,1,4. Two sonatas for two flutes. *Oxford University Press. £1.10* VRNUE (B73-51268)
ISBN 0 19 357590 6

London College of Music. Examinations in pianoforte playing and singing: sight reading tests, sight singing tests as set throughout 1972: grades 1-8 and diplomas. *Ashdown. £0.30* Q/EG (B73-50289)

Long and the short: violin solo. (Wuorinen, Charles). *Peters. Unpriced* SPMJ (B73-50371)

Long trail: piano duet. (Parfrey, Raymond). *Composer to Player Edition. Unpriced* QNV (B73-50708)

Longmire, John.
Paradise islands: 3 miniatures for piano. *Bosworth. £0.20* QPJ (B73-51175)
Trotting to the fair: pianoforte duet. *Bosworth. £0.20* QNV (B73-51163)

Lorca, Federico Garcia. Bogenschutzen: Vokalise für eine hohe Singstimme und Klavier. (Reutter, Hermann). *Schott. £1.44* KFTDW (B73-51095)

Lord, David. Most glorious Lord of lyfe!: SATB. *Oxford University Press. Unpriced* DH/LL (B73-50959)
ISBN 0 19 350346 8

Lord dismiss us with thy blessing: a choral benediction, for four-part chorus of mixed voices a cappella. (Ford, Virgil T). *Schirmer. Unpriced* EZDM (B73-50088)

Love came down at Christmas: carol. (Noble, Harold). *Studio Music. Unpriced* JDP/LF (B73-51051)

Love in your eyes. (Theodorakis, Mikis). *Dick James Music. £0.20* KDW (B73-50211)

Love-song: for four-part chorus of mixed voices a cappella. (Heath, Fenno). *Schirmer. Unpriced* EZDW (B73-50117)

Low minuet: bassoon or contrabassoon and piano. (Hughes, Eric). *Spring House, Ampleforth, Yorkshire: June Emerson. Unpriced* VWPHR (B73-50433)

Loxam, Arnold. Operettas. Selections: arr. Gems of Sullivan Vol.1. (Sullivan, *Sir* Arthur Seymour). *Regina Music. Unpriced* PWPK/CF (B73-50287)

Loyd, Rob. Rob Loyd folio of graduated guitar solos. *Kadence Music, Affiliated Music. £0.75* TSPMJ (B73-51249)

Lucas, Leighton. A waltz overture. *R. Smith. Unpriced* WMHW (B73-50887)

Luci care, luci bello = Eyes of beauty, eyes flashing bright. K.346: nocturne. (Mozart, Wolfgang Amadeus). *Schirmer. Unpriced* FDW (B73-50144)

Ludwig van Beethoven: a study in text and pictures. (Fischer, Hans Conrad). *Macmillan. £4.00* BBJ(N) (B73-03211) ISBN 0 333 12114 7

Lullaby. (Keel, Frederick). *Galaxy: Galliard. Unpriced* DW (B73-50976)

Lullay, lullay, thou lytil child: SATB unacc. (Gardner, Ward). *Banks. £0.03* EZDP/LF (B73-50995)

Lullay myn lykyng: for mixed voice choir with soprano solo, unaccompanied. (Monelle, Raymond). *Roberton. £0.10* EZDP/LF (B73-50998)

Lully, Jean Baptiste. Thésée.. March: arr. Processional march. *Ashdown. £0.20* RK/AGM (B73-50349)

Lunn, Jean. Magnificat. Vocal score. Magnificat = My soul doth magnify the Lord: five-part chorus and organ (piano) or five-part string accompaniment (or only 2 violins) and thorough-bass. (Buxtehude, Dietrich). *Peters: Hinrichsen. £0.45* DGKK (B73-50945)

Luntan dalla suna Clori: solo cantata for soprano and basso continuo. (Scarlatti, Alessandro). First edition. *Bärenreiter. £1.20* KFLDX (B73-50223)

Lutyens, Elisabeth. A goldfish bowl. *Cassell. £4.00* BLU(N) (B73-04669) ISBN 0 304 93663 4

Lwowskie piosenki
Cześć 1: Jak sie rodzily lwowskie piosenki. (Uhma, Stefan). *240 King's St., W6 9JT: Kola Lwowian. £0.50* ADW/G(YMUL) (B73-31510)
Cześć 2: Kobieta i milość. (Uhma, Stefan). *240 King's St., W6 9JT: Kola Lwowian. £0.50* ADW/G(YMUL) (B73-31511)
Cześć 3: Pod znakiem Marsa. (Uhma, Stefan). *240 King's St., W6 9JT: Kola Lwowian. £0.50* ADW/G(YMUL) (B73-24206) ISBN 0 9503005 0 0

Lynn, George. Two chorales. *Schirmer. Unpriced* EZDM (B73-50090)

Lyon, David. Variations, nocturne and finale on an old English sea song for piano and orchestra. Op.60: arr. Variations, nocturne and finale on an old English sea song: for piano and orchestra. Op.60. (Bush, Alan). *Novello. £1.75* QNUK (B73-50290)

M. J. *See* Jacobson, Maurice.

Macaulay-Jones, Ken. Rob Gordon's book of Scottish music. (Gordon, Rob). *Kerr. Unpriced* QPK/AH/AYDL (B73-50316)

McCabe, John.
Dance-prelude for oboe d'amore (or clarinet) and piano. *Novello. £0.50* VTQPJ (B73-51288)
Gaudí: study no.3, for piano. *Novello. £1.00* QPJ (B73-50305)
Notturni ed alba: for soprano and orchestra. *Novello. £2.50* KFLE/MDX (B73-50644)
Symphony no.2. *Novello. £6.00* MME (B73-51115)

McCabe, Peter.
Apple to the core. *Sphere. £0.40* AKDW/GB/E(P) (B73-05834) ISBN 0 7221 5899 8
Apple to the core: the unmaking of the Beatles. *37 Museum St., W.C.1: Martin Brian and O'Keeffe Ltd. £2.00* AKDW/GB(P) (B73-05835)
ISBN 0 85616 090 3

McCullough, James. Tonus primus operis musici. Regem natum. Regem natum = Our king is born: for 4-part chorus of mixed voices unaccompanied. (Handl, Jacob). *Roberton. Unpriced* EZDJ/LF (B73-50538)

Macdonald, Hugh.
New edition of the complete works of Hector Berlioz
Vol.2a: Les Troyens. Acts 1-2; edited by Hugh MacDonald. (Berlioz, Hector). *Bärenreiter. Unpriced* C/AZ (B73-50479)
Vol.2b: Les Troyens. Acts 3-5; edited by Hugh Macdonald. (Berlioz, Hector). *Bärenreiter. Unpriced* C/AZ (B73-50480)

Macdonald, Hugh. New edition of the complete works of Hector Berlioz
Vol.2c: Les Troyens; supplement, edited by Hugh Macdonald. (Berlioz, Hector). *Bärenreiter. Unpriced* C/AZ (B73-50481)

McGrady, Richard J. Four thirteenth century pieces. *Chester. Unpriced* VSN/AY (B73-50412)

McIntyre, William M. Sing life, sing love: songs. (Lewis, Pete). *Holmes McDougall. Unpriced* JFDM/AY (B73-51064) ISBN 0 7157 1005 2

Mackay, Angus. A collection of ancient piobaireachd or highland pipe music. *E.P. Publishing. £3.00* VY/T/AYDL (B73-50436) ISBN 0 85409 821 6

Macleod, A C. The Skye boat song: arr. The Skye boat song. *Cramer. £0.15* QPK/DW (B73-50750)

Macleod, Christina. Music from the heart: a memorial tribute being 15 selected songs. (Macleod, Kenneth Iain Eachainn). *John Blackburn. Unpriced* KDW (B73-50207)

Macleod, Kenneth Iain Eachainn. Music from the heart: a memorial tribute being 15 selected songs. *John Blackburn. Unpriced* KDW (B73-50207)

Macmillan jazz masters series. *(Macmillan)* Stewart, Rex. Jazz masters of the thirties. *Macmillan: Collier-Macmillan. £1.90* AMT/E(M/XN21) (B73-08421) ISBN 0 02 614690 8

McNess-Eames, Vera. Rhythm and action songs for tiny tots. *Stockwell. £0.25* JFDW/GR (B73-51073)
ISBN 0 7223 0403 x

MacRae, Donald. A life of song: the story of Kenny MacRae. *38 Lilybank Gardens, Glasgow G12 8SA: D. MacRae. £0.40* AKG/E(P) (B73-05260)
ISBN 0 9502730 0 7

Madgwick, Donald. The Savoyards. Vocal score. The Savoyards: a new operetta. (Robinson, Stanford). *Boosey and Hawkes. £3.00* CF (B73-50489)

Madrigal. (Roche, Jerome). *Hutchinson. £2.60* AEZDU(YJ) (B73-02066) ISBN 0 09 113260 6

Madrigales. Las Canas. Las Canas = The lancers: for four-part chorus of mixed voices a cappella. (Brudieu, Joan). *Roberton. Unpriced* EZDU (B73-50546)

Madrigali a cinque voci. Pastorella gratiosella. Shepherd maiden, fair and graceful: for 5-part chorus of mixed voices unaccompanied. (Vecchi, Horatio). *Roberton. Unpriced* EZDU (B73-50550)

Madrigals and motets of four centuries: a choral songbook of 18 European classics, for mixed voices. (Richter, Clifford). *Associated Music. Unpriced* CB/AY (B73-50933)

Magee, Bryan. Aspects of Wagner. *Panther. £0.35* BWCAC (B73-00360) ISBN 0 586 03774 8

Magidoff, Robert. Yehudi Menuhin: the story of the man and the musician. 2nd ed. *Hale. £3.00* AS/E(P) (B73-24889) ISBN 0 7091 3351 0

Maguire, John. Come day, go day, God send Sunday: the songs and life story, told in his own words, of John Maguire, traditional singer and farmer from Co. Fermanagh. *Routledge and Kegan Paul. £2.95* AKGDW/G/E(P) (B73-24205) ISBN 0 7100 7634 7

Mahler, Gustav. Thou spirit of love divine: SATB accompanied. (Chapman, Edward). *Roberton. Unpriced* DH (B73-50024)

Maine, Basil. Elgar, his life and works. *Chivers. £2.85(to members of the Library Association)* BEP(N) (B73-14761) ISBN 0 85594 835 3

Mairants, Ivor. Flamenco guitar albums
Album no.3. *Belwin-Mills. Unpriced* TSPMH/G/AYK (B73-51246)

Make music fun. (Dankworth, Avril). *Dryad Press. £0.45* AX/BC (B73-10168)

Making the nations sing: the birth of the Llangollen International Eisteddfod. (Tudor, Harold). *61 Lockwood Rd, Northfield, Birmingham: H. Tudor. Private circulation* AD(YDKRL/WB/XPG3) (B73-19495)
ISBN 0 9502935 0 4

Makris, Andreas. String quartet in one movement. *Galaxy Music: Galliard. Unpriced* RXNS (B73-51216)

Malcolm Sargent: a biography. (Reid, Charles, *b.1900*). *Hodder and Stoughton. £0.60* A/EC(P) (B73-25531)
ISBN 0 340 17662 8

Mallarmé, Stéphane. Trois poèmes de Stéphane Mallarmé: songs for solo voice and piano. (Debussy, Claude). *Peters. Unpriced* KDW (B73-50634)

Man of La Mancha. (Leigh, Mitch). *KPM. £0.85* QPK/JR (B73-50323)

Man with the blue guitar: for four-part chorus of mixed voices with piano accompaniment. (Beyer, Frederick). *Schirmer. Unpriced* DW (B73-50043)

Manchester Public Libraries. *Henry Watson Music Library. See* Henry Watson Music Library.

Mandyczewski, Eusebius. Works, string instruments. Complete chamber music for strings. (Schubert, Franz). *Dover: Constable. £2.25* RXN/AZ (B73-51214)
ISBN 0 486 21463 x

Manger carol: for soli and SATB unaccompanied. (Hedges, Anthony). *Novello. £0.07* EZDP/LF (B73-50996)

Marble threshing floor: a collection of Greek folksongs. (Frye, Ellen). *Texas University Press for the American Folklore Society. Unpriced* JDW/G/AYPE (B73-51058)
ISBN 0 292 75005 6

March, Ivan. The stereo record guide
Vol.8: Composer index Me-Z. *Squires Gate, Station Approach, Blackpool, Lancs. FY82 SP: Long Playing Record Library Ltd. £1.95* A/FF(WT) (B73-08019)
ISBN 0 901143 06 5

March for all seasons: march. (Goldman, Edwin Franko). *Boosey and Hawkes. £1.75* UMMGM (B73-50398)

March for peace. (Goldman, Edwin Franko). *Boosey and Hawkes. £1.75* UMMGM (B73-50399)

March of the champions. (Laudan, Stanley). *Peter Maurice. Unpriced* UMMGM (B73-51253)

March to the scaffold. (Berlioz, Hector). *Oxford University Press. £1.75* MGM (B73-50658) ISBN 0 19 362158 4

Marcha del tambor: Caribbean impression, for percussion ensemble, (6 players). (Fink, Siegfried). *Simrock. Unpriced* XNQGM (B73-51309)

Marching and waltzing. (Rapley, Felton). *Chappell. £0.40* RK/AAY (B73-50348)

Mare, Walter de la. *See* De la Mare, Walter.

Marek, George Richard. Gentle genius: the story of Felix Mendelssohn. *Hale. £4.50* BMJ(N) (B73-16142)
ISBN 0 7091 3900 4

Marenzio, Luca.
Madrigali a quattro voci.. Non vidi mai. Non vidi mai = After a rainy evening: for four-part chorus of mixed voices a cappella. *Schirmer. Unpriced* EZDU (B73-50107)
Il quinto libro de madrigale a sei voci. Leggiadre ninfe. Leggiadre ninfe = You graceful nymphs: for six-part chorus of mixed voices a cappella. *Schirmer. Unpriced* EZDU (B73-50548)
Il secondo libro de madrigali a sei voce.. In un bel bosco. In un bel bosco = In a fair greenwood: for six-part chorus of mixed voices a cappella. *Schirmer. Unpriced* EZDU (B73-50109)
Il terzo libro de madrigali a cinque voci.. Togli, dolce ben mio. Togli, dolce ben mio = Take thou, my sweetheart, these lovely flow'rs: for five-part chorus of mixed voices a cappella. *Chappell. Unpriced* EZDU (B73-50110)

Maria. (Trapp, Maria Augusta). *Coverdale House: Distributed ... by Hodder and Stoughton. £1.75* AKDW/G/E(P) (B73-25530) ISBN 0 902088 42 4

Marie Lloyd & music hall. (Farson, Daniel). *28 Maiden La., WC2E 7JP: Tom Stacey Ltd. £3.00* AKFDW/JV/E(P) (B73-03721) ISBN 0 85468 082 9

Markel, Roberta. Parents' and teachers' guide to music education. *Macmillan: Collier-Macmillan. £2.65* A(V) (B73-05833) ISBN 0 02 579750 6

Marks, Charles.
Quartet for strings, no.1, in D minor. Op. posth. String quartet, no.1, in D minor. Op. posth. (Ireland, John). *Boosey and Hawkes. Unpriced* RXNS (B73-50364)
Quartet for strings, no.2, in C minor. Op. posth. String

quartet, no.2, C minor. Op. posth. (Ireland, John). *Boosey and Hawkes. £0.85* RXNS (B73-50363)
Marlow, Richard. The preces and responses: T.T.B.B. unacc. *Oxford University Press. Unpriced* GEZDGMM (B73-50167) ISBN 0 19 351640 3
Marquina, Pascual. Spanish gipsy dance: arr. Spanish gipsy dance: paso doble. *Schauer and May. Unpriced* WSPK/AHSW (B73-50467)
Marr, Peter.
Four medieval pieces: for organ. *Peters. Unpriced* R/AY (B73-50328)
Four medieval pieces: for organ. (Marr, Peter). *Peters. Unpriced* R/AY (B73-50328)
Martin, Frank. Mass. Messe für zwei vierstimmige Chöre. *Bärenreiter. £1.80* EZDG (B73-50057)
Martinu, Bohuslav. Rhapsody concerto for viola: arr. Rhapsody-concerto for viola and orchestra. *Bärenreiter. £1.95* SQPK/LF (B73-50378)
Mary Agnes Cecilia, *Sister. See* Agnes Cecilia, *Sister.*
Mary of the wilderness: carol for SATB and flute. (Rudland, Malcolm). *Thames. Unpriced* EVRDH/LF (B73-50054)
Maschera, Florentio. Libro primo de canzoni da sonare. La Maggia. Canzona 'La Maggia'. *Oxford University Press. Unpriced* LNS (B73-50657) ISBN 0 19 341204 7
Mason, Barbara Kirkby-. *See* Kirkby-Mason, Barbara.
Masque at the Earl of Somerset's marriage. (Campion, Thomas). *Scolar Press. £2.75* BCBNACPF (B73-31563) ISBN 0 85967 129 1
Mass.. A simple song. A simple song. (Bernstein, Leonard). *Amberson: Schirmer. Unpriced* KDW (B73-50200)
Mass.. Almighty Father. Almighty Father: chorale for four part chorus of mixed voices a cappella. (Bernstein, Leonard). *Amberson: Schirmer. Unpriced* EZDH (B73-50070)
Mass. The word of the Lord. The word of the Lord. (Bernstein, Leonard). *Amberson: Schirmer. Unpriced* KDW (B73-50201)
Master musicians series. *(Dent)*
Davies, Laurence, *b.1926.* Franck. *Dent. £1.90* BFT(N) (B73-12434) ISBN 0 460 03134 1
Garden, Edward. Tchaikovsky. *Dent. £1.95* BTD(N) (B73-11185) ISBN 0 460 03105 8
Hutchings, Arthur. Schubert. Revised ed. *Dent. £2.00* BSF(N) (B73-04216) ISBN 0 460 03139 2
Lesznai, Lajos. Bartók. *26 Albemarle St., W1X 4QY: Dent. £2.50* BBG(N) (B73-24886) ISBN 0 460 03136 8
Masterpieces of music before 1750: an anthology of musical examples from Gregorian chant to J.S. Bach. (Parrish, Carl). *Faber. £2.25* C/AY (XA1750) (B73-50477) ISBN 0 571 10248 4
Masterton, James. Lochnagar. (Gibson, Isabella Mary). *Kerr. Unpriced* KDW (B73-50205)
Mater ora filium: Irish folk song. (Wood, Charles). *Novello. £0.10* FLDP/LF (B73-50575)
Mathias, William.
Concerto for harp. Op.50. Harp concerto. Op.50. *Oxford Unpversity Press. £3.00* MPTQF (B73-50686) ISBN 0 19 365588 8
The law of the Lord. Op.61, no.2: an introit, SATB unacc. *Oxford University Press. £0.05* EZDK (B73-50990) ISBN 0 19 350341 7
Lift up your head, O ye gates. Op. 44, no.2. *Oxford University Press. Unpriced* DK (B73-50962) ISBN 0 19 350344 1
Magnificat and Nunc dimittis. Op.53: SATB. *Oxford University Press. £0.30* DGPP (B73-50503) ISBN 0 19 351636 5
Matthews, David. Owen Wingrave. Vocal score. Owen Wingrave. Op 35: an opera in two acts. (Britten, Benjamin). *Faber. £10.00* CC (B73-50488)
Matthews, Denis.
Brahms's three phases: an inaugural lecture-recital delivered before the University of Newcastle upon Tyne on Monday 24 January 1972 and repeated on Wednesday 2 February 1972. *Newcastle upon Tyne NE1 7RU: University of Newcastle upon Tyne. £0.30* BBTAL (B73-10166) ISBN 0 900565 79 9
Sonata for piano in A major. K.331. Sonata in A. K.331. (Mozart, Wolfgang Amadeus). *Associated Board of the Royal Schools of Music. £0.35* QPE (B73-50721)
Sonata for piano in C major. K.309. Sonata in C. (Mozart, Wolfgang Amadeus). *Associated Board of the Royal Schools of Music. £0.35* QPE (B73-51168)
Sonata for piano in D major. K.576. Sonata in D. K.576. (Mozart, Wolfgang Amadeus). *Associated Board of the Royal Schools of Music. £0.35* QPE (B73-50722)
Sonata for piano in F major. K.332. Sonata in F. K.332. (Mozart, Wolfgang Amadeus). *Associated Board of the Royal Schools of Music. £0.35* QPE (B73-50723)
Sonata for piano in F major. K.533. Sonata in F. K.533. (Mozart, Wolfgang Amadeus). *Associated Board of the Royal Schools of Music. £0.35* QPE (B73-50724)
Matz, Arnold. Scale and chord studies for viola. *Peters. Unpriced* SQ/AF (B73-50374)
Maurer, Ludwig. 12 kleine Stücke. Selections. Four fancies: a serenade in E flat for brass band. *Novello. £1.25* WMJ (B73-50438)
Maurer, Ludwig. Zwolf kleine Stücke. *See* Maurer, Ludwig. 12 kleine Stücke.
Maurier, George du. *See* Du Maurier, George.
Maw, Nicholas.
Five Irish songs: for mixed chorus a cappella
1: I shall not die for thee; words by Douglas Hyde. *Boosey and Hawkes. £0.09* EZDW (B73-50556)
2: Dear dark head; words by Samuel Ferguson. *Boosey and Hawkes. £0.09* EZDW (B73-50557)
3: Popular song; words anon. *Boosey and Hawkes. £0.09* EZDW (B73-50558)
4: Ringleted youth of my love; words by Douglas Hyde. *Boosey and Hawkes. £0.14* EZDW (B73-50559)
5: Jig; words by Cecil Day-Lewis. *Boosey and Hawkes. £0.20* EZDW (B73-50560)
May, Helmut.
Concerto for viola in B flat major: arr. Konzert für Viola, B-dur. (Stamitz, Anton). *Schott. £1.70* SQPK/LF (B73-50379)
Prometheus. Op.43. *Excerpts.* Pastorale, Opus 43. (Beethoven, *Ludwig van*). *Schott. £1.60* MJ (B73-50246)

May Magnificat: three choruses for mixed voices by John Paynter. (Paynter, John). *Oxford University Press. £0.35* EZDW (B73-50126) ISBN 0 19 343692 2
Mayer, *Sir* Robert.
The anatomy of a miracle: Campbell-Orde memorial lecture 1972. *Smythe. £0.45(non-net)* A(W/YD/XLQ76) (B73-28188) ISBN 0 900675 87 x
My first hundred years: the revised version of an informal address given at the British Institute of Recorded Sound, on Friday 3rd December 1971. *Smythe. £0.85(non-net)* A(KK/P) (B73-29206) ISBN 0 900675 77 2
Maynard, John.
In tune: over 60 hymns and songs, for churches schools and groups. *Vanguard. Unpriced* JDM/AY (B73-50172)
It's all in the book: 20 hymns and songs for young people. *Vanguard Music. Unpriced* JFDM/GJ/AY (B73-50618)
Mazas, Jacques Féréol.
75 études mélodiques et progressives pour violon. Op.36, nos. 1-30. Etudes spéciales. Op.36, nos 1-30: for the viola. *Schirmer. Unpriced* SQ/AC (B73-50373)
75 études mélodiques et progressives pour violon. Op.36, nos.31-56. Etudes brillantes. Op.36, nos 31-56. *Schirmer. Unpriced* SQ/AC (B73-50372)
Mediaeval pageant: easy piano pieces. (George, Jon). *Oxford University Press. £0.40* QPJ (B73-50730) ISBN 0 19 372719 6
Medieval men: march. (Porter-Brown, Reginald). *Studio Music. Unpriced* WMK/AGM (B73-50898)
Medinger, Gregor.
Anthems for choirs
Volume 1. (Jackson, Francis). *Oxford University Press. £0.12* DH/AY (B73-50506) ISBN 0 19 353215 8
Beggar's opera. Selections. Four songs. (Gay, John). *Oxford University Press. £0.12* EZDW (B73-50555) ISBN 0 19 343673 6
Meditation and impromptu: organ. (Kennaway, Lamont). *Paxton. £0.35* RJ (B73-51194)
Meerwein, Georg.
Quintet for woodwind & piano quintet in D major. Op.54, no.2. Quintet in D major. Opus 54, no.2: for piano, flute, oboe, clarinet, and bassoon. (Danzi, Franz). *Musica rara. £3.00* NWPNR (B73-50278)
Quintet for woodwind & piano quintet in F major. Op.53, no.1. Quintet in F major. Opus 53, no.1: for piano, flute, oboe, clarinet and bassoon. (Danzi, Franz). *Musica rara. Unpriced* NWPNR (B73-50279)
Melba: a biography. (Hetherington, John, *b.1907*). *Faber. £1.40* AKFL/E(P) (B73-11782) ISBN 0 571 10286 7
'Melody Maker' file
1974. *161 Fleet St., EC4P 4AA: IPC Specialist and Professional Press Ltd. £1.00* AKDW/GB/E(M) (B73-31505) ISBN 0 617 00093 x
Memo 1: for solo contra bass. (Rands, Bernard). *Universal. Unpriced* SSPMJ (B73-50809)
Memorias de 'El Cimarron'. (Henze, Hans Werner). *Schott. £1.60* TSPMK (B73-50826)
Memories of morning. Night: a monodrama for mezzosoprano and orchestra. (Crosse, Gordon). *Oxford University Press. £3.00* KFNE/MDX (B73-50650) ISBN 0 19 362487 7
Memory lane, 1890 to 1925: ragtime, jazz, foxtrot and other popular music and music covers. (Wilk, Max). *14 West Central St., WC1A 1JH: Studioart. £6.75* A(RC/XLK36) (B73-30839) ISBN 0 902063 14 6
Mendelssohn, Felix.
Athalia.. War march of the priests. War march of the priests. *Cramer. £0.24* RK/AGM (B73-50350)
Fruhlingsfeier. Op.48, no.3. Spring repose: for four-part chorus of mixed voices a cappella. *Schirmer. Unpriced* EZDW (B73-50123)
Hear my prayer. Op.39, no.1: arr. O for the wings of a dove. *Cornelius. Unpriced* WTPK/DH (B73-50917)
Hear my prayer. Op.39, no.1: arr. O for the wings of a dove. *Cornelius. Unpriced* WUPK/DH (B73-50922)
Psalm 115. Op 31. Vocal score. Not unto us, O Lord. Op 31: for chorus of mixed voices and soprano, tenor and baritone solos. *Schirmer. Unpriced* DR (B73-50974)
Merewether, Richard. Symphonies. Complete horn parts of the four symphonies. (Brahms, Johannes). *Horn Centre. £1.50* WTPME/AZ (B73-50474)
Merril, Marlin. Di pera mora = Cruel they beauty: 16th century Spanish dance song, for 4-part chorus of mixed voices unaccompanied. *Roberton. Unpriced* EZDU (B73-50549)
Merrill, Marlin. Madrigales. Las Canas. Las Canas = The lancers: for four-part chorus of mixed voices a cappella. (Brudieu, Joan). *Roberton. Unpriced* EZDU (B73-50546)
Merton, Thomas. Evening: for voice and piano. (Niles, John Jacob). *Schirmer. Unpriced* KDW (B73-50208)
Meryll, Jane. Vocabulary ramblebuggies and educational wordopolis. Vocal score. Vocabulary ramblebuggies and educational wordopolis. *Belwin-Mills. £0.40* JFDX/GJ (B73-50625)
Meslanges liv 2. S'ebahit-on si je vous aime. How can my love: chanson for SATB. (Le Jeune, Claude). *J.A. Parkinson. Unpriced* EZDU (B73-50547)
Messiah. Vocal score. Der Messias = The Messiah: oratorio in three parts. (Handel, George Frideric). *Bärenreiter. £2.10* DD (B73-50495)
Messias = The Messiah: oratorio in three parts. (Handel, George Frideric). *Bärenreiter. £2.10* DD (B73-50495)
Metamorphoses (Symphony no.2). (Gerhard, Roberto). Revised ed.: edited by Alan Boustead. *Belwin-Mills. Unpriced* MME (B73-50669)
Metastasio, Pietro.
Ecco quel fiero istante = Lo, now the hour of parting. K.436. (Mozart, Wolfgang Amadeus). *Schirmer. Unpriced* FDW (B73-50143)
Luci care, luci bello = Eyes of beauty, eyes flashing bright. K.346: nocturne. (Mozart, Wolfgang Amadeus). *Schirmer. Unpriced* FDW (B73-50144)
Mi lagnero tacendo = Silent, I long for thy love. K.437: nocturne. (Mozart, Wolfgang Amadeus). *Chappell. Unpriced* FDW (B73-50145)
Methinks I hear the full celestial choir: for 5-part chorus of mixed voices unaccompanied. (Crotch, William). *Roberton. £0.13* EZDH (B73-50533)
Meyer, Ernst Hermann.
Quintet for clarinet in A & strings. Quintett für Klarinette in A, zwei Violinen, Viola und Violoncello. *Peters Hinrichsen. £1.20* NVVQNR (B73-50276)
Toccata für Orchester. *Peters. Unpriced* MMJ (B73-50259)
Trio 1948: für Violine, Violoncello und Klavier. *Peters. Unpriced* NXNT (B73-50282)
Meyerolbersleben, Ernst. Sonata for two flutes & basso continuo in E flat major. Sonata in E flat major for two flutes (violins) and basso continuo. (Graun, Carl Heinrich). *Bärenreiter. £1.80* VRNTPWE (B73-50404)
Mi lagnero tacendo = Silent, I long for thy love. K.437: nocturne. (Mozart, Wolfgang Amadeus). *Chappell. Unpriced* FDW (B73-50145)
Middleton, John.
Contrasts: for harpsichord. *Thames. Unpriced* QRPJ (B73-50326)
Fantaisie: for organ. *Thames. Unpriced* RJ (B73-50340)
Mikis Theodorakis: music and social change. (Giannaris, George). *Allen and Unwin. £3.95* BTF(N) (B73-20238) ISBN 0 04 920038 0
Miller, Lewis M. The faucet: for four-part chorus of men's voices with piano accompaniment. *Schirmer. Unpriced* GDW (B73-50165)
Mills, Alan. Favorite French folk songs: sixty-five traditional songs of France and Canada. *Oak Publications: Music Sales. £0.95* JE/TSDW/G/AYSXH (B73-50178)
Milner, Anthony. Blessed art thou, O God of our fathers: anthem for SATB and organ. *Boosey and Hawkes. £0.14* DK (B73-50036)
Milner, John. The scout show book. *Brown Son and Ferguson. £0.75* JGDW (B73-51079)
Milner-Gulland, N J. Terpsichore.. Selections: arr. Dance suite. (Praetorius, Michael). *Boosey and Hawkes. £5.90* MK/AH (B73-50250)
Milner-White, E. Our day of praise is done: SATB. (Harris, *Sir* William Henry). *Oxford University Press. Unpriced* DH (B73-50504) ISBN 0 19 351118 5
Mil'shteyn, Y I. The complete preludes & études for pianoforte solo. (Scriabin, Alexander). *Constable. £2.00* QPJ (B73-51176) ISBN 0 486 22919 x
Mingled chime: leaves from an autobiography. (Beecham, *Sir* Thomas, *bart*). *White Lion Publishers. £2.25* A/EC(P/XA1923) (B73-20240) ISBN 0 85617 163 8
Miniature scores:.
Antoniou, Theodor. Kinesis ABCD. Op.31: for two groups of strings. *Bärenreiter. £1.50* RXMJ (B73-50354)
Antoniou, Theodor. Op ouverture: for orchestra and three groups of loudspeakers. *Bärenreiter. £1.50* MMJ (B73-50256)
Banks, Don. Concerto for violin and orchestra. *Schott. £2.50* MPSF (B73-51121)
Bialas, Günter. Quartet for strings, no.3. Drittes Streichquartett. *Bärenreiter. £1.50* RXNS (B73-50783)
Binkerd, Gordon. Portrait interieur: for mezzo-soprano and violin and cello. *Boosey and Hawkes. £1.25* KFNE/SPLSRDW (B73-51092)
Binkerd, Gordon. Three songs for mezzo soprano and string quartet. *Boosey and Hawkes. £6.25* KFNE/RXNSDW (B73-50651)
Brian, Havergal. Symphony 8. *Musica Viva. Unpriced* MME (B73-50666)
Brian, Havergal. Symphony 10. *Musica Viva. Unpriced* MME (B73-50667)
Brian, Havergal. Symphony 21. *Musica Viva. Unpriced* MME (B73-50668)
Delius, Frederick. A village Romeo and Juliet. Vocal score. A village Romeo and Juliet. *Boosey and Hawkes. £7.50* CC (B73-50005)
Glazunov, Alexander. The seasons: ballet in one act and four tableaux. *Belaieff: Hinrichsen. £4.50* MM/HM (B73-50664)
Goehr, Alexander. Romanza for cello and orchestra. Op.24. *Schott. £2.50* MPSR (B73-51122)
Greene, Maurice. Overture no.5 in D major. *Eulenburg. £0.60* MRJ (B73-51124)
Greene, Maurice. Overture no.6 in E flat major. *Eulenburg. £0.60* MRJ (B73-51125)
Hamilton, Iain. Ecossaise for orchestra. *Schott. £1.50* MMHJQ (B73-50675)
Handel, George Frideric. Concerto grosso in A major. Op.6, no.11. *Eulenburg. £0.41* RXMF (B73-50766)
Handel, George Frideric. Concerto grosso in A minor. Op. 6, no.4. *Eulenburg. £0.41* RXMF (B73-50767)
Handel, George Frideric. Concerto grosso in B flat major. Op. 6, no.7. *Eulenburg. £0.41* RXMF (B73-50768)
Handel, George Frideric. Concerto grosso in B minor. Op.6, no.12: by George Frideric Handel. *Eulenburg.*

£0.41 RXMF (B73-50769)
Handel, George Frideric. Concerto grosso in C minor. Op: 6, no.8. *Eulenburg. £0.41* RXMF (B73-50770)
Handel, George Frideric. Concerto grosso in D major. Op. 6, no.5. *Eulenburg. £0.41* MRF (B73-50689)
Handel, George Frideric. Concerto grosso in D minor. Op. 6, no.10. *Eulenburg. £0.41* RXMF (B73-50771)
Handel, George Frideric. Concerto grosso in E minor. Op. 6, no.3. *Eulenburg. £0.41* RXMF (B73-50772)
Handel, George Frideric. Concerto grosso in F major. Op. 6, no.2. *Eulenburg. £0.41* MRF (B73-50690)
Handel, George Frideric. Concerto grosso in F major. Op.6, no.9. *Eulenburg. £0.41* RXMF (B73-50773)
Handel, George Frideric. Concerto grosso in G major. Op. 6, no.1. *Eulenburg. £0.41* MRF (B73-50691)
Handel, George Frideric. Concerto grosso in G minor. Op. 6, no.6. *Eulenburg. £0.41* MRF (B73-50692)
Haubenstock-Ramati, Roman. Chants et prismes = Gesange und prismen. Revised 1967. *Universal. Unpriced* MRJ (B73-51126)
Haydn, Joseph. Mass no.3 in D minor, 'Nelson Mass'. Messe D-moll, (Nelson-Messe): für vierstimmigen Chor, Soli, Orchester und Orgel. *Peters: Hinrichsen. Unpriced* EMDG (B73-50049)
Haydn, Joseph. Symphony no.51 in B flat major. *Eulenburg. £0.75* MME (B73-50670)
Haydn, Joseph. Symphony no.54 in G major. *Eulenburg. £1.00* MME (B73-50671)
Haydn, Joseph. Symphony no.59 in A major. *Eulenburg. £1.00* MME (B73-51114)
Haydn, Joseph. Symphony no.69, in C major, 'Laudon'. *Bärenreiter. Unpriced* MRE (B73-50268)
Ireland, John. Quartet for strings, no.1, in D minor. Op. posth. String quartet, no.1, in D minor. Op. posth. *Boosey and Hawkes. Unpriced* RXNS (B73-50364)
Ireland, John. Quartet for strings, no.2, in C minor. Op. posth. String quartet, no.2, C minor. Op. posth. *Boosey and Hawkes. £0.85* RXNS (B73-50363)
Meyer, Ernst Hermann. Quintet for clarinet in A & strings. Quintett für Klarinette in A, zwei Violinen, Viola und Violoncello. *Peters: Hinrichsen. £1.20* NVVQNR (B73-50276)
Panufnik, Andrzej. Rhapsody for orchestra. *Boosey and Hawkes. £1.00* MMJ (B73-50682)
Panufnik, Andrzej. Sinfonia elegaica. *Boosey and Hawkes. Unpriced* MME (B73-50252)
Poot, Marcel. Mosaïque pour huit instruments a vent bois. *Universal. Unpriced* VNN (B73-51263)
Schumann, Robert. Symphony in G minor. Sinfonie, G-moll für Orchester. *Litolff: Peters. £3.00* MME (B73-50674)
Scriabin, Alexander. Reverie. Opus 24: for orchestra. *Belaieff: Hinrichsen. £0.85* MMJ (B73-50683)
Stamitz, Johann. Concerto for clarinet in B flat major. Concerto, B flat major: for clarinet and orchestra. *Bärenreiter. £0.50* MPVVF (B73-50265)
Stiles, Frank. Interlude for strings. *Mixolydian Press. Unpriced* RXMJ (B73-50775)
Stiles, Frank. Quartet for strings. String quartet: by Frank Stiles. *Mixolydian Press. Unpriced* RXNS (B73-50788)
Stiles, Frank. Sonnet: for soprano voice and string orchestra. *Mixolydian Press. Unpriced* KFLE/RXMDW (B73-50648)
Tippett, *Sir* Michael. Suite in D major. Suite for the birthday of Prince Charles. *Eulenburg. £0.80* MMG (B73-50255)
Williamson, Malcolm. Epitaphs for Edith Sitwell: for string orchestra. *Weinberger. Unpriced* RXMJ (B73-50358)
Miniatures: for wind trio and three violins. (Hewson, Richard). *Boosey and Hawkes. £1.25* NVNQ (B73-50271)
Minister of Justice: opera. (Elton, Antony). *Antony Elton. Unpriced* CQC (B73-50939)
Miramichi ballad: a suite for orchestra. (Jones, Kelsey). *Boosey and Hawkes. £4.85* MJ (B73-50249)
Miroglio, Francis. Réfractions. *Universal. Unpriced* NYDR (B73-51133)
Mirth: anthem for female or boy's voices and organ. (Rose, Michael). *Novello. £0.14* FDH (B73-51016)
Missa 'L'Homme armé': for mixed choir (SATB) a cappella. (Dufay, Guillaume). *Boosey and Hawkes. £1.00* EZDG (B73-50981)
Missa sine credo a 4. (Naylor, Bernard). *Roberton. £0.18* EZDG (B73-50531)
Missae totius anni: Missa O magnum mysterium. Santus: arr. Sanctus = Holy holy holy. (Victoria, Tomás Luis de). *Schirmer. Unpriced* FEZDGE (B73-50149)
Missarum liber primus. (Animuccia, Giovanni). 1st ed. reprinted. *Gregg. £12.60* ADG (B73-00361) ISBN 0 576 28220 0
Modes and modulations: piano solo. (Parfrey, Raymond). *Composer to Player Edition. Unpriced* QPJ (B73-50737)

Mogill, Leonard. 75 études mélodiques et progressives pour violon. Op.36, nos. 1-30. Etudes spéciales. Op.36, nos 1-30: for the viola. (Mazas, Jacques Féréol). *Schirmer. Unpriced* SQ/AC (B73-50373)
Mohr, Joseph. Stille Nacht, heilige Nacht: arr. Silent night. (Gruber, Franz). *Thames. Unpriced* FEZDP/LF (B73-50152)
Moisy, Heinz von. Brazilian carnival march: for percussion ensemble (6 players). *Simrock. Unpriced* XNQGM (B73-50927)
Mond = The moon: a little theatre of the world; English text by Maria Pelikan, vocal score by Hans Bergese. (Orff, Carl). *Schott. £9.60* CC (B73-50934)
Mond. Vocal score. Der Mond = The moon: a little theatre of the world; English text by Maria Pelikan, vocal score by Hans Bergese. (Orff, Carl). *Schott. £9.60* CC (B73-50934)
Mondonville, Joseph de. Titon et l'Aurore. *Gregg International. £8.40* CQC (B73-50491) ISBN 0 576 28987 6
Monelle, Raymond. Lullay myn lykyng: for mixed voice choir with soprano solo, unaccompanied. *Roberton. £0.10* EZDP/LF (B73-50998)
Monteverdi, Claudio. L'Orfeo: favola in musica. 2nd ed. reprinted. *Gregg. £7.20* BMNAC (B73-16144) ISBN 0 576 28177 8
Moore, Elizabeth. Second book of music for the ballet class. *Cramer. £0.48* QPK/CC/AY (B73-51183)
Moore, Jack. Themes from TV and film classics. (Bolton, Cecil). *Robbins Affiliated Music. £0.75* RK/JS (B73-51207)
Moore, Mavor. Anne of Green Gables. Vocal score. Anne of Green Gables. (Campbell, Norman). *Chappell. £2.00* CM (B73-50937)
Moore, Philip. Immortal babe: carol for accompanied two-part chorus. *Thames. Unpriced* FDP/LF (B73-50566)
Moore, Thomas.
At the mid hour of night, (from Moore's Irish melodies). (Pasfield, William Reginald). *Ashdown. £0.05* FLDW (B73-50576)
The last rose of summer, (from Moore's Irish melodies). (Pasfield, William Reginald). *Ashdown. £0.05* FLDW (B73-50577)
The young may moon, (from Moore's Irish melodies). (Pasfield, William Reginald). *Ashdown. £0.05* FLDW (B73-50578)
More carols for recorder, with simple harmonies for auto-harp, chimes or guitar. (Sadleir, Richard). *British and Continental Music. £0.20* VSPLTQTK/DP/LF/AY (B73-51278)
More songs for music time: for unison voices, with tuned and rhythmic percussion accompaniments. (Wilson, Mabel). *Oxford University Press. £0.50* JFE/NYLDW/GJ/AY (B73-50194) ISBN 0 19 330876 2
Morehen, John. Liber secundus sacrarum cantionum. Miserere. Miserere mei = Look on me in mercy: SATBB. (Byrd, William). Revised ed. *Oxford University Press. Unpriced* EZDGKH/LHLN (B73-50532) ISBN 0 19 352053 2
Morley, Thomas. Madrigalls to foure voyces. Ho! who comes here? Ho! who comes here?: Madrigal. *Schott. £1.00* VSNSK/DU (B73-50415)
Morley-Pegge, Reginald. The French horn: some notes on the evolution of the instrument and of its technique. 2nd ed. *E. Benn. £3.95* AWT/B (B73-15417) ISBN 0 510 36601 5
Morovitz, Joseph. Captain Noah and his floating zoo. Vocal score. Captain Noah and his floating zoo: cantata in popular style. (Flanders, Michael). *Novello. £0.69* DE (B73-50496)
Morrissey, LeRoy John. The Grub-Street opera. (Fielding, Henry). *Oliver and Boyd. £2.00* ACLMBM (B73-31566) ISBN 0 05 002755 7
Morton, Robin. Come day, go day, God send Sunday: the songs and life story, told in his own words, of John Maguire, traditional singer and farmer from Co. Fermanagh. (Maguire, John). *Routledge and Kegan Paul. £2.95* AKGDW/G/E(P) (B73-24205) ISBN 0 7100 7634 7
Mosaic for brass band. (Howarth, Elgar). *Paxton. £2.50* WMJ (B73-51296)
Mosaïque pour huit instruments a vent bois. (Poot, Marcel). *Universal. Unpriced* VNN (B73-51263)
Moscheles, Ignaz. Grande due concertante: für Gitarre & Klavier. *Simrock. Unpriced* TSPMJ (B73-51250)
Most glorious Lord of lyfe!: SATB. (Lord, David). *Oxford University Press. Unpriced* DH/LL (B73-50959) ISBN 0 19 350346 8
Moteca. Cantate Domino. Cantate Domino. Sing unto the Lord: for 4-part chorus of mixed voices with optional organ. (Vecchi, Horatio). *Roberton. Unpriced* EZDR (B73-50545)
Motecta. O regem coeli. In festo natalis Domini: for 4-part chorus of mixed voices unaccompanied. (Victoria, Tomas Luis de). *Roberton. Unpriced* EZDJ/LF (B73-50539)
Mottl, Felix. Tristan und Isolde. (Wagner, Richard). *Dover: Constable. £3.75* CQC (B73-50941) ISBN 0 486 22915 7
Mould, Clifford. The musical manuscripts of St George's Chapel, Windsor Castle: a descriptive catalogue. (Windsor Castle. *St George's Chapel*). *2 Victoria St., Windsor, Berks.: Oxley and Son (Windsor) Ltd for the Dean and Canons of St George's Chapel in Windsor Castle. £1.25* AD/LD(YDEUW/TE) (B73-09262) ISBN 0 902187 16 3
Mountain of the Lord: anthem for SATB and organ. (Griffin, Jack). *Roberton. £0.10* DK (B73-50034)
Moyse, Louis.
First solos for the flute player. *Schirmer. Unpriced* VRPK/AAY (B73-50408)
Three French songs: music, based on French melodies. *Schirmer. Unpriced* EVQNTQDW/G/AYH (B73-50053)

Mozart, Wolfgang Amadeus.
Andante for flute clock in F major. K.616: arr. Andante, F Dur, KV616: ein Stück für eine Walze in eine kleine Orgel. *Schott. £1.20* VRNSK (B73-50841)
Concerto for flute, harp & orchestra in C major. K.299: arr. Konzert für Flöte, Harfe und Orchester, C-Dur. KV299. *Peters. £3.60* VRPK/LF (B73-50844)
Dixit Dominus and Magnificat. Vocal score. Dixit Dominus and Magnificat. K.193. *Schirmer. Unpriced* DGKB (B73-50498)
Duets for two horns. K.487: arr. 12 easy duets for winds Volume 1: For flutes, oboes (and saxophones). *Schirmer. Unpriced* UNUK (B73-50837)
Duets for two horns. K.487: arr. 12 easy duets for winds Volume 2: for clarinets trumpets (and F horns). *Schirmer. Unpriced* UNUK (B73-50838)
Ecco quel fiero istante = Lo, now the hour of parting. K.436. *Schirmer. Unpriced* FDW (B73-50143)
Galimathias musicum. KV32: 2 violins, viola, bass, 2 oboes, 2 horns, bassoon and cembalo. *Peters. £1.80* MRJ (B73-51127)
Luci care, luci bello = Eyes of beauty, eyes flashing bright. K.346: nocturne. *Schirmer. Unpriced* FDW (B73-50144)
Mass. K.262.. Sanctus. Vocal score. Sanctus = Holy holy holy. *Schirmer. Unpriced* DGE (B73-50015)
Mi lagnero tacendo = Silent, I long for thy love. K.437: nocturne. *Chappell. Unpriced* FDW (B73-50145)
Quartet for string instruments in C major. K.157: arr. Divertimento, C-Dur. *Schott. £1.20* RXMK (B73-50359)

Quintet for horn & strings in E flat major. K 407: arr. Horn quintet in E flat. *Schirmer. Unpriced* WTPK (B73-51307)
Sonata for piano in A major. K.331. Sonata in A. K.331. *Associated Board of the Royal Schools of Music. £0.35* QPE (B73-50721)
Sonata for piano in C major. K.309. Sonata in C. *Associated Board of the Royal Schools of Music. £0.35* QPE (B73-51168)
Sonata for piano in D major. K.576. Sonata in D. K.576. *Associated Board of the Royal Schools of Music. £0.35* QPE (B73-50722)
Sonata for piano in F major. K.332. Sonata in F. K.332. *Associated Board of the Royal Schools of Music. £0.35* QPE (B73-50723)
Sonata for piano in F major. K.533. Sonata in F. K.533. *Associated Board of the Royal Schools of Music. £0.35* QPE (B73-50724)
Symphony no.38 in D major. K.504, 'Prague'. Sinfonie in D, (Prager Sinfonie). KV504. *Bärenreiter. £3.50* MME (B73-50672)
Die Zauberflöte. The golden flute: an opera for schools in two acts based on Mozart's 'The magic flute'. *Novello. £1.00* CN (B73-50008)
Muczynski, Robert. Sonata for alto saxophone and piano. Op.29. *Schirmer. Unpriced* VUSPE (B73-50426)
Muffat, Georg. Florilegium.. Suites. Suites from the 'Florilegium': for four or five parts (string or wind instruments). *Bärenreiter. £1.95* NXNSG (B73-50280)
Mulgan, D M.
Quartet for oboe & strings. Op.7, no.4. Quartet. Opus 7, no.4: for oboe, violin, viola and violoncello. (Vanhal, Jan). *Musica rara. Unpriced* NVTNT (B73-50275)
Quartet for oboe & strings. Op.7, no.5. Quartet. Opus 7, no.5: for oboe, violin and violoncello. (Vanhal, Jan). *Musica rara. Unpriced* NVTNS (B73-50273)
Quartet for oboe & strings. Op.7, no.6. Quartet. Opus 7, no.6: for oboe, violin and violoncello. (Vanhal, Jan). *Musica rara. Unpriced* NVTNS (B73-50274)
Murray, Margaret. Nine carols. *Schott. £0.25* JFE/NYESDP/LF/AYD (B73-51076)
Music and history of the baroque trumpet before 1721. (Smithers, Don L). *Dent. £8.00* AWS(XA1721) (B73-32170) ISBN 0 460 03991 1
Music and integrated studies in the secondary school: a bulletin. (Schools Council. *Music Committee*). *160 Great Portland St., W.1: Schools Council. Free* A(VF) (B73-11781) ISBN 0 901681 28 8
Music & meaning: a theoretical introduction to musical aesthetics. (Coker, Wilson). *Free Press: Collier-Macmillan. £4.50* A/CC (B73-05832) ISBN 0 02 906350 7
Music and painting: a study in comparative ideas from Turner to Schoenberg. (Lockspeiser, Edward). *Cassell. £4.25* A(ZF) (B73-14124) ISBN 0 304 29149 8
Music and the BBC. (Curran, Charles John). *British Broadcasting Corporation. Free* A(W/Q/P) (B73-07798) ISBN 0 563 10209 8
Music for guitar and lute. (Exeter City Library). *Castle St., Exeter, Devon EX4 3PQ: Exeter City Library. £0.10* ATS(TC) (B73-27122) ISBN 0 904128 00 8
Music from the heart: a memorial tribute being 15 selected songs. (Macleod, Kenneth Iain Eachainn). *John Blackburn. Unpriced* KDW (B73-50207)
Music group
Book 4. (Horton, John). *Schott. Unpriced* CB/AY (B73-50004)
Book 5. (Horton, John). *Schott. £1.30* CB/AY (B73-50485)
Book 6. (Horton, John). *Schott. £1.30* CB/AY (B73-50486)
Music in Edinburgh: consumers' guide to places of music. *19 Coates Cres., Edinburgh EH3 7AF: Ramsay Head Press. £0.25* A(YDLH) (B73-08420) ISBN 0 902859 10 2
Music in the elementary school. (Nye, Robert Evans). 3rd ed. *Prentice-Hall. £4.75* A(VG) (B73-03023) ISBN 0 13 608141 x
Music in the modern age. *See* Sternfeld, F W.
Music in the service of the king: France in the seventeenth century. (Isherwood, Robert M). *Cornell University Press. £7.90* A(YH/XCQ316) (B73-17451) ISBN 0 8014 0734 6
Music of Berlioz. (Dickinson, Alan Edgar Frederic). *Faber. £8.00* BBM (B73-00878) ISBN 0 571 09618 2
Music of Claudio Monteverdi: a discography. (Westerlund, Gunnar). *29 Exhibition Rd, S.W.7: British Institute of Recorded Sound. £2.00* BMN/FD(WT) (B73-01061) ISBN 0 900208 05 8

Music of the Americas: an illustrated music ethnology of the Eskimo and American Indian peoples. (Collaer, Paul). *Curzon Press. £6.50* BZP (B73-02064) ISBN 0 7007 0004 8
Music that brings sweet sleep: song cycle for high voice and piano. (Stoker, Richard). *Peters. Unpriced* KFTDW (B73-50231)
Music trade directory
1972-73: 5th ed.. *10a High St., Tunbridge Wells, Kent: Music Industry Publications. £1.80* A(YC/BC) (B73-05003) ISBN 0 903224 00 3
Music trades international year book
1973. *157 Hagden La., Watford, Herts. WD1 8LW: Trade Papers (London) Ltd. £1.55* A(YC/BC) (B73-14513) ISBN 0 903462 01 x
Music with everything. (Hope-Brown, Margaret). *F. Warne. £3.00* A/D(VG) (B73-30643) ISBN 0 7232 1722 x
Musica Britannica: a national collection of music
Vol.34: Pelham Humfrey: Complete church music I; transcribed and edited by Peter Dennison. *Stainer and Bell. Unpriced* C/AYD (B73-50478)
Vol.37: Sterndale Bennett: piano and chamber music. *Stainer and Bell. Unpriced* C/AYD (B73-50002)
Musical instruments: an illustrated history. (Buchner, Alexander). *Octopus Books. £4.25* AL/B(X) (B73-24887) ISBN 0 7064 0015 1
Musical instruments through the ages. *See* Buchner, Alexander.
Musiche sacre. Magnificat. Vocal score. Magnificat for double chorus, cornetti (trumpets), trombones, strings, and keyboard continuo. (Cavalli, Francesco). *Faber Music. Unpriced* DGKK (B73-50946)
My first hundred years: the revised version of an informal address given at the British Institute of Recorded Sound, on Friday 3rd December 1971. (Mayer, *Sir* Robert). *Smythe. £0.85(non-net)* A(KK/P) (B73-29206) ISBN 0 900675 77 2
My heart's in the highlands: chamber opera in two acts. (Beeson, Jack). *Boosey and Hawkes. £10.00* CC (B73-50487)
My little garden plot: unison children's voices. (King, Audrey). *Bosworth. £0.10* JFDW (B73-51069)
My own trumpet. (Boult, *Sir* Adrian). *Hamilton. £3.25* A/EC(P) (B73-26819) ISBN 0 241 02445 5
My young years. (Rubinstein, Arthur). *Cape. £4.50* AQ/E(P/XLG31) (B73-29558) ISBN 0 224 00926 5
Naiades: fantasy sonata, for flute and harp. (Alwyn, William). *Boosey and Hawkes. Unpriced* VRPLTQE (B73-50846)
Naidu, Sarojini. Five Indian poems: for mixed choir and small orchestra. (Hughes, Robert). *Chappell. Unpriced* DW (B73-50516)
Najera, Edmund. Ad flumina Babylonis: for double chorus of mixed voices a cappella. *Schirmer. Unpriced* EZDR (B73-50102)
Narcisse-Mair, Denise. Buddy Lindo: folk songs of Trinidad and Tobago, for unison voices and guitar. (Harvey, John). *Oxford University Press. £0.25* JE/TSDW/G/AYULM (B73-50608) ISBN 0 19 330450 3
Nathan, Robert. Be not afraid because the sun goes down: for four-part chorus of mixed voices a cappella. (Fast, Willard S). *Schirmer. Unpriced* EZDW (B73-50114)
National Operatic and Dramatic Association. Year book
1973. *1 Crestfield St., WC1H 8AU: National Operatic and Dramatic Association. £2.50* AC/E(YC/Q) (B73-08999) ISBN 0 901318 05 1
Nativity: SATB unacc. (Dickson, Andrew). *Banks. £0.05* EZDP/LF (B73-50994)
Naylor, Bernard.
Come Holy Ghost, eternal God: set for SATBB and organ. *Roberton. £0.10* DH/LN (B73-50960)
Exultet mundus gaudio: introduction and sequence of nine carols for the Christian year, for SSAATTBB chorus, SATB soli and two-part chorus of trebles. *Roberton. £0.50* EZDP (B73-50094)
Invitation to music: anthem for SATB and organ. *Roberton. £0.13* DH (B73-50026)
Missa sine credo a 4. *Roberton. £0.18* EZDG (B73-50531)
The preces and responses: SSATB unacc. *Oxford University Press. Unpriced* EZDGMM (B73-50061) ISBN 0 19 351641 1
Six poems from 'Miserere'. *Roberton. £0.30* EZDW (B73-50124)
Speaking from the snow: suite for high voice and piano. *Roberton. £0.40* KFTDW (B73-51094)
Neal, Mary. English folk-song and dance. (Kidson, Frank). *E.P. Publishing. £2.10* ADW/G(YD) (B73-00881) ISBN 0 85409 917 4
Neander, Valentin. Uns ist geborn ein Kindelein. Cradle: SSATB unacc. *Banks. £0.04* EZDP/LF (B73-50999)
Neighbour, Oliver. Three anonymous keyboard pieces. (Byrd, William). *Novello. £0.30* QSQ/AY (B73-50751)
Nelly Gray: plantation song. (Hanby, B R). *Schott. £0.30* GEZDW (B73-50583)
Nelson, Havelock. You must have that true religion: negro spiritual, for soprano and alto accompanied. *Keith Prowse Music. Unpriced* FDW/LC (B73-51037)
Neue Gitarren-Schule
Band 1. (Zanoskar, Hubert). *Schott. £1.125* TS/AC (B73-51241)
Neue Kinderlieder: für Kinder - und Familiengottesdienst. (Behr, Heinz Otto). *Bosse: Bärenreiter. £0.60* JFEZDM/GJ/AY (B73-50195)
Neue Musik
Heft 9: Neue Violin-Duos. (Doflein, Erich). Neuausgabe 1972. *Schott. £1.40* S/AY (B73-50365)
Neugebor'ne Kindelein. Vocal score. The little newborn Jesus Child: for chorus of mixed voices (SATB) with organ or instrumental accompaniment. (Buxtehude, Dietrich). *Lawson-Gould: Roberton. £0.32* DE/LF (B73-50942)
Neuhaus, Heinrich. The art of piano playing. 2nd ed.. *Barrie and Jenkins. £3.50* AQ/E (B73-14764) ISBN 0 214 65364 1
Neuss, Franz. The symphony. (Rauchhaupt, Ursula von). *Thames and Hudson. £8.50* AMME (B73-26166) ISBN 0 500 01099 4
Neville, Paul. Sword of honour: concert march for band. *Boosey and Hawkes. £5.40* UMMGM (B73-50832)
New child songs: Christian songs for under-eights. (Buzzing, Pauline). *Denholme House Press. £1.50* JFDM/GJ/AY (B73-51065) ISBN 0 85213 074 0
New dictionary of music. (Jacobs, Arthur). 3rd ed. *Penguin. £0.50* A(C) (B73-31504) ISBN 0 14 051012 5
New edition of the complete works of Hector Berlioz
Vol.2c: Les Troyens; supplement, edited by Hugh Macdonald. (Berlioz, Hector). *Bärenreiter. Unpriced* C/AZ (B73-50481)
New encyclopedia of the opera. (Ewen, David). *Vision Press. £7.20* AC(C) (B73-32163) ISBN 0 85478 033 5
New English Mass, series 3. (Appleford, Patrick). *Weinberger. £0.25* JDGS (B73-50170)
New music for Holy Week. (Bevenot, Laurence). *Chapman. £0.40* DFF/LH (B73-50013)
New Oxford history of music
Vol.7: The Age of Enlightenment, 1745-1790. *Oxford University Press. £8.00* A(X) (B73-31506) ISBN 0 19 316307 1
Newbury, Kent A.
Break forth into joy: festival anthem, for four-part chorus of mixed voices with organ or piano accompaniment. *Schirmer. Unpriced* DK (B73-50037)
Give ear to my words: general anthem, for four-part chorus of mixed voices a cappella. *Schirmer. Unpriced* EZDK (B73-50082)
Gloria: a Christmas fanfare or introit, for four-part chorus of mixed voices with piano or organ accompaniment. *Schirmer. Unpriced* DH/LF (B73-50029)
How lovely is thy dwelling place: for four-part chorus of mixed voices a cappella. *Schirmer. Unpriced* EZDK (B73-50083)
I long for thy salvation: general anthem, for four-part chorus of mixed voices a cappella. *Schirmer. Unpriced* EZDK (B73-50084)
Let the word of Christ dwell in you richly: general anthem, for four-part chorus of mixed voices a cappella. *Schirmer. Unpriced* EZDK (B73-50085)
Newcastle upon Tyne University. *See* University of Newcastle upon Tyne.
Newe lustige Volten, Couranten zu 5 Stimmen, nos. 11, 16, 17, 25. First set of quintets for 2 descant, treble, tenor and bass (or tenor) recorder. (Brade, William). *Chester. Unpriced* VSNRK/AH (B73-50413)
Newell, Norman.
The first Christmas. (Green, Philip). *Belwin-Mills. £0.20* KDP/LF (B73-51085)
The love in your eyes. (Theodorakis, Mikis). *Dick James Music. £0.20* KDW (B73-50211)
Newley, Anthony. 'The good old bad old days!': a new musical. (Bricusse, Leslie). *Peter Maurice Music, (KPM Music Group). £0.75* KDW (B73-50204)
Newsom, Lerona. The family motoring book. (Elsworth, Cecilie). *Tom Stacey. £1.00* JE/TSDW/AY (B73-50605) ISBN 0 85468 025 x
Newsome, R. Tantalising tubas: brass septet. *R. Smith. Unpriced* WNP (B73-50909)
Newsome, Roy.
The bass in the balloon: solo for E flat bass. *Studio Music. Unpriced* WMJ (B73-51297)
Tenor trombone rag: trombone solo and brass band. *Studio Music. Unpriced* WMPWU (B73-50906)
Nfance du Christ. L'Adieu des bergers. Vocal score: arr. Thou must leave thy lowly dwelling. The shepherds farewell to the Holy Family. (Berlioz, Hector). *Novello. £0.10* GDH/LF (B73-51044)
Nichols, Roger. Debussy. *Oxford University Press. £1.20* BDJ (B73-24201) ISBN 0 19 315426 9
Nicholson, Ralph. Herrick's carol: for women's voices and piano. *Weinberger. £0.08* FDP/LF (B73-50138)
Nieman, Alfred. Five adventures: for piano. *Boosey and Hawkes. £0.40* QPJ (B73-50308)
Night pieces: for piano. (Sculthorpe, Peter). *Faber. Unpriced* QPJ (B73-51177)
Night spot: piano solo. (Parfrey, Raymond). *Composer to Player Edition. Unpriced* QPJ (B73-50738)
Night thoughts. (Homage to Ives): piano solo. (Copland, Aaron). *Boosey and Hawkes. £0.60* QPJ (B73-51173)
Nikiprowetzky, Tolia. Treize etudes pour piano. *Boosey and Hawkes. £1.75* QP/AF (B73-51166)
Niles, John Jacob. Evening: for voice and piano. *Schirmer. Unpriced* KDW (B73-50208)
Nine short pieces from three centuries. (Thackray, Roy). *Oxford University Press. £0.90* VTPK/AAY (B73-50423) ISBN 0 19 359080 8
Nine variants for piano. (Hudes, Eric). *Thames. Unpriced* QP/T (B73-50718)
Noad, Frederick McNeill. Playing the guitar: a self-instruction guide to technique and theory. Revised and expanded ed. *Collier Books: Collier-Macmillan. £0.70* ATS/E (B73-05836) ISBN 0 02 080950 6
Noble, Harold.
The fairy tailor: unison song. *Bosworth. £0.10* JFDW (B73-51070)
The happy vagabond: bassoon and piano. *Peters. £0.48* VWPJ (B73-50877)
The harebell: unison song. *Studio Music. Unpriced* JFDW (B73-51071)
Love came down at Christmas: carol. *Studio Music. Unpriced* JDP/LF (B73-51051)
Noble numbers: five songs for counter-tenor (or contralto) and piano (or harpsichord). (Roe, Betty). *Thames. Unpriced* KHNDW (B73-50241)
Noche pasiva del sentido, (San Juan de la Cruz). (Halffter, Cristóbal). *Universal. Unpriced* KFLE/NYLNUDE (B73-50647)
Nocturnes and cadenzas. Op.62: for cello and orchestra. (Hoddinott, Alun). *Oxford University Press. £2.00* MPSR (B73-50264) ISBN 0 19 364497 5
Noel Coward collection: songs
Volume 1. (Coward, *Sir* Noel). *Chappell. £0.60* KDW/AZ (B73-50630)
Non vidi mai = After a rainy evening: for four-part chorus of mixed voices a cappella. (Marenzio, Luca). *Schirmer. Unpriced* EZDU (B73-50107)
Non vos relinquam orphanos = I will not leave you fatherless: SSA or T.T. Bar. (Donati, Ignazio). *Oxford University Press. Unpriced* FDJ (B73-50135) ISBN 0 19 350336 0
Non vos relinquam orphanos = I will not leave you fatherless: SSA or T.T. Bar. (Donati, Ignazio). *Oxford University Press. Unpriced* FDJ (B73-51035) ISBN 0 19 350336 0
Nonomiya. Op 27: for piano. (Goehr, Alexander). *Schott. £0.80* QPJ (B73-50731)
Not unto us, O Lord. Op 31: for chorus of mixed voices and soprano, tenor and baritone solos. (Mendelssohn, Felix). *Schirmer. Unpriced* DR (B73-50974)
Notation in new music: a critical guide to interpretation and realisation. (Karkoschka, Erhard). *c/o A. Kalmus, 38 Eldon Way, Paddock Wood, Tonbridge, Kent: Universal Edition. £8.00* A(QU/XN53) (B73-06589) ISBN 0 900938 28 5
Notturni ed alba: for soprano and orchestra. (McCabe, John). *Novello. £2.50* KFLE/MDX (B73-50644)
Notturno concertante, Op 68: for piano violin and horn (violin) or piano and violin. (Dussek, Jan Ladislav). *Bärenreiter. £3.30* NUNT (B73-50694)
Notturno: for solo harp. (Van Delden, Lex). *Lengnick. £0.45* TQPMJ (B73-50391)
November sunlight: piano solo. (Parfrey, Raymond). *Composer to Player Edition. Unpriced* QPJ (B73-50739)
Now the most high is born = Nunc natus est altissimus: carol for female or boys' voices and organ. (Rose, Michael). *Novello. £0.14* JFDP/LF (B73-51067)
Noyes, Alfred. Lullaby. (Keel, Frederick). *Galaxy: Galliard. Unpriced* DW (B73-50976)
Nr 10 = Carré: für 4 orchester und Chöre
Nr.1. (Stockhausen, Karlheinz). *Universal. Unpriced* EMDX (B73-50523)
Nr.2. (Stockhausen, Karlheinz). *Universal. Unpriced* EMDX (B73-50521)
Nr.3. (Stockhausen, Karlheinz). *Universal. Unpriced* EMDX (B73-50520)
Nr.4. (Stockhausen, Karlheinz). *Universal. Unpriced* EMDX (B73-50522)
Nursery rhyme of innocence and experience: song for medium voice and piano. (Roe, Betty). *Thames. Unpriced* KFVDW (B73-50234)
Nye, Robert Evans. Music in the elementary school. 3rd ed. *Prentice-Hall. £4.75* A(VG) (B73-03023) ISBN 0 13 608141 x
Nye, Vernice Trousdale. Music in the elementary school. (Nye, Robert Evans). 3rd ed. *Prentice-Hall. £4.75* A(VG) (B73-03023) ISBN 0 13 608141 x
Nyman, Michael.
Concerto grosso in A major. Op.6, no.11. (Handel, George Frideric). *Eulenburg. £0.41* RXMF (B73-50766)
Concerto grosso in A minor. Op. 6, no.4. (Handel, George Frideric). *Eulenburg. £0.41* RXMF (B73-50767)
Concerto grosso in B flat major. Op. 6, no.7. (Handel, George Frideric). *Eulenburg. £0.41* RXMF (B73-50768)
Concerto grosso in B minor. Op.6, no.12: by George Frideric Handel. (Handel, George Frideric). *Eulenburg. £0.41* RXMF (B73-50769)
Concerto grosso in C minor. Op: 6, no.8. (Handel, George Frideric). *Eulenburg. £0.41* RXMF (B73-50770)
Concerto grosso in D major. Op. 6, no.5. (Handel, George Frideric). *Eulenburg. £0.41* MRF (B73-50689)
Concerto grosso in D minor. Op. 6, no.10. (Handel, George Frideric). *Eulenburg. £0.41* RXMF (B73-50771)
Concerto grosso in E minor. Op. 6, no.3. (Handel, George Frideric). *Eulenburg. £0.41* RXMF (B73-50772)
Concerto grosso in F major. Op. 6, no.2. (Handel, George Frideric). *Eulenburg. £0.41* MRF (B73-50690)
Concerto grosso in F major. Op.6, no.9. (Handel, George Frideric). *Eulenburg. £0.41* RXMF (B73-50773)
Concerto grosso in G major. Op. 6, no.1. (Handel, George Frideric). *Eulenburg. £0.41* MRF (B73-50691)
Concerto grosso in G minor. Op. 6, no.6. (Handel, George Frideric). *Eulenburg. £0.41* MRF (B73-50692)
O be joyful: for six-part chorus of mixed voices, SSA-TBB a cappella. (Hoag, Charles K). *Schirmer. Unpriced* EZDGNT (B73-50063)
O clap your hands: SATB. (Rutter, John). *Oxford University Press. Unpriced* DK (B73-50963) ISBN 0 19 350347 6
O come let us sing unto the Lord: for two-part chorus of female, male or mixed voices with piano accompaniment. (Swann, Donald). *Roberton. Unpriced* DGNPV (B73-50016)
O come, thou spirit divinest: introit for SATB. (Statham, Heathcote). *Cramer. £0.06* EZDH (B73-50076)
O Duinn, Micheal. Seinn suas port: ceol don fheadog. *John*

F. Kennedy Drive, Naas Rd, Dublin 12: Folens. Unpriced VSPMK/DW/G/AYDM (B73-51280)
O for the wings of a dove. (Mendelssohn, Felix). *Cornelius. Unpriced* WTPK/DH (B73-50917)
O for the wings of a dove. (Mendelssohn, Felix). *Cornelius. Unpriced* WUPK/DH (B73-50922)
O God of every race and creed: for four-part chorus of mixed voices with organ or piano accompaniment. (Grieb, Herbert). *Schirmer. Unpriced* DM (B73-50040)
O good ale: unison song with piano accompaniment (and ad lib. parts for violins, descant recorders, guitars, tambourine, glockenspiel, cymbals and drums). (Hunt, Reginald). *Ashdown. £0.10* JFDW (B73-51068)
O Lord, thou hast searched me. (Lekberg, Sven). *Schirmer. Unpriced* KDK (B73-50199)
O men from the fields: SATB unacc. (Deale, Edgar Martin). *Oxford University Press. Unpriced* EZDP/LF (B73-50993) ISBN 0 19 343038 x
O sinner man. (Sansom, Clive A). *Studio Music. Unpriced* FDM (B73-51019)
Oboe music for beginners, with piano accompaniment. (Szeszler, Tiber). *Boosey and Hawkes. £0.85* VTPK/AAY (B73-50859)
Ockeghem, Johannes. *See* Okeghem, Jean.
Ode to music. (Williamson, Malcolm). *Weinberger. Unpriced* JFDX (B73-50192)
Offer, Charles Karel. Up and down the River Danube: twelve Czecholsovak folk songs. (Tausky, Vilem). *Roberton. Unpriced* JFDW/G/AYF (B73-50191)
Ohl, John F. Masterpieces of music before 1750: an anthology of musical examples from Gregorian chant to J.S. Bach. (Parrish, Carl). *Faber. £2.25* C/AY (XA1750) (B73-50477) ISBN 0 571 10248 4
Ohlsen, Oscar. Elizebethan duets for two guitars. (Spencer, Robert). *Stainer and Bell. Unpriced* TSNUK/AAY (B73-50817)
Okeghem, Jean. Mass, 'L'homme armé'. Missa 'L'homme armé': for mixed choir (S.Ms.A.T., Bar, B) a cappella. *Boosey and Hawkes. £1.00* EZDG (B73-50058)
Old songs and singing games. (Chase, Richard). *Dover: Constable. Unpriced* JFEZDW/GS/AYT (B73-51078) ISBN 0 486 22879 7
Oliver, Paul. The story of the blues. *Penguin. £0.75* AKDW/HHW(X) (B73-00879) ISBN 0 14 003509 5
On a Brittany beach: piano solo. (Parfrey, Raymond). *Composer to Player Edition. Unpriced* QPJ (B73-50740)

Only a miner: studies in recorded coal-mining songs. (Green, Archie). *University of Illinois Press. £5.65* ADW/GNGC(YT) (B73-06593) ISBN 0 252 00181 8
Ono, Yoko. Lennon remembers: the 'Rolling Stone' interviews with John Lennon and Yoko Ono. (Wenner, Jann). *Talmy. £2.25* AKG/E(P) (B73-07792) ISBN 0 900735 10 4
'Onozó, Jones. Horn music for beginners, with piano accompaniment. *Boosey and Hawkes. £0.85* WTPK/AAY (B73-50916)
Onslow, George. Sonata for viola & piano in C minor. Op.16, no.2. Sonata in C minor for viola (or violoncello) and piano. Op.16, no.2. *Bärenreiter. £3.30* SQPE (B73-50796)
Op ouverture: for orchestra and three groups of loudspeakers. (Antoniou, Theodor). *Bärenreiter. £1.50* MMJ (B73-50256)
Opera and its future in America. (Graf, Herbert). *Kennikat Press. £9.75* AC(XA1940) (B73-24202) ISBN 0 8046 1744 9
Opera in Dublin, 1705-1797: the social scene. (Walsh, T J). *Allen Figgis. £5.00* AC(YDN/XFE93) (B73-30858) ISBN 0 900372 74 5
Operas of Verdi
1: From 'Oberto' to 'Rigoletto'. (Budden, Julian). *Cassell. £6.00* BVEAC (B73-13585) ISBN 0 304 93756 8
Operatic airs. (Campra, André). *Oxford University Press, for the University of Hull. £3.50* KDW (B73-50629)
Ophenbeidt. Fugue on 'Hey diddle diddle': for SATB unaccompanied. *Thames. Unpriced* EZDW (B73-50125)
Orange carol book. (Horder, Mervyn, *Baron*). *Schott. £0.50* DP/LF/AY (B73-50972) ISBN 0 901938 10 6
Ord-Hume, Arthur Wolfgang Julius Gerald. Clockwork music: an illustrated history of mechanical musical instruments from the musical box to the pianola, from automaton lady virginal players to orchestrion. *Allen and Unwin. £5.95* A/FH/B (B73-14765) ISBN 0 04 789004 5
Orfeo: favola in musica. (Monteverdi, Claudio). 2nd ed. reprinted. *Gregg. £7.20* BMNAC (B73-16144) ISBN 0 576 28177 8
Orff. Schulwerk. *(Schott)* Jones, E Olwen. Chwe can werin gymreig = Six Welsh folk songs. *Schott. £1.00* JFE/XMDW/G/AYDK (B73-51077)
Orff, Carl. Der Mond. Vocal score. Der Mond = The moon: a little theatre of the world; English text by Maria Pelikan, vocal score by Hans Bergese. *Schott. £9.60* CC (B73-50934)
Orff-Schulwerk. *(Schott)* Murray, Margaret. Nine carols. *Schott. £0.25* JFE/NYESDP/LF/AYD (B73-51076)
Organ music for services of thanksgiving. (Trevor, Caleb Henry). *Oxford University Press. £0.75* R/AY (B73-50752) ISBN 0 19 375854 7
Organs, rides and engines on parade
Vol.2. (Fair Organ Preservation Society). *3 Bentley Rd, Denton, Manchester M34 AH2: F.O.P.S. £0.50* A/FM (B73-04221) ISBN 0 9502701 0 5
Ornadel, Cyril. The piano can be fun. (Junkin, Harry). *Paul. £2.50* AQ/E (B73-05262) ISBN 0 09 115200 3
Orphée: cantata for high voice, flute, violin and continuo. (Clérambault, Louis Nicolas). *Faber Music. Unpriced* KFTE/NURNTDX (B73-50232)
Osborne, Charles, *b.1927.* Richard Wagner - stories and essays. (Wagner, Richard). *Owen. £3.25* BWC(D) (B73-13014) ISBN 0 7206 0122 3
O'Shaughnessy, Arthur. We are the music-makers: for four-part chorus of mixed voices with descant a cappella. (Lekberg, Sven). *Schirmer. Unpriced* EZDW (B73-50121)
Oswin, Mary. A grain of wheat: 12 songs of grouping and growing. *Mayhew-McCrimmon. £0.47* JDM (B73-50601)

Other man's shoes: a modern spiritual. (Cookridge, John Michael). *Janay. £0.06* JFDM (B73-50181)
Ottman, Robert W. Advanced harmony: theory and practice. 2nd ed. *Prentice-Hall. £5.00* A/R (B73-03715) ISBN 0 13 012955 0
Ouellette, Fernand. Edgard Varèse. *Calder and Boyars. £3.95* BVB(N) (B73-07096) ISBN 0 7145 0208 1
Our day of praise is done: SATB. (Harris, *Sir* William Henry). *Oxford University Press. Unpriced* DH (B73-50504) ISBN 0 19 351118 5
Owen, Ivor.
Gorwyd Iesu Grist = Christus natus est: two part carol by Gordon Weston; traditional words, Welsh version by Ivor Owen. (Weston, Gordon). *University of Wales Press. £0.15* FDP/LF (B73-51026)
Seren Bethlehem = Star of Bethlehem: TTBB. (Weston, Gordon). *University of Wales Press. £0.15* GEZDP/LF (B73-51045)
Owen Wingrave. Op 35: an opera in two acts. (Britten, Benjamin). *Faber. £10.00* CC (B73-50488)
Oxford library of African literature. *(Clarendon Press)* Deng, Francis Mading. The Dinka and their songs. *Clarendon Press. £6.50* BZNDADW/G (B73-27559) ISBN 0 19 815138 1
Oxford studies of composers. *(Oxford University Press)* Nichols, Roger. Debussy. *Oxford University Press. £1.20* BDJ (B73-24201) ISBN 0 19 315426 9
Oxley, Harrison. Mater ora filium: arr. Mater ora filium: Irish folk song. (Wood, Charles). *Novello. £0.10* FLDP/LF (B73-50575)
Pachelbel, Johann. Works, organ. Selections. Selected organ works
5. *Bärenreiter. £1.20* RJ (B73-50341)
Paganini, Nicolo. Concerto for violin, no.1, in D major. Op.6: arr. Konzert no.1, D-Dur. Opus 6: für Violine und Orchester. *Schott. £1.40* SPK/LF (B73-50368)
Page, Martin, *b.1938.* Kiss me goodnight, Sergeant Major: the songs and ballads of World War II. *Hart-Davis, MacGibbon. £1.60* ADW/KG(XPE7) (B73-29557) ISBN 0 246 10748 0
Paget, Michael. Adam and the apple: an occasional carol for various combinations of voices percussion and optional trumpets. *Schirmer. £0.15* FE/XRUDP/LF (B73-50571)

Painful plough: a portrait of the agricultural labourer in the nineteenth century from folk songs and ballads and contemporary accounts. (Palmer, Roy). *Cambridge University Press. £0.80(non-net)* ADW/GNFF (B73-02068) ISBN 0 521 08512 8
Pair of pieces
for 2 flutes and clarinet. (Blezard, William). *British and Continental. Unpriced* VNT (B73-50403)
Pair of pieces: for 2 flutes and clarinet. (Blezard, William). *British and Continental. Unpriced* VNT (B73-50840)
Palestrina's style: a practical introduction. (Boyd, Malcolm). *Oxford University Press. £0.95* BPC/R (B73-07791) ISBN 0 19 315224 x
Palmer, Christopher. Impressionism in music. *Hutchinson. £3.00* A(XHK111) (B73-20236) ISBN 0 09 115140 6
Palmer, King. Compose music. 2nd ed. *Teach Yourself Books. £0.65* A/D (B73-07097) ISBN 0 340 05552 9
Palmer, Roy.
The painful plough: a portrait of the agricultural labourer in the nineteenth century from folk songs and ballads and contemporary accounts. *Cambridge University Press. £0.80(non-net)* ADW/GNFF (B73-02068) ISBN 0 521 08512 8
Songs of the Midlands. *E.P. Publishing. Unpriced* JE/LDW/G/AYDG (B73-50175) ISBN 0 7158 0377 8
The valiant sailor: sea songs and ballads and prose passages illustrating life on the lower deck in Nelson's navy. *Cambridge University Press. Unpriced* JE/TSDW/KC/AYD(XFYK36) (B73-50611) ISBN 0 521 20101 2
Paloma. (Yradier, Sebastian). *Fisher & Lane. Unpriced* RPVK/AHVR (B73-50353)
Pan book of great composers. *See* Hughes, Gervase.
Panufnik, Andrzej.
Concerto for violin. Violin concerto. *Boosey and Hawkes. £4.75* RXMPSF (B73-51213)
Rhapsody for orchestra. *Boosey and Hawkes. £1.00* MMJ (B73-50682)
Sinfonia elegiaca. *Boosey and Hawkes. Unpriced* MME (B73-50252)
Song to the Virgin Mary: for mixed chorus a cappella or 6 solo voices. Revised edition. *Boosey and Hawkes. £0.40* EZDJ/LF (B73-50081)
Paradise islands: 3 miniatures for piano. (Longmire, John). *Bosworth. £0.20* QPJ (B73-51175)
Paraphrase: für einen Flötisten und einen Pianisten. (Wyttenbach, Jurg). *Ars viva: Schott. £3.00* VRPJ (B73-50407)
Parents' and teachers' guide to music education. (Markel, Roberta). *Macmillan: Collier-Macmillan. £2.65* A(V) (B73-05833) ISBN 0 02 579750 6
Parfrey, Raymond.
A Highland tale: piano solo. *Composer to Player Edition. Unpriced* QPJ (B73-50733)
Autumn song: piano solo. *Composer to Player Edition. Unpriced* QPJ (B73-50734)
Background of brass: piano solo. *Composer to Player Edition. Unpriced* QPJ (B73-50735)
A dance from the mountains: piano duet. *Composer to Player Edition. Unpriced* QNVH (B73-50709)
Double bill: piano duet. *Composer to Player Edition. Unpriced* QNV (B73-50707)
A flute from afar: piano solo. *Composer to Player Edition. Unpriced* QPJ (B73-50736)
A long trail: piano duet. *Composer to Player Edition. Unpriced* QNV (B73-50708)
Modes and modulations: piano solo. *Composer to Player Edition. Unpriced* QPJ (B73-50737)
Night spot: piano solo. *Composer to Player Edition. Unpriced* QPJ (B73-50738)
November sunlight: piano solo. *Composer to Player Edition. Unpriced* QPJ (B73-50739)
On a Brittany beach: piano solo. *Composer to Player Edition. Unpriced* QPJ (B73-50740)
Salt caked smokestack: piano solo. *Composer to Player Edition. Unpriced* QPJ (B73-50741)
Serenade in pastels: piano solo. *Composer to Player Edition. Unpriced* QPJ (B73-50742)
Southern sun: piano trio. *Composer to Player Edition. Unpriced* QNVQ (B73-50715)
Suite on three pages: piano solo. *Composer to Player Edition. Unpriced* QPG (B73-50726)
Toy bandstand: piano solo. *Composer to Player Edition. Unpriced* QPJ (B73-50743)
Two little chorales: piano solo. *Composer to Player Edition. Unpriced* QPJ (B73-50744)
Youth at the helm: piano solo. *Composer to Player Edition. Unpriced* QPJ (B73-50745)
Parker, Alice.
Fum fum fum!: Traditional Spanish carol. *Schirmer. Unpriced* FDP/LF (B73-50139)
The parting glass: Irish folk song. *Roberton. £0.10* GEZDW (B73-50584)
Parker, Andrew. Adoramus te, Christe: SATB unacc. (Lasso, Orlando di). *Oxford University Press. Unpriced* EZDJ (B73-50537) ISBN 0 19 350332 8
Parkinson, John Alfred. Meslanges liv 2. S'ebahit-on si je vous aime. How can my love: chanson for SATB. (Le Jeune, Claude). *J.A. Parkinson. Unpriced* EZDU (B73-50547)
Parkinson, Stephen R. Meslanges liv 2. S'ebahit-on si je vous aime. How can my love: chanson for SATB. (Le Jeune, Claude). *J.A. Parkinson. Unpriced* EZDU (B73-50547)
Parliament Street blues. (Barratt, Bernard). *R. Smith. Unpriced* WMJ (B73-50888)
Parrish, Carl. Masterpieces of music before 1750: an anthology of musical examples from Gregorian chant to J.S. Bach. *Faber. £2.25* C/AY (XA1750) (B73-50477) ISBN 0 571 10248 4
Parrott, Ian. Flamingoes: song for medium voice and piano. *Thames. Unpriced* KFVDW (B73-50233)
Parry, William Howard. Four winds: unison, with optional second part. *Lengnick. £0.06* JFDW (B73-50188)
Parsons, Robert. Ave Maria: SAAT Bar B. *Oxford University Press. £0.15* EZDJ (B73-50988) ISBN 0 19 350335 2
Parting glass: Irish folk song. (Parker, Alice). *Roberton. £0.10* GEZDW (B73-50584)
Pas de deux: for clarinet (B flat) and piano. (Williamson, Malcolm). *Weinberger. Unpriced* VVPH (B73-50428)
Pasfield, William Reginald.
At the mid hour of night, (from Moore's Irish melodies). *Ashdown. £0.05* FLDW (B73-50576)
The last rose of summer, (from Moore's Irish melodies). *Ashdown. £0.05* FLDW (B73-50577)
The young may moon, (from Moore's Irish melodies). *Ashdown. £0.05* FLDW (B73-50578)
Passagen-Ubungen. Op.26.. Selections. 101 exercises: for piano. (Czerny, Carl). *Chappell. Unpriced* Q/AF (B73-50288)
Passion of Christ: a devotional service of nine lessons and hymns (or chorales) based on the St Matthew Passion narrative. (Ratcliffe, Desmond). *Novello. £0.35* DFDM/LH (B73-50012)
Pastorale, Opus 43. (Beethoven, *Ludwig van*). *Schott. £1.60* MJ (B73-50246)
Pastorale prelude: organ solo. (Gilbert, Norman). *Cramer. £0.24* RJ (B73-50337)
Patterson, Paul.
Comedy for five winds: flute, oboe, clarinet in B flat, horn in F and bassoon. *Weinberger. Unpriced* UNR (B73-51260)
Interludium: for organ. *Weinberger. Unpriced* RJ (B73-50342)
Visions: for organ. *Weinberger. Unpriced* RJ (B73-50343)
Paul Simon - now and then. (Leigh, Spencer). *C52 The Temple, 24 Dale St., Liverpool L2 5RL: Raven Books. £0.60* AKDW/GB/E(P) (B73-28187) ISBN 0 85977 008 7
Pauly, Reinhard. Exultabunt sancti: arr. Thou art mighty: for four-part chorus of mixed voices. (Haydn, Michael). *Schirmer. Unpriced* EZDJ (B73-50987)
Pauly, Reinhard G. Tenebrae factae sunt = Darkness was over all: for four-part chorus of mixed voices a cappella. (Biber, Carl Heinrich). *Schirmer. Unpriced* EZDGKH/LK (B73-50060)
Paynter, Elizabeth. Fog: for voices and instruments. (Paynter, John). *Universal. Unpriced* FE/LDW (B73-50569)
Paynter, John.
Fog: for voices and instruments. *Universal. Unpriced* FE/LDW (B73-50569)
The high school band: SSATB (S. solo) unacc. *Oxford University Press. Unpriced* EZDW (B73-51009)

ISBN 0 19 343039 8

May Magnificat: three choruses for mixed voices by John Paynter. *Oxford University Press. £0.35* EZDW (B73-50126) ISBN 0 19 343692 2

The space-dragon of Galatar: an opera-workshop project for schools, for voices, sound effects and piano. *Universal. Unpriced* CQN (B73-50009)

Three pieces: for oboe and piano. *Oxford University Press. £0.45* VTPJ (B73-50421) ISBN 0 19 358130 2

Paz, Elena. Favorite Spanish folksongs: traditional songs from Spain and Latin America. *Oak Publications: Music Sales. £0.95* JE/TSDW/G/AYU (B73-50179)

Pearsall, Robert Lucas. Duetto for two cats with an accompaniment for the pianoforte. (Berthold, G). *Schott. £0.50* JNFEDW (B73-50628)

Pearsall, Ronald. Victorian popular music. *David and Charles. £3.50* A/GB(XHS65) (B73-03713) ISBN 0 7153 5689 5

Peasant songs: for violin and piano. (Standford, Patric). *Novello. £0.75* SPJ (B73-51223)

Pêcheurs de perles. Au fond du temple saint: arr. Au fond du temple saint: duet. (Bizet, Georges). *United Music. Unpriced* JNGEDW (B73-51081)

Pedley, David. Five folk tunes. *British and Continental Music. £0.30* VVNTK/DW/G/AYD (B73-50868)

Pedrette, Edward. Is it nothing to you?: for four-part chorus of mixed voices with organ or piano accompaniment. *Schirmer. Unpriced* DK/LH (B73-50039)

Pegge, Reginald Morley-. *See* Morley-Pegge, Reginald.

Pehkonen, Elis. Kyries: for treble voices in 2 or 4 parts with soli and organ with optional side drum. *Chappell. Unpriced* FLDH (B73-50161)

Pelikan, Maria. Der Mond. Vocal score. Der Mond = The moon: a little theatre of the world; English text by Maria Pelikan, vocal score by Hans Bergese. (Orff, Carl). *Schott. £9.60* CC (B73-50934)

Penderecki, Krzystof. De natura sonoris no.2: per orchestra. *Schott. £2.00* MMJ (B73-50260)

Penguin book of accompanied songs. (Harewood, Marion). *Penguin Books. £0.75* JFDW/AY (B73-50190) ISBN 0 14 070839 1

Penguin reference books. *(Penguin)* Jacobs, Arthur. A new dictionary of music. 3rd ed. *Penguin. £0.50* A(C) (B73-31504) ISBN 0 14 051012 5

Pentatonic music
 Vol.4: 140 Churash melodies. (Kodály, Zoltán). *Boosey and Hawkes. £0.30* JFEZDW/PP/AY (B73-50196)

Pepusch, Johann Christoph. Beggar's opera. Selections. Four songs. (Gay, John). *Oxford University Press. £0.12* EZDW (B73-50555) ISBN 0 19 343673 6

Percussion studio. *(N. Simrock)* Fink, Siegfried. Tablature 72. *N. Simrock; 67 Belsize La., NW3 5AX: Distributed by R. Schauer. £0.45* AX(QU) (B73-16796) ISBN 0 9502847 0 x

Performer's guide to Baroque music. (Donington, Robert). *Faber. £7.00* A/E(XDYQ176) (B73-27556) ISBN 0 571 09797 9

Pergolesi, Giovanni Battista. La Serva padrona. Vocal score. La Serva padrona = From maid to mistress. *Schirmer. Unpriced* CC (B73-50935)

Periodicals:, *New periodicals and those issued with changed titles.*
 The Baton: official journal of the Philatelic Music Circle
 Vol.1, no.1- ; 1969- . *c/o Hon. Editor, Irene Lawford, 22 Bouverie Gardens, Kenton, Middx HA3 0RG: Philatelic Music Circle. Unpriced* A(ZD/B) (B73-18101)
 Listen Easy
 No.1- ; Oct. 1972-. *43 Queen St., Hitchin, Herts.: B.C. Enterprises. £0.20* A/GB(B) (B73-08998)
 The Radio One story of pop: the first encyclopaedia of pop
 Vol.1, no.1- ; 24th Sept. 1973-. *49 Poland St., W1A 2LG: Phoebus Publishing Co. £0.25* ADW/GB(XPN21) (B73-29553)
 Sounding Brass; and, The Conductor
 Vol.1-, no.1- ; Apr. 1972-. *Novello. £0.15* AWM(B) (B73-26820)

Perkins, Polly. Songs for the liberated woman. *Kahn and Averill. £0.70* KFE/TSDW/AY (B73-51090) ISBN 0 900707 24 0

Perrault, Charles. La Belle au bois dormant. *Adaptations.* The sleeping beauty. (Chappell, Warren). *Kaye and Ward. £1.25* AM/HMBN (B73-24333) ISBN 0 7182 0949 4

Peter Honri presents - working the halls: the Honris in one hundred years of British music hall ... (Honri, Peter). *D.C. Heath. £2.80* 792.70280922 (B73-29564) ISBN 0 347 00013 4

Petit livre des formes musicales = Spiel mit musikalischen Formen. Op.83: acht leichter Stücke, für Flöte ober Oboe und Klavier. (Schulé, Bernard). *Bosse: Bärenreiter. £1.80* VRPJ (B73-50843)

Pezel, Johann.
 Bicinia variorum instrumentum, no.75. Bicinia 75 for clarino (trumpet in C), bassoon and continuo. *Musica rara. Unpriced* NWNT (B73-50277)
 Bicinia variorum instrumentum, nos 63-4, 67-8. Sonatinas no.63,64,67,68: for two cornetti (trumpets) and basso continuo. *Musica rara. Unpriced* WSNTPW (B73-50410)
 Bicinia variorum instrumentum, nos 69-70, 72-3. Sonatinas no.69,70,72,73: for two clarini (trumpets), and basso continuo. *Musica rara. Unpriced* WSNTPW (B73-50464)

Pfau, Hans. Bläserspielbuch: 156 leichte Spielsatz, Lieder und Tanze, für Gruppen und Bläserspielkreise
 Band 1: Aufbauband (Übungsstücke). *Schott. £3.60* WN/AF (B73-51301)

Pfitzner, Hans. Quartet for strings in D minor. String quartet in D minor. *Bärenreiter. £3.60* RXNS (B73-50786)

Philatelic Music Circle. The Baton: official journal of the Philatelic Music Circle
 Vol.1, no.1- ; 1969- . *c/o Hon. Editor, Irene Lawford, 22 Bouverie Gardens, Kenton, Middx HA3 0RG: Philatelic Music Circle. Unpriced* A(ZD/B) (B73-18101)

Phillips, Gordon.
 English organ music of the eighteenth century
 Volume 1. *Peters. Unpriced* R/AYD (B73-51185)
 Volume 2. *Peters. Unpriced* R/AYD (B73-51186)

Phillips, Ivan C. Danzas espanolas, vol.2. Andaluza. Spanish dance, no.5. (Granados, Enrique). *Oxford University Press. £0.35* WTPK/AH (B73-50472) ISBN 0 19 356830 6

Phillips, John C. Symphony no.9 in D minor. Op.125. Freude, schöner Götterfunken: arr. Hymn of joy. (Beethoven, Ludwig van). *Paxton. £0.25* RK/DW (B73-51206)

Photography of rock. (Hirsch, Abby). *Cobb House, Nuffield, Henley-on-Thames, Oxon. RG9 5RU: Aidan Ellis Publishing Ltd. £1.95* AKDW/HK(M//M) (B73-22267) ISBN 0 85628 006 2

Piaf. (Berteaut, Simone). *Penguin. £0.60* AKF/E(P) (B73-25529) ISBN 0 14 003669 5

Piano can be fun. (Junkin, Harry). *Paul. £2.50* AQ/E (B73-05262) ISBN 0 09 115200 3

Piano lessons
 Book 2. (Waterman, Fanny). *Faber Music. Unpriced* Q/AC (B73-51139)
 Book 3. (Waterman, Fanny). *Faber Music. Unpriced* Q/AC (B73-51140)

'Piano World and Music Trades Review' year book. *For later issues of this annual see* Music trades international year book.

Pianos and their makers: a comprehensive history of the development of the piano from the monochord to the concert grand player piano. (Dolge, Alfred). *Dover Publications: Constable. £2.50* AQ/B(XA1910) (B73-15416) ISBN 0 486 22856 8

Piccini, Niccolò. Iphigénie en Tauride. *Gregg International. £12.00* CQC (B73-50492) ISBN 0 576 28239 1

Picken, Laurence. Ancient Chinese tunes: nine pieces arranged for recorders, tuned percussion, rhythmic percussion, plucked strings, guitar and optional clarinet in B flat. *Oxford University Press. £1.50* NYESK/AYVS (B73-50700) ISBN 0 19 344895 5

Pieces for the growing band. (Benoy, A W). *Hinrichsen. Unpriced* WMK/AAY (B73-50896)

Pied piper: songs from the film. (Leitch, Donovan). *Donovan Music. £0.30* KDW/JR (B73-50215)

Piers, Olaf.
 Holberg suite. Op.40. Sarabande: arr. Sarabande. (Grieg, Edvard). *Cornelius. Unpriced* SQPK/AHVL (B73-50797)
 Holberg suite. Op.40. Sarabande: arr. Sarabande. (Grieg, Edvard). *Cornelius. Unpriced* SRPK/AHVL (B73-50807)
 Holberg suite. Op.40. Sarabande: arr. Sarabande. (Grieg, Edvard). *Cornelius. Unpriced* WUPK/AHVL (B73-50921)

Piggott, Patrick. The life and music of John Field, 1782-1837, creator of the nocturne. *Faber. £10.00* BFK(N) (B73-31512) ISBN 0 571 10145 3

Pilgrims to Bethlehem: two-part song with piano. (Thiman, Eric Harding). *Roberton. £0.10* FDP/LF (B73-50140)

Pinkham, Daniel.
 Magnificat. Vocal score. Magnificat = My soul doth magnify the Lord: five-part chorus and organ (piano) or five-part string accompaniment (or only 2 violins) and thorough-bass. (Buxtehude, Dietrich). *Peters: Hinrichsen. £0.45* DGKK (B73-50945)
 Traité de l'harmonie, liv.3.. Laboravi clamans. Laboravi clamans: motet for SSATB and organ. (Rameau, Jean Philippe). *Peters. Unpriced* DJ (B73-50032)

Piper, Myfanwy. Owen Wingrave. Vocal score. Owen Wingrave. Op 35: an opera in two acts. (Britten, Benjamin). *Faber. £10.00* CC (B73-50488)

Pitter, Ruth. A cycle of cats: three songs for soprano and alto voices with piano. (Price, Beryl). *Oxford University Press. £0.60* FDW (B73-50146) ISBN 0 19 337853 1

Plaint: for tenor recorder and harpsichord (or piano). (Hand, Colin). *Schott. £0.50* VSTPJ (B73-50856)

Plantagenets: a symphonic study, for brass band. (Gregson, Edward). *R. Smith. Unpriced* WMJ (B73-50889)

Platt, Richard.
 Music for flute and basso continuo, 1700-1750: ten pieces. *Oxford University Press. £0.90* VRP/AY(XF51) (B73-50405) ISBN 0 19 358270 8
 Overture no.5 in D major. (Greene, Maurice). *Eulenburg. £0.60* MRJ (B73-51124)
 Overture no.6 in E flat major. (Greene, Maurice). *Eulenburg. £0.60* MRJ (B73-51125)

Platts, Kenneth.
 Dance overture. Op. 10: for orchestra. *Ashdown. £3.00* MMH (B73-51116)
 A shepherd's carol. Opus 12: for treble voices and piano. *Ashdown. £0.05* FLDP/LF (B73-51043)

Plaudite: for triple chorus of mixed voices. (Gabrieli, Giovanni). *Schirmer. Unpriced* DJ (B73-50961)

Play time: Longman first recorder course
 Stage 1. (Fagan, Margo). *Longman. Unpriced* VS/AC (B73-50847) ISBN 0 582 18536 x
 Stage Two. (Fagan, Margo). *Longman. £0.25* VS/AC (B73-51269) ISBN 0 582 18537 8

Playford, John. English dancing master. Selections: arr. Three English dances from Playford's 'English Dancing Master' (1650). *Boosey and Hawkes. £1.80* MK/AH/AYD (B73-51110)

Playing the guitar: a self-instruction guide to technique and theory. (Noad, Frederick McNeill). Revised and expanded ed. *Collier Books: Collier-Macmillan. £0.70* ATS/E (B73-05836) ISBN 0 02 080950 6

Pli selon pli
 No.5: Tombeau. (Boulez, Pierre). *Universal. Unpriced* MMJ (B73-50678)

Polwarth, Gwen. Folk songs and dance tunes from the North with fiddle tunes, pipe tunes and street cries. *Frank Graham. £0.60* JE/TSDW/G/AYDJJ (B73-51062) ISBN 0 900409 93 2

Polwarth, Mary. Folk songs and dance tunes from the North with fiddle tunes, pipe tunes and street cries. (Polwarth, Gwen). *Frank Graham. £0.60* JE/TSDW/G/AYDJJ (B73-51062) ISBN 0 900409 93 2

Pont, Kenneth. Ancient Chinese tunes: nine pieces arranged for recorders, tuned percussion, rhythmic percussion, plucked strings, guitar and optional clarinet in B flat. (Picken, Laurence). *Oxford University Press. £1.50* NYESK/AYVS (B73-50700) ISBN 0 19 344895 5

Pooler, Marie. The water is wide: Scottish folk song, arranged for four-part chorus of mixed voices with piano accompaniment. *Schirmer. Unpriced* DW (B73-50977)

Poot, Marcel. Mosaïque pour huit instruments a vent bois. *Universal. Unpriced* VNN (B73-51263)

Pop-song without words: piano. (Wilson, Robert Barclay). *Cramer. Unpriced* QPJ (B73-51180)

Porteous, Chris. Sing me a story. *Church Pastoral Aid Society. £0.35* QPK/DW/GJ/JT/AY (B73-50321) ISBN 0 85491 834 5

Porter-Brown, Reginald. The medieval men: march. *Studio Music. Unpriced* WMK/AGM (B73-50898)

Portrait intérieur: for mezzo-soprano and violin and cello. (Binkerd, Gordon). *Boosey and Hawkes. £1.50* KFNE/SPLSRDW (B73-50652)

Portrait interieur: for mezzo-soprano and violin and cello. (Binkerd, Gordon). *Boosey and Hawkes. £1.25* KFNE/SPLSRDW (B73-51092)

Poulton, Diana. Works, psalms. Complete psalms for SATB. (Dowland, John). *Stainer and Bell. Unpriced* EZDR/AZ (B73-51005) ISBN 0 85249 168 9

Pound, Ezra. Heaven conserve thy course in quietness: for women's chorus and viola, or piano. (Cobb, Donald). *Galaxy Music: Galliard. Unpriced* FE/SQDH (B73-51039)

Praetorius, Michael. Terpsichore.. Selections: arr. Dance suite. *Boosey and Hawkes. £5.90* MK/AH (B73-50250)

Praise ye the Lord: anthem for double choir (unaccompanied). (Rose, Bernard). *Novello. £0.18* EZDK (B73-50540)

Praises of heaven and earth: for solo soprano piano, and electronic tape. (Johnson, Robert Sherlaw). *Oxford University Press. £1.20* KFLDH (B73-50221) ISBN 0 19 345480 7

Praxis der Chorprobe: Arbeitsheft für die Choreinstudierung. (Eberhardt, Carl). *Peters. £2.50* EZ/AF (B73-50528)

Prayer: for treble voices and organ. (Lloyd, Richard). *Lengnick. £0.06* FLDH (B73-50160)

Prelude and capriccio: for cornet and band. (Gregson, Edward). *R. Smith. Unpriced* WMPWR (B73-51300)

Prelude and fugue. Op.36: organ. (Barrell, Bernard). *Thames. Unpriced* R/Y (B73-50754)

Prelude for Christmas: for school orchestra. (Benoy, Arthur William). *Oxford University Press. Unpriced* M/LF (B73-51103) ISBN 0 19 361940 7

Prelude in canon: viola or horn in F. (Anderson, Muriel Bradford). *Boosey and Hawkes. £0.40* SQP/X (B73-50794)

Prelude no.1 (on a 15th century French melody) and Prelude no.2. (Hughes-Jones, Llifon). *Bosworth. £1.60* MJ (B73-50661)

Prelude on the hymn tune 'Rhosymedre'. (Vaughan Williams, Ralph). *Stainer and Bell. Unpriced* VSNSK (B73-51273)

Prelude, song and dance: for clarinet and piano. (Burnett, Michael). *Ricordi. Unpriced* VVPJ (B73-50870)

Prelude to a ceremony: for orchestra. (Taylor, Herbert F). *Bosworth. £0.37* MJ (B73-51107)

Preston, Michael J. A complete concordance to the songs of the early Tudor court. *Hudson Rd, Leeds LS9 7DL: W.S. Maney and Son. £6.50* ADWBP (B73-20977) ISBN 0 901286 03 6

Preston, Simon. Vox dicentis. *Novello. £0.45* RJ (B73-50344)

Price, Beryl. A cycle of cats: three songs for soprano and alto voices with piano. *Oxford University Press. £0.60* FDW (B73-50146) ISBN 0 19 337853 1

Priestley, Leslie.
 Make music fun. (Dankworth, Avril). *Dryad Press. £0.45* AX/BC (B73-10168)
 Voices and instruments. (Dankworth, Avril). *Hart-Davis. £1.50* A/DZ(VF) (B73-27555) ISBN 0 247 12513 x

Prill, Emil. Concerto for flute, harp & orchestra in C major. K.299: arr. Konzert für Flöte, Harfe und Orchester, C-Dur. KV299. (Mozart, Wolfgang Amadeus). *Peters. £3.60* VRPK/LF (B73-50844)

Primmer, Brian. The Berlioz style. *Oxford University Press. £3.75* BBM (B73-05259) ISBN 0 19 713136 0

Primo libro delli motetti concertati.. Ut flos, ut rosa. Ut flos, ut rosa. = Like flowers, like roses bloom the crowns: S.S. or T.T. (Crivelli, Giovanni Battista). *Oxford University Press. Unpriced* FLDJ (B73-50162) ISBN 0 19 350337 9

Prince of Denmark's march: arr. Trumpet voluntary. (Clarke, Jeremiah). *Cramer. £0.24* RK/AGM (B73-50765)

Processional march. (Lully, Jean Baptiste). *Ashdown. £0.20* RK/AGM (B73-50349)

Prometheus. Op.43. *Excerpts.* Pastorale, Opus 43. (Beethoven, *Ludwig van*). *Schott. £1.60* MJ (B73-50246)

Psalm 116: für Sopran, Flöte, Vibraphon. (Wernert, Wolfgang). *Bosse: Bärenreiter. £1.50* KFLE/VRPLXTRTDR (B73-50226)

Psalm of praise: for full chorus of mixed voices with organ or piano accompaniment. (Hedges, Hazel). *Schirmer. Unpriced* DGNT (B73-50019)

Psalm praise: for choir or congregation. *Falcon: Church Pastoral Aid Society. Unpriced* DR/AY (B73-50975)

Psalmen Davids, 1619. Die mit Tränen säen. Die mit Tränen säen: motet for two five-part choirs and basso continuo. (Schütz, Heinrich). *Bärenreiter. £1.50* EWUNPPWDH (B73-50527)

Pueri concinite: for four equal voices SSSA or SSAA a cappella. (Handl, Jacob). *Roberton. Unpriced* EZDJ/LF (B73-50080)

Purcell, Henry.
Hear my prayer, O Lord. *Roberton. £0.07* FDK (B73-50136)
Instrumental works. Selections. Music for strings and keyboard. *Novello. £0.80* NX (B73-51130)

Queen Elizabeth's dances: for piano. (Judd, Margaret). *Bosworth. £0.30* QPH (B73-51171)

Queen's garland: pieces by Elizabethan composers. (Veal, Arthur). *Ashdown. Unpriced* QNVK/AAY (B73-51165)

Quickenden, Beatrice. In that poor stable: carol for voice(s) and piano or organ. (Bacon, Ernst). *Novello. £0.10* FDP/LF (B73-51021)

Quine, Hector.
Brother James's air. (James, *Brother*). *Oxford University Press. £0.20* TSPMK/DR (B73-50395) ISBN 0 19 358403 4
Sir John in love.. Fantasia on Greensleeves. Fantasia on 'Greensleeves'. (Vaughan Williams, Ralph). *Oxford University Press. £0.30* TSPMK (B73-50394) ISBN 0 19 359309 2

Quinto libro de madrigale a sei voci. Leggiadre ninfe. Leggiadre ninfe = You graceful nymphs: for six-part chorus of mixed voices a cappella. (Marenzio, Luca). *Schirmer. Unpriced* EZDU (B73-50548)

Radford, Anthony. And wilt thou leave me thus?: For SSATBB unaccompanied. *Thames. Unpriced* EZDW (B73-50561)

Radio One story of pop: the first encyclopaedia of pop
Vol.1, no.1- ; 24th Sept. 1973-. *49 Poland St., W1A 2LG: Phoebus Publishing Co. £0.25* ADW/GB(XPN21) (B73-29553)

Rahere. This spiritual house almighty God shall inhabit. Op 146: motet for unaccompanied 4-part choir. (Rubbra, Edmund). *Lengnick. £0.12* EZDH (B73-50534)

Ramati, Roman Haubenstock-. *See* Hauenstock-Ramati.

Rameau, Jean Philippe. Traité de l'harmonie, liv.3.. Laboravi clamans. Laboravi clamans: motet for SSATB and organ. *Peters. Unpriced* DJ (B73-50032)

Ramsbotham, A. Liber primus sacrarum cantionum. Laetentur coeli. Laetentur coeli = Be glad ye heavens: SATBB by William Byrd. (Byrd, William). Revised ed. *Oxford University Press. Unpriced* EZDJ (B73-50536) ISBN 0 19 352058 3

Rands, Bernard. Memo 1: for solo contra bass. *Universal. Unpriced* SSPMJ (B73-50809)

Raphael, Mark. 3 D.H. Lawrence love poems: for high voice and piano. *Thames. Unpriced* KFTDW (B73-50230)

Rapley, Felton. Marching and waltzing. *Chappell. £0.40* RK/AAY (B73-50348)

Rastall, Richard. Two Coventry carols: for 3 voices (S/ATB) with optional instruments. *Antico. Unpriced* EZDP/LF (B73-51000)

Ratcliffe, Desmond.
The Passion of Christ: a devotional service of nine lessons and hymns (or chorales) based on the St Matthew Passion narrative. *Novello. £0.35* DFDM/LH (B73-50012)
Sixty interludes for service use. *Novello. £1.00* RJ (B73-51195)
The story of Christmas: a new presentation of the Festival of Nine Lessons. *Novello. £0.40* DPDF/LF (B73-50973)

Rauchhaupt, Ursula von. The symphony. *Thames and Hudson. £8.50* AMME (B73-26166) ISBN 0 500 01099 4

Raven, Jon. Songs of a changing world. *Ginn. Unpriced* JE/TSDW/GM/AYC (B73-50180) ISBN 0 602 21848 9

Rawsthorne, Alan.
Concerto for clarinet & string orchestra: arr. Concerto for clarinet & string orchestra. *Oxford University Press. £1.50* VVPK/LF (B73-50875) ISBN 0 19 366905 6
Quintet for clarinet, horn, violin, cello and piano. *Oxford University Press. £1.50* NUNR (B73-50269) ISBN 0 19 358572 3
Theme and four studies. *Oxford University Press. Unpriced* QP/T (B73-50296) ISBN 0 19 373571 7

Raynor, Henry. Yehudi Menuhin: the story of the man and the musician. (Magidoff, Robert). 2nd ed. *Hale. £3.00* AS/E(P) (B73-24889) ISBN 0 7091 3351 0

Raynor, John, *b.1909.* A Westminster childhood. *Cassell. £3.25* BRGY(N/XA1921) (B73-24203) ISBN 0 304 29183 8

Reading, John. The preces and responses. Responses in A Sharpe: SATB unacc. *Oxford University Press. Unpriced* EZDGMM (B73-50062) ISBN 0 19 351637 3

Reaks, Brian. As fit as a fiddle: six health education songs for younger children. *British and Continental. Unpriced* JFDW (B73-50624)

Recorder profiles. (Thomson, John Mansfield). *48 Great Marlborough St., W.1: Schott and Co. Ltd. £1.00* AVS/E(M) (B73-05837) ISBN 0 901938 09 2

Recordmasters. *(Allan)*
Blyth, Alan. Janet Baker. *Allan. £1.75* AKFQ/E(P) (B73-21632) ISBN 0 7110 0424 2
Greenfield, Edward. André Previn. *Allan. £2.25* A/EC(P) (B73-21633) ISBN 0 7110 0370 x

Rectanus, Hans. Quartet for strings in D minor. String quartet in D minor. (Pfitzner, Hans). *Bärenreiter. £3.60* RXNS (B73-50786)

Red Sea. Chorus score. The Red Sea: opera in one act. (Williamson, Malcolm). *Weinberger. £0.30* DAC (B73-50010)

Red Sea: opera in one act. (Williamson, Malcolm). *Weinberger. Unpriced* CC (B73-50007)

Red Sea: opera in one act. (Williamson, Malcolm). *Weinberger. £0.30* DAC (B73-50010)

Red Sea. Vocal score. The Red Sea: opera in one act. (Williamson, Malcolm). *Weinberger. Unpriced* CC (B73-50007)

Reda, Siegfried. Fünf Madrigale: für gemischten Chor. *Bärenreiter. £0.40* EZDH (B73-50067)

Reed, Phyllis Luidens. I have a dream: for mixed chorus and piano with soprano solo. *Galaxy Music: Galliard. Unpriced* DH (B73-50956)

Reed, William Henry. Elgar as I knew him. 2nd ed.. *Gollancz. £2.60* BEP(N/XMB33) (B73-16141) ISBN 0 575 01641 8

Rees, Howard. Honeywell: for three groups of instruments and/or voices. *Universal. Unpriced* LJ (B73-50656)

Reflections: two solos for B flat clarinet. (Hinton, Alistair). *Cornelius. Unpriced* VVPJ (B73-50872)

Réfractions. (Miroglio, Francis). *Universal. Unpriced* NYDR (B73-51133)

Regem natum = Our king is born: for 4-part chorus of mixed voices unaccompanied. (Handl, Jacob). *Roberton. Unpriced* EZDJ/LF (B73-50538)

Regions 3: for clarinet, trombone and violoncello. (Lehmann, Hans Ulrich). *Ars viva: Schott. Unpriced* NVNT (B73-50272)

Regnard, Jacques. Tricinia. Selections: arr. Deutsche dreistimmige Lieder nach Art der Neapolitanen oder welschen Villanellen. *Bärenreiter. £0.75* VSNTK/DW (B73-50853)

Regner, Hermann. Chorstudien: for mixed choir. *Schott. Unpriced* EZ/AF (B73-50056)

Reicha, Joseph. Concerto for cello in C major. Op.2, Livre 2: arr. Concerto, C major: for violoncello and orchestra. *Simrock. Unpriced* SRPK/LF (B73-51232)

Reichert, Heinz. The Czarevitch: songs from the operetta. (Lehár, Franz). *Glocken Verlag. Unpriced* KDW (B73-50206)

Reid, Charles, *b.1900.*
Fifty years of Robert Mayer concerts, 1923-1972. *Smythe. £0.55(non-net)* A(W/Q/P) (B73-28190) ISBN 0 900675 78 0
Malcolm Sargent: a biography. *Hodder and Stoughton. £0.60* A/EC(P) (B73-25531) ISBN 0 340 17662 8

Rejoice in the Lamb. Op 30: festival cantata. (Britten, Benjamin). *Boosey and Hawkes. £1.00* FDE (B73-50564)

Rejoice in the Lamb. Op.30. Vocal score: arr. Rejoice in the Lamb. Op 30: festival cantata. (Britten, Benjamin). *Boosey and Hawkes. £1.00* FDE (B73-50564)

Renaissance: songs and dances by French and German composers of the sixteenth and seventeenth centuries. (Stone, David). *Boosey and Hawkes. Unpriced* UNSK/AH/AYH (B73-51262)

Requiem for the living: for speaker, mezzo-soprano or baritone solo, mixed chorus, percussion, cimbalom and piano. (Swann, Donald). *Roberton. Unpriced* KHYE/NYLDE (B73-50242)

Requiescat: canon for two-part high voices (or children's two-part choir). (Stoker, Richard). *Ashdown. £0.10* FTDW/X (B73-50581)

Resonet in laudibus = Joseph dearest, Joseph mine: for four-part chorus of mixed voices. (Handl, Jacob). *Roberton. Unpriced* EZDP/LF (B73-50098)

Responses: musical essays and reviews. (Cairns, David, *b.1926*). *Secker and Warburg. £3.75* A(D) (B73-13013) ISBN 0 436 08090 7

Responsorial psalms for the Sundays of the year, year 1
22nd to 34th Sunday of the yearly cycle. *St Thomas More Centre for Pastoral Liturgy. Unpriced* JDGKAD/AY (B73-50585)
Advent to the Baptism of our Lord. *St Thomas More Centre for Pastoral Liturgy. Unpriced* JDGKAD/AY (B73-50586)
Second Sunday of Easter to Pentecost. *St Thomas More Centre for Pastoral Liturgy. Unpriced* JDGKAD/AY (B73-50587)
Second Sunday of the yearly cycle to Fifth Sunday of Lent. *St Thomas More Centre for Pastoral Liturgy. Unpriced* JDGKAD/AY (B73-50588)
Trinity Sunday to 21st Sunday of the year. *St Thomas More Centre for Pastoral Liturgy. Unpriced* JDGKAD/AY (B73-50589)

Responsorial psalms for the Sundays of the year, year 2
26th-34th Sundays. *St Thomas More Centre for Pastoral Liturgy. Unpriced* JDGKAD/AY (B73-50590)
Advent to the Baptism of our Lord. *St Thomas More Centre for Pastoral Liturgy. Unpriced* JDGKAD/AY (B73-50591)
Second Sunday of Easter to Pentecost. *St Thomas More Centre for Pastoral Liturgy. Unpriced* JDGKAD/AY (B73-50592)
Second Sunday of the yearly cycle to Fifth Sunday of Lent. *St Thomas More Centre for Pastoral Liturgy. Unpriced* JDGKAD/AY (B73-50593)
Trinity Sunday to 21st Sunday of the year. *St Thomas More Centre for Pastoral Liturgy. Unpriced* JDGKAD/AY (B73-50594)
Twenty second Sunday of the yearly cycle to the thirty-fourth Sunday. *St Thomas More Centre for Pastoral Liturgy. Unpriced* JDGKAD/AY (B73-50595)

Responsorial psalms for the Sundays of the year, year 3
2nd Sunday of Easter to Pentecost. *St Thomas More Centre for Pastoral Liturgy. Unpriced* JDGKAD/AY (B73-50596)
23rd Sunday of the year to 34th Sunday of the year. *St Thomas More Centre for Pastoral Liturgy. Unpriced* JDGKAD/AY (B73-50597)
Advent to Epiphany. *St Thomas More Centre for Pastoral Liturgy. Unpriced* JDGKAD/AY (B73-50598)
Trinity Sunday to 22nd Sunday of the year. *St Thomas More Centre for Pastoral Liturgy. Unpriced* JDGKAD/AY (B73-50599)

Reutter, Hermann.
Bogenschutzen: Vokalise für eine hohe Singstimme und Klavier. *Schott. £1.44* KFTDW (B73-51095)
Chamber music: four selected poems, for low male voice and piano. *Schott. £1.20* KFXDW (B73-50655)
Fünf Lieder: für mittlere Stimme und Klavier. *Schott. £1.20* KFVDW (B73-50653)
Neun Lieder: für eine Manner oder Frauenstimme (mittel bis hoch) und Klavier. *Schott. £1.50* KDW (B73-50636)
Vier Lieder: für mittlere Stimme und Klavier. *Schott. £1.20* KFVDW (B73-50654)

Reverie. Opus 24: for orchestra. (Scriabin, Alexander). *Belaieff: Hinrichsen. £0.85* MMJ (B73-50683)

Reynolds, Gordon. The choirmaster in action. *Novello. £0.50* AD/E (B73-15415) ISBN 0 85360 057 0

Rhapsody concerto for viola: arr. Rhapsody-concerto for viola and orchestra. (Martinu, Bohuslav). *Bärenreiter. £1.95* SQPK/LF (B73-50378)

Rhapsody for orchestra. (Panufnik, Andrzej). *Boosey and Hawkes. £1.00* MMJ (B73-50682)

Rhodes, Willard. Music of the Americas: an illustrated music ethnology of the Eskimo and American Indian peoples. (Collaer, Paul). *Curzon Press. £6.50* BZP (B73-02064) ISBN 0 7007 0004 8

Rhys, Jean. Memories of morning. Night: a monodrama for mezzosoprano and orchestra. (Crosse, Gordon). *Oxford University Press. £3.00* KFNE/MDX (B73-50650) ISBN 0 19 362487 7

Rhythm and action songs for tiny tots. (McNess-Eames, Vera). *Stockwell. £0.25* JFDW/GR (B73-51073) ISBN 0 7223 0403 x

Richard III. Prelude: arr. Prelude. (Walton, *Sir* William). *Boosey and Hawkes. £4.50* UMMK/JR (B73-50835)

Richards, Nansi. Cwpwrdd Nansi. *Gwasg Gomer. £0.75* ATQ/E(P) (B73-19501)

Richardson, Alan. Second book of oboe solos. (Craxton, Janet). *Faber Music. Unpriced* VTPK/AAY (B73-50422)

Richardson, Norman.
Eye level: theme from the Thames TV series 'Van der Valk'. (Trombey, Jack). *Boosey and Hawkes. Unpriced* WMK/AGM/JS (B73-51298)
Richard III. Prelude: arr. Prelude. (Walton, *Sir* William). *Boosey and Hawkes. £4.50* UMMK/JR (B73-50835)

Richter, Clifford. Madrigals and motets of four centuries: a choral songbook of 18 European classics, for mixed voices. *Associated Music. Unpriced* CB/AY (B73-50933)

Richter, Franz Xaver. Sinfonia a quattro for string orchestra in C minor. Sinfonia a quattro, C-moll: für Streicher. *Peters. £1.80* RXMJ (B73-50774)

Richter, Werner. Concerto for flute, harp & orchestra in C major. K.299: arr. Konzert für Flöte, Harfe und Orchester, C-Dur. KV299. (Mozart, Wolfgang Amadeus). *Peters. £3.60* VRPK/LF (B73-50844)

Riddle song: SATB. (Rutter, John). *Oxford University Press. Unpriced* DW (B73-50517) ISBN 0 19 343031 2

Ridley, George. George Ridley, Gateshead poet and vocalist. *Graham. £0.40* AKDW/G/E(YDJHT/P) (B73-19498) ISBN 0 902833 81 2

Ridout, Alan. Music for three violoncelli. *Schott. £0.75* SRPMJ (B73-50386)

Riethmüller, G. Concerto for cello in C major. Op.2, Livre 2: arr. Concerto, C major: for violoncello and orchestra. (Reicha, Joseph). *Simrock. Unpriced* SRPK/LF (B73-51232)

Right on march. (Goldman, Edwin Franko). *Boosey and Hawkes. £1.75* UMMGM (B73-50400)

Rilke, Rainer Maria.
Love-song: for four-part chorus of mixed voices a cappella. (Heath, Fenno). *Schirmer. Unpriced* EZDW (B73-50117)
Portrait intérieur: for mezzo-soprano and violin and cello. (Binkerd, Gordon). *Boosey and Hawkes. £1.50* KFNE/SPLSRDW (B73-50652)
Portrait interieur: for mezzo-soprano and violin and cello. (Binkerd, Gordon). *Boosey and Hawkes. £1.25* KFNE/SPLSRDW (B73-51092)

Rimmer, Frederick. A history of Scottish music. (Elliott, Kenneth). *British Broadcasting Corporation. £0.90* A(YDL/X) (B73-25526) ISBN 0 563 12192 0

Ring of carols: for female or boys' voices and piano. (Adams, Jean). *Paxton. £0.27* FDP/LF (B73-51020)

Ring out, sing out: a festival carol for spring and summer, for unison voices, recorders, percussion, violins, cellos and piano. (Tate, Phyllis). *Oxford University Press. Unpriced* JFE/NYDSDP (B73-51074) ISBN 0 19 344943 9

Rive, Thomas. Classical polyphony. (Rubio, Samuel). *Blackwell. £3.45* A/RM (B73-04219) ISBN 0 631 11740 7
Rob Gordon's book of Scottish music. (Gordon, Rob). *Kerr. Unpriced* QPK/AH/AYDL (B73-50316)
Rob Loyd folio of graduated guitar solos. (Loyd, Rob). *Kadence Music, Affiliated Music. £0.75* TSPMJ (B73-51249)
Robert Schumann: the man and his music. (Walker, Alan, *b.1930*). *Barrie and Jenkins. £7.50* BSG (B73-04217) ISBN 0 214 66805 3
Roberts, John Storm. Black music of two worlds. *Allen Lane. £3.50* A/HG(X) (B73-16795) ISBN 0 7139 0536 0
Robertson, M. Da sangs at a'll sing ta dee: a book of Shetland songs. (Robertson, Thomas Alexander). *Shetland Folk Society. Unpriced* JEZDW/G/AYDLZN (B73-51063)
Robertson, Thomas Alexander. Da sangs at a'll sing ta dee: a book of Shetland songs. *Shetland Folk Society. Unpriced* JEZDW/G/AYDLZN (B73-51063)
Robinson, Stanford. The Savoyards. Vocal score. The Savoyards: a new operetta. *Boosey and Hawkes. £3.00* CF (B73-50489)
Rochberg, George. Caprice variations: for unaccompanied violin. *Galaxy: Galliard. Unpriced* SPM/T (B73-50793)
Roche, Elizabeth.
Concerti ecclesiastici. Op.4. *Excerpts.* Non vos relinquam orphanos = I will not leave you fatherless: SSA or T.T. Bar. (Donati, Ignazio). *Oxford University Press. Unpriced* FDJ (B73-50135) ISBN 0 19 350336 0
Concerti ecclesiastici. Op.4. Nun vos relinquam orphanos. Non vos relinquam orphanos = I will not leave you fatherless: SSA or T.T. Bar. (Donati, Ignazio). *Oxford University Press. Unpriced* FDJ (B73-51035) ISBN 0 19 350336 0
Il Primo libro delli motetti concertati.. Ut flos, ut rosa. Ut flos, ut rosa. = Like flowers, like roses bloom the crowns: S.S. or T.T. (Crivelli, Giovanni Battista). *Oxford University Press. Unpriced* FLDJ (B73-50162) ISBN 0 19 350337 9
Roche, Jerome.
Concerti ecclesiastici. Op.4. *Excerpts.* Non vos relinquam orphanos = I will not leave you fatherless: SSA or T.T. Bar. (Donati, Ignazio). *Oxford University Press. Unpriced* FDJ (B73-50135) ISBN 0 19 350336 0
Concerti ecclesiastici. Op.4. Nun vos relinquam orphanos. Non vos relinquam orphanos = I will not leave you fatherless: SSA or T.T. Bar. (Donati, Ignazio). *Oxford University Press. Unpriced* FDJ (B73-51035) ISBN 0 19 350336 0
The madrigal. *Hutchinson. £2.60* AEZDU(YJ) (B73-02066) ISBN 0 09 113260 6
Il Primo libro delli motetti concertati.. Ut flos, ut rosa. Ut flos, ut rosa. = Like flowers, like roses bloom the crowns: S.S. or T.T. (Crivelli, Giovanni Battista). *Oxford University Press. Unpriced* FLDJ (B73-50162) ISBN 0 19 350337 9
Rock-a my soul: negro spiritual, for 3-part chorus of treble voices with piano accompaniment. (Barthelson, Joyce). *Roberton. £0.13* FLDW/LC (B73-50579)
Roe, Betty.
Away in a manger: carol for mixed choir and organ/piano. *Thames. Unpriced* DP/LF (B73-50041)
Away in a manger: carol for mixed choir and organ/piano. *Thames. Unpriced* JDP/LF (B73-50604)
Come all ye children: carol for unison voices and piano (organ). *Thames. Unpriced* JFDP/LF (B73-50184)
Deck the hall: carol for mixed voices. *Thames. Unpriced* EZDP/LF (B73-50543)
Firstlings: three songs, for medium voice, flute, (clarinet or violin) and guitar. *Thames. Unpriced* KFVE/VRPLTSDW (B73-50239)
Jubilate Deo: for SATB and organ. *Thames. Unpriced* DGNT (B73-50500)
Noble numbers: five songs for counter-tenor (or contralto) and piano (or harpsichord). *Thames. Unpriced* KHNDW (B73-50241)
Nursery rhyme of innocence and experience: song for medium voice and piano. *Thames. Unpriced* KFVDW (B73-50234)
Sing for Christmas: 6 songs for unison voices (optional 2nd part). *Thames. Unpriced* JFDP/LF (B73-50620)
Summer suite
five easy pieces for guitar. *Thames. Unpriced* TSPMG (B73-50393)
Summer suite: five easy pieces for guitar. *Thames. Unpriced* TSPMG (B73-50819)
Roger Evans book of folk songs and how to play them: all guitar chords, melody, lyrics & easy to understand guitar accompaniments. (Evans, Roger). *Robbins, Francis, Day & Hunter. £0.60* KE/TSDW/G/AY (B73-50217)
Rokos, Kurt W. Il Cimento dell'armonia e dell'invenzione. Op.8, no.3. La Caccia: arr. The hunt from 'Autumn' (The four seasons). (Vivaldi, Antonio). *Bosworth. £0.57* MK (B73-51108)
'Rolling Stone'. Lennon remembers: the 'Rolling Stone' interviews with John Lennon and Yoko Ono. (Wenner, Jann). *Talmy. £2.25* AKG/E(P) (B73-07792) ISBN 0 900735 10 4
Roman Catholic Church. *Liturgy and ritual.* Missarum liber primus. (Animuccia, Giovanni). 1st ed. reprinted. *Gregg. £12.60* ADG (B73-00361) ISBN 0 576 28220 0
Romance. (Wagner, Richard). *Chappell. Unpriced* RXMK (B73-51212)
Romani, G. Sonate à tre in G minor. Adagio: arr. Adagio in G minor on two thematic fragments and a figured bass. (Albinoni, Tommaso). *Ricordi. Unpriced* RSPMK (B73-51210)
Romanza for cello and orchestra. Op.24. (Goehr, Alexander). *Schott. £2.50* MPSR (B73-51122)
Rombaut, John. A grain of wheat: 12 songs of grouping and growing. (Oswin, Mary). *Mayhew-McCrimmon. £0.47* JDM (B73-50601)
Rondeau for organ. (Cole, Bruce). *Boosey and Hawkes. £0.65* R/W (B73-50753)
Roper, Keith.
Landscapes: for two clarinets. *Thames. Unpriced* VVNU (B73-50869)
Triptych: horn and piano. *Thames. Unpriced* WTPJ (B73-50914)
Rorate coeli desuper = Drop down, ye heavens: SAATB. (Byrd, William). *Oxford University Press. Unpriced* EZDGKAD/LEZ (B73-50059) ISBN 0 19 352062 1
Rorem, Ned.
Bertha. Vocal score. Bertha: one act opera. *Boosey and Hawkes. £2.00* CC (B73-50936)
Day music: for violin and piano. *Boosey and Hawkes. £1.25* SPJ (B73-50366)
Rose, Bernard.
Cathedral music.. Bow down thine ear. Bow down thine ear, O Lord: SATB (SS Soli). (Hayes, William). *Oxford University Press. £0.25* DK (B73-50035) ISBN 0 19 350334 4
Cathedral music. *Excerpts.* Bow down thine ear, O Lord: SATB (SS Soli). (Hayes, William). *Oxford University Press. £0.25* DK (B73-50035) ISBN 0 19 350334 4
Praise ye the Lord: anthem for double choir (unaccompanied). *Novello. £0.18* EZDK (B73-50540)
Rose, Fred.
'Deed I do: arr. 'Deed I do: march. (Hirsch, Walter). *Keith Prowse. Unpriced* UMMK/DW (B73-51256)
'Deed I do: arr. 'Deed I do: march. (Hirsch, Walter). *Keith Prowse. Unpriced* WMK/DW (B73-51299)
Rose, Gregory.
God's strange ways: SATB a cappella. *Boosey and Hawkes. £0.14* EZDH (B73-50984)
It's snowing: S.A.T.B. *Boosey and Hawkes. £0.15* EZDW (B73-51010)
Rose, Michael.
Mirth: anthem for female or boy's voices and organ. *Novello. £0.14* FDH (B73-51016)
Now the most high is born = Nunc natus est altissimus: carol for female or boys' voices and organ. *Novello. £0.14* JFDP/LF (B73-51067)
Rosen, Charles. The classical style: Haydn, Mozart, Beethoven. *Faber. £2.00* A(X) (B73-04668) ISBN 0 571 10234 4
Rosenthal, Harold. Concise Oxford dictionary of opera. 1st ed. reprinted with corrections. *Oxford University Press. £2.00* AC(C) (B73-30857) ISBN 0 19 311305 8
Rosetti, Christina. Love came down at Christmas: carol. (Noble, Harold). *Studio Music. Unpriced* JDP/LF (B73-51051)
Rosetti, Franz Anton.
Concerto for oboe in C major. Konzert für Oboe und Kammerorchester, C-Dur. *Peters. £3.00* MPVTF (B73-50688)
Concerto for oboe in C major: arr. Konzert für Oboe und Kammerorchester, C-Dur. *Peters. £2.20* VTPK/LF (B73-50860)
Ross, Walter. Concerto for trombone: arr. Trombone concerto. *Boosey and Hawkes. £2.50* WUPK/LF (B73-50923)
Rossetti, Christina. In the bleak mid winter: carol for SATB unaccompanied. (Walker, Robert). *Novello. £0.07* EZDP/LF (B73-51003)
Rossini, Gioacchino Antonio.
Duetto for two cats with an accompaniment for the pianoforte. (Berthold, G). *Schott. £0.50* JNFEDW (B73-50628)
Prelude, thème et variations pour cor. Prelude, theme and variations for horn and piano. *Peters. Unpriced* WTP/T (B73-50468)
Rota, Nina. The godfather: themes for easy play piano. *Famous Chappell. £0.40* QPK/JR (B73-50324)
Rothenberg, Peter.
Dance melodies: for 2 manuals and pedal. *Schott. £1.20* RPVK/AAY (B73-50352)
Rund um die Weihnacht: für l-manualige Orgel. *Schott. £1.40* RK/DP/LF/AY (B73-51205)
Rothke, Georg. Quartet for string instruments in C major. K.157: arr. Divertimento, C-Dur. (Mozart, Wolfgang Amadeus). *Schott. £1.20* RXMK (B73-50359)
Rothko chapel. (Feldman, Morton). *Universal. Unpriced* ENYJDW (B73-50524)
Roussel, Hubert. The Houston Symphony Orchestra, 1913-1971. *University of Texas Press. £3.40* AMM/E(QB/XMN59) (B73-10709) ISBN 0 292 73000 4
Routh, Francis. Early English organ music from the Middle Ages to 1837. *Barrie and Jenkins. £6.75* AR(XCQ438) (B73-04220) ISBN 0 214 66804 5
Rowe, Winston Hugh. Communion service, Series 3: for congregation and choir. *Cramer. £0.09* JDGS (B73-51048)
Roxburgh, Edwin.
Images for oboe and piano. *United Music. Unpriced* VTPJ (B73-51286)
Partita for solo violoncello. *United Music. Unpriced* SRPMG (B73-51234)
Royal College of Organists. Year book
1972-1973. *Kensington Gore, SW7 2QS: Royal College of Organists. £0.75* AR(YC/VP/Q) (B73-04670) ISBN 0 902462 03 2
Royal School of Church Music. English church music: a collection of essays
1973. *Addington Palace, Croydon, CR9 5AD: Royal School of Church Music. £0.90* AD/LD(YD/D) (B73-18105) ISBN 0 85402 052 7
Rubbra, Edmund.
Fanfare for Europe on the notes EEC. Op.142: for six trumpets in C. *Lengnick. £1.00* WSNQGN (B73-50911)
Symphony no.8, 'Hommage à Teilhard de Chardin'. Op. 132. *Lengnick. £2.00* MME (B73-50673)
This spiritual house almighty God shall inhabit. Op 146: motet for unaccompanied 4-part choir. *Lengnick. £0.12* EZDH (B73-50534)
Trio for violin, cello & piano, no.2. Op. 138. Piano trio. Op. 138: for piano, violin and violoncello. *Lengnick. £1.00* NXNT (B73-51132)
Rubinstein, Arthur. My young years. *Cape. £4.50* AQ/E(P/XLG31) (B73-29558) ISBN 0 224 00926 5
Rubio, Samuel. Classical polyphony. *Blackwell. £3.45* A/RM (B73-04219) ISBN 0 631 11740 7
Rudland, Malcolm.
Carol of Joseph: for SATB choir. *Thames. Unpriced* EZDP/LF (B73-50099)
Mary of the wilderness: carol for SATB and flute. *Thames. Unpriced* EVRDH/LF (B73-50054)
Ruf, Hugo.
Eight fugues for keyboard. Acht Fugen für Cembalo oder Orgel. (Kirnberger, Johann Philipp). *Schott. £1.80* PWP/Y (B73-51137)
Simphonies for two instruments, liv. 1, suite 2, liv. 2, suites. 1, 2. Simphonies: three easy duets for recorders, flutes, oboes or other melodic instruments. (Chedeville, Esprit Philippe). *Schott. £1.08* LNU (B73-51099)
Rund um die Weihnacht: für l-manualige Orgel. (Rothenberg, Peter). *Schott. £1.40* RK/DP/LF/AY (B73-51205)
Runze, Klaus. Zwei Hande- zwölf Tasten
Band 2: Spiel mit Noten. *Schott. Unpriced* LNU (B73-51101)
Rushton, Julian. New edition of the complete works of Hector Berlioz
Vol.5: Huit scenes de Faust; edited by Julian Rushton. (Berlioz, Hector). *Bärenreiter. Unpriced* C/AZ (B73-50482)
Ruskin, John. For lo the winter is past: for full chorus of mixed voices a cappella. (Chorbajian, John). *Schirmer. Unpriced* EZDW (B73-50111)
Russell, Raymond. The harpsichord and clavichord: an introductory study. 2nd ed. *Faber. £7.50* AQR/B(XA1900) (B73-17453) ISBN 0 571 04795 5
Russell, Ross. Bird lives! *27 Goodge St., W1P 1FD: Quartet Books Ltd. £3.75* AVU/HX(P) (B73-22801) ISBN 0 7043 2007 x
Russell-Smith, Geoffrey. Pentatonic music
Vol.4: 140 Churash melodies. (Kodály, Zoltán). *Boosey and Hawkes. £0.30* JFEZDW/PP/AY (B73-50196)
Russell-Smith, Geoffry.
Fiddle-dee: SSAA unaccompanied. (Kodály, Zoltán). *Boosey and Hawkes. £0.05* FEZDW (B73-51041)
Have good courage: SSA unaccompanied. (Kodaly, Zoltán). *Boosey and Hawkes. £0.14* FEZDW (B73-50574)
The wedding ring: SSAA and piano. *Boosey and Hawkes. £0.09* FDW (B73-50568)
Russian music and its sources in chant and folk-song. (Swan, Alfred Julius). *J. Baker. £4.50* A(YM/XA1950) (B73-22799) ISBN 0 212 98421 7
Rutherford, Robert. Show album: songs and sketches. (Wilcock, Frank). *Brown, Son and Ferguson. £0.75* JDW (B73-51057)
Rutter, John.
Carols for schools: twelve carols for unison voices, recorders or flutes, percussion, guitar and piano. *Oxford University Press. £1.60* JFE/NYDPDP/LF/AY (B73-50193) ISBN 0 19 330665 4
Fancies. Riddle song. Riddle song: SATB. *Oxford University Press. Unpriced* DW (B73-50517) ISBN 0 19 343031 2
Fancies. Vocal score. Fancies: a cycle of choral settings with small orchestra. *Oxford University Press. Unpriced* DW (B73-50045) ISBN 0 19 338071 4
O clap your hands: SATB. *Oxford University Press. Unpriced* DK (B73-50963) ISBN 0 19 350347 6
Sing we to this merry company: SATB. *Oxford University Press. Unpriced* DP/LF (B73-50042) ISBN 0 19 343037 1
Ryman, James. Now the most high is born = Nunc natus est altissimus: carol for female or boys' voices and organ. (Rose, Michael). *Novello. £0.14* JFDP/LF (B73-51067)
Sabeth: for alto flute (G), cor anglais (F), (viola), and harp. (Huber, Klaus). *Ars viva. £5.00* NVPNT (B73-50695)
Sachs, Nelly. Vier Lieder: für mittlere Stimme und Klavier. (Reutter, Hermann). *Schott. £1.20* KFVDW (B73-50654)
Sackett, S J. The faucet: for four-part chorus of men's voices with piano accompaniment. (Miller, Lewis M). *Schirmer. Unpriced* GDW (B73-50165)
Sacrae symphoniae, bk.1. Plaudite. Vocal score. Plaudite: for triple chorus of mixed voices. (Gabrieli, Giovanni). *Schirmer. Unpriced* DJ (B73-50961)
Sacred harp. Three hymns: arranged for four-part chorus of mixed voices with tenor solo a cappella
1: Paradise. *Chappell. Unpriced* EZDM (B73-50091)
2: The morning trumpet. *Chappell. Unpriced* EZDM (B73-50092)

Sacred harp. Three hymns: arranged for four-part chorus of mixed voices with tenor solo a cappella
3: Sweet rivers. *Chappell. Unpriced* EZDM (B73-50093)
Sadie, Stanley.
Sonata for piano in A major. K.331. Sonata in A. K.331. (Mozart, Wolfgang Amadeus). *Associated Board of the Royal Schools of Music. £0.35* QPE (B73-50721)
Sonata for piano in C major. K.309. Sonata in C. (Mozart, Wolfgang Amadeus). *Associated Board of the Royal Schools of Music. £0.35* QPE (B73-51168)
Sonata for piano in D major. K.576. Sonata in D. K.576. (Mozart, Wolfgang Amadeus). *Associated Board of the Royal Schools of Music. £0.35* QPE (B73-50722)
Sonata for piano in F major. K.332. Sonata in F. K.332. (Mozart, Wolfgang Amadeus). *Associated Board of the Royal Schools of Music. £0.35* QPE (B73-50723)
Sonata for piano in F major. K.533. Sonata in F. K.533. (Mozart, Wolfgang Amadeus). *Associated Board of the Royal Schools of Music. £0.35* QPE (B73-50724)
Sadleir, Richard. More carols for recorder, with simple harmonies for auto-harp, chimes or guitar. *British and Continental Music. £0.20* VSPLTQTK/DP/LF/AY (B73-51278)
Sadler, Graham. Operas. Selections. Operatic airs. (Campra, André). *Oxford University Press, for the University of Hull. £3.50* KDW (B73-50629)
Saffe, Ferdinand. Erstlinge musicalischer Andachten.. Jauchzet Gott, alle Lande. Jauchzet Gott, alle Lande = Make a joyful noise unto God: sacred concerto for soprano, two violins and basso continuo. (Weiland, Julius Johann). *Bärenreiter. £1.50* KFLE/SNTPWDE (B73-50225)
Sailing by: words and music by Ronald Binge. (Binge, Ronald). *Mozart Edition. Unpriced* KDW (B73-50203)
St George's Chapel, Windsor Castle. *See* Windsor Castle. *St George's Chapel.*
St Pancras Library. *See* Camden *(London Borough). Libraries and Arts Department. St Pancras Library.*
Saint-Saens, Camille.
Le Carnival des animaux. Le Cygne: arr. The swan. *Studio Music. Unpriced* WMPWTWK (B73-50904)
Carnival des animaux. Le Cygne: arr. Le Cygne = The swan. *Paxton. £0.25* SRPK (B73-50384)
Saint-Saens, Charles. Samson et Dalila. Mon coeur s'ouvre à ta voix: arr. Softly awakes my heart. *Studio Music. Unpriced* WMK/DW (B73-50899)
Salon Mexico. (Copland, Aaron). *Boosey and Hawkes. £7.50* UMK (B73-50397)
Salt caked smokestack: piano solo. (Parfrey, Raymond). *Composer to Player Edition. Unpriced* QPJ (B73-50741)

Salvation Army Brass Band Journal (Festival series).
Nos 349-352. *Salvationist Publishing and Supplies. Unpriced* WM/AY (B73-50878)
Samson et Dalila. Mon coeur s'ouvre à ta voix: arr. Softly awakes my heart. (Saint-Saens, Charles). *Studio Music. Unpriced* WMK/DW (B73-50899)
San Casciano: for recorder ensemble, solo sopranino, descants, trebles, tenors. (Kear, Warrick). *Tomus. Unpriced* VSNPG (B73-51270)
Sandner, Wolfgang. Adagio and rondo for wind sextet. Adagio und Rondo für 2 Klarinetten, 2 Horner und 2 Fagotte. (Weber, Carl Maria, *Freiherr von*). *Schott. £2.88* UNQ/W (B73-51259)
Sandy, Stephen. Home from the range: for full chorus of mixed voices a cappella. (Wilson, Richard). *Schirmer. Unpriced* EZDX (B73-50132)
Sanford, Herb. Tommy and Jimmy - the Dorsey years. *Allan. £2.95* AMT(P) (B73-18107)
ISBN 0 7110 0416 1
Sangs at a'll sing ta dee: a book of Shetland songs. (Robertson, Thomas Alexander). *Shetland Folk Society. Unpriced* JEZDW/G/AYDLZN (B73-51063)
Sansom, Clive A.
Favourites for recorder
No.3. *British and Continental. £0.25* VSPMK/DW/G/AY (B73-50417)
Jubilate jazz: for SATB with instrumental accompaniment. *Paterson. Unpriced* ELDGNT (B73-50048)
O sinner man. *Studio Music. Unpriced* FDM (B73-51019)

Saroyan, William. My heart's in the highlands. Vocal score. My heart's in the highlands: chamber opera in two acts. (Beeson, Jack). *Boosey and Hawkes. £10.00* CC (B73-50487)
Savoyards: a new operetta. (Robinson, Stanford). *Boosey and Hawkes. £3.00* CF (B73-50489)
Savoyards. Vocal score. The Savoyards: a new operetta. (Robinson, Stanford). *Boosey and Hawkes. £3.00* CF (B73-50489)
Scale and chord studies for viola. (Matz, Arnold). *Peters. Unpriced* SQ/AF (B73-50374)
Scarborough Fair: rhythmic version for piano solo. (Dexter, Harry). *Ashdown. £0.20* QPK/DW (B73-50318)
Scarlatti, Alessandro.
Il Giardino di amore.. Sinfonia. Sinfonia for trumpet and strings. *Musica rara. Unpriced* RXMPWS (B73-50360)
Il Giardino di amore. Sinfonia. Sinfonia: for trumpet and strings. *Musica rara. Unpriced* WSPK (B73-50466)
Io son pur solo: solo cantata for soprano and basso continuo. First edition. *Bärenreiter. £1.20* KFLDX (B73-50222)
Luntan dalla suna Clori: solo cantata for soprano and basso continuo. First edition. *Bärenreiter. £1.20* KFLDX (B73-50223)
Symphony for flute and string ochestra, no,6, in A minor. Sinfonia Nr,6 a-moll: Flöte, Streicher und Basso continuo. *Peters. Unpriced* RXMPVRE (B73-50778)
Symphony for flute & string orchestra, no 7, in G minor. Sinfonia Nr. 7, g-moll: Flöte, Streicher und Basso continuo. *Peters. Unpriced* RXMPVRE (B73-50779)
Symphony for flute & string orchestra, no.8, in G major. Sinfonia Nr. 8, G-dur: Flöte, Streicher und Basso continuo. *Peters. Unpriced* RXMPVRE (B73-50782)
Symphony for flute & string orchestra, no. 9, in G minor. Sinfonia, Nr.9,g-moll: Flöte, Streicher und Basso continuo. *Peters. Unpriced* RXMPVRE (B73-50777)
Symphony for flute & string orchestra, No. 10, in A minor. Sinfonia Nr. 10, a-moll: Flöte. Streicher und Basso continuo. *Peters. Unpriced* RXMPVRE (B73-50780)
Symphony for flute & string orchestra, no. 11, in C major. Sinfonia Nr. 11, C-dur: Flöte, Streicher und Basso continuo. *Peters. Unpriced* RXMPVRE (B73-50781)
Scenes from childhood: for piano. (Schumann, Robert). *Chappell. Unpriced* QPJ (B73-50309)
Schein, Johann Hermann.
Banchetto musicale.. Suites. Three suites for five string or wind instruments. *Bärenreiter. £2.70* RXNRG (B73-50361)
Israelsbrünnlein. Zion spricht: arr. Zion spricht = Zion speaks. *Roberton. Unpriced* EZDH (B73-50535)
Schenker, Friedrich. Fünf Bagatellen: für Posaune und Klavier. *Peters. Unpriced* VWPJ (B73-50434)
Scherzino. Op 27a: for piccolo, three flutes, three B flat clarinets and B flat bass clarinet. (Tull, Fisher). *Boosey and Hawkes. £4.00* VNN (B73-50839)
Scherzo for B flat clarinet and piano. (Johnson, Thomas Arnold). *British and Continental Music. Unpriced* VVPJ (B73-51293)
Scherzo for Christmas: for school orchestra. (Benoy, Arthur William). *Oxford University Press. Unpriced* M/LF (B73-51104) ISBN 0 19 361966 0
Scherzo for piano duet, 'The keys of Canterbury'. (Hamilton, Alasdair). *Roberton. £0.40* QNV (B73-51162)
Schmidt, Harold. Motecta. O regem coeli. In festo natalis Domini: for 4-part chorus of mixed voices unaccompanied. (Victoria, Tomas Luis de). *Roberton. Unpriced* EZDJ/LF (B73-50539)
Schmidt, Peter. Airs francais = Cantate francaise: for soprano and basso continuo. (Handel, George Frideric). First ed. *Bärenreiter. £1.50* KFLDX (B73-50643)
Schmitt, Meinrad. Fantasia piccola: für Streichquartett. *Bosse: Bärenreiter. £2.10* RXNS (B73-50787)
Schnebel, Dieter.
Für Stimmen (... missa est)!
Nr. 3: Madrisha II; fur 3 Chorgruppen. *Schott. £4.80* EZDW (B73-51011)
Für Stimmen (... missa est)
Nr.1,2: Choralvorspiele 1/2, für Orgel, Nebeninstrumente und Tonband. *Schott. Unpriced* NYFXP (B73-50284)
Schneider, Eta Harich-. *See* Harich-Schneider, Eta.
Schneider, Max. Messiah. Vocal score. Der Messias = The Messiah: oratorio in three parts. (Handel, George Frideric). *Bärenreiter. £2.10* DD (B73-50495)
Schneider, Willy.
Spielstucke und Etüden: für Trompete oder Flugelhorn oder Kornett. *Schott. £1.44* WS/AF (B73-51304)
Suite for two trumpets in B and two trombones. Suite für zwei Trompeten in B und zwei Posaunen. (Szelenyi, Istvan). *Schott. £2.40* WNSG (B73-51303)
Scholes, Percy Alfred. The concise Oxford dictionary of music. 2nd ed. reprinted with corrections. *Oxford University Press. £1.50* A(C) (B73-30855)
ISBN 0 19 311302 3
Schonfeld, Robert David.
Apple to the core. (McCabe, Peter). *Sphere. £0.40* AKDW/GB/E(P) (B73-05834) ISBN 0 7221 5899 8
Apple to the core: the unmaking of the Beatles. (McCabe, Peter). *37 Museum St., W.C.1: Martin Brian and O'Keeffe Ltd. £2.00* AKDW/GB(P) (B73-05835)
ISBN 0 85616 090 3
School of English Church Music. *See* Royal School of Church Music.
Schools Council. *Music Committee.* Music and integrated studies in the secondary school: a bulletin. *160 Great Portland St., W.1: Schools Council. Free* A(VF) (B73-11781) ISBN 0 901681 28 8
Schott, Howard. The harpsichord and clavichord: an introductory study. (Russell, Raymond). 2nd ed. *Faber. £7.50* AQR/B(XA1900) (B73-17453)
ISBN 0 571 04795 5
Schroeder, Hermann. Sonatina for piano, no.3, in C minor. Sonatina no.3 in C minor: piano solo. *Simrock. Unpriced* QPEM (B73-50725)
Schubert, Franz.
Schubert and Schumann songs and translations. *Melbourne University Press: Distributed by Angus and Robertson. £4.15* BSGADW (B73-13019) ISBN 0 522 83999 1
Sonatas for violin and piano. D.384, 385 & 408. *Bärenreiter. £2.10* SPE (B73-50790)
Symphony no.8 in B minor, 'Unfinished'. D759. Symphony in B minor, 'Unfinished'. *Chappell. Unpriced* MME (B73-50253)
Waltzes for piano. D.779, no.12, D.734, no.15 & D.924, no.9: arr. Three waltzes. *Cornelius. Unpriced* TSPMK/AHW (B73-50828)
Works, string instruments. Complete chamber music for strings. *Dover: Constable. £2.25* RXN/AZ (B73-51214)
ISBN 0 486 21463 x
Works, strings and piano. Complete chamber music for pianoforte and strings. *Dover: Constable. £2.25* NX/AZ (B73-51131) ISBN 0 486 21527 x
Schubert. (Hutchings, Arthur). Revised ed. *Dent. £2.00* BSF(N) (B73-04216) ISBN 0 460 03139 2
Schubert and Schumann songs and translations. *Melbourne University Press: Distributed by Angus and Robertson. £4.15* BSGADW (B73-13019) ISBN 0 522 83999 1
Schubert's songs. (Capell, Richard). 3rd ed.. *Pan Books. £0.95* BSFAKDW (B73-29556) ISBN 0 330 23775 6
Schulé, Bernard. Petit livre des formes musicales = Spiel mit musikalischen Formen. Op.83: acht leichter Stücke, für Flöte ober Oboe und Klavier. *Bosse: Bärenreiter. £1.80* VRPJ (B73-50843)
Schulten, Gustav. Draussen am Rain = Uti var hage: Schwedisches Volkslied, für gemischten Chor a cappella. (Steinfeld, Karl-Heinz). *Bosworth. £0.10* EZDW (B73-50562)
Schumann, Clara.
Works, piano. Piano music of Robert Schumann
Series 1. (Schumann, Robert). *Dover: Constable. £2.25* QP/AZ (B73-50310) ISBN 0 486 21459 1
Works piano. Piano music of Robert Schumann
Series 2. (Schumann, Robert). *Dover: Constable. £2.25* QP/AZ (B73-50311) ISBN 0 486 21461 3
Schumann, Robert.
Adagio and allegro. Op.70: for horn (or violin, or viola, or cello) and piano. *Schirmer: Chappell. Unpriced* WTPJ (B73-51305)
Adagio and allegro. Op.70: for horn (or violin, or viola, or cello) and piano. *Schirmer: Chappell. Unpriced* WTPJ (B73-51306)
Kinderscenen. Op.15. Scenes from childhood: for piano. *Chappell. Unpriced* QPJ (B73-50309)
Kinderscenen. Op.15. Traümerei: arr. Traümerei. *Cornelius. Unpriced* VVNSK (B73-50866)
Schubert and Schumann songs and translations. *Melbourne University Press: Distributed by Angus and Robertson. £4.15* BSGADW (B73-13019) ISBN 0 522 83999 1
Sketches for pedal-piano. Op.58. Four sketches. *Oxford University Press. £0.65* RJ (B73-50762)
ISBN 0 19 375732 x
Symphony in G minor. Sinfonie, G-moll für Orchester. *Litolff: Peters. £3.00* MME (B73-50674)
Works, piano. Piano music of Robert Schumann
Series 1. *Dover: Constable. £2.25* QP/AZ (B73-50310)
ISBN 0 486 21459 1
Works piano. Piano music of Robert Schumann
Series 2. *Dover: Constable. £2.25* QP/AZ (B73-50311)
ISBN 0 486 21461 3
Schurmann, Gerard.
Attack and celebration: for orchestra. *Novello. £1.25* MMJ (B73-51118)
Concerto for clarinet & string orchestra: arr. Concerto for clarinet & string orchestra. (Rawsthorne, Alan). *Oxford University Press. £1.50* VVPK/LF (B73-50875)
ISBN 0 19 366905 6
Serenade for solo violin. *Novello. £1.20* SPMJ (B73-50370)
Schütz, Heinrich. Psalmen Davids, 1619. Die mit Tränen säen. Die mit Tränen säen: motet for two five-part choirs and basso continuo. *Bärenreiter. £1.50* EWUNPPWDH (B73-50527)
Schwartz, Elliot. Electronic music: a listener's guide. *Secker and Warburg. £5.00* APV (B73-16150)
ISBN 0 436 44410 0
Schwartz, Stephen.
Godspell: film souvenir song book. *Valando Music. £1.00* KDW/JR (B73-50638)
Mass.. A simple song. A simple song. (Bernstein, Leonard). *Amberson: Schirmer. Unpriced* KDW (B73-50200)
Mass.. Almighty Father. Almighty Father: chorale for four part chorus of mixed voices a cappella. (Bernstein, Leonard). *Amberson: Schirmer. Unpriced* EZDH (B73-50070)
Mass. The word of the Lord. The word of the Lord. (Bernstein, Leonard). *Amberson: Schirmer. Unpriced* KDW (B73-50201)
Scott, Anthony. Easter: a marriage anthem, SATB and organ. *Boosey and Hawkes. £0.20* DH/LL (B73-50031)
Scott, Barbara. Folk songs of France: 25 traditional French songs with guitar chords, in both French and English. *Oak Publications: Music Sales. £0.95* JE/TSDW/G/AYH (B73-50177)
Scott, David.
Invitation to madrigals
6: for SSATB and SSAT Ba B; transcribed and edited by David Scott. (Dart, Thurston). *Stainer and Bell. Unpriced* EZDU/AY (B73-50551)
ISBN 0 903000 02 4
Invitation to madrigals: for S S A T B & S S A T B a B
Volume 7. *Stainer and Bell. Unpriced* EZDU/AY (B73-51007) ISBN 0 85249 167 0
Scott, Ralph Henry Forster. Jean-Baptiste Lully. *Owen. £3.00* BLT(N) (B73-14125) ISBN 0 7206 0432 x
Scott-Sutherland, Colin. Arnold Bax. *Dent. £3.50* BBH(N) (B73-15413) ISBN 0 460 03861 3
Scottish folk directory
1973. *12 Mansfield Rd, Scone, Perth: Sheila Douglas. £0.20* A/G/E(YDL/Q) (B73-14762)
ISBN 0 903919 00 1
Scout show book. (Milner, John). *Brown Son and Ferguson. £0.75* JGDW (B73-51079)
Scriabin, Alexander.
The complete preludes & études for pianoforte solo. *Constable. £2.00* QPJ (B73-51176)
ISBN 0 486 22919 x
Reverie. Opus 24: for orchestra. *Belaieff: Hinrichsen. £0.85* MMJ (B73-50683)
Sculthorpe, Peter.
Autumn song: for unaccompanied chorus (SAT Bar B). *Faber Music. Unpriced* EZDW (B73-50127)
Night pieces: for piano. *Faber. Unpriced* QPJ (B73-51177)

Sun music 3: for orchestra. *Faber Music. Unpriced* MMJ (B73-50261)

Sun music II: for orchestra. *Faber. Unpriced* MMJ (B73-51119)
Sea: for chorus and piano. (Jones, Daniel). *Eisteddfod genedlaethol frenhinol Cymru. Unpriced* DW (B73-50044)
Searle, Humphrey. Ballet music: an introduction. Second revised ed. *Dover Publications: Constable. £1.50* AMM/HM (B73-32165) ISBN 0 486 22917 3
Sears E H. An air composed for Holsworthy Church bells. It came upon the midnight clear. (Wesley, Samuel Sebastian). *Oxford University Press. Unpriced* EZDP/LF (B73-50544) ISBN 0 19 343041 x
Seasons: ballet in one act and four tableaux. (Glazunov, Alexander). *Belaieff: Hinrichsen. £4.50* MM/HM (B73-50664)
Seasons of love. (Cookridge, John Michael). *Janay. £0.06* JDW (B73-50174)
Seasons: suite. (Carr, John). *R. Smith. Unpriced* WMG (B73-50881)
Second book of music for the ballet class. (Moore, Elizabeth). *Cramer. £0.48* QPK/CC/AY (B73-51183)
Second book of oboe solos. (Craxton, Janet). *Faber Music. Unpriced* VTPK/AAY (B73-50422)
Second service = Magnificat and Nunc dimittis. Op.62: SATB. (Leighton, Kenneth). *Oxford University Press. £0.30* DGPP (B73-50021) ISBN 0 19 395236 x
Second year piano lessons
Book 1. (Waterman, Fanny). *Faber Music. Unpriced* Q/AC (B73-51141)
Secondo libro de madrigali a sei voce.. In un bel bosco. In un bel bosco = In a fair greenwood: for six-part chorus of mixed voices a cappella. (Marenzio, Luca). *Schirmer. Unpriced* EZDU (B73-50109)
Seeger, Peter. Steel drums, how to play them and make them: an instruction manual. *Oak Publications; 78 Newman St., W.1: Music Sales Ltd. £1.25* AXRQ/BC(YUH) (B73-03214) ISBN 0 9502654 0 3
Seeger, Peter. Steel drums of Kim Loy Wong. *See* Seeger, Peter. Steel drums, how to play them and make them.
Seidel, Uwe. Neue Kinderlieder: für Kinder - und Familiengottesdienst. (Behr, Heinz Otto). *Bosse Bärenreiter. £0.60* JFEZDM/GJ/AY (B73-50195)
Seinn suas port: ceol don fheadog. (O Duinn, Micheal). *John F. Kennedy Drive, Naas Rd, Dublin 12: Folens. Unpriced* VSPMK/DW/GJ/AYDM (B73-51280)
Self-banished. Minuet: arr. Minuet. (Blow, John). *Cornelius. Unpriced* SRNTK/AHR (B73-50802)
Senaillé, Jean Baptiste. Sonata for violin & basso continuo in D minor. Sarabanda, Allegro; arr. Introduction and allegro spiritoso. *Fenette Music, Breitkopf and Härtel. Unpriced* VVPK (B73-50430)
Senallié, Jean Baptiste. Sonata for violin & basso continuo, liv. 5, no.5 in E minor. Sonata in E minor for violin and continuo. *Oxford University Press. £0.90* SPE (B73-51220) ISBN 0 19 358796 3
Seren Bethlehem = Star of Bethlehem: TTBB. (Weston, Gordon). *University of Wales Press. £0.15* GEZDP/LF (B73-51045)
Serenade for solo violin. (Schurmann, Gerard). *Novello. £1.20* SPMJ (B73-50370)
Serenade for string orchestra. Op.48. Waltz: arr. Waltz. (Tchaikovsky, Peter). *Cornelius. Unpriced* TSPMK/AHW (B73-50829)
Serenade in pastels: piano solo. (Parfrey, Raymond). *Composer to Player Edition. Unpriced* QPJ (B73-50742)
Serenade to Christmas: for mezzo-soprano solo mixed chorus and orchestra. (Tate, Phyllis). *Oxford University Press. Unpriced* DE/LF (B73-50943) ISBN 0 19 338419 1
Serenade to Christmas. Vocal score. Serenade to Christmas: for mezzo-soprano solo mixed chorus and orchestra. (Tate, Phyllis). *Oxford University Press. Unpriced* DE/LF (B73-50943) ISBN 0 19 338419 1
Sergei Rachmaninoff: his life and music. (Threlfall, Robert). *Boosey and Hawkes. £0.75* BRC(N) (B73-22268) ISBN 0 85162 009 4
Serva padrona. Vocal score. La Serva padrona = From maid to mistress. (Pergolesi, Giovanni Battista). *Schirmer. Unpriced* CC (B73-50935)
Seven easy duets for piano. (Johnson, Thomas Arnold). *Freeman. £0.20* QNV (B73-50706)
Seven short and easy studies: for beginners on the Spanish guitar. (White, Tony). *Cornelius. Unpriced* TS/AF (B73-50813)
Shakespeare, William.
Lady Macbeth: a scena for mezzo-soprano and piano. (Horovitz, Joseph). *Novello. £0.65* KFNDX (B73-50227)
Music that brings sweet sleep: song cycle for high voice and piano. (Stoker, Richard). *Peters. Unpriced* KFTDW (B73-50231)
A Shakespeare sequence. Op.66.. Who is Sylvia? Who is Sylvia?: SSAA. (Gardner, John). *Oxford University Press. Unpriced* FDW (B73-50142) ISBN 0 19 342594 7
Shakespearian rhapsody, 'Prospero and Miranda'. (Heath, Reginald). *R. Smith. Unpriced* WMJ (B73-50892)
Sharp, Cecil James. English folk song - some conclusions. 4th revised ed. *E.P. Publishing. £1.75* ADW/G(YD) (B73-02067) ISBN 0 85409 929 8
Sharpe, Frederick. The church bells of Herefordshire: their inscriptions and founders
Vol.4: Putley-Yazor. *'Derwen', Launton, Oxon.: F. Sharpe. £1.75* AXSR(YDHR) (B73-00362) ISBN 0 9500835 8 5
Shaw, Robert. Fum fum fum!: Traditional Spanish carol. (Parker, Alice). *Schirmer. Unpriced* FDP/LF (B73-50139)
Shaw, Watkins.
Works, organ. Thirty voluntaries and verses for the organ. (Blow, John). Revised edition. *Schott. £2.30* R/AZ (B73-50331)
Works, organ. Selections. Ten selected organ pieces. (Blow, John). *Schott. £1.40* RJ (B73-50336)
She walks in beauty: for three-part chorus of mixed voices a cappella. (Lekberg, Sven). *Schirmer. Unpriced* EZDW (B73-50119)
Shelley, Percy Bysshe. A widow bird sate mourning: SATB unaccompanied. (Dare, Marie). *Roberton. £0.07* EZDW (B73-50113)
Shephard, Richard. The Addington service: Holy Communion, Series 3. *Royal School of Church Music. Unpriced* JDGS (B73-51049)
Shepherd maiden, fair and graceful: for 5-part chorus of mixed voices unaccompanied. (Vecchi, Horatio). *Roberton. Unpriced* EZDU (B73-50550)
Shepherd's carol. Opus 12: for treble voices and piano. (Platts, Kenneth). *Ashdown. £0.05* FLDP/LF (B73-51043)
Shepherd's story: Christmas chorus for mixed voice choir with piano or orchestra. (Thiman, Eric). *Roberton. £0.10* DP/LF (B73-50970)
Shepherd's story. Vocal score. The shepherd's story: Christmas chorus for mixed voice choir with piano or orchestra. (Thiman, Eric). *Roberton. £0.10* DP/LF (B73-50970)
Shipbuilders: suite for brass band. (Yorke, Peter). *Chappell. Unpriced* WMG (B73-50884)
Shipp, Clifford. Canzonets to three voyces.. Come merry lads, let us away: arr. Come merry lads, let us away. (Youll, Henry). *Roberton. £0.10* FEZDU (B73-50156)
Shipp, Mary Jane.
First set of madrigals.. Corydon would kiss her then: arr. Corydon would kiss her then. (East, Michael). *Roberton. £0.10* FEZDU (B73-50154)
First set of madrigals. In the merry month of May: arr. In the merry month of May. (East, Michael). *Roberton. £0.10* FEZDU (B73-50155)
Shires suite.. Come, let us sing you a song in canon. Vocal score. Come, let us sing you a song in canon: cantata. (Tippett, *Sir* Michael). *Schott. £0.50* DX/X (B73-50047)
Shirtcliff, J Stanley. Thésée.. March: arr. Processional march. (Lully, Jean Baptiste). *Ashdown. £0.20* RK/AGM (B73-50349)
Short, Don. Engelbert Humperdinck: the authorised biography. *New English Library. £0.40* AKDW/GB/E(P) (B73-02065) ISBN 0 450 01453 3
Short and easy classics
Ser 1. (Brahms, Johannes). *Cornelius. Unpriced* TSPMK (B73-50824)
Short exercises in position changing for the cello
Bk 1: Position 2 to 5. (Wheeler, Eunice). *Cornelius. Unpriced* SR/AF (B73-50800)
Bk 2: Positions 6, 7 and thumb. (Wheeler, Eunice). *Cornelius. Unpriced* SR/AF (B73-50801)
Show album: songs and sketches. (Wilcock, Frank). *Brown, Son and Ferguson. £0.75* JDW (B73-51057)
Showbooth for bold pianists. (Steinbrenner, Wilfried). *Schott. £1.40* QP/AY (B73-50716)
Sieben Formen. *See* 7 Formen.
Siebert, Edrich.
Le Chasseur maudit: arr. The accursed huntsman. (Franck, Cesar). *Studio Music. Unpriced* WMK (B73-50895)
Dear to my heart: air varié. *Studio Music. Unpriced* WM/T (B73-50879)
'Deed I do: arr. 'Deed I do: march. (Hirsch, Walter). *Keith Prowse. Unpriced* WMK/DW (B73-51299)
The good old bad old days. Selections: arr. The good old bad old days. (Bricusse, Leslie). *Peter Maurice. Unpriced* UMMK/CM (B73-50401)
The good old bad old days. Selections: arr. The good old bad old days. (Bricusse, Leslie). *Peter Maurice. Unpriced* WMK/CM (B73-50439)
Hawaiian hoe-down. *Studio Music. Unpriced* WMHME (B73-50885)
Singalong
Selection no.1. *KPM Music. Unpriced* WMK/DW (B73-50440)
Singalong: selection no.1. *Keith Prowse. Unpriced* UMMK/DW (B73-51257)
Spanish gipsy dance: arr. Spanish gipsy dance: paso doble. (Marquina, Pascual). *Schauer and May. Unpriced* WSPK/AHSW (B73-50467)
Tango taquin: for brass band. (Barratt, Bob). *Affiliated Music. Unpriced* WMHVR (B73-51295)
Silcock, Norman. Two George Herbert songs: for medium voice and cello. *Thames. Unpriced* KFVE/SRDW (B73-50238)
Silent night. (Gruber, Franz). *Thames. Unpriced* FEZDP/LF (B73-50152)
Silverman, Jerry. Favorite French folk songs: sixty-five traditional songs of France and Canada. (Mills, Alan). *Oak Publications: Music Sales. £0.95* JE/TSDW/G/AYSXH (B73-50178)
Simkins, Cyril Frank.
Newe lustige Volten, Couranten zu 5 Stimmen, nos. 11, 16, 17, 25. First set of quintets for 2 descant, treble, tenor and bass (or tenor) recorder. (Brade, William). *Chester. Unpriced* VSNRK/AH (B73-50413)
Resonet in laudibus = Joseph dearest, Joseph mine: for four-part chorus of mixed voices. (Handl, Jacob). *Roberton. Unpriced* EZDP/LF (B73-50098)
Tomus primus operis musici.. Pueri concinite. Pueri concinite: for four equal voices SSSA or SSAA a cappella. (Handl, Jacob). *Roberton. Unpriced* EZDJ/LF (B73-50080)
Simon, Paul. The songs of Paul Simon. *Joseph. £2.95* KDW (B73-50209)
Simple song. (Bernstein, Leonard). *Amberson: Schirmer. Unpriced* KDW (B73-50200)
Simpson, Gordon. Sing life, sing love: songs. (Lewis, Pete). *Holmes McDougall. Unpriced* JFDM/AY (B73-51064) ISBN 0 7157 1005 2
Simpson, Harold. Singers to remember. *Oakwood Press. £3.00* AK/E(M/XN53) (B73-06591) ISBN 0 85361 113 0
Simpson, John. Wi'a hundred pipers an' a': SAB. *British and Continental. Unpriced* DW (B73-50978)
Sinatra and the great song stylists. (Barnes, Ken). *Allan. £3.00* AKDW/GB/E(M/XN52) (B73-00880) ISBN 0 7110 0400 5
Sinfonia elegaica. (Panufnik, Andrzej). *Boosey and Hawkes. Unpriced* MME (B73-50252)
Sinfonia: organ. (Spooner, Ian). *Boosey and Hawkes. £0.40* RJ (B73-51196)
Sinfonie in D, (Prager Sinfonie). KV504. (Mozart, Wolfgang Amadeus). *Bärenreiter. £3.50* MME (B73-50672)
Sing a song for Christmas: a selection from the Southern Independent Television series. *High-Fye. £1.25* QP/LF/JS/AY (B73-51167)
Sing for Christmas: 6 songs for unison voices (optional 2nd part). (Roe, Betty). *Thames. Unpriced* JFDP/LF (B73-50620)
Sing for joy: twenty seven songs for infants. (Coyle, Margaret). *Mayhew-McGrimmon. £0.50* JFDM/GJ (B73-50617) ISBN 0 85597 019 7
Sing life, sing love: songs. (Lewis, Pete). *Holmes McDougall. Unpriced* JFDM/AY (B73-51064) ISBN 0 7157 1005 2
Sing me a story. (Porteous, Chris). *Church Pastoral Aid Society. £0.35* QPK/DW/GJ/JT/AY (B73-50321) ISBN 0 85491 834 5
Sing, say and play. (Adams-Jeremiah, Dorothy). *Lengnick. £0.20* MJ (B73-50245)
Sing we to this merry company: SATB. (Rutter, John). *Oxford University Press. Unpriced* DP/LF (B73-50042) ISBN 0 19 343037 1
Singalong
Selection no.1. (Siebert, Edrich). *KPM Music. Unpriced* WMK/DW (B73-50440)
Singalong: selection no.1. (Siebert, Edrich). *Keith Prowse. Unpriced* UMMK/DW (B73-51257)
Singalong tunes for recorder. (Verrall, Pamela). *British and Continental. £0.25* VSPMK/AAY (B73-50416)
Singers: a directory of freelance amateur singers in London and the Home Counties
'73: 2nd ed. *14 Barlby Rd, W10 6AR: Autolycus Publications. £0.35* ADW/G(YD) (B73-20239) ISBN 0 903413 10 8
Singers to remember. (Simpson, Harold). *Oakwood Press. £3.00* AK/E(M/XN53) (B73-06591) ISBN 0 85361 113 0
Sir Gawayn carols: SATB. (Crawley, Christopher). *Oxford University Press. Unpriced* DP/LF (B73-50966) ISBN 0 19 343042 8
Sir John in love.. Fantasia on Greensleeves. Fantasia on 'Greensleeves'. (Vaughan Williams, Ralph). *Oxford University Press. £0.30* TSPMK (B73-50394) ISBN 0 19 359309 2
Sir Thomas Browne Institute. Publications: general series. *(Leiden University Press for the Sir Thomas Browne Institute, Leiden)* Curtis, Alan. Sweelinck's keyboard music: a study of English elements in seventeenth-century Dutch composition. 2nd ed. *Leiden University Press for the Sir Thomas Browne Institute, Leiden: Distributed by Oxford University Press. £7.75* BSXAPW (B73-09001) ISBN 0 19 647470 1
Six favourite concertos.. Selections. Organ solos. (Arne, Thomas Augustine). *Peters. Unpriced* RJ (B73-50335)
Six introductory sentences: for SATB and organ. (Thiman, Eric Harding). *Novello. £0.10* DGMKAD (B73-50947)
Six 'nonsense' songs: for piano trio, one, two or three players
Book 1: Nos.1 to 3. (Enoch, Yvonne). *Bosworth. £0.25* QNVQ (B73-50292)
Book 2: Nos.4 to 6. (Enoch, Yvonne). *Bosworth. £0.25* QNVQ (B73-50293)
Six poems from 'Miserere'. (Naylor, Bernard). *Roberton. £0.30* EZDW (B73-50124)
Sixty interludes for service use. (Ratcliffe, Desmond). *Novello. £1.00* RJ (B73-51195)
Skelton, Geoffrey. Wagner writes from Paris: stories, essays and articles by the young composer. (Wagner, Richard). *Allen and Unwin. £3.85* A(D) (B73-19496) ISBN 0 04 780022 4
Sketches for three: for violin, cello and piano. (Grace, Norah). *Forsyth. Unpriced* NXNT (B73-50281)
Sketches on a Tudor psalm based on a setting of the second psalm: for military band. (Tull, Fisher). *Boosey and Hawkes. £12.50* UMMJ (B73-51255)
Skye boat song. (Macleod, A C). *Cramer. £0.15* QPK/DW (B73-50750)
Skye boat song: arr. The Skye boat song. (Macleod, A C). *Cramer. £0.15* QPK/DW (B73-50750)
Slatford, Rodney. Duet for double bass, no.1. Grand duetto 1: for double bass. (Bottesini, Giovanni). *Yorke. Unpriced* SSNU (B73-50387)
Sleep little baby: Christmas song. (Kelly, Bryan). *Novello. £0.07* DP/LF (B73-50969)
Sleep little baby: Christmas song for unison voices and piano. (Kelly, Bryan). *Novello. £0.07* JDP/LF (B73-51050)
Sleeping beauty. (Chappell, Warren). *Kaye and Ward. £1.25* AM/HMBN (B73-24333) ISBN 0 7182 0949 4
Smalley, Roger. Strata: for fifteen solo strings. *Faber. Unpriced* RXMJ (B73-50356)
Smart, Christopher.
A cycle of cats: three songs for soprano and alto voices

with piano. (Price, Beryl). *Oxford University Press. £0.60* FDW (B73-50146) ISBN 0 19 337853 1
Mirth: anthem for female or boy's voices and organ. (Rose, Michael). *Novello. £0.14* FDH (B73-51016)
Rejoice in the Lamb. Op.30. Vocal score: arr. Rejoice in the Lamb. Op 30: festival cantata. (Britten, Benjamin). *Boosey and Hawkes. £1.00* FDE (B73-50564)
Smet, Robert de. *See* De Smet, Robert.
Smet, Robin de. *See* De Smet, Robin.
Smith, Aubrey George. New child songs: Christian songs for under-eights. (Buzzing, Pauline). *Denholme House Press. £1.50* JFDM/GJ/AY (B73-51065) ISBN 0 85213 074 0
Smith, Derek. Theme and variations: trumpet, horn, trombone. *Thames. Unpriced* WNT/T (B73-50462)
Smith, Geoffry Russell-. *See* Russel-Smith, Geoffry. Russell-Smith, Geoffry.
Smith, Geoffry-Russell. *See* Russell-Smith, Geoffry.
Smith, Henry Charles.
Duets for two horns. K.487: arr. 12 easy duets for winds Volume 1: For flutes, oboes (and saxophones). (Mozart, Wolfgang Amadeus). *Schirmer. Unpriced* UNUK (B73-50837)
Duets for two horns. K.487: arr. 12 easy duets for winds Volume 2: for clarinets trumpets (and F horns). (Mozart, Wolfgang Amadeus). *Schirmer. Unpriced* UNUK (B73-50838)
Smith, John Christopher. The fairies.. Overture. Overture: for strings and continuo (with optional oboes and optional trumpets). *Oxford University Press. £1.00* RXMJ (B73-50357) ISBN 0 19 367637 0
Smith, Peter Melville. Eastern monarchs: SATB unacc. *Banks. Unpriced* EZDP/LFP (B73-51004)
Smith Brindle, Reginald. Variants on two themes of J.S. Bach: guitar solo B-A-C-H and the fugue subject of the G minor fugue Book 1 of the '48'. *Peters. Unpriced* TSPM/T (B73-51245)
Smithers, Don L. The music and history of the baroque trumpet before 1721. *Dent. £8.00* AWS(XA1721) (B73-32170) ISBN 0 460 03991 1
Snape Maltings Foundation. Aldeburgh anthology. (Blythe, Ronald). *Snape Maltings Foundation Ltd; 38 Russell Sq., W.C.1: Distributed by Faber Music Ltd. £6.00* A(D) (B73-04215) ISBN 0 571 10003 1
Snowdrop: unison song. (Craxton, Harold). *Cramer. Unpriced* JFDW (B73-50623)
Softly, Barbara. Come all ye children: carol for unison voices and piano (organ). (Roe, Betty). *Thames. Unpriced* JFDP/LF (B73-50184)
Softly awakes my heart. (Saint-Saens, Charles). *Studio Music. Unpriced* WMK/DW (B73-50899)
Soixante-quinze études mélodiques et progressives pour violon. *See* 75 études mélodiques et progressives pour violon.
Soldier, soldier, won't you marry me? (Langstaff, John). *World's Work. £1.20* ADW/G(YD) (B73-20978) ISBN 0 437 54105 3
Soler, Antonio.
Concertos for 2 keyboard instruments, nos 1-6. VI conciertos de dos organos obligados: oder zwei Cembali, zwei Clavichorde, zwei Klaviere, eine Orgel und ein Cembalo
Band 2. *Schott. £1.70* PWNUF (B73-51135)
Concertos for 2 keyboard instruments, nos.1-6. VI conciertos de dos organos obligados: oder zwei und ein Cembalo
Band 1. *Schott. £1.70* PWNUF (B73-51136)
Sollima, Eliodoro. Sonata for treble recorder and piano. *Schott. £1.40* VSSPE (B73-50855)
Solo recital: the reminiscences of Michael Kelly. (Kelly, Michael, *b.1762*). Abridged ed.. *Folio Society. £2.90 to members of the Society only* AKGH/E(P) (B73-03213) ISBN 0 85067 055 1
Solstice carol. Op. 115. (Gardner, John). *Chappell. Unpriced* DP (B73-50964)
Solus ad victimam: SATB. (Leighton, Kenneth). *Oxford University Press. Unpriced* DH/LK (B73-50958) ISBN 0 19 350349 2
Somebody's knockin' at your door: spiritual, for 4-part chorus of mixed voices with piano. (Barthelson, Joyce). *Roberton. Unpriced* DW/LC (B73-50519)
Someone's singing, Lord: hymns and songs for children with piano accompaniments, with chords for guitar, and with parts for descant recorders, glockenspiel, chime bars and percussion. (Harrop, Beatrice). *Black. Unpriced* JFDM/AY (B73-50182) ISBN 0 7136 1355 6
Somfai, Laszlo. Symphony no.38 in D major. K.504, 'Prague'. Sinfonie in D, (Prager Sinfonie). KV504. (Mozart, Wolfgang Amadeus). *Bärenreiter. £3.50* MME (B73-50672)
Sommer, Jürgen.
Concerto for oboe, violin, string orchestra in C minor: arr. Concerto in C minor for oboe, violin, strings and basso continuo. (Bach, Johann Sebastian). *Bärenreiter. £2.25* NUTNTK/LF (B73-50270)
Rhapsody concerto for viola: arr. Rhapsody-concerto for viola and orchestra. (Martinu, Bohuslav). *Bärenreiter. £1.95* SQPK/LF (B73-50378)
Sonatina for violin and piano. (Srebotnjak, Alojz). *Schirmer. Unpriced* SPEM (B73-51222)
Sonatinas for piano. Opus 36. (Clementi, Muzio). *Chappell. Unpriced* QPEM (B73-50298)
Song of wandering Aengus: SATB a cappella by Doreen Droste. (Droste, Doreen). *Galaxy: Galliard. Unpriced* EZDW (B73-50553)
Song to the Virgin Mary: for mixed chorus a cappella or 6 solo voices. (Panufnik, Andrzej). Revised edition. *Boosey and Hawkes. £0.40* EZDJ/LF (B73-50081)
Songs and Southern breezes: country folk and country ways. (Copper, Bob). *Heinemann. £3.50* ADW/G(YDCV) (B73-27558) ISBN 0 434 14456 8
Songs by Sinatra, 1939-1970. (Hainsworth, Brian). *Little Timbers, Wyncroft Grove, Bramhope, Leeds LS16 9DG: B. Hainsworth. £1.00* AKG/FD(P/WT) (B73-12708) ISBN 0 9502861 0 9
Songs for singing together: fifty songs from around the world, taken from the B B C's music programme for schools 'Singing together'. (Coombes, Douglas). *British Broadcasting Corporation. £1.25* JFDW/G/JT/AY (B73-51072)
Songs for the liberated woman. (Perkins, Polly). *Kahn and Averill. £0.70* KFE/TSDW/AY (B73-51090) ISBN 0 900707 24 0
Songs for the primaries (with percussion). (Dainton, Marie Cleeve). *British and Continental. £0.30* NYL (B73-50702)
Songs of a changing world. (Raven, Jon). *Ginn. Unpriced* JE/TSDW/GM/AYC (B73-50180) ISBN 0 602 21848 9
Songs of celebration: a collection of new hymns featured in the Southern Television Hymn Competition 1973, appropriate for family service, communion service, wedding service, baptism service, harvest festival. *Weinberger. £0.75* DM/JS/AY (B73-50513)
Songs of Paul Simon. (Simon, Paul). *Joseph. £2.95* KDW (B73-50209)
Songs of the Midlands. (Palmer, Roy). *E.P. Publishing. Unpriced* JE/LDW/G/AYDG (B73-50175) ISBN 0 7158 0377 8
Songs of work and freedom. Songs of work and protest. (Fowke, Edith). *Dover: Constable. £1.75* JDW/KJ/AY (B73-51059) ISBN 0 486 22899 1
Songs of work and protest. (Fowke, Edith). *Dover: Constable. £1.75* JDW/KJ/AY (B73-51059) ISBN 0 486 22899 1
Sonnet: for soprano voice and string orchestra. (Stiles, Frank). *Mixolydian Press. Unpriced* KFLE/RXMDW (B73-50648)
Sonnets: for two double basses. (Cole, Bruce). Revised ed. *Yorke. Unpriced* SSNU (B73-51236)
Sonnets for two double basses. (Cole, Bruce). Revised ed. *Yorke. Unpriced* SSNU (B73-51237)
Sorozat = Series. Op.19: for chamber ensemble. (Bozay, Attila). *Boosey and Hawkes. £1.50* NYDPNM (B73-50283)
Sounding Brass; and, The Conductor
Vol.1-, no.1- ; Apr. 1972-. *Novello. £0.15* AWM(B) (B73-26820)
Sounds like folk
No.2: The railways in song. *E F D S. £0.30* JE/TSDW/G/AY (B73-50606)
No.3: Growing up songs. *EFDS Publications. £0.30* JE/TSDW/G/AY (B73-51061)
Southern sun: piano trio. (Parfrey, Raymond). *Composer to Player Edition. Unpriced* QNVQ (B73-50715)
Space-dragon of Galatar: an opera-workshop project for schools, for voices, sound effects and piano. (Paynter, John). *Universal. Unpriced* CQN (B73-50009)
Spada, Pietro. Duettinos for piano. Wotquenne 24-5. Two duettinos: for piano, four hands. (Clementi, Muzio). *Schirmer. Unpriced* QNV (B73-51161)
Spanish dance, no.5. (Granados, Enrique). *Oxford University Press. £0.35* WTPK/AH (B73-50472) ISBN 0 19 356830 6
Spanish gipsy dance: paso doble. (Marquina, Pascual). *Schauer and May. Unpriced* WSPK/AHSW (B73-50467)
Speaking from the snow: suite for high voice and piano. (Naylor, Bernard). *Roberton. £0.40* KFTDW (B73-51094)
Spearing, Robert. A hymn to the Virgin. Opus 20: Christmas anthem for two part female, or boys, voices, trumpet (optional) and organ. *Novello. £0.07* FDP/LF (B73-51025)
Spell respell. Op 14: for electric basset clarinet (or clarinet in A) and piano. (Gilbert, Anthony). *Schott. £0.75* VVXPJ (B73-50876)
Spencer, Robert. Elizebethan duets for two guitars. *Stainer and Bell. Unpriced* TSNUK/AAY (B73-50817)
Spencer, Williametta. Wassail wassail all over the town: a madrigal for Christmas time, for four-part chorus of mixed voices a cappella. *Associated Music. Unpriced* EZDP/LF (B73-50100)
Spenser, Edmund. Most glorious Lord of lyfe!: SATB. (Lord, David). *Oxford University Press. Unpriced* DH/LL (B73-50959) ISBN 0 19 350346 8
Spielstucke und Etüden: für Trompete oder Flugelhorn oder Kornett. (Schneider, Willy). *Schott. £1.44* WS/AF (B73-51304)
Spies, Claudio. Bagatelle: piano solo. *Boosey and Hawkes. £0.75* QPJ (B73-50746)
Spooner, Ian. Sinfonia: organ. *Boosey and Hawkes. £0.40* RJ (B73-51196)
Sprague, Richard L. Gloria in excelsis Deo: for four-part chorus of mixed voices a cappella. *Schirmer. Unpriced* EZDH/LF (B73-50077)
Spring repose: for four-part chorus of mixed voices a cappella. (Mendelssohn, Felix). *Schirmer. Unpriced* EZDW (B73-50123)
Spruchmotetten
1: Motets by Wolfgang Carl Briegel, Andreas Raselins and anonymous works. (Ameln, Konrad). *Bärenreiter. £0.90* EZDJ/AYE (B73-50078)
2: Motets by Johann Christenius and others. (Ameln, Konrad). *Bärenreiter. £0.90* EZDJ/AYE (B73-50079)
Spurgeon, O M. The young child's carol. (Evans, E L). *British and Continental. Unpriced* EZDP (B73-50095)
Srebotnjak, Alojz.
Sonata for violin & piano, no.2. Second sonata for violin and piano. *Schirmer. Unpriced* SPEM (B73-51221)
Sonatina for violin & piano, no.1. Sonatina for violin and piano. *Schirmer. Unpriced* SPEM (B73-51222)
St. Margaret's Communion, Series 3: for congregation and choir in unison (optional SATB) with organ or piano. (Gibbs, Alan). *Royal School of Church Music. Unpriced* JDGS (B73-51047)
Staatstheater: szenische Komposition, 1967-70. (Kagel, Mauricio). *Universal. Unpriced* C/J (B73-50484)
Stamitz, Anton. Concerto for viola in B flat major: arr. Konzert für Viola, B-dur. *Schott. £1.70* SQPK/LF (B73-50379)
Stamitz, Johann. Concerto for clarinet in B flat major. Concerto, B flat major: for clarinet and orchestra. *Bärenreiter. £0.50* MPVVF (B73-50265)
Standford, Patric.
Bagatelles. Opus 22: for string quartet. *Novello. Unpriced* RXNS (B73-51217)
Four preludes for bassoon and piano. *Novello. Unpriced* VWPJ (B73-50435)
Peasant songs: for violin and piano. *Novello. £0.75* SPJ (B73-51223)
Suite française: for wind quintet. *Novello. £1.10* UNRG (B73-51261)
Stanza 1: per chitarra, arpa, pianoforte, celesta, vibrafono e voce feminile (soprano). (Takemitsu, Toru). *Universal. Unpriced* KFLE/NYGNRDW (B73-51091)
Statham, Heathcote. O come, thou spirit divinest: introit for SATB. *Cramer. £0.06* EZDH (B73-50076)
Steel drums, how to play them and make them: an instruction manual. (Seeger, Peter). *Oak Publications; 78 Newman St., W.1: Music Sales Ltd. £1.25* AXRQ/BC(YUH) (B73-03214) ISBN 0 9502654 0 3
Steel drums of Kim Loy Wong. *See* Seeger, Peter.
Steinbrenner, Wilfried. The showbooth for bold pianists. *Schott. £1.40* QP/AY (B73-50716)
Steinfeld, Karl-Heinz. Draussen am Rain = Uti var hage: Schwedisches Volkslied, für gemischten Chor a cappella. *Bosworth. £0.10* EZDW (B73-50562)
Steinitz, Nicholas. Ave Maria: SAAT Bar B. (Parsons, Robert). *Oxford University Press. £0.15* EZDJ (B73-50988) ISBN 0 19 350335 2
Stereo record guide
Vol.8: Composer index Me-Z. *Squires Gate, Station Approach, Blackpool, Lancs. FY82 SP: Long Playing Record Library Ltd. £1.95* A/FF(WT) (B73-08019) ISBN 0 901143 06 5
Sternfeld, Frederick William.
A history of Western music
1: Music from the Middle Ages to the Renaissance. *Weidenfeld and Nicolson. £7.00* A(X) (B73-32161) ISBN 0 297 99594 4
5: Music in the modern age. *Weidenfeld and Nicolson. £6.50* A(X) (B73-18797) ISBN 0 297 99561 8
The new Oxford history of music
Vol.7: The Age of Enlightenment, 1745-1790. *Oxford University Press. £8.00* A(X) (B73-31506) ISBN 0 19 316307 1
Sternhold, Thomas. Fantasia (quasi variazione) on the 'Old 104th' psalm tune: for solo piano, mixed chorus and orchestra. (Vaughan Williams, Ralph). *Oxford University Press. £1.75* EMDR (B73-50050) ISBN 0 19 338922 3
Stevens, Bernard. Choriamb for orchestra. Op. 41. *Novello. £2.50* MMJ (B73-51120)
Stevens, Wallace. The man with the blue guitar: for four-part chorus of mixed voices with piano accompaniment. (Beyer, Frederick). *Schirmer. Unpriced* DW (B73-50043)
Stevenson, Ronald. Concerto for piano, no.1, 'Faust triptych': arr. Piano concerto, no.1. *Novello. £1.75* QNUK/LF (B73-50704)
Stewart, Rex. Jazz masters of the thirties. *Macmillan: Collier-Macmillan. £1.90* AMT/E(M/XN21) (B73-08421) ISBN 0 02 614690 8
Sticks and stones: a classroom music project for young children and audience. (Chatterley, Albert). *Novello. £0.64* JFE/LPDX/GR (B73-50626)
Stiles, Frank.
Four pieces for solo viola. *Mixolydian Press. Unpriced* SQPMJ (B73-50799)
Interlude for strings. *Mixolydian Press. Unpriced* RXMJ (B73-50775)
Quartet for strings. String quartet: by Frank Stiles. *Mixolydian Press. Unpriced* RXNS (B73-50788)
Sonnet: for soprano voice and string orchestra. *Mixolydian Press. Unpriced* KFLE/RXMDW (B73-50648)
Still: for orchestra. (Berio, Luciano). *Universal. Unpriced* MMJ (B73-51117)
Stille Nacht, heilige Nacht: arr. Silent night. (Gruber, Franz). *Thames. Unpriced* FEZDP/LF (B73-50152)
Stingl, Anton. Grande ouverture. Op 61. (Giuliani, Mauro). *Schott. £0.80* TSPMJ (B73-50823)
Stockhausen, Karlheinz.
Nr 10 = Carré: für 4 orchester und Chöre
Nr.1. *Universal. Unpriced* EMDX (B73-50523)
Nr.2. *Universal. Unpriced* EMDX (B73-50521)
Nr.3. *Universal. Unpriced* EMDX (B73-50520)
Nr.4. *Universal. Unpriced* EMDX (B73-50522)
Stockhausen: life and work. (Wörner, Karl Heinrich). *Faber. £6.00* BSO(N) (B73-03714) ISBN 0 571 08997 6
Stockmeier, Wolfgang. Works, organ. Selections. Selected organ works

5. (Pachelbel, Johann). *Bärenreiter. £1.20* RJ (B73-50341)
Stoker, Richard.
Aspects 1 in 3: song cycle for medium voice and piano. *Peters. Unpriced* KFVDW (B73-50235)
Fireworks: 6 little pieces for piano. *Ashdown. £0.30* QPJ (B73-51178)
Johnson preserv'd: opera in 3 acts. (Watt, Jill). *Hinrichsen. Unpriced* BSNKAC (B73-09577)
A little organ book. *Boosey and Hawkes. £0.40* RJ (B73-51197)
Music that brings sweet sleep: song cycle for high voice and piano. *Peters. Unpriced* KFTDW (B73-50231)
Requiescat: canon for two-part high voices (or children's two-part choir). *Ashdown. £0.10* FTDW/X (B73-50581)

Three improvisations: organ. *Boosey and Hawkes. £0.40* RJ (B73-51198)
Three improvisations: organ. *Boosey and Hawkes. £0.40* RJ (B73-51199)
Stokowski, Leopold. Stokowski: essays in analysis of his art. (Johnson, Edward). *Triad Press. £1.95* A/EC(P/D) (B73-14763) ISBN 0 902070 06 1
Stone, Brian. A hymn to the Virgin. Opus 20: Christmas anthem for two part female, or boys, voices, trumpet (optional) and organ. (Spearing, Robert). *Novello. £0.07* FDP/LF (B73-51025)
Stone, David.
Le Docteur Miracle.. Overture: arr. Overture. (Bizet, Georges). *Oxford University Press. £2.50* MJ (B73-50247) ISBN 0 19 361673 4
English dancing master. Selections: arr. Three English dances from Playford's 'English Dancing Master' (1650). (Playford, John). *Boosey and Hawkes. £1.80* MK/AH/AYD (B73-51110)
La Fille mal gardée. Clog dance. Clog dance. (Hérold, Ferdinand). *Oxford University Press. Unpriced* MH/HM (B73-51105) ISBN 0 19 364251 4
La Fille mal gardée. Flute dance. Flute dance. (Hérold, Ferdinand). *Oxford University Press. Unpriced* MH/HM (B73-51106) ISBN 0 19 364275 1
La Renaissance: songs and dances by French and German composers of the sixteenth and seventeenth centuries. *Boosey and Hawkes. Unpriced* UNSK/AH/AYH (B73-51262)
Wesendonck Lieder. Träume. Träume = Dreams: study for 'Tristan and Isolde'. (Wagner, Richard). *Boosey and Hawkes. £0.75* MPVVK/DW (B73-50266)
Wesendonck Lieder. Träume. Träume = Dreams: study for 'Tristan and Isolde'. (Wagner, Richard). *Boosey and Hawkes. £0.50* VVPK/DW (B73-50431)
Stone, Robert. The Lord's Prayer: SATB unacc. *Oxford University Press. £0.05* EZDTF (B73-51006) ISBN 0 19 350345 x
Stories of Britain in song. (Stuart, Forbes). *Longman Young Books. £2.75* KDW/G/AYC (B73-50213) ISBN 0 582 15330 1
Story of Ceol Chumann na nOg. (Ceol Chumann na nOg). *Smythe. £0.50(non-net)* A(W/Q/YDN/XA1972) (B73-28189) ISBN 0 900675 80 2
Story of Christmas: a new presentation of the Festival of Nine Lessons. (Ratcliffe, Desmond). *Novello. £0.40* DPDF/LF (B73-50973)
Story of music. (Ingman, Nicholas). *Ward Lock. £2.00* A(X) (B73-00877) ISBN 0 7063 1306 2
Story of the blues. (Oliver, Paul). *Penguin. £0.75* AKDW/HHW(X) (B73-00879) ISBN 0 14 003509 5
Strata: for fifteen solo strings. (Smalley, Roger). *Faber. Unpriced* RXMJ (B73-50356)
Strauss family. Works, orchestra. Selections: arr. The Strauss family: greatest hits for all organ. *Chappell. £1.00* RK/AH (B73-50351)
Stravinsky, Igor.
Canon for concert introduction or encore: a Russian popular tune. *Boosey and Hawkes. £0.50* MM/X (B73-51113)
Four Norwegian moods: for orchestra. *Schott. Unpriced* MMJ (B73-50262)
Stravinsky, Thedor. Catherine and Igor Stravinsky: a family album. *Boosey and Hawkes. £6.50* BSV(N/XLB39/EM) (B73-13584) ISBN 0 85162 008 6
Strawinsky, Igor. *See* Stravinsky, Igor.
Strawinsky, Theodore. *See* Stravinsky, Thedor.
Street, Allan. Great film themes for brass. *Chappell. Unpriced* WMK/JR (B73-50900)
String quartet: by Frank Stiles. (Stiles, Frank). *Mixolydian Press. Unpriced* RXNS (B73-50788)
Strouse, Charles. 'Applause' song book: songs from a new musical by Charles Strouse. *Edwin H. Morris. £1.25* KDW (B73-50210)
Stuart, Alice V. A Christmas fable. (Douglas, James). *Roberton. £0.07* EZDP/LF (B73-50097)
Stuart, Forbes. Stories of Britain in song. *Longman Young Books. £2.75* KDW/G/AYC (B73-50213) ISBN 0 582 15330 1
Studies in church music. *(Barrie and Jenkins)* Routh, Francis. Early English organ music from the Middle Ages to 1837. *Barrie and Jenkins. £6.75* AR(XCQ438) (B73-04220) ISBN 0 214 66804 5
Studies in Eastern Chant
Vol.3. (Wellesz, Egon). *Oxford University Press. £6.00* ADTDS (B73-22800) ISBN 0 19 316320 9
Study no.1 for unaccompanied cello. (Lees, Benjamin). *Boosey and Hawkes. £0.65* SRPMJ (B73-50385)
Sturgeon, Shirlem M. The Christmas carol book: words and music of 24 popular carols chosen and arranged by Brian V. Burdett in collaboration with Shirley M. Sturgeon. (Burdett, Brian V). *Jarrold. Unpriced* JDP/LF/AY (B73-51052) ISBN 0 85306 437 7
Suantrái: S S A. (Agnes Cecilia, *Sister*). *McCullough, Pigott. Unpriced* FDH (B73-51015)
Suffer little children. (Green, Philip). *Belwin-Mills. £0.20* FDH (B73-51017)
Suite bergamasque. Clair de lune: arr. Clair de lune. (Debussy, Claude). *Cornelius. Unpriced* TSPMK (B73-50825)
Suite Blaen Myherin: for 2 trumpets, 2 trombones. (Burnett, Michael). *Ricordi. Unpriced* WNSG (B73-50910)
Suite for seven: 2 flutes, oboe, 3 clarinets, bassoon. (Hanmer, Ronald). *Emerson. Unpriced* VNPG (B73-51264)
Suite for the birthday of Prince Charles. (Tippett, *Sir* Michael). *Eulenburg. £0.80* MMG (B73-50255)
Suite française: for wind quintet. (Standford, Patric). *Novello. £1.10* UNRG (B73-51261)
Suite on three pages: piano solo. (Parfrey, Raymond). *Composer to Player Edition. Unpriced* QPG (B73-50726)
Sullivan, *Sir* Arthur Seymour.
Operettas. Selections: arr. Gems of Sullivan
Vol.1. *Regina Music. Unpriced* PWPK/CF (B73-50287)
The Savoyards. Vocal score. The Savoyards: a new operetta. (Robinson, Stanford). *Boosey and Hawkes. £3.00* CF (B73-50489)
Summer suite
five easy pieces for guitar. (Roe, Betty). *Thames. Unpriced* TSPMG (B73-50393)
Summer suite: five easy pieces for guitar. (Roe, Betty). *Thames. Unpriced* TSPMG (B73-50819)
Sumsion, Herbert. Blessed are they that dwell in thy house: anthem for a dedication festival, or general use. *Lengnick. £0.18* DK (B73-50038)
Sun music 3: for orchestra. (Sculthorpe, Peter). *Faber Music. Unpriced* MMJ (B73-50261)
Sun music II: for orchestra. (Sculthorpe, Peter). *Faber. Unpriced* MMJ (B73-51119)
Sun, the great luminary of the universe. Op.76. (Hoddinott, Alun). *Oxford University Press. £1.50* MMJ (B73-50257) ISBN 0 19 364564 5
Superstar or son of God? (Forristal, Desmond). *Pranstown House, Booterstown Ave., Booterstown, Dublin: Veritas Publications: Talbot Press. £0.15* BWKRACM/LH (B73-25528) ISBN 0 901810 60 6
Surge equilo; et veni auster. Op 60: Paraphrase uber ein Thema von Igor Stravinsky, für Orgel. (Klebe, Giselher). *Bärenreiter. £1.05* RJ (B73-50761)
Surinach, Carlos. Acrobats of God: symphonic version of the ballet for orchestra. *Associated Music. Unpriced* MM/HM (B73-51112)
Sutherland, Colin Scott-. *See* Scott-Sutherland, Colin.
Swan, Alfred Julius. Russian music and its sources in chant and folk-song. *J. Baker. £4.50* A(YM/XA1950) (B73-22799) ISBN 0 212 98421 7
Swan. (Saint-Saens, Camille). *Studio Music. Unpriced* WMPWTWK (B73-50904)
Swann, Donald.
Festival Matins.. Blessed be the Lord God of Israel. Blessed be the Lord God of Israel: for two-part chorus of female, male or mixed voices with piano or organ accompaniment. *Roberton. Unpriced* DGNS (B73-50018)
Festival Matins.. O come let us sing unto the Lord. O come let us sing unto the Lord: for two-part chorus of female, male or mixed voices with piano accompaniment. *Roberton. Unpriced* DGNPV (B73-50016)
A modern Te Deum: We praise thee, O God: for equal voices with piano or organ accompaniment. *Roberton. £0.18* FDGNQ (B73-50134)
Requiem for the living: for speaker, mezzo-soprano or baritone solo, mixed chorus, percussion, cimbalom and piano. *Roberton. Unpriced* KHYE/NYLDE (B73-50242)
The rope of love. Around the earth in song: an anthology of contemporary carols. *The Bodley Head. £2.50* DP/AY (B73-50514) ISBN 0 370 01272 0
Swarsenski, H.
Estampes: piano solo. (Debussy, Claude). *Peters. Unpriced* QPJ (B73-50303)
Prelude for piano. Book1, no.6. Des pas sur la neige = Footprints in the snow. (Debussy, Claude). *Peters. Unpriced* QPJ (B73-51174)
Sweelinck's keyboard music: a study of English elements in seventeenth-century Dutch composition. (Curtis, Alan). 2nd ed. *Leiden University Press for the Sir Thomas Browne Institute, Leiden: Distributed by Oxford University Press. £7.75* BSXAPW (B73-09001) ISBN 0 19 647470 1
Sweets for woodwind quintet. (Buchanan, Gary Robert). *Galaxy: Galliard. Unpriced* VNRG (B73-51265)
Swing and sing: Tanzsuite für gemischten Chor (auch Kammerchor) und Rhythmusgruppe. (Fussan, Werner). *Schott. Unpriced* DW/AY (B73-50518)
Swingin' Samson: a cantata in popular style for unison voices (with divisions) and piano with guitar chord-symbols. (Hurd, Michael). *Novello. £0.35* FDE (B73-51013)
Sword of honour: concert march for band. (Neville, Paul). *Boosey and Hawkes. £5.40* UMMGM (B73-50832)
Swords into plowshares: for four-part chorus of mixed voices a cappella. (Vernon, Knight). *Schirmer. Unpriced* EZDK (B73-50086)
Sykes, Harold Hinchcliff. As we sailed out of London river: male voice chorus (TTBB) and piano. *Roberton. £0.10* GDW (B73-50166)
Symonds, John Addington. Adventante Deo = Lift up your heads, gates of my heart: anthem for SATB and organ. (Leighton, Kenneth). *Novello. £0.21* DH (B73-50025)
Symphonie fantastique. Op.14. Marche au supplice: arr. March to the scaffold. (Berlioz, Hector). *Oxford University Press. £1.75* MGM (B73-50658) ISBN 0 19 362158 4
Symphony. (Rauchhaupt, Ursula von). *Thames and Hudson. £8.50* AMME (B73-26166) ISBN 0 500 01099 4
Symphony in yellow. Op. 15b: for high voice and harp (or piano). (Blyton, Carey). *Boosey and Hawkes. £0.40* KFTE/TQDW (B73-51096)
Symphony no.8, 'Hommage à Teilhard de Chardin'. Op. 132. (Rubbra, Edmund). *Lengnick. £2.00* MME (B73-50673)
System of harmonics for violin
Vol.1. (Heller, Henryk). *Simrock. £0.75* S/AF (B73-51218)
Szelényi, István. Sonatina for two violins, no.2. Sonata no.2 for two violins. *Boosey and Hawkes. £0.65* SNUE (B73-51219)
Szelenyi, Istvan.
Suite for two trumpets in B and two trombones. Suite für zwei Trompeten in B und zwei Posaunen. *Schott. £2.40* WNSG (B73-51303)
Works, piano. Piano works
Vol.3: Hungarian rhapsodies 1, nos.1-9. (Liszt, Franz). *Bärenreiter. £2.40* QP/AZ (B73-50717)
Szeszler, Tiber. Oboe music for beginners, with piano accompaniment. *Boosey and Hawkes. £0.85* VTPK/AAY (B73-50859)
Szkharos, Andrew Horvath de. Have good courage: SSA unaccompanied. (Kodaly, Zoltán). *Boosey and Hawkes. £0.14* FEZDW (B73-50574)
Taberer, Alfred A. Dux animorum. Leader of faithful souls. *Bankhead Press. £0.01* DM (B73-50512)
Tablature 72. (Fink, Siegfried). *N. Simrock; 67 Belsize La., NW3 5AX: Distributed by R. Schauer. £0.45* AX(QU) (B73-16796) ISBN 0 9502847 0 x
Takemitsu, Teru. Valeria: per violino, violoncello, chitarra, organo elettrice e due offavani. *Universal. Unpriced* NUPNQ (B73-51128)
Takemitsu, Toru. Stanza 1: per chitarra, arpa, pianoforte, celesta, vibrafono e voce feminile (soprano). *Universal. Unpriced* KFLE/NYGNRDW (B73-51091)
Talba: for oboe solo. (Camilleri, Charles). *Novello. £0.50* VTPMJ (B73-50425)
Talbot, Michael.
Il Giardino di amore.. Sinfonia. Sinfonia for trumpet and strings. (Scarlatti, Alessandro). *Musica rara. Unpriced* RXMPWS (B73-50360)
Il Giardino di amore. Sinfonia. Sinfonia: for trumpet and strings. (Scarlatti, Alessandro). *Musica rara. Unpriced* WSPK (B73-50466)
Tantalising tubas: brass septet. (Newsome, R). *R. Smith. Unpriced* WNP (B73-50909)
Tanze der Volker: ein Spielbuch fur Blas-, Streich-, Zupf- und Schlaginstrumente mit Improvisations- Möglichkeiten
Heft 2. (Werdin, Eberhard). *Schott. £1.00* NYEH/G/AY (B73-50698)
Tanzmusik. Op.33: for solo piano. (Barrell, Joyce). *Thames. Unpriced* QPH (B73-50727)
Tate, Phyllis.
Ring out, sing out: a festival carol for spring and summer, for unison voices, recorders, percussion, violins, cellos and piano. *Oxford University Press. Unpriced* JFE/NYDSDP (B73-51074) ISBN 0 19 344943 9
Serenade to Christmas. Vocal score. Serenade to Christmas: for mezzo-soprano solo mixed chorus and orchestra. *Oxford University Press. Unpriced* DE/LF (B73-50943) ISBN 0 19 338419 1
Tatlock, Richard. The Passion of Christ: a devotional service of nine lessons and hymns (or chorales) based on the St Matthew Passion narrative. (Ratcliffe, Desmond). *Novello. £0.35* DFDM/LH (B73-50012)
Tausky, Vilem. Up and down the River Danube: twelve Czecholsovak folk songs. *Roberton. Unpriced* JFDW/G/AYF (B73-50191)
Taylor, Cecily. As I went riding by: carol for unison voices with optional descant, and piano. (Graves, Richard). *Novello. £0.07* JFDP/LF (B73-51066)
Taylor, Colin. Whimsies: four miniatures for piano
Second set. *Boosey and Hawkes. £0.60* QPJ (B73-50747)
Taylor, Derek. As time goes by. *Davis-Poynter. £2.00* A/GB (B73-21631) ISBN 0 7067 0027 9
Taylor, Herbert F. Prelude to a ceremony: for orchestra. *Bosworth. £0.37* MJ (B73-51107)
Taylor, John. The water babies. Selections: arr. The water babies: simplified children's selection for easy piano/organ/guitar, etc. *Chappell. £0.80* PWPK/CM (B73-51138)
Tchaikovsky, Peter.
Selections: arr. Tchaikovsky's greatest hits: for all organ. *Chappell. Unpriced* RK (B73-51203)
Serenade for string orchestra. Op.48. Waltz: arr. Waltz. *Cornelius. Unpriced* TSPMK/AHW (B73-50829)
The sleeping beauty. (Chappell, Warren). *Kaye and Ward. £1.25* AM/HMBN (B73-24333) ISBN 0 7182 0949 4
Tchaikovsky. (Garden, Edward). *Dent. £1.95* BTD(N) (B73-11185) ISBN 0 460 03105 8
Tchaikovsky. (Warrack, John). *Hamilton. £5.00* BTD(N) (B73-26164) ISBN 0 241 02403 x
Tchaikovsky's greatest hits: for all organ. (Tchaikovsky, Peter). *Chappell. Unpriced* RK (B73-51203)
Tcherepnin, Alexander. Twelve preludes for piano. Opus 85. New ed. *Belaieff: Hinrichsen. £1.40* QPJ (B73-50312)
Te Deum and Jubilate: SATB. (Farrant, John, *b.1575*). Revised ed. *Oxford University Press. £0.30* DGNP (B73-50499) ISBN 0 19 352106 7
'Te Deum laudamus': Konzert für Orgel, drei Trompeten und drei Posaunen. (Baudach, Ulrich). *Bärenreiter. £2.10* WNPRF (B73-50461)
Teach me how to look: a collection of new hymns. *Weinberger. £0.50* JDM/AY (B73-50602)
Teach yourself books. *(Teach Yourself Books)* Palmer, King. Compose music. 2nd ed. *Teach Yourself Books.*

£0.65 A/D (B73-07097) ISBN 0 340 05552 9
Temperley, Nicholas. New edition of the complete works of Hector Berlioz
Vol.16: Symphonie fantastique; edited by Nicholas Temperley. (Berlioz, Hector). *Bärenreiter. Unpriced* C/AZ (B73-50483)
Ten bicinia of the 16th century. (Unger, Harald). *Bärenreiter. £0.75* VSNUK/DW/AY (B73-50854)
Ten little studies: for oboe and piano. (Jacob, Gordon). *Oxford University Press. £0.60* WTPJ (B73-50470) ISBN 0 19 357359 8
Ten tunes. (Houghton, Frank). *OMF. Unpriced* DM (B73-50511)
Tennyson, Alfred, *Baron Tennyson.* Music that brings sweet sleep: song cycle for high voice and piano. (Stoker, Richard). *Peters. Unpriced* KFTDW (B73-50231)
Tenor trombone rag: trombone solo and brass band. (Newsome, Roy). *Studio Music. Unpriced* WMPWU (B73-50906)
Terpsichore.. Selections: arr. Dance suite. (Praetorius, Michael). *Boosey and Hawkes. £5.90* MK/AH (B73-50250)
Thackray, Roy. Nine short pieces from three centuries. *Oxford University Press. £0.90* VTPK/AAY (B73-50423) ISBN 0 19 359080 8
Thal, Herbert Van. *See* Van Thal, Herbert.
The constant lover: early 18th century songs. (Dexter, Harry). *Ashdown. Unpriced* GEZDW (B73-50168)
The rope of love. Around the earth in song: an anthology of contemporary carols. (Swann, Donald). *The Bodley Head. £2.50* DP/AY (B73-50514) ISBN 0 370 01272 0
The water is wide: Scottish folk song, arranged for four-part chorus of mixed voices with piano accompaniment. (Pooler, Marie). *Schirmer. Unpriced* DW (B73-50977)
Theme and four studies. (Rawsthorne, Alan). *Oxford University Press. Unpriced* QP/T (B73-50296) ISBN 0 19 373571 7
Themes from TV and film classics. (Bolton, Cecil). *Robbins Affiliated Music. £0.75* RK/JS (B73-51207)
Theodorakis, Mikis. The love in your eyes. *Dick James Music. £0.20* KDW (B73-50211)
There is a silence: for full chorus of mixed voices a cappella. (Chorbajian, John). *Schirmer. Unpriced* EZDW (B73-50112)
Thésée.. March: arr. Processional march. (Lully, Jean Baptiste). *Ashdown. £0.20* RK/AGM (B73-50349)
They can make music. (Bailey, Philip). *Oxford University Press. £1.75* A(VMX) (B73-16551) ISBN 0 19 311913 7
Thiman, Eric. The shepherd's story. Vocal score. The shepherd's story: Christmas chorus for mixed voice choir with piano or orchestra. *Roberton. £0.10* DP/LF (B73-50970)
Thiman, Eric Harding.
Five hymn-tune variants: for organ. *Roberton. Unpriced* RJ (B73-50345)
Listening: three-part song for female voices and piano. *Roberton. £0.10* FDW (B73-50147)
Pilgrims to Bethlehem: two-part song with piano. *Roberton. £0.10* FDP/LF (B73-50140)
Six introductory sentences: for SATB and organ. *Novello. £0.10* DGMKAD (B73-50947)
Think afresh about the voice: a reappraisal of the teaching of Ernest George White. (Hewlett, Arthur Donald). 2nd ed. *Hillcrest, Ringwood, Deal, Kent: Ernest George White Society. £0.75* AB/E(VC/P) (B73-19499) ISBN 0 9501610 1 2
Thirty voluntaries and verses for the organ. (Blow, John). Revised edition. *Schott. £2.30* R/AZ (B73-50331)
This bird ...: soprano, flute, clarinet. (Walker, Eldon). *Thames. Unpriced* KFLE/VRPLVVDW (B73-50649)
This spiritual house almighty God shall inhabit. Op 146: motet for unaccompanied 4-part choir. (Rubbra, Edmund). *Lengnick. £0.12* EZDH (B73-50534)
This train: folk spiritual, SSA. (Arch, Gwyn). *British and Continental. Unpriced* FDW/LC (B73-51036)
Thomas, Bernard.
Canzone e sonate (1615): for trumpets, optional horns, and trombones
Canzon 1: for 2 trumpets and 3 trombones (2 trumpets, horn, and trombones). (Gabrieli, Giovanni). *Musica rara. Unpriced* WN (B73-50441)
Canzon 2: for 3 trumpets and 3 trombones, (3 trumpets, horn and 2 trombones). (Gabrieli, Giovanni). *Musica rara. Unpriced* WN (B73-50442)
Canzon 3: for 2 trumpets and 4 trombones, (2 trumpets, horn and 3 trombones). (Gabrieli, Giovanni). *Musica rara. Unpriced* WN (B73-50443)
Canzon 4: for 4 trumpets and 2 trombones. (Gabrieli, Giovanni). *Musica rara. Unpriced* WN (B73-50444)
Canzon 5: for 4 trumpets and 3 trombones (4 trumpets, and 2 trombones). (Gabrieli, Giovanni). *Musica rara. Unpriced* WN (B73-50445)
Canzon 6: for 4 trumpets and 3 trombones, (4 trumpets, horn and 2 trombones). (Gabrieli, Giovanni). *Musica rara. Unpriced* WN (B73-50446)
Canzon 7: for 4 trumpets and 3 trombones, (4 trumpets, horn and 2 trombones). (Gabrieli, Giovanni). *Musica rara. £2.00* WN (B73-50447)
Canzon 8: for 3 trumpets and 5 trombones. (Gabrieli, Giovanni). *Musica rara. Unpriced* WN (B73-50448)
Canzon 9: for 3 trumpets and 5 trombones (3 trumpets, horn and 4 trombones). (Gabrieli, Giovanni). *Musica rara. £2.50* WN (B73-50449)
Canzon 10: for 4 trumpets and 4 trombones (4 trumpets, 2 horns and 2 trombones). (Gabrieli, Giovanni). *Musica rara. £2.50* WN (B73-50450)
Canzon 11: for 4 trumpets and 4 trombones. (Gabrieli, Giovanni). *Musica rara. £2.50* WN (B73-50451)
Canzon 12: for 2 trumpets and 6 trombones, (2 trumpets, 2 horns and 4 trombones). (Gabrieli, Giovanni). *Musica rara. £2.50* WN (B73-50452)
Canzon 13: for 4 trumpets and 4 trombones, (4 trumpets, 2 horns and 2 trombones). (Gabrieli, Giovanni). *Musica rara. £2.50* WN (B73-50453)
Canzon 14: for 6 trumpets and 4 trombones. (Gabrieli, Giovanni). *Musica rara. £2.50* WN (B73-50454)
Canzon 15: for 4 trumpets and 6 trombones, (4 trumpets, 2 horns and 4 trombones). (Gabrieli, Giovanni). *Musica rara. £3.00* WN (B73-50455)
Canzon 16: for 6 trumpets and 6 trombones, (6 trumpets, 3 horns and 3 trombones). (Gabrieli, Giovanni). *Musica rara. £3.00* WN (B73-50456)
Canzon 17: for 6 trumpets and 6 trombones. (Gabrieli, Giovanni). *Musica rara. £3.00* WN (B73-50457)
Canzon 18: for 4 trumpets and 10 trombones, (4 trumpets, 2 horns and 8 trombones). (Gabrieli, Giovanni). *Musica rara. Unpriced* WN (B73-50458)
Canzon 19: for trumpets and 12 trombones, (3 trumpets, 3 horns and 9 trombones). (Gabrieli, Giovanni). *Musica rara. £3.50* WN (B73-50459)
Canzon 20: for 5 trumpets and 17 trombones, (5 trumpets, 4 horns and 13 trombones). (Gabrieli, Giovanni). *Musica rara. Unpriced* WN (B73-50460)
Thomas, Gwyn. Sea: for chorus and piano. (Jones, Daniel). *Eisteddfod genedlaethol frenhinol Cymru. Unpriced* DW (B73-50044)
Thomas, Madeline. Listening: three-part song for female voices and piano. (Thiman, Eric Harding). *Roberton. £0.10* FDW (B73-50147)
Thomas, Mansel. Sing, say and play. (Adams-Jeremiah, Dorothy). *Lengnick. £0.20* MJ (B73-50245)
Thompson, Kenneth. A dictionary of twentieth-century composers, 1911-1971. *Faber. £12.00* A/D(M/XML61/C) (B73-09574) ISBN 0 571 09002 8
Thomson, John Mansfield. Recorder profiles. *48 Great Marlborough St., W.1: Schott and Co. Ltd. £1.00* AVS/E(M) (B73-05837) ISBN 0 901938 09 2
Thomson, Katherine. Songs of the Midlands. (Palmer, Roy). *E.P. Publishing. Unpriced* JE/LDW/G/AYDG (B73-50175) ISBN 0 7158 0377 8
Thou art mighty: for four-part chorus of mixed voices. (Haydn, Michael). *Schirmer. Unpriced* EZDJ (B73-50987)
Thou must leave thy lowly dwelling. The shepherds farewell to the Holy Family. (Berlioz, Hector). *Novello. £0.10* GDH/LF (B73-51044)
Thou, O God, art praised in Sion: SATB anthem for harvest festival or general use. (Hare, Ian). *Oxford University Press. Unpriced* DK/LP (B73-50510) ISBN 0 19 350340 9
Thou spirit of love divine: SATB accompanied. (Chapman, Edward). *Roberton. Unpriced* DH (B73-50024)
Thou spirit of love divine: unison song. (Chapman, Edward). *Roberton. £0.09* JDH (B73-50171)
Three classical pieces. (Gange, Kenneth). *Bosworth. £0.50* MK/AAY (B73-51109)
Three D.H. Lawrence love poems. *See* Raphael, Mark.
Three English dances from Playford's 'English Dancing Master' (1650). (Playford, John). *Boosey and Hawkes. £1.80* MK/AH/AYD (B73-51110)
Three hundred and thirtythree reading exercises. *See* Kodály, Zoltán.
Three improvisations: organ. (Stoker, Richard). *Boosey and Hawkes. £0.40* RJ (B73-51198)
Three improvisations: organ. (Stoker, Richard). *Boosey and Hawkes. £0.40* RJ (B73-51199)
Three inns
for two guitars. (Barrell, Joyce). *Thames. Unpriced* TSNU (B73-50392)
Three preludes for organ founded on Welsh hymn tunes, no.2. Prelude on the hymn tune 'Rhosymedre'. (Vaughan Williams, Ralph). *Stainer and Bell. Unpriced* VSNSK (B73-51273)
Three rhythmic pianoforte pieces. (Hunt, Reginald). *Ashdown. £0.30* QPH (B73-51170)
Three romances: for viola and pianoforte. (Kiel, Friedrich). *Musica rara. Unpriced* SQPJ (B73-50377)
Three songs for mezzo soprano and string quartet. (Binkerd, Gordon). *Boosey and Hawkes. £6.25* KFNE/RXNSDW (B73-50651)
Three stanzas. Op 8: for harp solo. (Harries, David). *Stainer & Bell. Unpriced* TQPMJ (B73-50811)
Threlfall, Robert.
Sergei Rachmaninoff: his life and music. *Boosey and Hawkes. £0.75* BRC(N) (B73-22268) ISBN 0 85162 009 4
Songs. Selections. Ten songs. (Delius, Frederick). *Galliard. Unpriced* KDW (B73-50635)
Tidy, Bill. Kiss me goodnight, Sergeant Major: the songs and ballads of World War II. (Page, Martin, *b.1938*). *Hart-Davis, MacGibbon. £1.60* ADW/KG(XPE7) (B73-29557) ISBN 0 246 10748 0
Time twisters: five contrapuntal pieces for piano, each with a rhythmic twist. (Last, Joan). *Oxford University Press. £0.30* QP/NM (B73-50295) ISBN 0 19 373146 0
Timpany, John. And out of his knapsack he drew a fine fiddle: an introduction to the technique of English fiddling. *English Folk Dance and Song Society. £0.50* AS/G/E (B73-19500) ISBN 0 85418 088 5
Tintagel. (Bax, *Sir* Arnold). *Chappell. Unpriced* MMJ (B73-50676)
Tippett, *Sir* Michael.
The Shires suite.. Come, let us sing you a song in canon. Vocal score. Come, let us sing you a song in canon: cantata. *Schott. £0.50* DX/X (B73-50047)
Suite in D major. Suite for the birthday of Prince Charles. *Eulenburg. £0.80* MMG (B73-50255)
Titon et l'Aurore. (Mondonville, Joseph de). *Gregg International. £8.40* CQC (B73-50491) ISBN 0 576 28987 6
To mercy, pity, peace and love: for four-part chorus of mixed voices a cappella. (Fast, Willard S). *Schirmer. Unpriced* EZDH (B73-50073)
Tobin, C. Colour piping
Book 1. *Helicon Press. Unpriced* VSR/AC (B73-51281)
Tobin, John. Messiah. Vocal score. Der Messias = The Messiah: oratorio in three parts. (Handel, George Frideric). *Bärenreiter. £2.10* DD (B73-50495)
Toccata, 'Hommage ▮a Ravel: piano solo. (Westbrook, Francis). *Peters. Unpriced* QPJ (B73-50748)
Todhunter, Rebecca. The harebell: unison song. (Noble, Harold). *Studio Music. Unpriced* JFDW (B73-51071)
Togli, dolce ben mio = Take thou, my sweetheart, these lovely flow'rs: for five-part chorus of mixed voices a cappella. (Marenzio, Luca). *Chappell. Unpriced* EZDU (B73-50110)
Tomlins, Greta. Who would true valour see: S.S.A. with piano or organ. *Roberton. £0.09* FDM (B73-50137)
Tomlinson, Fred.
8 songs: for medium voice and piano. (Warlock, Peter). *Thames. Unpriced* KFVDW (B73-50236)
The curlew: for tenor solo, flute, English horn, and string quartet. (Warlock, Peter). *Stainer and Bell. Unpriced* KGHE/NVPNQDX (B73-51097)
Tomlinson, Geoffrey. Contrasts: seven miniatures for school orchestra. *Boosey and Hawkes. £4.90* MJ (B73-50662)
Tomlinson, Geoffrey R. Ten miniatures for young pianists. *Forsyth. Unpriced* QPJ (B73-51179)
Tommy and Jimmy - the Dorsey years. (Sanford, Herb). *Allan. £2.95* AMT(P) (B73-18107) ISBN 0 7110 0416 1
Tomorrow shall be my dancing day: English traditional carol. (Carter, Andrew). *Banks. £0.05* FDP/LF (B73-51022)
Tonus primus operis musici. Regem natum. Regem natum = Our king is born: for 4-part chorus of mixed voices unaccompanied. (Handl, Jacob). *Roberton. Unpriced* EZDJ/LF (B73-50538)
Tostevin, E. An air composed for Holsworthy Church bells. It came upon the midnight clear. (Wesley, Samuel Sebastian). *Oxford University Press. Unpriced* EZDP/LF (B73-50544) ISBN 0 19 343041 x
Touchin, Colin M. Sonata for recorder group, (2 descants, 2 trebles, 2 tenors, bass). Op. 2. *Tomus Publications. Unpriced* VSNPE (B73-50848)
Townsend, Paul. The space-dragon of Galatar: an opera-workshop project for schools, for voices, sound effects and piano. (Paynter, John). *Universal. Unpriced* CQN (B73-50009)
Toy bandstand: piano solo. (Parfrey, Raymond). *Composer to Player Edition. Unpriced* QPJ (B73-50743)
Traherne, Thomas. The fire of heaven: for unaccompanied triple choir. (Burgon, Geoffrey). *Stainer and Bell. Unpriced* EZDE (B73-50529)
Traité de l'harmonie, liv.3.. Laboravi clamans. Laboravi clamans: motet for SSATB and organ. (Rameau, Jean Philippe). *Peters. Unpriced* DJ (B73-50032)
Trant, Brian. The Virgin Mary had a baby boy: carol from the West Indies. *Oxford University Press. Unpriced* DP/LF (B73-50971) ISBN 0 19 343040 1
Trapp, Maria Augusta. Maria. *Coverdale House: Distributed ... by Hodder and Stoughton. £1.75* AKDW/G/E(P) (B73-25530) ISBN 0 902088 42 4
Träume = Dreams: study for 'Tristan and Isolde'. (Wagner, Richard). *Boosey and Hawkes. £0.75* MPVVK/DW (B73-50266)
Träume = Dreams: study for 'Tristan and Isolde'. (Wagner, Richard). *Boosey and Hawkes. £0.50* VVPK/DW (B73-50431)
Traümerei. (Schumann, Robert). *Cornelius. Unpriced* VVNSK (B73-50866)
Trees in the valley. Op. 40
1: The plane: unison and piano. (Le Fleming, Christopher). *Boosey and Hawkes. £0.05* FDW (B73-51029)
2: Beeches (copper and green): two part or unison and piano. (La Fleming, Christopher). *Boosey and Hawkes. £0.05* FDW (B73-51028)
3: The holly: SSA and piano. (Le Fleming, Christopher). *Boosey and Hawkes. £0.05* FDW (B73-51030)
4: The willow: unison and piano. (Le Fleming, Christopher). *Boosey and Hawkes. £0.05* FDW (B73-51031)
5: The yew: SA and piano. (Le Fleming, Christopher). *Boosey and Hawkes. £0.05* FDW (B73-51032)
6: The elm: SSA and piano. (Le Fleming, Christopher). *Boosey and Hawkes. £0.05* FDW (B73-51033)
7: Poplars: unison and piano. (Le Fleming, Christopher). *Boosey and Hawkes. £0.05* FDW (B73-51034)
8: The oak: two part or unison and piano. (Le Flemming, Christopher). *Boosey and Hawkes. £0.05* FDW (B73-51035)
Trees stand silent: for five-part chorus of mixed voices SSATB a cappella. (Lekberg, Sven). *Schirmer. Unpriced* EZDW (B73-50120)
Treize etudes pour piano. (Nikiprowetzky, Tolia). *Boosey and Hawkes. £1.75* QP/AF (B73-51166)
Tremens: szenische Montage eines Tests, für zwei Darsteller, elektrische Instrumente, Schlagzeug, Tonbänder und Projektionen. (Kagel, Mauricio). *Universal. Unpriced* CQM (B73-50493)
Trevor, Caleb Henry.
Organ music for manuals
Book 3. *Oxford University Press. £0.75* R/AY (B73-50329) ISBN 0 19 375850 4
Book 4. *Oxford University Press. £0.75* R/AY

(B73-50330) ISBN 0 19 375851 2
Organ music for services of thanksgiving. *Oxford University Press. £0.75* R/AY (B73-50752) ISBN 0 19 375854 7
Sketches for pedal-piano. Op.58. Four sketches. (Schumann, Robert). *Oxford University Press. £0.65* RJ (B73-50762) ISBN 0 19 375732 x
Two Passiontide anthems. *Novello. £0.07* FEZDH/LGZ (B73-50151)
Triade for xylophon, vibraphone, marimbaphone and three cymbals (3 players). (Konietzny, Heinrich). *Schott. £1.44* XNT (B73-51310)
Tricinia. Selections: arr. Deutsche dreistimmige Lieder nach Art der Neapolitanen oder welschen Villanellen. (Regnard, Jacques). *Bärenreiter. £0.75* VSNTK/DW (B73-50853)
Trio 1948: für Violine, Violoncello und Klavier. (Meyer, Ernst Hermann). *Peters. Unpriced* NXNT (B73-50282)
Tripelfuge. (Bach, Wilhelm Friedemann). *Tomus. Unpriced* VSNRK/Y (B73-51271)
Tripelfuge for keyboard in F major. Falck 19: arr. Tripelfuge. (Bach, Wilhelm Friedemann). *Tomus. Unpriced* VSNRK/Y (B73-51271)
Triptych: horn and piano. (Roper, Keith). *Thames. Unpriced* WTPJ (B73-50914)
Triptych. Op.25
No.1: Naboth's vineyard. (Goehr, Alexander). *Schott. £3.00* CQC (B73-50940)
Triptych. Op.100: three movements for orchestra. (Gál, Hans). *Simrock. Unpriced* MMG (B73-50254)
Triptych: organ. (Freedman, Hermann L). *Thames. Unpriced* RJ (B73-50758)
Tristan und Isolde. (Wagner, Richard). *Dover: Constable. £3.75* CQC (B73-50941) ISBN 0 486 22915 7
Trois ballads de François Villon: songs for solo voice and piano. (Debussy, Claude). *Peters. Unpriced* KDW (B73-50632)
Trois chansons de France, and Trois poèmes de Tristan l'Hermite: songs for solo voice and piano. (Debussy, Claude). *Peters. Unpriced* KDW (B73-50633)
Trois poèmes de Stéphane Mallarmé: songs for solo voice and piano. (Debussy, Claude). *Peters. Unpriced* KDW (B73-50634)
Trombey, Jack. Eye level: theme from the Thames TV series 'Van der Valk'. *Boosey and Hawkes. Unpriced* WMK/AGM/JS (B73-51298)
Trombone: the instrument and its music. (Gregory, Robin). *Faber. £6.50* AWU (B73-06594) ISBN 0 571 08816 3
Trotting to the fair: pianoforte duet. (Longmire, John). *Bosworth. £0.20* QNV (B73-51163)
Trumpet and trombone: an outline of their history, development and construction. (Bate, Philip). 2nd ed. *Benn. £3.00* AWS/B (B73-13587) ISBN 0 510 36411 x
Trumpet carol: for mixed voices and trumpets. (Copley, ian). *Thames. Unpriced* EWSNTDP/LF (B73-50526)
Trumpet tango: a short and easy solo for trumpet and piano. (Baker, Mervyn). *Cornelius. Unpriced* WSPHVR (B73-50912)
Trumpet voluntary. (Clarke, Jeremiah). *Cramer. £0.24* RK/AGM (B73-50765)
Tudor, Harold. Making the nations sing: the birth of the Llangollen International Eisteddfod. *61 Lockwood Rd, Northfield, Birmingham: H. Tudor. Private circulation* AD(YDKRL/WB/XPG3) (B73-19495) ISBN 0 9502935 0 4
Tull, Fisher.
Scherzino. Op 27a: for piccolo, three flutes, three B flat clarinets and B flat bass clarinet. *Boosey and Hawkes. £4.00* VNN (B73-50839)
Sketches on a Tudor psalm based on a setting of the second psalm: for military band. *Boosey and Hawkes. £12.50* UMMJ (B73-51255)
Tunley, David. Cantates françoises, liv.1. Orphée. Orphée: cantata for high voice, flute, violin and continuo. (Clérambault, Louis Nicolas). *Faber Music. Unpriced* KFTE/NURNTDX (B73-50232)
Twelve pieces from the Glogauer Liederbuch. *Bärenreiter. £0.75* VSNTK/DW (B73-50852)
Twenty years of pop. (Barnes, Ken). *K. Mason: Distributed by Barrie and Jenkins. £0.75* ADW/GB(XPK24) (B73-30278) ISBN 0 85937 024 0
Two Chinese sketches: for piano solo. (Anson, George). *Schroeder and Gunther. Unpriced* QPJ (B73-50299)
Two chorales. (Lynn, George). *Schirmer. Unpriced* EZDM (B73-50090)
Two contrasts. (Gibson, Arthur J). *Ashdown. Unpriced* RK (B73-50347)
Two Coventry carols: for 3 voices (S/ATB) with optional instruments. (Rastall, Richard). *Antico. Unpriced* EZDP/LF (B73-51000)
Two festal contrasts: organ solo
No.1: in C. (Brown, Frank Edwin). *Cramer. £0.24* RJ (B73-50755)
No.2: in D. (Brown, Frank Edwin). *Cramer. £0.24* RJ (B73-50756)
Two George Herbert songs: for medium voice and cello. (Silcock, Norman). *Thames. Unpriced* KFVE/SRDW (B73-50238)
Two little chorales: piano solo. (Parfrey, Raymond). *Composer to Player Edition. Unpriced* QPJ (B73-50744)
Two national songs: SATB unaccompanied
1: The robin's last will. (Laloux, Fernand). *Boosey and Hawkes. Unpriced* EZDW (B73-51008)
Two nightsongs. (Fox, Peter). *Cornelius. Unpriced* SQPK/DW (B73-50798)
Two nightsongs. (Fox, Peter). *Cornelius. Unpriced* SRPK/DW (B73-50808)
Two nightsongs. (Fox, Peter). *Cornelius. Unpriced* WTPK/DW (B73-50918)
Two of the tops: a duet for E flat soprano and B flat cornets. (Carr, John). *R. Smith. Unpriced* WMPWRNU (B73-50902)
Two Passiontide anthems. (Trevor, Caleb Henry). *Novello. £0.07* FEZDH/LGZ (B73-50151)
Uhl, Alfred. Zwanzig Etuden für Viola. *Schott. £1.30* SQ/AF (B73-51224)
Uhland, L. Fruhlingsfeier. Op.48, no.3. Spring repose: for four-part chorus of mixed voices a cappella. (Mendelssohn, Felix). *Schirmer. Unpriced* EZDW (B73-50123)
Uhma, Stefan.
Lwowskie piosenki
Cześć 1: Jak sie rodzily lwowskie piosenki. *240 King's St., W6 9JT: Kola Lwowian. £0.50* ADW/G(YMUL) (B73-31510)
Cześć 2: Kobieta i milość. *240 King's St., W6 9JT: Kola Lwowian. £0.50* ADW/G(YMUL) (B73-31511)
Cześć 3: Pod znakiem Marsa. *240 King's St., W6 9JT: Kola Lwowian. £0.50* ADW/G(YMUL) (B73-24206) ISBN 0 9503005 0 0
Understanding music. (Glennon, James). *Hale. £6.00* A (B73-04214) ISBN 0 7091 3539 4
Unger, Harald.
Deutsche weltliche Gesäng unnd Täntze
1: For descant, treble, tenor and bass recorder. (Franck, Melchior). *Bärenreiter. £0.90* VSNSK/DW (B73-50850)
2: For descant recorder, 2 treble recorders and tenor recorder. (Franck, Melchior). *Bärenreiter. £0.90* VSNSK/DW (B73-50851)
Glogau Songbook. Selections: arr. Twelve pieces from the Glogauer Liederbuch. *Bärenreiter. £0.75* VSNTK/DW (B73-50852)
Ten bicinia of the 16th century. *Bärenreiter. £0.75* VSNUK/DW/AY (B73-50854)
Tricinia. Selections: arr. Deutsche dreistimmige Lieder nach Art der Neapolitanen oder welschen Villanellen. (Regnard, Jacques). *Bärenreiter. £0.75* VSNTK/DW (B73-50853)
University of Durham. Publications. *(Oxford University Press)* Primmer, Brian. The Berlioz style. *Oxford University Press. £3.75* BBM (B73-05259) ISBN 0 19 713136 0
University of Exeter. Inaugural lectures. *(University of Exeter)* Doe, Paul Maurice. The craft of music: an inaugural lecture delivered in the University of Exeter on 2 November 1972. *University of Exeter. £0.30* A (B73-06588) ISBN 0 900771 69 0
University of Exeter. *American Arts Documentation Centre.* The literature of American music: a fully annotated catalogue of the books and song collections in Exeter University Library. (University of Exeter. *Library*). *Northcote House, The Queen's Drive, Exeter, Devon: University of Exeter (American Arts Documentation Centre): University of Exeter Library. £1.00* A(YT/T) (B73-13195) ISBN 0 902746 02 2
University of Exeter. *Library.* The literature of American music: a fully annotated catalogue of the books and song collections in Exeter University Library. *Northcote House, The Queen's Drive, Exeter, Devon: University of Exeter (American Arts Documentation Centre): University of Exeter Library. £1.00* A(YT/T) (B73-13195) ISBN 0 902746 02 2
University of Newcastle upon Tyne. Inaugural lectures. *(University of Newcastle upon Tyne)* Matthews, Denis. Brahms's three phases: an inaugural lecture-recital delivered before the University of Newcastle upon Tyne on Monday 24 January 1972 and repeated on Wednesday 2 February 1972. *Newcastle upon Tyne NE1 7RU: University of Newcastle upon Tyne. £0.30* BBTAL (B73-10166) ISBN 0 900565 79 9
Unless love prevails: a modern spiritual for SA with pianoforte accompaniment. (Cookridge, John Michael). *McCullough, Pigott. £0.10* FDM (B73-51018)
Uns ist geborn ein Kindelein. Cradle: SSATB unacc. (Neander, Valentin). *Banks. £0.04* EZDP/LF (B73-50999)
Up and down the River Danube: twelve Czecholsovak folk songs. (Tausky, Vilem). *Roberton. Unpriced* JFDW/G/AYF (B73-50191)
Ut flos, ut rosa. = Like flowers, like roses bloom the crowns: S.S. or T.T. (Crivelli, Giovanni Battista). *Oxford University Press. Unpriced* FLDJ (B73-50162) ISBN 0 19 350337 9
Vaczi, Karoly. Piano duet music for beginners. *Boosey and Hawkes. £0.85* QNVK/AAY (B73-50714)
Vale, Charles.
Christ's carol: SATB unaccompanied. *Roberton. £0.07* EZDP/LF (B73-51001)
Even such is time. Vocal score. Even such is time: cantata for tenor solo, chorus and orchestra (or organ). *Thames. Unpriced* DE (B73-50011)
Fugue on 'Hey diddle diddle': for SATB unaccompanied. (Ophenbeidt). *Thames. Unpriced* EZDW (B73-50125)
Valente, Antonio. Works, harpsichord. Intavolatura de cimbalo. *Clarendon Press. £11.00* QRP/AZ (B73-50325) ISBN 0 19 816121 2
Valeria: per violino, violoncello, chitarra, organo elettrice e due offavani. (Takemitsu, Teru). *Universal. Unpriced* NUPNQ (B73-51128)
Valiant sailor: sea songs and ballads and prose passages illustrating life on the lower deck in Nelson's navy. (Palmer, Roy). *Cambridge University Press. Unpriced* JE/TSDW/KC/AYD(XFYK36) (B73-50611) ISBN 0 521 20101 2
Valse des fleurs. Op 87: for 2 flutes and piano. (Kohler, Ernesto). *Emerson. Unpriced* VRNTQHW (B73-51267)
Valse: piano duet. (Johnson, Thomas Arnold). *Freeman. £0.20* QNVHW (B73-50712)
Valsette: piano duet. (Johnson, Thomas Arnold). *Freeman. £0.20* QNVHW (B73-50713)
Van Beethoven, Ludwig. *See* Beethoven, Ludwig van.
Van Beethoven, Ludwig van. *See* Beethoven, Ludwig van.
Van Delden, Lex. Notturno: for solo harp. *Lengnick. £0.45* TQPMJ (B73-50391)
Van Eyck, Johann Jacob. *See* Eyck, Johann Jacob van.
Van Thal, Herbert. Solo recital: the reminiscences of Michael Kelly. (Kelly, Michael, *b.1762*). Abridged ed.. *Folio Society. £2.90 to members of the Society only* AKGH/E(P) (B73-03213) ISBN 0 85067 055 1
Vančura, Bořek. Musical instruments: an illustrated history. (Buchner, Alexander). *Octopus Books. £4.25* AL/B(X) (B73-24887) ISBN 0 7064 0015 1
Vanhal, Jan.
Quartet for oboe & strings. Op.7, no.4. Quartet. Opus 7, no.4: for oboe, violin, viola and violoncello. *Musica rara. Unpriced* NVTNT (B73-50275)
Quartet for oboe & strings. Op.7, no.5. Quartet. Opus 7, no.5: for oboe, violin and violoncello. *Musica rara. Unpriced* NVTNS (B73-50273)
Quartet for oboe & strings. Op.7, no.6. Quartet. Opus 7, no.6: for oboe, violin and violoncello. *Musica rara. Unpriced* NVTNS (B73-50274)
Varèse, Louise. Varèse: a looking-glass diary
Vol.1: 1883-1928. *Davis-Poynter. £3.00* BVB(N) (B73-04218) ISBN 0 7067 0057 0
Varèse: a looking-glass diary
Vol.1: 1883-1928. (Varèse, Louise). *Davis-Poynter. £3.00* BVB(N) (B73-04218) ISBN 0 7067 0057 0
Variantes for one percussionist. (Brouwer, Leo). *Schott. £1.10* XPM/T (B73-50928)
Variants for organ. (Cooper, Paul). *Chester. Unpriced* R/T (B73-51187)
Variants on two themes of J.S. Bach: guitar solo B-A-C-H and the fugue subject of the G minor fugue Book 1 of the '48'. (Smith Brindle, Reginald). *Peters. Unpriced* TSPM/T (B73-51245)
Variations, nocturne and finale on an old English sea song: for piano and orchestra. Op.60. (Bush, Alan). *Novello. £1.75* QNUK (B73-50290)
Variations on a Dorian theme: for alto saxophone and piano. (Jacob, Gordon). *Emerson. Unpriced* VUSP/T (B73-50863)
Vaughan, Henry. The nativity: SATB unacc. (Dickson, Andrew). *Banks. £0.05* EZDP/LF (B73-50994)
Vaughan Williams, Ralph.
Concerto for piano. Piano concerto: for one piano or two pianos and orchestra. *Oxford University Press. £6.00* MPQF (B73-50685) ISBN 0 19 369273 2
Fantasia (quasi variazione) on the 'Old 104th' psalm tune: for solo piano, mixed chorus and orchestra. *Oxford University Press. £1.75* EMDR (B73-50050) ISBN 0 19 338922 3
Sir John in love.. Fantasia on Greensleeves. Fantasia on 'Greensleeves'. *Oxford University Press. £0.30* TSPMK (B73-50394) ISBN 0 19 359309 2
Three preludes for organ founded on Welsh hymn tunes, no.2. Prelude on the hymn tune 'Rhosymedre'. *Stainer and Bell. Unpriced* VSNSK (B73-51273)
Vaughan Williams, Ursula. Ode to music. (Williamson, Malcolm). *Weinberger. Unpriced* JFDX (B73-50192)
Veal, Arthur.
The Queen's garland: pieces by Elizabethan composers. *Ashdown. Unpriced* QNVK/AAY (B73-51165)
Tango: piano duet. *Ashdown. £0.30* QNVHVR (B73-51164)
Vecchi, Horatio.
Madrigali a cinque voci. Pastorella gratiosella. Shepherd maiden, fair and graceful: for 5-part chorus of mixed voices unaccompanied. *Roberton. Unpriced* EZDU (B73-50550)
Moteca. Cantate Domino. Cantate Domino. Sing unto the Lord: for 4-part chorus of mixed voices with optional organ. *Roberton. Unpriced* EZDR (B73-50545)
Velimirović, Miloš Milorad. Studies in Eastern Chant
Vol.3. (Wellesz, Egon). *Oxford University Press. £6.00* ADTDS (B73-22800) ISBN 0 19 316320 9
Vernon, Knight. Swords into plowshares: for four-part chorus of mixed voices a cappella. *Schirmer. Unpriced* EZDK (B73-50086)
Verrall, Pamela.
Around the world. Vocal score. Around the world: songs with chorus and accompaniment for recorders and percussion. *British and Continental. £0.40* CN (B73-50938)
Clarinets in concert: clarinet trio. *British and Continental. £0.40* VVNT (B73-51291)
Singalong tunes for recorder. *British and Continental. £0.25* VSPMK/AAY (B73-50416)
Versuch eines Agon um ...?: for 7 vocalists and orchestra. (Fortner, Wolfgang). *Schott. £3.84* JNAYME/MDX (B73-51080)
Vester, Frans. Cantatas. Selections: arr. Flute obbligatos from the cantatas. (Bach, Johann Sebastian). *Universal. Unpriced* VRPMK/DE (B73-50409)
Vetter, Karl. Von allerlei Hunden: eine frohliche Kantate, für Kinderchor, Klavier, Glockenspiel, Zupfbass, und Schlagwerk, (grosse und kleine Trommel, Holztrommel, Tamburin, Becken, Triangel). (Desch, Rudolf). *Schott. £1.40* FE/NYLDX (B73-50570)
Victoria, Tomás Luis de. Missae totius anni: Missa O magnum mysterium. Santus: arr. Sanctus = Holy holy holy. *Schirmer. Unpriced* FEZDGE (B73-50149)
Victoria, Tomas Luis de. Motecta. O regem coeli. In festo natalis Domini: for 4-part chorus of mixed voices unaccompanied. *Roberton. Unpriced* EZDJ/LF (B73-50539)

32 THE BRITISH CATALOGUE OF MUSIC

Victorian popular music. (Pearsall, Ronald). *David and Charles. £3.50* A/GB(XHS65) (B73-03713) ISBN 0 7153 5689 5
Vienna marches: a march fantasy based on melodies by Schubert, Mozart, Beethovan, and J. Strauss (father and son). (Hanmer, Ronald). *Studio Music. Unpriced* WMK/AGM (B73-50897)
Vier Lieder: für mittlere Stimme und Klavier. (Reutter, Hermann). *Schott. £1.20* KFVDW (B73-50654)
Vieuxtemps, Henri. Capriccio for viola. Op. 55, no.9. Capriccio für Viola. Op post. *Schott. £0.80* SQPMJ (B73-51227)
Village Romeo and Juliet. (Delius, Frederick). *Boosey and Hawkes. £7.50* CC (B73-50005)
Village Romeo and Juliet. Vocal score. A village Romeo and Juliet. (Delius, Frederick). *Boosey and Hawkes. £7.50* CC (B73-50005)
Villon, François. Trois ballads de François Villon: songs for solo voice and piano. (Debussy, Claude). *Peters. Unpriced* KDW (B73-50632)
Vintage operetta book. (Drinkrow, John). *Osprey Publishing. £1.95* ACFBN (B73-03717) ISBN 0 85045 102 7
Vinter, Gilbert. Entertainments. *R. Smith. Unpriced* WMG (B73-50883)
Viola in my life (IV). (Feldman, Morton). *Universal. Unpriced* MMJ (B73-50680)
Violin. (Wechsberg, Joseph). *Calder and Boyars. £5.00* AS/B(X) (B73-29559) ISBN 0 7145 1020 3
Virgin Mary had a baby boy: carol from the West Indies. (Trant, Brian). *Oxford University Press. Unpriced* DP/LF (B73-50971) ISBN 0 19 343040 1
Visions: for organ. (Patterson, Paul). *Weinberger. Unpriced* RJ (B73-50343)
Vivaldi, Antonio.
Il Cimento dell'armonia e dell'invenzione. Op.8, no.3. La Caccia: arr. The hunt from 'Autumn' (The four seasons). *Bosworth. £0.57* MK (B73-51108)
Il Cimento dell'armonia e dell'invenzione. Op.8, no.4. Largo: arr. Largo from the 'Winter' concerto for violin and strings. *Cramer. Unpriced* RK (B73-51204)
Vocabulary ramblebuggies and educational wordopolis. (Meryll, Jane). *Belwin-Mills. £0.40* JFDX/GJ (B73-50625)
Vocabulary ramblebuggies and educational wordopolis. Vocal score. Vocabulary ramblebuggies and educational wordopolis. (Meryll, Jane). *Belwin-Mills. £0.40* JFDX/GJ (B73-50625)
Voice of angels, steps of shepherds: carol for SATB and organ. (Cameron, Gordon). *Novello. £0.07* DP/LF (B73-50965)
Voices and instruments. (Dankworth, Avril). *Hart-Davis. £1.50* A/DZ(VF) (B73-27555) ISBN 0 247 12513 x
Von allerlei Hunden: eine frohliche Kantate, für Kinderchor, Klavier, Glockenspiel, Zupfbass, und Schlagwerk, (grosse und kleine Trommel, Holztrommel, Tamburin, Becken, Triangel). (Desch, Rudolf). *Schott. £1.40* FE/NYLDX (B73-50570)
Von Dadelsen, Georg. *See* Dadelsen, Georg von.
Von Moisy, Heinz. *See* Moisy, Heinz von.
Von Rauchhaupt, Ursula. *See* Rauchhaupt, Ursula von.
Von Weber, Carl Maria. *See* Weber, Carl Maria, Freiherr von.
Von Wittgenstein, Ludwig. *See* Wittgenstein, Ludwig von.
Vorholz, Dieter. Sonata for violin & harpsichord in B flat major. Sonate, B-Dur, für Violine und Klavier (Cembalo). (Boccherini, Luigi). *Peters. £1.50* SPE (B73-50789)
Vox dicentis. (Preston, Simon). *Novello. £0.45* RJ (B73-50344)
Waddell, Helen. Solus ad victimam: SATB. (Leighton, Kenneth). *Oxford University Press. Unpriced* DH/LK (B73-50958) ISBN 0 19 350349 2
Wagner, Marian.
Lwowskie piosenki
Cześć 1: Jak sie rodzily lwowskie piosenki. (Uhma, Stefan). *240 King's St., W6 9JT: Kola Lwowian. £0.50* ADW/G(YMUL) (B73-31510)
Cześć 2: Kobieta i milość. (Uhma, Stefan). *240 King's St., W6 9JT: Kola Lwowian. £0.50* ADW/G(YMUL) (B73-31511)
Cześć 3: Pod znakiem Marsa. (Uhma, Stefan). *240 King's St., W6 9JT: Kola Lwowian. £0.50* ADW/G(YMUL) (B73-24206) ISBN 0 9503005 0 0
Wagner, Richard.
Albumblatt for piano in E flat major: arr. Romance. *Chappell. Unpriced* RXMK (B73-51212)
Polonaise for piano. *Novello. £0.27* QPHVHM (B73-50728)
Richard Wagner - stories and essays. *Owen. £3.25* BWC(D) (B73-13014) ISBN 0 7206 0122 3
Tristan und Isolde. *Dover: Constable. £3.75* CQC (B73-50941) ISBN 0 486 22915 7
Wagner writes from Paris: stories, essays and articles by the young composer. *Allen and Unwin. £3.85* A(D) (B73-19496) ISBN 0 04 780022 4
Wesendonck Lieder. Träume. Träume = Dreams: study for 'Tristan and Isolde'. *Boosey and Hawkes. £0.75* MPVVK/DW (B73-50266)
Wesendonck Lieder. Träume. Träume = Dreams: study for 'Tristan and Isolde'. *Boosey and Hawkes. £0.50* VVPK/DW (B73-50431)
Wagner writes from Paris: stories, essays and articles by the young composer. (Wagner, Richard). *Allen and Unwin. £3.85* A(D) (B73-19496) ISBN 0 04 780022 4
Waifs' carol: for unison voices (optional second part) and piano. (Copley, Ian). *Thames. Unpriced* JDP/LF (B73-50603)
Wales, Tony.
Folk directory
1973. *English Folk Dance and Song Society. £1.25 (£0.75 to members of the English Folk Dance and Song Society)* A/G(BC) (B73-07790) ISBN 0 85418 087 7
Folk song to-day
Vol.2. *E F D S. £0.20* JEZDW/G/AY (B73-50614)
Vol.4. *E F D S. £0.20* JEZDW/G/AY (B73-50615)
Folk song today
Vol.5. *E F D S. £0.20* JEZDW/G/AY (B73-50616)
I'll sing you two o: words of more familiar folk songs for campfire, ceilidh and club. *English Folk Dance and Song Society. £0.40* ADW/G(YC) (B73-22269) ISBN 0 85418 089 3
Walker, Alan, *b.1930.* Robert Schumann: the man and his music. *Barrie and Jenkins. £7.50* BSG (B73-04217) ISBN 0 214 66805 3
Walker, Arthur D.
George Frideric Handel - the Newman Flower Collection in the Henry Watson Music Library: a catalogue. (Henry Watson Music Library). *Central Library, Manchester M2 5PD: Manchester Public Libraries. £3.50* BHC(WJ) (B73-00557) ISBN 0 901315 18 4
Polonaise for piano. (Wagner, Richard). *Novello. £0.27* QPHVHM (B73-50728)
Walker, Eldon.
Elegy: soprano, flute horn, cello. *Thames. Unpriced* KFLE/NVNTDW (B73-50645)
This bird ...: soprano, flute, clarinet. *Thames. Unpriced* KFLE/VRPLVVDW (B73-50649)
Walker, Raymond. Die Zauberflöte. The golden flute: an opera for schools in two acts based on Mozart's 'The magic flute'. (Mozart, Wolfgang Amadeus). *Novello. £1.00* CN (B73-50008)
Walker, Robert.
Adam lay ybounden: carol for SATB unaccompanied. *Novello. £0.07* EZDP/LF (B73-51002)
In the bleak mid winter: carol for SATB unaccompanied. *Novello. £0.07* EZDP/LF (B73-51003)
Waller, Edmund. Go, lovely rose: for full chorus of mixed voices a cappella. (Fast, Willard S). *Schirmer. Unpriced* EZDW (B73-50115)
Walsh, John. The preces and responses. Responses in A Sharpe: SATB unacc. (Reading, John). *Oxford University Press. Unpriced* EZDGMM (B73-50062) ISBN 0 19 351637 3
Walsh, T J. Opera in Dublin, 1705-1797: the social scene. *Allen Figgis. £5.00* AC(YDN/XFE93) (B73-30858) ISBN 0 900372 74 5
Walters, Gareth.
Flourish for brass. *R. Smith. Unpriced* WMJ (B73-50893)
Sonata for cello and piano. *Ricordi. Unpriced* SRPE (B73-50382)
Walton, *Sir* William.
Jubilate Deo: SSAATTBB and organ. *Oxford University Press. Unpriced* DGNT (B73-50501) ISBN 0 19 351642 x
Richard III. Prelude: arr. Prelude. *Boosey and Hawkes. £4.50* UMMK/JR (B73-50835)
Waltz emperors: the life and times and music of the Strauss family. (Wechsberg, Joseph). *Weidenfeld and Nicolson. £4.25* BSQB(N) (B73-30279) ISBN 0 297 76594 9
Waltz for a beguiling lady. (Heath, Reginald). *R. Smith. Unpriced* WMHW (B73-50886)
Waltz overture. (Lucas, Leighton). *R. Smith. Unpriced* WMHW (B73-50887)
Wanek, Friedrich.
Concerto for violin, no.1, in D major. Op.6: arr. Konzert no.1, D-Dur. Opus 6: für Violine und Orchester. (Paganini, Nicolo). *Schott. £1.40* SPK/LF (B73-50368)
The showbooth for bold pianists. (Steinbrenner, Wilfried). *Schott. £1.40* QP/AY (B73-50716)
Wanhal, Jan. *See* Vanhal, Jan.
War march of the priests. (Mendelssohn, Felix). *Cramer. £0.24* RK/AGM (B73-50350)
Warburton, K M. The shepherd's story. Vocal score. The shepherd's story: Christmas chorus for mixed voice choir with piano or orchestra. (Thiman, Eric). *Roberton. £0.10* DP/LF (B73-50970)
Warburton, Kathleen. Pilgrims to Bethlehem: two-part song with piano. (Thiman, Eric Harding). *Roberton. £0.10* FDP/LF (B73-50140)
Ward, John Owen. The concise Oxford dictionary of music. (Scholes, Percy Alfred). 2nd ed. reprinted with corrections. *Oxford University Press. £1.50* A(C) (B73-30855) ISBN 0 19 311302 3
Ward method of teaching music. (Cambridge Ward Method Centre). *12 Grange Rd, Cambridge CB3 9DX: Cambridge Ward Method Centre. Unpriced* A(VC) (B73-08419) ISBN 0 9502782 0 3
Warlock, Peter.
8 songs: for medium voice and piano. *Thames. Unpriced* KFVDW (B73-50236)
The curlew: for tenor solo, flute, English horn, and string quartet. *Stainer and Bell. Unpriced* KGHE/NVPNQDX (B73-51097)
Warner, Sylvia Townsend. Liber secundus sacrarum cantionum. Miserere. Miserere mei = Look on me in mercy: SATBB. (Byrd, William). Revised ed. *Oxford University Press. Unpriced* EZDGKH/LHLN (B73-50532) ISBN 0 19 352053 2
Warrack, John.
Concise Oxford dictionary of opera. (Rosenthal, Harold) 1st ed. reprinted with corrections. *Oxford University Press. £2.00* AC(C) (B73-30857) ISBN 0 19 311305 8
Tchaikovsky. *Hamilton. £5.00* BTD(N) (B73-26164) ISBN 0 241 02403 x
Warship: theme from the B B C - TV series. (Isaac, Anthony). *Valentine. £0.20* QPK/AGM/JS (B73-50749)
Wassail wassail all over the town: a madrigal for Christmas time, for four-part chorus of mixed voices a cappella. (Spencer, Williametta). *Associated Music. Unpriced* EZDP/LF (B73-50100)
Wastall, Peter. The B and H recorder cards: a programmed method
Set 1. *Boosey and Hawkes. £3.00* VS/AC (B73-50411)
Water babies. Selections: arr. The water babies: simplified children's selection for easy piano/organ/guitar, etc. (Taylor, John). *Chappell. £0.80* PWPK/CM (B73-51138)
Water babies: simplified children's selection for easy piano/organ/guitar, etc. (Taylor, John). *Chappell. £0.80* PWPK/CM (B73-51138)
Waterman, Fanny.
Piano lessons
Book 2. *Faber Music. Unpriced* Q/AC (B73-51139)
Book 3. *Faber Music. Unpriced* Q/AC (B73-51140)
Second year piano lessons
Book 1. *Faber Music. Unpriced* Q/AC (B73-51141)
Watermill. (Binge, Ronald). *Inter-Art. £0.12* FDW (B73-50141)
Waters, Charles Frederick.
Festive processional: organ solo. *Cramer. £0.24* RJ (B73-50763)
Impromptu: organ solo. *Cramer. Unpriced* RJ (B73-51200)
Watkins, David.
Fantasy: for harp. (Dodgson, Stephen). *Stainer and Bell. £0.66* TQPMJ (B73-50390)
Nocturne: for harp. (Berkeley, Lennox). *Stainer and Bell. £0.50* TQPMJ (B73-50389)
Three stanzas. Op 8: for harp solo. (Harries, David). *Stainer & Bell. Unpriced* TQPMJ (B73-50811)
Watson (Henry) Music Library. *See* Henry Watson Music Library.
Watson, Walter. Affirmation: for organ. *Schirmer. Unpriced* RJ (B73-50346)
Watt, Jill. Johnson preserv'd: opera in 3 acts. *Hinrichsen. Unpriced* BSNKAC (B73-09577)
Watters, Cyril. A Cotswold lullaby. *Studio Music. Unpriced* WMJ (B73-50894)
Watts, Isaac.
Come, sound his praise abroad: for four-part chorus of mixed voices a cappella. (Ford, Virgil T). *Schirmer. Unpriced* EZDH (B73-50075)
When I survey the wondrous cross: Passiontide anthem founded on the folk tune 'O waly waly', for SATB and organ. (Eldridge, Guy). *Novello. £0.10* DH/LGZ (B73-50030)
Wayfaring stranger: for 2/3 part chorus of female or children's voices unaccompanied. (De Cormier, Robert). *Roberton. £0.07* FEZDM (B73-50573)
Wayfaring stranger: for 4-part chorus of mixed voices unaccompanied. (De Cormier, Robert). *Roberton. £0.10* EZDM (B73-50541)
We are the music-makers: for four-part chorus of mixed voices with descant a cappella. (Lekberg, Sven). *Schirmer. Unpriced* EZDW (B73-50121)
We make music. (Grindea, Carola). *Kahn and Averill. £0.75* QP/D/AY (B73-50294) ISBN 0 900707 14 3
Weber, Carl Maria, *Freiherr von.* Adagio and rondo for wind sextet. Adagio und Rondo für 2 Klarinetten, 2 Horner und 2 Fagotte. *Schott. £2.88* UNQ/W (B73-51259)
Webster, John. Elegy: soprano, flute horn, cello. (Walker, Eldon). *Thames. Unpriced* KFLE/NVNTDW (B73-50645)
Wechsberg, Joseph. Glory of the violin. *See* Wechsberg, Joseph. The violin.
Wechsberg, Joseph.
The violin. *Calder and Boyars. £5.00* AS/B(X) (B73-29559) ISBN 0 7145 1020 3
The waltz emperors: the life and times and music of the Strauss family. *Weidenfeld and Nicolson. £4.25* BSQB(N) (B73-30279) ISBN 0 297 76594 9
Wedding fanfare: organ. (Farmer, John A). *Coastal Music Studios. Unpriced* RGN/KDD (B73-50334)
Wedding music: suite for organ. (Gange, Kenneth). *Cramer. Unpriced* RG/KDD (B73-51193)
Wedding ring: SSAA and piano. (Russell-Smith, Geoffry). *Boosey and Hawkes. £0.09* FDW (B73-50568)
Weeks, John. The Sir Gawayn carols: SATB. (Crawley, Christopher). *Oxford University Press. Unpriced* DP/LF (B73-50966) ISBN 0 19 343042 8
Weelkes, Thomas.
Christ rising again: verse anthem for two sopranos, two altos, chorus and organ. *Novello. £0.18* DK (B73-50509)
Magnificat and Nunc dimittis no.5, 'in medio chori'. Evening service no.5, 'in medio chori': for two altos, tenor, two basses, chorus and organ. *Novello. £0.34* DGPP (B73-50949)
Weep you no more, sad fountains: for four-part chorus of mixed voices a cappella. (Lekberg, Sven). *Schirmer. Unpriced* EZDW (B73-50122)
Weep you no more, sad fountains: for four-part chorus of women's voices a cappella. (Carter, John). *Schirmer. Unpriced* FEZDW (B73-50157)
Wegner, Uwe. Sonata for viola & piano in C minor. Op.16, no.2. Sonata in C minor for viola (or violoncello) and piano. Op.16, no.2. (Onslow, George). *Bärenreiter. £3.30* SQPE (B73-50796)
Wegweiser: a 17th century German organ tutor. *Peters. Unpriced* R/AC (B73-50327)
Weihnacht wie bist so schon = Christmas so wondrous fair: carol from Upper Austria, for four-part chorus of mixed voices a cappella. (Czajanek, Victor). *Schirmer. Unpriced* EZDP/LF (B73-50096)
Weiland, Julius Johann. Erstlinge musicalischer Andachten..

Jauchzet Gott, alle Lande. Jauchzet Gott, alle Lande = Make a joyful noise unto God: sacred concerto for soprano, two violins and basso continuo. *Bärenreiter. £1.50* KFLE/SNTPWDE (B73-50225)
Weismann, Wilhelm. Mass no.3 in D minor, 'Nelson Mass'. Messe D-moll, (Nelson-Messe): für vierstimmigen Chor, Soli, Orchester und Orgel. (Haydn, Joseph). *Peters Hinrichsen. Unpriced* EMDG (B73-50049)
Welcome the Christ-child: seven carols for junior voices. (Bennett, F Roy). *Ashdown. £0.18* JFDP/LF (B73-50619)
Wellesz, Egon.
The new Oxford history of music
Vol.7: The Age of Enlightenment, 1745-1790. *Oxford University Press. £8.00* A(X) (B73-31506) ISBN 0 19 316307 1
Studies in Eastern Chant
Vol.3. *Oxford University Press. £6.00* ADTDS (B73-22800) ISBN 0 19 316320 9
Wenner, Jann. Lennon remembers: the 'Rolling Stone' interviews with John Lennon and Yoko Ono. *Talmy. £2.25* AKG/E(P) (B73-07792) ISBN 0 900735 10 4
Werdin, Eberhard. Tanze der Volker: ein Spielbuch fur Blas-, Streich-, Zupf- und Schlaginstrumente mit Improvisations- Möglichkeiten
Heft 2. *Schott. £1.00* NYEH/G/AY (B73-50698)
Wernert, Wolfgang. Psalm 116: für Sopran, Flöte, Vibraphon. *Bosse: Bärenreiter. £1.50* KFLE/VRPLXTRTDR (B73-50226)
Wesendonck Lieder. Träume. Träume = Dreams: study for 'Tristan and Isolde'. (Wagner, Richard). *Boosey and Hawkes. £0.75* MPVVK/DW (B73-50266)
Wesendonck Lieder. Träume. Träume = Dreams: study for 'Tristan and Isolde'. (Wagner, Richard). *Boosey and Hawkes. £0.50* VVPK/DW (B73-50431)
Wesley, Charles. Dux animorum. Leader of faithful souls. (Taberer, Alfred A). *Bankhead Press. £0.01* DM (B73-50512)
Wesley, Samuel. Trio for two flutes & pianoforte. *Oxford University Press. £1.60* VRNTQ (B73-51266) ISBN 0 19 359505 2
Wesley, Samuel Sebastian. An air composed for Holsworthy Church bells. It came upon the midnight clear. *Oxford University Press. Unpriced* EZDP/LF (B73-50544) ISBN 0 19 343041 x
Westbrook, Francis.
Faith of our fathers: anthem for a Dedication service. *Roberton. £0.10* DH (B73-50027)
Toccata, 'Hommage a Ravel: piano solo. *Peters. Unpriced* QPJ (B73-50748)
Westerlund, Gunnar. Music of Claudio Monteverdi: a discography. *29 Exhibition Rd, S.W.7: British Institute of Recorded Sound. £2.00* BMN/FD(WT) (B73-01061) ISBN 0 900208 05 8
Western overture. (George, Thom Ritter). *Boosey and Hawkes. £10.00* UMMJ (B73-50834)
Westminster childhood. (Raynor, John, *b.1909*). *Cassell. £3.25* BRGY(N/XA1921) (B73-24203) ISBN 0 304 29183 8
Westminster Te Deum: for SATB and organ. (Hall, Ian). *Weinberger. £0.25* DGNQ (B73-50017)
Westmore, Peter. It's who you're with that counts: SATB. (Hughes, Edward). *British and Continental. Unpriced* DP/LF (B73-50968)
Weston, Gordon.
Gorwyd Iesu Grist = Christus natus est: two part carol by Gordon Weston; traditional words, Welsh version by Ivor Owen. *University of Wales Press. £0.15* FDP/LF (B73-51026)
Seren Bethlehem = Star of Bethlehem: TTBB. *University of Wales Press. £0.15* GEZDP/LF (B73-51045)
Wette, Adelheid. Hänsel und Gretel. Vocal score. Hänsel und Gretel: Märchenspiel in drei Bildern. (Humperdinck, Engelbert). *Peters: Hinrichsen. Unpriced* CC (B73-50006)
Wheeler, Eunice.
Short exercises in position changing for the cello
Bk 1: Position 2 to 5. *Cornelius. Unpriced* SR/AF (B73-50800)
Bk 2: Positions 6, 7 and thumb. *Cornelius. Unpriced* SR/AF (B73-50801)
When I survey the wondrous cross: Passiontide anthem founded on the folk tune 'O waly waly', for SATB and organ. (Eldridge, Guy). *Novello. £0.10* DH/LGZ (B73-50030)
When I was one-and-twenty: for four-part chorus of mixed voices a cappella. (Fast, Willard S). *Schirmer. Unpriced* EZDW (B73-50116)
Whimsies: four miniatures for piano
Second set. (Taylor, Colin). *Boosey and Hawkes. £0.60* QPJ (B73-50747)
White, E Milner-. *See* Milner-White, E.
White (Ernest George) Society *See* Ernest George White Society.
White, Tony. Seven short and easy studies: for beginners on the Spanish guitar. *Cornelius. Unpriced* TS/AF (B73-50813)
Whittemore, Reed. The high school band: SSATB (S. solo) unacc. (Paynter, John). *Oxford University Press. Unpriced* EZDW (B73-51009) ISBN 0 19 343039 8
Whittier, John Greenleaf. All as God wills: for four-part chorus of mixed voices a cappella. (Ford, Virgil T). *Schirmer. Unpriced* EZDH (B73-50074)
Who is Sylvia?: SSAA. (Gardner, John). *Oxford University Press. Unpriced* FDW (B73-50142) ISBN 0 19 342594 7
Who would true valour see: S.S.A. with piano or organ. (Tomlins, Greta). *Roberton. £0.09* FDM (B73-50137)
Whyte, Hamish B.
Carol of Joseph: for SATB choir. (Rudland, Malcolm). *Thames. Unpriced* EZDP/LF (B73-50099)
Mary of the wilderness: carol for SATB and flute. (Rudland, Malcolm). *Thames. Unpriced* EVRDH/LF (B73-50054)
Wi'a hundred pipers an' a': SAB. (Simpson, John). *British and Continental. Unpriced* DW (B73-50978)
Wickham, E H.
Bang on a drum: songs from Play School and Play Away, the B.B.C. Television programmes. *British Broadcasting Corporation, Keith Prowse Music. £0.60* QPK/DW/GJ/JS/AY (B73-50320)
How to play the flageolet (penny whistle). *Keith Prowse. £0.20* VSQQ/AC (B73-50418)
Wicks, Allan. Communion service, series 3: unison (and optional SATB). (Dearnley, Christopher). *Oxford University Press. Unpriced* JDGS (B73-50600) ISBN 0 19 351645 4
Widdicombe, Trevor. As we sailed out of London river: male voice chorus (TTBB) and piano. (Sykes, Harold Hinchcliff). *Roberton. £0.10* GDW (B73-50166)
Widow bird sate mourning: SATB unaccompanied. (Dare, Marie). *Roberton. £0.07* EZDW (B73-50113)
Wilcock, Frank. Show album: songs and sketches. *Brown, Son and Ferguson. £0.75* JDW (B73-51057)
Wilde, Oscar. Symphony in yellow. Op. 15b: for high voice and harp (or piano). (Blyton, Carey). *Boosey and Hawkes. £0.40* KFTE/TQDW (B73-51096)
Wilhelm, Roger.
Cantemus Domino = Sing unto God: for 3-part chorus of mixed voices with organ. (Brunetti, Domenico). *Roberton. £0.13* DJ (B73-50508)
Moteca. Cantate Domino. Cantate Domino. Sing unto the Lord: for 4-part chorus of mixed voices with optional organ. (Vecchi, Horatio). *Roberton. Unpriced* EZDR (B73-50545)
Wiliam, Urien. Gentle are its songs. (Wright, Kenneth Anthony). *P.O. Box 775, W9 1LN: Sir Gerald Nabarro (Publications) Ltd. £3.50* AD(YDKRL/WB/XPG26) (B73-16140) ISBN 0 903699 00 1
Wilk, Max. Memory lane, 1890 to 1925: ragtime, jazz, foxtrot and other popular music and music covers. *14 West Central St., WC1A 1JH: Studioart. £6.75* A(RC/XLK36) (B73-30839) ISBN 0 902063 14 6
Wilkins, Nigel.
Three madrigals: for 3 voices and/or instruments. (Jacopo da Bologna). *Antico. Unpriced* EZDU (B73-50104)
Three madrigals: for 3 voices and/or instruments. (Jacopo da Bologna). *Antico. Unpriced* EZDU (B73-50105)
William Boyce suite. (Boyce, William). *Paxton. £0.45* RK (B73-51202)
Williams, Bryn. Three Welsh folk songs = Tair cânwerin: for female voices with piano. *Roberton. £0.18* FEZDW/G/AYDK (B73-50158)
Williams, Gilbert. Voice of angels, steps of shepherds: carol for SATB and organ. (Cameron, Gordon). *Novello. £0.07* DP/LF (B73-50965)
Williams, John. Guitar transcriptions from the Cube L.P., 'The height below'. *Essex Music. Unpriced* TSNUK/AAY (B73-51243)
Williams, Ralph Vaughan. *See* Vaughan Williams, Ralph.
Williams, Ursula Vaughan. *See* Vaughan Williams, Ursula.
Williamson, Malcolm.
Carols of King David: for unison choir, congregation and organ
No.3: Together in unity: Psalm 133. *Weinberger. £0.05* JDR (B73-51056)
Epitaphs for Edith Sitwell: for string orchestra. *Weinberger. Unpriced* RXMJ (B73-50358)
I will lift up mine eyes. Psalm 121: anthem for chorus, echo chorus and organ. *Weinberger. £0.05* FDR (B73-50567)
Ode to music. *Weinberger. Unpriced* JFDX (B73-50192)
Pas de deux: for clarinet (B flat) and piano. *Weinberger. Unpriced* VVPH (B73-50428)
The Red Sea. Chorus score. The Red Sea: opera in one act. *Weinberger. £0.30* DAC (B73-50010)
The Red Sea. Vocal score. The Red Sea: opera in one act. *Weinberger. Unpriced* CC (B73-50007)
The winter star. Vocal score. The winter star: a cassation for audience and instruments. *Weinberger. Unpriced* FDE/LF (B73-51014)
Wills, Arthur. Let all men everywhere rejoice: anthem for SATB and organ (or brass, percussion and organ). *Novello. £0.14* DH (B73-50028)
Wilmer, Valerie. Jazz people. 2nd ed. *Allison and Busby. £1.00* AMT/E(M) (B73-00882) ISBN 0 85031 085 7
Wilson, Christopher. Green groves: more English folk songs. (Hamer, Fred). *EFDS. £0.75* KE/TSDW/G/AYD (B73-50218)
Wilson, Jane. Flamingoes: song for medium voice and piano. (Parrott, Ian). *Thames. Unpriced* KFVDW (B73-50233)
Wilson, Jo Manning.
The jolly swagman. (Binge, Ronald). *Mozart Edition. Unpriced* KDW (B73-50202)
The watermill. (Binge, Ronald). *Inter-Art. £0.12* FDW (B73-50141)
Wilson, Mabel. More songs for music time: for unison voices, with tuned and rhythmic percussion accompaniments. *Oxford University Press. £0.50* JFE/NYLDW/GJ/AY (B73-50194) ISBN 0 19 330876 2
Wilson, Richard. Home from the range: for full chorus of mixed voices a cappella. *Schirmer. Unpriced* EZDX (B73-50132)
Wilson, Robert Barclay.
Heard ye the mighty roar?: Song. *Cramer. Unpriced* KDW (B73-50212)
Pop-song without words: piano. *Cramer. Unpriced* QPJ (B73-51180)
Wilson, Thomas. Sinfonietta for brass band. *R. Smith. Unpriced* WMEM (B73-50880)
Wilson-Dickson, Andrew. Jesu, send us peace: SATB. *Banks. Unpriced* DH (B73-50505)
Wilton, Dorothy R. New child songs: Christian songs for under-eights. (Buzzing, Pauline). *Denholme House Press. £1.50* JFDM/GJ/AY (B73-51065) ISBN 0 85213 074 0
Wimbush, Roger. 'The Gramophone' jubilee book. *177 Kenton Rd, Harrow, Middx: General Gramophone Publications Ltd. £2.50* A/FD(XNC51/D) (B73-13020) ISBN 0 902470 04 3
Windsor Castle. *St George's Chapel.* The musical manuscripts of St George's Chapel, Windsor Castle: a descriptive catalogue. *2 Victoria St., Windsor, Berks.: Oxley and Son (Windsor) Ltd for the Dean and Canons of St George's Chapel in Windsor Castle. £1.25* AD/LD(YDEUW/TE) (B73-09262) ISBN 0 902187 16 3
Winners got scars too. Johnny Cash - winners got scars too. (Wren, Christopher, *b.1936*). *W.H. Allen. £2.00* AKDW/GCW/(P) (B73-09000) ISBN 0 491 00794 9
Winter star: a cassation for audience and instruments. (Williamson, Malcolm). *Weinberger. Unpriced* FDE/LF (B73-51014)
Winters, Geoffrey. Stories of Britain in song. (Stuart, Forbes). *Longman Young Books. £2.75* KDW/G/AYC (B73-50213) ISBN 0 582 15330 1
Wise, Michael. Magnificat and Nunc dimittis: SATBB. *Oxford University Press. £0.15* DGPP (B73-50950) ISBN 0 19 351635 7
Wittgenstein, Ludwig von. Stanza 1: per chitarra, arpa, pianoforte, celesta, vibrafono e voce feminile (soprano). (Takemitsu, Toru). *Universal. Unpriced* KFLE/NYGNRDW (B73-51091)
Wizard of Oz: song album from the film. (Arlen, Harold). *Robbins Music, Francis, Day & Hunter. £0.75* KDW/JR (B73-50639)
Woehl, Waldemar. Florilegium.. Suites. Suites from the 'Florilegium': for four or five parts (string or wind instruments). (Muffat, Georg). *Bärenreiter. £1.95* NXNSG (B73-50280)
Wohltemperirte Clavier. Prelude no.23. S.868: arr. Prelude no.23. S.868. (Bach, Johann Sebastian). *Cornelius. Unpriced* TSNTK (B73-50815)
Wolfe, Daniel. Sacrae symphoniae, bk.1. Plaudite. Vocal score. Plaudite: for triple chorus of mixed voices. (Gabrieli, Giovanni). *Schirmer. Unpriced* DJ (B73-50961)
Wolff, Harold. Rejoice in the Lamb. Op.30. Vocal score: arr. Rejoice in the Lamb. Op 30: festival cantata. (Britten, Benjamin). *Boosey and Hawkes. £1.00* FDE (B73-50564)

Wood, Charles. Mater ora filium: arr. Mater ora filium: Irish folk song. *Novello. £0.10* FLDP/LF (B73-50575)
Wood, John. Yeoman's carol: for SSS unaccompanied. *Novello. £0.07* FLEZDP/LF (B73-50580)
Word of the Lord. (Bernstein, Leonard). *Amberson: Schirmer. Unpriced* KDW (B73-50201)
Working the halls. *See* Honri, Peter.
Wörner, Karl Heinrich. Stockhausen: life and work. *Faber. £6.00* BSO(N) (B73-03714) ISBN 0 571 08997 6
Wren, Christopher, *b.1936*. Johnny Cash - winners got scars too. *W.H. Allen. £2.00* AKDW/GCW/(P) (B73-09000) ISBN 0 491 00794 9
Wright, Kenneth Anthony. Gentle are its songs. *P.O. Box 775, W9 1LN: Sir Gerald Nabarro (Publications) Ltd. £3.50* AD(YDKRL/WB/XPG26) (B73-16140) ISBN 0 903699 00 1
Wright, Laurence.
Chansons musicales. Selections: arr. Eight chansons: for recorders (Tr T T B or D Tr T B)
Vol.1. (Attaingnant, Pierre). *Schott. £0.75* VSNSK/DU/AY (B73-51274)
Chansons musicales. Selections: arr. Eight chansons: for recorders (Tr T T B or D Tr T B)
Vol.2. (Attaingnant, Pierre). *Schott. £0.75* VSNSK/DU/AY (B73-51275)
Wright, Paul. Missa brevis: for men's voices. *Thames. Unpriced* GEZDG (B73-50582)
Write your own pop song with Rolf Harris. (Harris, Rolf). *Wolfe: Keith Prowse Music Publishing Co. Ltd. £2.00* ADW/GB/D (B73-26165) ISBN 0 7234 0509 3
Wuorinen, Charles. The long and the short: violin solo. *Peters. Unpriced* SPMJ (B73-50371)
Wurzburger, Walter.
Ensemble studies
2: Oboe and clarinet. *Thames. Unpriced* VTPLVV (B73-50424)
Klavierstück: for solo piano. *Thames. Unpriced* QPJ (B73-50313)
Wyatt, *Sir* Thomas. And wilt thou leave me thus?: For SSATBB unaccompanied. (Radford, Anthony). *Thames. Unpriced* EZDW (B73-50561)
Wye, Trevor. Valse des fleurs. Op 87: for 2 flutes and piano. (Kohler, Ernesto). *Emerson. Unpriced* VRNTQHW (B73-51267)
Wyttenbach, Jurg. Paraphrase: für einen Flötisten und einen Pianisten. *Ars viva: Schott. £3.00* VRPJ (B73-50407)
Yale studies in English. *(Yale University Press)* Johnson, Paula. Form and transformation in music and poetry of the English Renaissance. *Yale University Press. £3.50* A(YD/XDY81/ZB) (B73-03716) ISBN 0 300 01544 5
Yeats, William Butler.
The curlew: for tenor solo, flute, English horn, and string quartet. (Warlock, Peter). *Stainer and Bell. Unpriced* KGHE/NVPNQDX (B73-51097)
The song of wandering Aengus: SATB a cappella by

Doreen Droste. (Droste, Doreen). *Galaxy: Galliard.*
Unpriced EZDW (B73-50553)
Yehudi Menuhin: the story of the man and the musician.
(Magidoff, Robert). 2nd ed. *Hale. £3.00* AS/E(P)
(B73-24889)   ISBN 0 7091 3351 0
Yeoman's carol: for SSS unaccompanied. (Wood, John).
Novello. £0.07 FLEZDP/LF (B73-50580)
Yorke, Peter. The shipbuilders: suite for brass band.
Chappell. Unpriced WMG (B73-50884)
You asked for it: for acoustic guitar solo. (Bedford, David).
Universal. Unpriced TSPMJ (B73-51247)
You must have that true religion: negro spiritual, for
soprano and alto accompanied. (Nelson, Havelock).
Keith Prowse Music. Unpriced FDW/LC (B73-51037)
Youll, Henry. Canzonets to three voyces.. Come merry lads,
let us away: arr. Come merry lads, let us away.
Roberton. £0.10 FEZDU (B73-50156)
Young, Percy. Classical songs for children. The Penguin
book of accompanied songs. (Harewood, Marion).
Penguin Books. £0.75 JFDW/AY (B73-50190)
                                        ISBN 0 14 070839 1
Young, Percy Marshall.
Airs francais = Cantate francaise: for soprano and basso
continuo. (Handel, George Frideric). First ed.
Bärenreiter. £1.50 KFLDX (B73-50643)
Bartók. (Lesznai, Lajos). *26 Albemarle St., W1X 4QY:*
Dent. £2.50 BBG(N) (B73-24886)
                                        ISBN 0 460 03136 8
Young child's carol. (Evans, E L). *British and Continental.*
Unpriced EZDP (B73-50095)
Young may moon, (from Moore's Irish melodies). (Pasfield,
William Reginald). *Ashdown. £0.05* FLDW (B73-50578)

Young person's guide to playing the piano. (Harrison,
Sidney). 2nd ed. *Faber. £1.50* AQ/E (B73-20241)
                                        ISBN 0 571 04787 4
Youth at the helm: piano solo. (Parfrey, Raymond).
Composer to Player Edition. Unpriced QPJ (B73-50745)

Yradier, Sebastian. La Paloma: arr. La Paloma. *Fisher &*
Lane. Unpriced RPVK/AHVR (B73-50353)
Zanoskar, Hubert.
Neue Gitarren-Schule
Band 1. *Schott. £1.125* TS/AC (B73-51241)
Übungen und Spielstücke: Beiheft zu Band 1 der neuen
Gitarren-Schule. *Schott. £0.90* TS/AF (B73-51242)
Zauberflöte. The golden flute: an opera for schools in two
acts based on Mozart's 'The magic flute'. (Mozart,
Wolfgang Amadeus). *Novello. £1.00* CN (B73-50008)
Zils, Diethard. Neue Kinderlieder: für Kinder - und
Familiengottesdienst. (Behr, Heinz Otto). *Bosse*
Bärenreiter. £0.60 JFEZDM/GJ/AY (B73-50195)
Zimmer, Ulrich W. Kirchengesäng: Psalmen und geistliche
Lieder.. Selections. Kirchengesänge, Psalmen und
geistliche Lieder: Choralsätz für gemischten Chor.
(Hassler, Hans Leo). *Bärenreiter. £1.35* EZDM
(B73-50089)
Zimmermann, Reiner.
Cinq poèmes de Charles Baudelaire: songs for solo voice
and piano. (Debussy, Claude). *Peters. Unpriced* KDW
(B73-50631)
Trois ballads de François Villon: songs for solo voice and
piano. (Debussy, Claude). *Peters. Unpriced* KDW
(B73-50632)
Trois chansons de France, and Trois poèmes de Tristan
l'Hermite: songs for solo voice and piano. (Debussy,
Claude). *Peters. Unpriced* KDW (B73-50633)
Trois poèmes de Stéphane Mallarmé: songs for solo voice
and piano. (Debussy, Claude). *Peters. Unpriced* KDW
(B73-50634)
Zion spricht = Zion speaks. (Schein, Johann Hermann).
Roberton. Unpriced EZDH (B73-50535)
Zipoli, Domenico. Sonate d'intavolatura for organ. Op. 1.
Parte 1. Toccata: arr. Toccata. *Boosey and Hawkes.*
£0.75 QPK (B73-51181)
Zironi, Yossi. Serenade for solo violin. (Schurmann, Gerard).
Novello. £1.20 SPMJ (B73-50370)
Zulu welcome: South African impression for percussion
ensemble, (6 players). (Fink, Siegfried). *Simrock.*
Unpriced XNQ (B73-51308)
Zwei Hande- zwölf Tasten
Band 2: Spiel mit Noten. (Runze, Klaus). *Schott. Unpriced*
LNU (B73-51101)
Zwei-Mann-Orchester. (Kagel, Mauricio). *Universal.*
Unpriced LNU (B73-51100)
Zwolf kleine Stücke. *See* Maurer, Ludwig. 12 kleine Stücke.

SUBJECT INDEX

LIST OF MUSIC PUBLISHERS

While every effort has been made to check the information given in this list with the publishers concerned, the Council of the British National Bibliography cannot hold itself responsible for any errors or omissions.

ALLAN & Co. (Pty.), Ltd., Australia.
British Agent: Freeman, H., & Co.

ALLEN, George, & Unwin, Ltd. 40 Museum St., London, W.C.2: *Tel:* 01-405 8577. *Grams:* Deucalion.
Trade: Park Lane, Hemel Hempstead, Herts.
Tel: 0442 3244

AMERICAN Institute of Musicology, U.S.A.
British Agent: Hinrichsen Edition, Ltd.

AMICI della Musica da Camera, Rome.
British Agent: Hinrichsen Edition, Ltd.

ARNOLD, Edward, (Publishers), Ltd. (Music Scores). *See* Novello & Co., Ltd.

ARTIA, Prague.
British Agent: Boosey & Hawkes Music Publishers, Ltd.

ASCHERBURG, Hopwood & Crew, 50 New Bond St., W1A 2BR. *Tel:* 01-629 7600. *Grams:* Symphony London.

ASHDOWN, Edwin, Ltd. 275-281 Cricklewood Broadway, London, NW2 6QR. *Tel:* 01-450 5237.

ASSOCIATED Board of the Royal Schools of Music (Publications Dept.). 14 Bedford Sq., London, WC1B 3JG. *Tel:* 01-636 6919. *Grams:* Musexam London WC1.

AVENUE Music Publishing Co., Ltd. 50 New Bond St., London, W1A 2BR. *Tel:* 01-629 7600. *Grams:* Symphony London.

BANK, Annie, Editions, Amsterdam.
British Agent: J. & W. Chester, Ltd.

BARENREITER, Ltd. 32 Gt. Titchfield St., London, W.1.
Tel: 01-580 9008

BARON, H. 136 Chatsworth Rd., London, NW2 5QU.
Tel: 01-459 2035. *Grams:* Musicbaron, London.

BARRY & Co., Buenos Aires.
British Agent: Boosey & Hawkes Music Publishers, Ltd.

BAYLEY & Ferguson, Ltd. 65 Berkeley St., Glasgow C3.
Tel: CENtral 7240. *Grams:* Bayley Glasgow.

BELWIN-MILLS Music, Ltd. 230 Purley Way, Croydon, CR9 4QD. *Tel:* 01-681 0855. *Grams:* Belmil Croydon.

BERLIN, Irving, Ltd. 14 St. George St., London, W.1.
Tel: 01-629 7600.

BESSEL, W. & Co. Paris.
British Agent: Boosey & Hawkes Music Publishers, Ltd.

BIELER, Edmund, Musikverlag, Cologne.
British Agent: J. & W. Chester, Ltd.

BLOSSOM Music, Ltd. 139 Piccadilly, London, W.1.
Tel: 01-629 7211. *Grams:* Leedsmusik London, W.1.

BOOSEY & Hawkes Music Publishers, Ltd. 295 Regent St., London, W1A 1BR. *Tel:* 01-580 2060.
Grams: Sonorous London W.1.

BOSTON Music Co., Boston (Mass.).
British Agent: Chappell & Co., Ltd.

BOSWORTH & Co., Ltd. 14-18 Heddon St., London, W.1. *Tel:* 01-734 4961/2. *Grams:* Bosedition Piccy London.

BOURNE MUSIC Ltd. 34/36 Maddox St., London, W1R 9PD.
Tel: 01-493 6412/6583. *Grams:* Bournemusic London, W.1.

BRADBURY Wood, Ltd. 16 St. George St., London, W.1.

BREGMAN, Vocco & Conn, Ltd. 50 New Bond St., London, W1A 1BR. *Tel:* 01-629 7600. *Grams:* Symphony London.

BREITKOPF & Härtel, Leipzig.
British Agent: Breitkopf & Härtel (London), Ltd.

BREITKOPF & Härtel (London), Ltd. 8 Horse and Dolphin Yard, London, W1V 7LG.

BREITKOPF & Härtel, Wiesbaden, W. Germany.
British Agent: Breitkopf & Härtel (London), Ltd.

BRITISH & Continental Music Agencies, Ltd. 64 Dean St., London, W.1. *Tel:* GERrard 9336. *Grams:* Humfriv Wesdo London.

BROCKHAUS, Max, Germany.
British Agent (Orchestral music only): Novello & Co., Ltd.

BRUZZICHELLI, Aldo, Florence.
British Agent: Hinrichsen Edition, Ltd.

CAMPBELL, Connelly, & Co., Ltd. *See* CONNELLY, Campbell, & Co., Ltd.

CARY, L.J., & Co. Ltd. 50 New Bond St., London, W1A 2BR.
Tel: 01-629 7600. *Grams:* Symphony London W1.

CEBEDEM Foundation, Brussels.
British Agent: Lengnick & Co., Ltd.

CHAPPELL & Co., Ltd. 50 New Bond St., London, W1A 2BR. *Tel:* 01-629 7600. *Grams:* Symphony London.

CHESTER, J. & W., Ltd. Eagle Court, London, E.C.1.
Tel: 01-253-6947. *Grams:* Guarnerius, London E.C.1.

CHURCH, John, Co., Pennsylvania.
British Agent: Alfred A. Kalmus, Ltd.

CLIFFORD Essex Music Co., Ltd. *See* ESSEX, Clifford, Music Co., Ltd.

COLLIER/DEXTER Music, Ltd. 50 New Bond St., London, W1A 2BR. *Tel:* 01-629 7600.

COLUMBIA Music Co., Washington, D.C.
British Agent: Breitkopf & Härtel (London) Ltd.

COMPASS Music Lyd. 93 Albert Embankment, London, SE1 7TY. *Tel:* 01-735 9291.

CONNELLY, Campbell & Co., Ltd. 10 Denmark St., London, W.C.2. *Tel:* TEMple Bar 1653. *Grams:* Dansmelodi Westcent London.

CONSTABLE & Co., Ltd. 10 Orange St., London, WC2H 7EG.
Tel: 01-930 0801. *Grams:* Dhagoba London WC2.
Trade: Tiptree Book Services Ltd., Tiptree, Colchester, Essex. *Tel:* Tiptree 6362/7

CRAMER, J. B., & Co., Ltd. 99 St. Martin's Lane, London, WC2N 4AZ. *Tel:* 01-240 1612.

CURWEN, J., & Sons, Ltd.
Agents: Faber Music, & Roberton Publications.

DELHI Publications, Inc., Cincinnati.
British Agent: Chappell & Co., Ltd.

DELRIEU, Georges, & Cie, Nice.
British Agent: Galliard, Ltd.

DE SANTIS, Rome.
British Agent: Hinrichsen Edition, Ltd.

DEUTSCH, André, Ltd. 105 Gt. Russell St., London, W.C.1.
Tel: 01-580 2746. *Grams:* Adlib London.
Trade: Amabel House, 14-24 Baches St., London, N.1.
Tel: 01-253 8589.

DE WOLFE, Ltd. 80-82 Wardour St., London, W1V 3LF.
Tel: 01-437 4933. *Grams:* Musicall London.

DISNEY, Walt, Music Co., Ltd. 52 Maddox St., London, W.1.
Tel: 01-629 7600.

DITSON, Oliver, Co., Pennsylvania.
British Agent: Alfred A. Kalmus, Ltd.

DOBLINGER Edition, Vienna.
British Agent: Alfred A. Kalmus, Ltd.

DONEMUS Foundation, Amsterdam.
British Agent: Alfred Lengnick, & Co., Ltd.

EDITIO Musica, Budapest.
British Agent: Boosey & Hawkes Music Publishers, Ltd.

EDITION Tonos, Darmstadt.
British Agent: Breitkopf & Härtel (London), Ltd.

EDIZIONI Bèrben, Ancona, Italy.
British Agent: Breitkopf & Härtel (London) Ltd.

EDIZIONI Suvini Zerboni, Milan.
British Agent: Schott & Co., Ltd.

EDWARD B. Marks Music Corporation, New York.
British Agent: Boosey & Hawkes Music Publishers, Ltd.

ELKIN & Co., Ltd. Borough Green, Sevenoaks, Kent. *Tel:* Borough Green 3261. *Grams:* Novellos Sevenoaks

ENGLISH Folk Dance and Song Society. Cecil Sharp House, 2 Regent's Park Road, London, NW1 7AY.
Tel: 01-485 2206.

ESCHIG, Max, Paris.
British Agent: Schott & Co., Ltd.

ESSEX, Clifford, Music Co., Ltd. 20 Earlham St., London, W.C.2. *Tel:* 01-836 2810. *Grams:* Triomphe London, W.C.2.

ESSEX Music Group. Essex House, 19/20 Poland St., London, W1V 3DD. *Tel:* 01-434 1621. *Grams:* Sexmus London.
Trade: Music Sales Ltd. 78 Newman St., London, W.1.

EULENBURG, Ernst, Ltd. 48 Great Marlborough St., London, W1V 2BN. *Tel:* 01-437 1246/8.

FABER Music, Ltd. 38 Russell Sq., London, WC1B 5DA.
Tel: 01-636 1344. *Grams:* Fabbaf London WC1.

FAITH Press, Ltd. Wing Rd, Leighton Buzzard, Beds.
LU7 7NQ. *Tel:* 052-53 3365.

FAMOUS Chappell, Ltd. 50 New Bond St., London, W1A 2BR. *Tel:* 01-629 7600. *Grams:* Symphony London.

FELDMAN, B., & Co., Ltd. 64 Dean St., London, W.1.
Tel: GERard 9336. *Grams:* Humfriv Wesdo London.

FISCHER, Carl, New York.
British Agent: Hinrichsen Edition, Ltd.

FOETISCH Freres, Éditions, Lausanne.
British Agent: J. & W. Chester, Ltd.

FORBERG, Robert, Bad Godesberg.
British Agent: Hinrichsen Edition, Ltd.

FORSYTH Brothers, Ltd. 190 Grays Inn Rd., London, WC1X 8EW. *Tel:* 01-837 4768.

FORTISSIMO-Verlag, Vienna.
British Agent: Clifford Essex Music Co., Ltd.

FOX, Sam, Publishing Co. *See* SAM Fox Publishing Co.

FRANCIS, Day & Hunter, Ltd. 138 Charing Cross Rd., London, W.C.2. *Tel:* 01-836 6699. *Grams:* Arpeggio London.
Westcent London.

FRANK Music Co., Ltd. 50 New Bond St., London, W1A 2BR. *Tel:* 01-629 7600. *Grams:* Symphony London.

FREEMAN, H., Ltd. 64 Dean St., London, W.1. *Tel:* 01-437 9336/9.

FRENCH, Samuel, Ltd. 26 Southampton St., Strand, London, W.C.2. *Tel:* 01-836 7513. *Grams:* Dramalogue London W.C.2.

G. & C. Music Corporation, New York.
British Agent: Chappell & Co., Ltd.

GALAXY Music Corporation, New York.
British Agent: Stainer & Bell, Ltd.

GALLIARD, Ltd. 82 High Rd, London N.2.

GLOCKEN Verlag, Ltd. 10-16 Rathbone St., London, W1P 2BJ. *Tel:* 01-580 2827. *Grams:* Operetta London W1.

GRAPHIC, Graz, Austria.
British Agent: Alfred A. Kalmus, Ltd.

GREGG International Publishers, Ltd. Westmead, Farnborough, Hants.

GWASG Prifysgol Cymru, Merthyr House, James St., Cardiff, CF1 6EU. *Tel:* Cardiff 31919.

HANSEN, Wilhelm, Edition, Copenhagen.
British Agent: J. & W. Chester, Ltd.

HANSSLER, Verlag, Germany.
British Agent: Novello & Co., Ltd.

HARGAIL Music Press, New York.
British Agent: Alfred A. Kalmus, Ltd.

HARMONIA Uitgave, Hilversum.
British Agent: Alfred A. Kalmus, Ltd.

HARRIS, Frederick, Music Co., Ltd.
British Agent: Alfred Lengnick & Co., Ltd.

HART, F. Pitman, & Co., Ltd. 99 St. Martin's Lane, London, WC2N 4AZ. *Tel:* 01-240 1612.

HEINRICHSHOFEN, Wilhelmshaven.
British Agent: Clifford Essex Music Co., Ltd.

HENLE, G., Verlag, Germany.
British Agent: Novello & Co., Ltd.

HENMAR Press, New York.
British Agent: Hinrichsen Edition, Ltd.

HEUWEKEMEIJER, Holland.
British Agent: Hinrichsen Edition, Ltd.

HINRICHSEN Edition, Ltd. Bach House, 10-12 Baches St., London, N1 6DN. *Tel:* 01-253 1638. *Grams:* Musipeters London.

HOFMEISTER, Friedrich, Hofheim, W. Germany.
British Agent: Breitkopf & Härtel (London) Ltd.

HOFMEISTER Figaro Verlag, Vienna.
British Agent: Alfred A. Kalmus, Ltd.

HUG & Co., Zurich.
British Agent: Hinrichsen Edition, Ltd.

HUGHES a'i Fab (Hughes & Son) Publishers, Ltd. 29 Rivulet Rd., Wrexham, Denbighshire, North Wales. *Tel:* Wrexham 4340.

HUNTZINGER, R. L., Inc., Cincinnati.
British Agent: Chappell & Co., Ltd.

IMPERIAL Society of Teachers of Dancing. 70 Gloucester Place, London, W1H 4AJ. *Tel:* 01-935 0825/6. *Grams:* Istod, London W1.

INTER-ART Music Publishers. 10-16 Rathbone St., London, W1P 2BJ. *Tel:* 01-580 2827. *Grams:* Operetta London W1.

INTERNATIONAL Music Co., New York.
British Agent: Alfred A. Kalmus, Ltd.

INTERNATIONALEN Musikbisliothek, Berlin.
British Agent: Breitkopf & Härtel (London), Ltd.

ISTITUTO Italiano per la Storia della Musica.
British Agent: Alfred A. Kalmus, Ltd.

JUSKO, Ralph, Publications, Inc., Cincinnati.
British Agent: Chappell & Co., Ltd.

KAHNT, C. F., Germany.
British Agent: Novello & Co., Ltd.

KALMUS, Alfred A., Ltd. 2-3 Fareham St., London, W1V 4DU. *Tel:* 01-437 5203. *Grams:* Alkamus London W.1.

KALMUS, Edwin, New York.
British Agent: Alfred A. Kalmus, Ltd.

KEITH Prowse Music Publishing Co., Ltd. 21 Denmark St., London, WC2H 8NE. *Tel:* 01-836 5501.

KISTNER & Siegel & Co., Germany.
British Agent: Novello & Co., Ltd.

KNEUSSLIN, Switzerland.
British Agent: Hinrichsen Edition, Ltd.

LAUDY & Co. c/o Bosworth & Co., Ltd. 14-18 Heddon St., London, W.1. *Tel:* 01-734 4961/2. *Grams:* Bosedition Piccy London.

LAWSON-GOULD Music Publications, New York.
British Agent: Roberton Publications.

LEA Pocket Scores, New York.
British Agent: Alfred A. Kalmus, Ltd.

LEEDS Music, Ltd. 139 Piccadilly, London, W.1. *Tel:* MAYfair 7211. *Grams:* Leedsmusik London.

LENGNICK, Alfred, & Co., Ltd. Purley Oaks Studios, 421a Brighton Rd., South Croydon, Sy. *Tel:* 01-660-7646.

LEONARD, Gould & Bolttler. 99 St. Martin's Lane, London, WC2N 4AZ. *Tel:* 01-240 1612.

LEUCKART, F. E. C., Germany.
British Agent: Novello & Co., Ltd.

LIENAU, Robert (Schlesinger), Germany.
British Agent: Hinrichsen Edition, Ltd.

LITOLFF Verlag. Bach House, 10-12 Baches St., London, N1 6DN. *Tel:* 01-253 1638.

LUVERNE Inc., New York.
British Agent: Boosey & Hawkes Music Publishers, Ltd.

LYCHE, Oslo.
British Agent: Hinrichsen Edition, Ltd.

McGINNIS & Marx, New York.
British Agent: Hinrichsen Edition, Ltd.

MADDOX Music Co., Ltd. 52 Maddox St., London, W.1. *Tel:* 01-629 7600.

MAURICE, Peter. *See* PETER Maurice.

MERION Music Co., Pennsylvania.
British Agent: Alfred A. Kalmus, Ltd.

MERSEBURGER Verlag, Berlin.
British Agent: Hinrichsen Edition, Ltd. ; Musica Rara.

METROPOLIS, Antwerp.
British Agent: Hinrichsen Edition, Ltd.

MEZHDUNARODNAJA Kniga, Moscow.
British Agent: Boosey & Hawkes Music Publishers, Ltd.

MIDLAND Music Ltd. 50 Ladbroke Grove, London, W.11. *Tel:* 01-229 1129

MOORIS, Edwin H., & CO., Ltd. 50 New Bond St., London, W1A 2BR. *Tel:* 01-629 0576.

MOSELER Verlag, Germany.
British Agent: Novello & Co., Ltd.

MÜLLER, Willy, Germany.
British Agent: Novello & Co., Ltd.

MUSIA International (Export and Import), Frankfurt.
British Agent: Hinrichsen Edition, Ltd.

MUSICA Islandica, Reykjavik.
British Agent: Alfred Lengnick & Co., Ltd.

MUSICA Rara. 2 Great Marlborough St., London, W.1. *Tel:* 01-437 1576.

NEW American Music Awards Series (Sigma Alpha Iota), New York.
British Agent: Hinrichsen Edition, Ltd.

NEW Music Edition, Pennsylvania.
British Agent: Alfred A. Kalmus, Ltd.

NEW Wind Music Co. 23 Ivor Pl., London, N.W.1. *Tel:* 01-262 3797.

NEW World Publishers, Ltd. 50 New Bond St., London, W.1. *Tel:* 01-629 7600. *Grams:* Symphony London.

NOETZEL, Wilhelmshaven, Germany.
British Agent: Hinrichsen Edition, Ltd.

NORDISKA Musikforlaget, Stockholm.
British Agent: J. & W. Chester, Ltd.

NORMAN Richardson Band Arrangements. 27 A'Becket's Avenue, Bognor Regis, Sussex, PO21 4LX.

NORSK Musikforlag, Oslo.
British Agent: J. & W. Chester, Ltd.

NORTHERN Songs, Ltd. 12 Bruton St., London, W.1. *Tel:* 01-499 0673. *Grams:* Atumusic London.
Telex: 28526.

NOVELLO & Co., Ltd. Borough Green, Sevenoaks, Kent. *Tel:* Borough Green 3261. *Grams:* Novello Sevenoaks

OCTAVA Music Co., Ltd.
British Agent: Josef Weinberger, Ltd.

OXFORD University Press (Music Department). 44 Conduit St., London, W1R ODE. *Tel:* 01-734 5364. *Grams and Cables:* Fulscore London W1.

PARAGON, New York.
British Agent: Hinrichsen Edition, Ltd.

PATERSON'S Publications, Ltd. 38 Wigmore St., London, W1H 0EX. *Tel:* 01-935 3551. *Grams:* Paterwia London W1.

PENNSYLVANIA State University Press. 70 Great Russell St., London, WC1B 3BY. *Tel:* 01-405 0182. *Grams:* Amunpress London.

PETER Maurice Music Co., Ltd. 21 Denmark St., London, WC2H 8NE. *Tel:* 01-836 5501. *Grams:* Mauritunes London WC2.

PETERS Edition, Bach House, 10-12 Baches St., London, N1 6DN. *Tel:* 01-253 1638. *Grams:* Musipeters London.

PITMAN, Hart, & Co., Ltd. *See* HART, F. Pitman, & Co., Ltd.

POLISH Music Publications, Poland.
British Agent: Alfred A. Kalmus, Ltd.

POLYPHONIC Reproductions Ltd. 89-91 Vicarage Rd, London, NW10 2VA. *Tel:* 01-459 6194.

PRESSER, Theodore, Co., Pennsylvania.
British Agent: Alfred A. Kalmus, Ltd.

PRO ART Publications, Inc. New York.
British Agent: Alfred A. Kalmus, Ltd.

PRO MUSICA Verlag, Leipzig.
British Agent: Breitkopf & Härtel (London) Ltd.

PROWSE, Keith, Music Publishing Co., Ltd. *See* KEITH Prowse Music Publishing Co., Ltd.

RAHTER, D. Lyra House, 67 Belsize La., London, NW3 5AX. *Tel:* 01-794 8038.

REGINA Music Publishing Co., Ltd. Old Run Rd., Leeds, LS10 2AA. *Tel:* Leeds 700527.

RICHARDSON, Norman, Ltd. *See* Norman Richardson Band Arrangements.

RIES & Erler, Berlin.
British Agent: Hinrichsen Edition, Ltd.

ROBBINS Music Corporation, Ltd. 1-6 Denmark Place, London, WC2H 8NL. *Tel:* 01-240 2156.

ROBERTON Publications. The Windmill, Wendover, Aylesbury, Bucks. *Tel:* Wendover 3107.

ROYAL Academy of Dancing. 48 Vicarage Cres., London, SW11 3LT. *Tel:* 01-223 0091. *Grams:* Radancing London SW11 3LT.

ROYAL School of Church Music. Addington Palace, Croydon, CR9 5AD. *Tel:* 01-654 7676. *Grams:* Cantoris, Croydon.

ROYAL Scottish Country Dance Society. 12 Coates Crescent, Edinburgh EH3 7AF. *Tel:* 031-225 3854.

RUBANK Inc. U.S.A.
   British agent: Novello & Co., Ltd.

ST. MARTINS Publications, Ltd. Addington Palace, Croydon CR9 5AD. *Tel:* 01-654 7676

SAM Fox Publishing Co., New York.
   British Agent: Keith Prowse Music Publishing Co., Ltd.

SCHIRMER, G., (Music Publishers), 140 Strand, London, W.C.2.

SCHMIDT, C. F., Heilbronn, Germany.
   British Agent: Hinrichsen Edition, Ltd.

SCHOFIELD & Sims, Ltd. 35 St. John's Rd., Huddersfield, Yorkshire HD1 5DT. *Tel:* Huddersfield 30684. *Grams:* Schosims, Huddersfield.

SCHOTT & Co. Ltd. 48 Great Marlborough St., London, W1V 2BN. *Tel:* 01-437 1246. *Grams:* Shotanco London.

SCRIPTURE Union. 5 Wigmore St., London, W.1.
   Tel: 01-486 2561.
   Trade: 79 Hackney Rd., London, E.2. *Tel:* 01-739 2941.

SOCIETAS Universalis Santae Ceciliae.
   British Agent: Alfred A. Kalmus, Ltd.

SIMROCK, N. Lyra House, 67 Belsize Lane, London, NW3 5AX. *Tel:* 01-794 8038.

SOUTHERN Music Company, San Antonio, Texas.
   British Agent: Boosey & Hawkes Music Publishers, Ltd.

STAINER & Bell, Ltd. 82 High Road, London, N2 9PW.
   Tel: 01-444 9135.

STEINGRABER Verlag, Germany.
   British Agent: Bosworth & Co., Ltd.

STUDIO Music Co. 89-91 Vicarage Rd, London, NW10 2VA.
   Tel: 01-459 6194/5

SUPRAPHON Czechoslovakia.
   British Agent: Alfred A. Kalmus, Ltd.

TALZEHN Music Corporation, New York.
   British Agent: Hinrichsen Edition, Ltd.

TAUNUS Verlag, Frankfurt.
   British Agent: Hinrichsen Edition, Ltd.

TURRET Books. 1B, 1C, 1D, Kensington Church Walk, London, W8 4NB.
   Tel: 01-937 7583.

UNIVERSAL Edition (London), Ltd. 2-3 Fareham St., London, W1V 4DU.

UNIVERSAL Edition Vienna-London-Zurich
   British Agent: Alfred A. Kalmus, Ltd.

UNIVERSITY of Wales Press. Merthyr House, James St., Cardiff, CF1 6EU. *Tel:* Cardiff 31919.

V.E.B. Deutscher Verlag für Musik, Leipzig.
   British Agent: Breitkopf & Härtel (London), Ltd.

V.E.B. Friedrich Hofmeister, Leipzig.
   British Agent: Breitkopf & Härtel (London), Ltd.

VALANDO Music Co., Ltd. 50 New Bond St., London, W1A 2BR. *Tel:* 01-629 7600. *Grams:* Symphony London.

VERLAG Neue Musik, Berlin.
   British Agent: Breitkopf & Härtel (London), Ltd.

VICTORIA Music Publishing Co., Ltd. 52 Maddox St., London, W.1. *Tel:* MAYfair 7600.

WALTON Music Corporation, California.
   British Agent: Walton Music, Ltd.

WALTON Music, Ltd. 50 New Bond St., London, W1A 2BR. *Tel:* 01-629 7600. *Grams:* Symphony London.

WARNE, Frederick, & Co., Ltd. 40 Bedford Sq., London, WC1B 3HE. *Tel:* 01-580 9622. *Grams:* Warne London WC1

WEINBERGER, Josef, Ltd. 10-16 Rathbone St., London, W1P 2BJ. *Tel;* 01-580 2827. *Grams;* Operetta London W.1.

WILHELMIANA Musikverlag, Frankfurt am Main.
   British Agent: J. & W. Chester, Ltd.

WILLIAMSON Music, Ltd. 138 Piccadilly, London, W1V 9FH.

WILLIS Music Co., Cincinnati (Ohio).
   British Agent: Chappell & Co., Ltd.

WOOD, B.F., Music Co., Ltd. See BELWIN-Mills Music Ltd.

WOOD, Bradbury, Ltd. See BRADBURY Wood Ltd.

ZANIBON Edition, Padua.
   British Agent: Hinrichsen Edition, Ltd.

ZIMMERMANN, Musikverlag, Germany.
   British Agent: Novello & Co., Ltd.